D1289451

MERRILL

FOCUS ON
LIFE
SCIENCE

AUTHOR

Charles H. Heimler
California State University—
Northridge, California

Content Consultants
James E. Kennedy, Professor of Biology,
Ohio Dominican College, Columbus, Ohio

Consultant

Lucy Daniel
Rutherfordton-Spindale High School—
Rutherfordton, North Carolina

William S. Kushner, Adjunct Professor of Biology,
Onondaga Community College, Syracuse, New York

MERRILL
PUBLISHING COMPANY
A Bell & Howell Company
Columbus, Ohio
Toronto   London   Sydney

A MERRILL SCIENCE PROGRAM

Focus on Life Science: *Student Edition*
Focus on Life Science: *Teacher Annotated Edition*
Focus on Life Science: *Teacher Resource Book*
Focus on Life Science: *Review and Reinforcement Guide*
Focus on Life Science: *Review and Reinforcement Guide, Teacher Annotated Edition*
Focus on Life Science: *A Learning Strategy for the Laboratory*
Focus on Life Science: *A Learning Strategy for the Laboratory, Teacher Annotated Edition*
Focus on Life Science: *Evaluation Program (Spirit Duplicating Masters)*
Life Science Skillcards
Focus on Earth Science Program
Focus on Physical Science Program

Charles H. Heimler is Professor of Science Education at California State University at Northridge, California. He received his B.S. degree from Cornell University and his M.A. and Ed.D. degrees from Columbia University and New York University. In his 33 years in education, Dr. Heimler has taught general science, biology, chemistry, and physics at the secondary school level as well as chemistry and biology at the university level. He currently teaches a science methods course and supervises student teachers in science. Dr. Heimler is a member of the American Association for the Advancement of Science, the National Science Teachers Association, and the National Association of Biology Teachers. He is coauthor of Merrill's *Focus on Physical Science* and author of Merrill's *Principles of Science, Book One* and *Principles of Science, Book Two*.

Lucy Daniel is a biology teacher at Rutherfordton-Spindale High School in Rutherfordton, North Carolina. In her 33 years of teaching, she has taught a variety of science courses and been chosen a Presidential Award Winner in Science from North Carolina. Ms. Daniel received her B.S. degree from the University of North Carolina at Greensboro and her M.A. degree in Science Education from Western Carolina University. She is a member of the National Association of Biology Teachers, the National Science Teachers Association, the American Institute of Biological Sciences, and the National Education Association. Ms. Daniel is coauthor of Merrill's *Biology: An Everyday Experience* program as well as author of various ancillary materials accompanying the *Focus on Life Science* program and Merrill's *Principles of Science* program.

Reading Consultant
Diane Wallace, William Penn High School, New Castle, Delaware

Computer Consultants
Henry Phillips, North Syracuse Junior High School, North Syracuse, New York
Bernard Schrilla, Cicero-North Syracuse High School, Cicero, New York

Special Features Consultant
Mike Bagby, Science Coordinator II, Dade County Schools, Miami, Florida

Special Needs Consultant
Janet Mansfield Davies, Boulder, Colorado

Reviewers
Mike Bagby, Science Coordinator II, Dade County Schools, Miami, Florida
John Denham Bernreuter, Assistant Science Supervisor, Dade County Schools, Miami, Florida
Peggy Sue Carnahan, Science Curriculum Specialist, San Antonio, Texas
Mary Ann Esquibel, District Science Coordinator, Albuquerque Public Schools, Albuquerque, New Mexico
Larry Alan Fegel, Outdoor Education Teacher Consultant, Grand Rapids, Michigan
William James Forward, Science Department Chairperson, Rio Linda Senior High School, Rio Linda, California
Bettye Lou Jerrel, Supervisor of Science (K–12), Evansville-Vanderburgh School Corporation, Evansville, Indiana
Harriet Knops, Life Science Teacher, Camerado Springs Middle School, Shingle Springs, California
Kenneth Relyea, Chairperson, Science and Mathematics Department, Wesleyan College, Macon, Georgia
Mary Kathryn Smith, Life Science Teacher, Dodgen Middle School, Marietta, Georgia

Series Editor: Terry B. Flohr; *Project Editor:* Carla J. Weiland; *Editors:* Angela E. Priestley, Mary Dylewski; *Book Designer and Project Artist:* Scott D. Sommers; *Illustrators:* David Dennis, Bill Robison; *Photo Editor:* Ruth E. Bogart; *Production Editor:* Victoria Morris Althoff

Cover Photograph: Trinidad Tree Frog: Breck P. Kent
Back Cover Photograph: Pink Edged Sulphur: John Gerlach/Tom Stack & Associates

ISBN 0-675-07401-0

Published by
MERRILL PUBLISHING COMPANY
A BELL & HOWELL COMPANY
Columbus, Ohio 43216

Copyright© 1987, 1986, 1984, 1981, 1977, 1974, 1969 by Bell & Howell. All rights reserved. No part of this book may be reproduced in any form, electronic or mechanical, including photocopy, recording, or any information retrieval system without written permission from the publisher.
Printed in the United States of America

To the Student

Most students enjoy the study of life science because they are curious about living things. In your study of life science, you will find answers to many questions. Further, you will find out why life science is an important and practical subject.

In using this textbook, you will increase your knowledge of topics such as behavior, reproduction, heredity, ecology, drugs, and disease. You will find out how plants make food and what enables some animals to see colors. You will learn how the life of one living creature can affect the lives of others. You will find out about the many changes that occur inside your own body.

A study of life science has many practical applications. For example, facts about nutrition can be used to help people choose foods that promote good health. Knowledge of heredity can be used to increase the world's supply of food obtained from living things. Information about microorganisms helps scientists prevent and cure diseases. Facts about the natural environment can help people learn how to clean up the air and water.

Many jobs and careers require a background in life science. Careers in veterinary medicine, plant breeding, horticulture, laboratory technology, nursing, and wildlife conservation involve areas of life science. In your life science class, you will be able to explore your interests in these fields and in many others. Learning about different careers and jobs will help you decide what field you may wish to enter when you finish school.

Life scientists use certain methods to solve problems and find answers. In this textbook, you will learn about scientific methods and how to use them. You will discover that you can use these same methods in your own life. Their use will increase your success in solving problems and accomplishing tasks.

Focus on Life Science contains many features that will help you learn. Each chapter begins with a photograph and brief introduction to the theme of the chapter. Goal statements identify what you can expect to learn as you study the chapter. Throughout the chapter, margin questions printed in blue emphasize the main ideas. Use these questions as self-checks to evaluate your progress. Major terms are highlighted in boldface type and are often spelled phonetically. Sets of review questions called *Making Sure* have been placed throughout the chapters. These questions provide another means of self evaluation.

At the end of each chapter are special sections of study and review materials. The *Summary* provides a list of the major points and ideas presented within the chapter. The *Vocabulary* lists important new terms. The section titled *Questions* contains questions that are useful as a review of the chapter's concepts and questions that require you to apply what you have learned. *Ideas to Explore* is a section that provides thought-provoking problems and ideas for projects. Sources of more information are listed in the *Readings* section.

Focus pages, located at the ends of all chapters, introduce you to *People and Careers* and *Frontiers* in life science. *Focus on Skills* pages offer tips on successful study of life science.

Included in certain chapters are *Technology* features. These features provide exciting information on new technological developments in life science.

A *Focus on Computers* feature located at the end of each unit offers you the opportunity to explore the use of computers as you study life science.

At the end of the textbook are the *Appendices*, *Glossary*, and *Index*. The *Appendices* contain tables and safety information. The *Glossary* contains definitions of the major terms presented in the textbook. The complete *Index* will help you quickly locate specific topics within the textbook.

This textbook has been written and organized to help you succeed in your science class. As you do your classwork and complete your assignments, you will gain the satisfaction of understanding life science and its applications in everyday life.

FOCUS ON
Skills

Textbook Inventory

A student's textbook is his or her primary learning tool. Therefore, an inventory is an excellent way to introduce a new textbook. An inventory introduces the general layout of the book. It points out the various features of the textbook, such as the number of chapters and how they are ordered, and highlights the different kinds of study aids.

Use your textbook to answer the questions.

A. Introduction
  1. What is the title of your textbook?
  2. Who is the author?
  3. Read To the Student on page iii. What will you learn about life science in this text?
  4. Look at the Table of Contents. How many chapters are in this book? In which section of Chapter 4 would you learn about scientific names?

B. Graphic Aids
  5. How is the photograph at the beginning of Unit 1 used to introduce the unit?
  6. Look at the beginning of Chapter 11. Why was the photograph chosen to begin Chapter 11?
  7. What two types of information are given in Table 6–1 on page 114?
  8. What kingdoms of organisms are classified in Table 4–1 on page 67?

C. Study Aids
  9. What should be your goals as you read Chapter 10?
  10. What is discussed in Section 10:2?
  11. How can you use the blue margin notes on page 92 to help you study?
  12. What is the purpose of section titles?
  13. Why are Making Sure questions included at the end of many sections?
  14. List the important terms you should know when you read Section 4:2 on pages 67–

  68. How did you know that these were the important terms?

D. Activities
  15. How is Activity 5–2 on page 93 different from Activity 5–3 on page 95?
  16. What question does Activity 5–2 ask?
  17. What materials are used in Activity 5–2?
  18. What is the purpose of the hand lens in Activity 11–2 on page 228?
  19. In Activity 6–1 on page 106, how many tables must be made for the Data and Observations section?
  20. Why is a microscope necessary for Activity 6–4 on page 116?

E. Chapter Review
  21. Look at the review of Chapter 6 that begins on page 123. What section would you re-read if you did not understand yeast fermentation?
  22. How many new terms are introduced?
  23. How many kinds of questions are introduced in Questions for Review?
  24. Where can you find project ideas to extend your knowledge of the chapter subjects?
  25. Where can you find additional information about the subjects of the chapter?

F. Other Features
  26. What is the purpose of the Focus on Frontiers page?
  27. What is the purpose of the Focus on Careers page?
  28. What learning skills are discussed in the eight Focus on Skills features?
  29. What information is provided in the appendices at the back of the book? How can this information be useful?
  30. In what section of the book are all vocabulary terms defined?
  31. In what section of the book could you find a listing of pages on which vertebrates are discussed?

TABLE OF CONTENTS

UNIT ONE
THE NATURE OF LIFE SCIENCE

UNIT TWO
SIMPLE ORGANISMS

UNIT THREE
PLANTS

UNIT FOUR
ANIMALS

UNIT FIVE
HUMAN LIFE

14   Support and Coordination

15   Body Transport Systems

UNIT SIX
HEREDITY AND EVOLUTION

UNIT SEVEN
THE ENVIRONMENT

22 The Biosphere

ACTIVITIES

THE NATURE OF LIFE SCIENCE

Scientist banding birds

UNIT 1

Throughout our history, people have been curious about the living world. From the first observations to present-day techniques, there has always been a basic need for us to understand nature. People who enjoy working with animals often spend years collecting data. The scientist bands birds to learn about their movements. The game warden may solve problems caused by raccoons. What other jobs do scientists have? What can we learn from nature?

Game warden removing raccoons

Science is discovery. It is a constant search for information and answers. We wonder about the living organisms around us and want to know how they live day-to-day. How do they get food? How do they protect themselves? How do their bodies function? To find answers to these questions, measurements must be made and records kept. These students are studying how the mammalian body works. What will they learn? What scientific methods will they use?

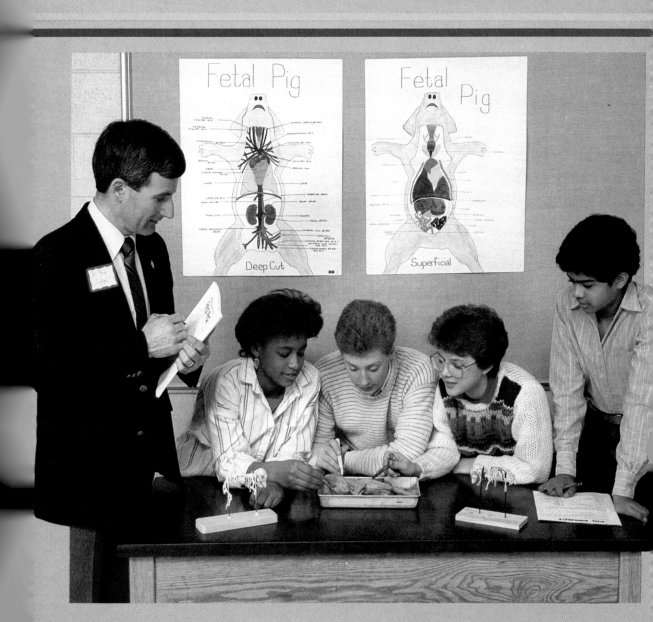

CHAPTER 1
METHODS OF LIFE SCIENCE

1:1 Life Science

Life science is the study of organisms through the use of scientific methods. An organism is a whole or complete living thing. Examples of organisms include a dog, rose bush, earthworm, apple tree, guppy, and the mold that grows on old bread. Every person is an organism.

Scientific methods are the ways in which scientists go about solving problems. In science, a problem is a question for which a scientist seeks an answer. For example, how do plants produce new plants from seeds? How does a heart pump blood? Here are three examples of problems currently studied by life scientists. How can insect pests be controlled? How do drugs affect the body? Why do some people experience motion sickness?

Technology (tek NAHL uh jee) is the use of scientific knowledge in a practical way. Knowing how plants produce offspring has led to the development of dwarf fruit trees. What scientists learn about the human heart is used to develop artificial hearts used in transplants. Dwarf fruit trees and artificial hearts are the products of technology. New medicines, vitamins made in laboratories, and methods of preserving food are products of technology, too.

GOALS:
1. You will learn how to use scientific methods to solve problems.
2. You will learn to make scientific measurements.
3. You will learn to use a microscope correctly.

What is life science?

Define and give three examples of technology.

5

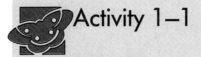

Activity 1–1   Life Science Research

Problem: What do life scientists study?

Materials   reference books, current newspapers and magazines, pencil, paper, scissors

Procedure   (1) Use reference books to look up the fields of study listed below. (2) Write a statement describing each field. (3) Cut out five articles or advertisements from newspapers or magazines. The articles should be related to life science. (4) Make a list of five topics in life science that are currently being researched.

agronomy	cytology	ichthyology
anatomy	ecology	microbiology
animal behavior	embryology	oceanography
anthropology	entomology	paleontology
bacteriology	genetics	taxonomy
biochemistry	herpetology	virology
botany	horticulture	zoology

Questions   (1) What is the meaning of the suffix -*logy?* (2) What is the difference between botany and zoology? (3) Which field includes the study of cockroaches? (4) How are all of the fields listed above related? (5) What field of study is represented by each of your research topics? (6) Which research topic do you believe is the most important? Explain why. (7) What do life scientists study?

FIGURE 1–1. The first step in scientific problem solving is to think of the problem. Often the problem is stated as a question.

1:2 Scientific Problem Solving

Scientists use scientific methods to solve problems. Often these methods are followed in a series of problem-solving steps. The following list shows some steps that might be used to solve a problem in life science.

1. *Identify the problem.* State the problem to be solved or the question to be answered.
2. *Collect information about the problem.* Facts and ideas may be obtained from books, journals, and other scientists. Some kinds of information are stored on film or magnetic disks and tapes used with computers.

FIGURE 1–2. After the problem is identified, research is done to find out what is already known about the problem. Then a hypothesis is formed, an experiment is done to test it, and the results are reported based on whether the hypothesis was accepted or rejected.

3. *Form a hypothesis* (hi PAHTH uh sus). A **hypothesis** is a proposed solution to a problem. It is a prediction or "best guess" based on known facts.
4. *Test the hypothesis*. A hypothesis is tested by making observations. An **observation** is something you learn through your senses. You observe things by seeing, hearing, touching, smelling, and tasting. One way to test a hypothesis is to do an experiment. In an **experiment,** a hypothesis is tested under carefully controlled conditions. By experimenting under these conditions, you can determine whether or not your observations support your hypothesis.
5. *Accept or reject the hypothesis*. If the information obtained from the tests does not show the hypothesis to be false, the hypothesis is accepted. Otherwise, the hypothesis is rejected or changed and tested again.
6. *Report the results*. Scientists publish the results of their work in journals so that their work can be used and repeated by other scientists.

Define observation.

Problem solving is not always a step-by-step process. Good scientists are creative people. They solve problems in many different ways. Imagination, skill, luck, hard work, and smart guesses are all part of scientific problem solving.

How do scientists solve problems?

Making Sure

1. What is the difference between observations and experiments? Explain.
2. How could you use scientific methods to determine the fastest way to get to school?
3. Why is problem solving not always a step-by-step process? Use examples to explain your answer.

1:3 Experiments

For a science fair project, a student decided to find out if temperature affects the growth of bean seeds. The student did some research and determined that bean seeds are unlikely to grow at cold temperatures. To test this hypothesis, the student got 20 bean seeds. Ten seeds were placed in a jar with moist cotton. The other 10 seeds were placed in another jar with moist cotton. One jar was kept in the classroom at room temperature. The other jar was kept in a refrigerator. After a week, the student observed each jar, Figure 1–3.

Experiments, such as the one described above, can be divided into four parts. These parts are the problem, procedure, observations, and conclusion. The **problem** is a question to be answered or a hypothesis to be tested. What is the problem in the bean experiment? The **procedure** part is what is done in the experiment. It usually involves the use of materials and equipment. In the bean experiment, the procedure is placing the beans with moist cotton into two jars, one kept at room temperature and the other refrigerated. Observations refer to what happens in an experiment. What changes were observed in the bean experiment? A **conclusion** is an answer or solution based on observations. Inferring is drawing conclusions based on your observations. What is your conclusion for the bean experiment? Should the student accept or reject the hypothesis?

It is important that the procedure and data for an experiment be carefully recorded. **Data** are the facts obtained through observations. For example, the fact that none of the refrigerated beans started to grow is part of the data for the bean experiment. A record of an experiment can be used for reference if the

What are the parts of an experiment?

FIGURE 1–3. In the bean experiment, the student observed that the beans in the refrigerated jar did not grow.

experiment is to be done again. Often an experiment is repeated with the procedure changed in some way to test a new hypothesis. The record can also be used if unexpected observations occur during an experiment. Records of what was done in the procedure may be used to explain the observations.

Every experiment has at least one variable (VER ee uh bul). A **variable** is something that can cause the changes observed in an experiment. In the bean experiment, temperature is one variable. Most experiments have a control. A **control** is the part of the experiment used for comparing the changes that occur. The control is the beans kept at room temperature. Failure of the beans in the refrigerator to grow is compared to the growth in the control jar. The student concluded that the difference was due to the cold temperature in the refrigerator. The observations in this experiment supported the hypothesis.

FIGURE 1—4. Many teachers assign science projects in which students report the results of experiments they have done to test hypotheses.

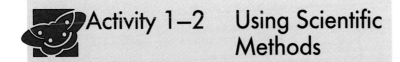

Activity 1—2 Using Scientific Methods

Problem: How are scientific methods used to answer questions?

Materials paper, pencil, reference books, magazines, newspapers

Procedure (1) Sugar, honey, saccharin, and aspartame are popular sweeteners. Predict an answer to the question, "Which of these sweeteners is sweetest?" (2) Read about sweeteners in reference books, magazines, and newspapers. (3) Using what you learn, write one paragraph about each sweetener. (4) Design an experiment to test your prediction. (You do not have to actually do the experiment.) List the materials that will be needed and the procedure steps to be followed. Be sure you have a control. (5) Make up a data table for recording observations.

Questions (1) What is the problem in your experiment? (2) How did you research the problem before you designed your experiment? (3) What was your hypothesis? (4) What are the variables? (5) What is the control? (6) Why do you need a control? (7) Upon what observations will your data be based? (8) How will you know whether to accept or reject your hypothesis? (9) Who might be interested in the results of your experiment? (10) How are scientific methods used to answer questions?

1:4 Theories

What is a theory?

How can a hypothesis become a theory?

Observations and conclusions are used to develop theories (THIHR eez). A **theory** is an idea that explains things or events. A good theory is based on a large number of observations. These observations may be made during experiments. A single experiment shows only that a hypothesis is or is not false under the conditions of that experiment. A hypothesis tested over and over again and not shown to be false may become a theory.

Theories can and do change. For example, people once believed that organisms come from decaying matter. This theory was an explanation of the people's observations. In the 1800s, some scientists did experiments to test the idea. The theory did not agree with the scientists' observations. If a theory does not agree with new observations and conclusions, it can no longer be accepted. It must be dropped or changed to account for the new data.

Most experiments lead to more questions for which scientists do more experiments to find answers. Therefore, there are always scientific questions that remain unanswered. Here are some examples of questions for which scientists are now seeking answers. Does life exist in other parts of the universe? How can cancer be prevented or cured? What is the safest way to dispose of nuclear wastes? You can probably think of many others.

FIGURE 1–5. Life scientists do many kinds of research to develop theories . A wildlife scientist prepares a sedative for a bear (a) and researchers study the effect of pollution on plants (b).

a

b

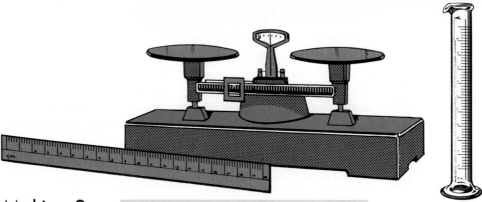

FIGURE 1–6. Scientists use meter sticks or metric rulers to measure length (a). They use balances to measure mass (b). They use graduated cylinders to measure volume (c).

Making Sure

4. In an experiment with a new medicine, two groups of animals are tested. One group is given the medicine. The other is not. Which group is the control? What is the variable? Explain.
5. State another hypothesis that could explain why the refrigerated beans in the experiment did not grow. Design an experiment to test this hypothesis.
6. What are three scientific questions that concern you? Explain why.

1:5 Scientific Measurement

Many observations make use of measurements. How high is a tree? What is the mass of a chicken egg? Numbers and units are used to measure height, weight, and other quantities. Many scientists use an international system of units called SI.

In SI, a unit of length is the **meter**. The height of a doorknob is about one meter.

A unit of mass is the **gram.** Mass means the amount of matter in something.

A common unit of volume is the **liter.** Volume tells us how much space something occupies. Liters are used to measure the volume of liquids and gases.

What units of length, volume, and mass do life scientists use?

Table 1–1

Units of Measure		
Unit	**Symbol**	**Used to measure**
meter	m	length
gram	g	mass
liter	L	volume

FIGURE 1–7. The Celsius temperature scale is named after Anders Celsius (1701–1744) who developed it.

What units of temperature do most people in the world use?

Prefixes are used with these units to change them to larger or smaller units. The prefix *milli-* means one thousandth. A millimeter is one thousandth of a meter. A milliliter is one thousandth of a liter. The prefix *centi-* means one hundredth. A centimeter is one hundredth of a meter. The prefix *kilo-* means one thousand. A kilogram is 1000 grams. A kilometer is 1000 meters.

Table 1–2

Prefixes		
Prefix	Symbol	Meaning
milli	m	0.001
centi	c	0.01
deci	d	0.1
deka	da	10.0
hecto	h	100.0
kilo	k	1000.0

Temperature is measured in units called degrees. The thermometer used by most of the people in the world measures temperature in degrees **Celsius** (SEL see us). Many scientists use the Celsius temperature scale. The symbol for Celsius temperature is °C.

The are 100 degrees between freezing and boiling points of water on the Celsius scale. The freezing point of pure water is 0°C and the boiling point is 100°C. The average human body temperature is 37°C on the Celsius scale. A pleasant room temperature is 21°C. If you remember these temperatures, you can use them as reference points for other Celsius temperatures. What might be the Celsius temperature on a hot summer day? In what season might the temperature outdoors be below 0°C?

Making Sure

7. What are the symbols for liter, meter, gram, and degrees Celsius?
8. How many grams are in two kilograms?
9. How many milliliters are in 0.5 liter? How many centimeters are in five meters?
10. How many millimeters are in a kilometer?
11. Would an outdoor temperature of 32°C be likely to occur in winter or summer?

Problem: What units do you use to measure length, mass, and volume?

Materials

10 leaves	paper cup
metric ruler	water
meter stick	ice cubes
balance	Celsius thermometer
graduated cylinder	stirring rod

Procedure

1. Use the metric ruler to measure the length and width of each leaf. (Use the longest and widest parts of the leaf.) Record your measurements in centimeters in a data table.
2. Using the meter stick, measure your height in meters. Record the measurement.
3. Fill the paper cup halfway with water. Using a balance, measure the mass of the cup of water. Record the mass in grams.
4. Pour the water into a graduated cylinder. Measure the volume of the water in milliliters. Record the volume.
5. Return the water to the cup. Using a Celsius thermometer, measure and record the temperature of the water.
6. Add ice cubes to the water. Use a stirring rod to stir until the temperature stops falling. **CAUTION:** *Never use a thermometer to stir*. Measure and record the new temperature.

Data and Observations

Object	Measurement

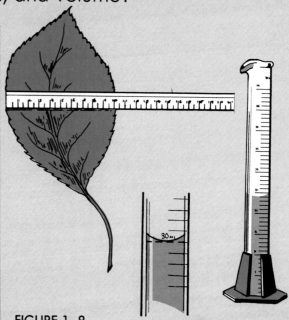

FIGURE 1–8.

Questions and Conclusions

1. What is the name of the unit of measurement on the metric ruler represented by the lines between the centimeter marks?
2. Why do you think the ruler is called a "metric" ruler? How is it different from other rulers?
3. What are the measurements of each leaf in millimeters?
4. What is your height in centimeters?
5. What is your height in millimeters?
6. How many grams are in a kilogram?
7. What temperature change occurred after you added ice to the water? How many degrees did it change?
8. What units described in Section 1:5 would you use to measure
   a. the amount of flour in a recipe?
   b. the distance between two cities?
   c. the width of a ring band?
9. What units do you use to measure length, mass, and volume?

FIGURE 1–9. A magnifying glass is a hand lens that makes an object appear larger than it actually is.

FIGURE 1–10. Anton van Leeuwenhoek made a microscope that enabled him to discover microbes.

1:6 Microscopes

Many of the organisms life scientists study are very tiny. Some are much less than a millimeter long. A **microscope** is a tool that magnifies objects. It is used to view objects that are too small to be seen by the unaided eye. Some of the first microscopes were made by Anton van Leeuwenhoek (LAY vun hook) (1632–1723), a Dutchman. Using his microscopes, Leeuwenhoek discovered microbes.

Have you ever used a magnifying glass to observe a tiny object? The curved glass that makes the object appear larger is a lens. A light microscope contains two or more lenses that magnify objects. A simple kind of light microscope has a tube with a magnifying lens at each end. One end of the tube is placed near an object. Then the object is viewed by looking through the lens at the other end of the tube. Light passes through the object, up through the lenses and tube to the eye. The magnification of the two lenses combines to focus an enlarged image of the object. Most light microscopes can enlarge an object hundreds of times. The most powerful light microscopes can magnify an object as much as 2000 times its actual size.

You can easily find the magnification of a light microscope if you know the "powers" of the lenses. The power of the eyepiece lens is marked on the part you look through. For example, an eyepiece lens may be marked 10×. This number means the eyepiece lens magnifies 10 times. The power of the objective lens is marked on the part near the object. If it is marked 45×, the objective lens magnifies 45 times. The total magnification is the power of the eyepiece lens multiplied by the power of the objective lens.

Power of eyepiece lens	times	Power of objective lens	equals	Magnification
10×	×	45×	=	450×

In this example, the total magnification of the microscope is 450×. That means the microscope magnifies objects 450 times their actual size.

Some microscopes are built with two or more objective lenses. The magnifying power of the microscope depends on which objective lens is being used to view an object. For example, many microscopes have low power (10×) and high power (45×) objective lenses and 10× eyepiece lenses. The magnification of these microscopes ranges from 100× to 450×.

An electron microscope is more powerful than a light microscope. It can magnify 100 000 times or more. Instead of light, an electron microscope uses a beam of electrons. Magnets, instead of lenses, focus the beam to form a picture. The picture is viewed on a screen that is like a television screen. Using electron microscopes, scientists can see parts of cells that cannot be seen with a light microscope.

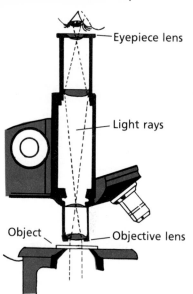

FIGURE 1−11. Most common microscopes have two lenses in the eyepiece that have a combined magnification of 10×. Many microscopes have two lenses in each objective. Note the path of light rays in the microscope.

How can you find the magnification of a light microscope?

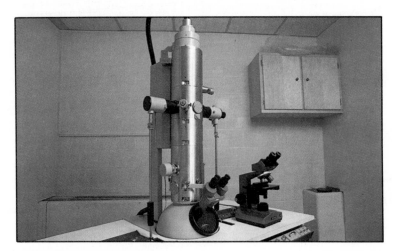

FIGURE 1−12. More powerful than a light microscope, an electron microscope can magnify more than 100 000 times. Magnets focus a beam of electrons to form a picture on a screen.

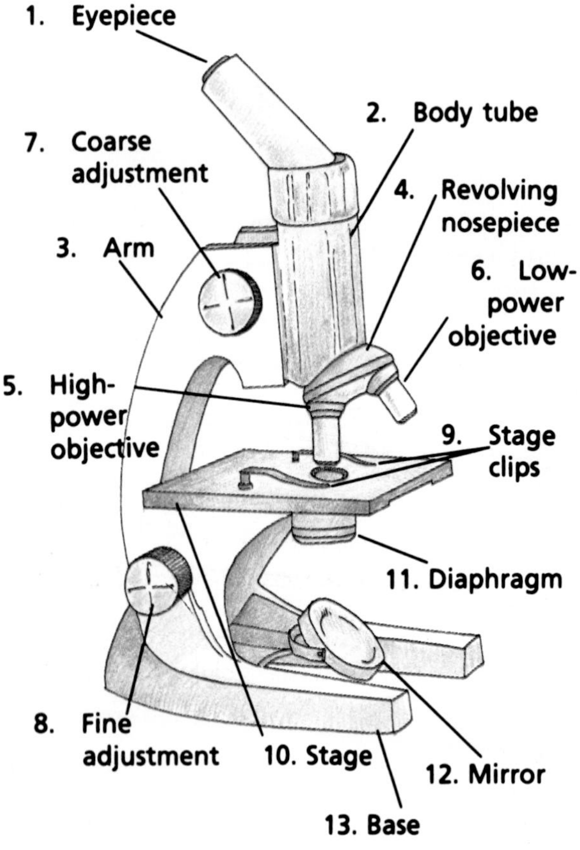

1:7 Microscope Parts

To use a light microscope properly, it is important to learn the name and purpose of each part. Locate in Figure 1–13 each part named below. Also learn the function of each part.

1. **Eyepiece**

7. **Coarse adjustment**

2. **Body tube**

4. **Revolving nosepiece**

3. **Arm**

6. **Low-power objective**

5. **High-power objective**

9. **Stage clips**

11. **Diaphragm**

8. **Fine adjustment**   10. **Stage**

12. **Mirror**

13. **Base**

FIGURE 1–13. Parts of the microscope.

What are the parts of a light microscope? Describe the function of each part.

1. Eyepiece	contains the magnifying lens you look through
2. Body tube	maintains the correct distance between the eyepiece and objective lens
3. Arm	supports the body tube
4. Nosepiece	holds high and low power objectives, can be rotated to change magnification
5. High power objective	provides the most magnification, usually $40\times$
6. Low power objective	provides the least magnification, usually $10\times$
7. Coarse adjustment	moves the body tube up and down for focusing
8. Fine adjustment	used to sharpen the image, moves body tube only slightly
9. Stage clips	hold the microscope slide in place
10. Stage	supports the microscope slide
11. Diaphragm	regulates the amount of light that enters the body tube
12. Mirror or light	sends light upward through the diaphragm, the object, and the lenses
13. Base	supports the microscope

1:8 Use of the Microscope

You must be careful when you use a microscope. Microscopes are easily broken if they are not used correctly. Follow these procedures whenever you handle or use a microscope.

1. Always carry the microscope with both hands. Hold the arm with one hand. Place the other hand beneath the base.
2. Place the microscope on the table gently with the arm toward you and the stage facing a light source. The top of the table should be cleared of other objects.
3. Look through the eyepiece and adjust the diaphragm so that light comes through the opening in the stage. The circle of light is called the field of view.
4. Turn the nosepiece so that the lower objective lens clicks into place.
5. Always focus first with the coarse adjustment and the low power objective lens. View the microscope from the side as you lower the objective. Raise the body tube and focus by turning the coarse adjustment.
6. Turn the nosepiece until the high power objective lens clicks into place. *Use only the fine adjustment with this lens.* There will be less light coming through the objective.
7. Be sure to keep your fingers from touching the lenses.
8. Use only special lens paper to clean the lenses.
9. Before putting the microscope away, always turn the low power objective into place over the stage.
10. Raise the body tube until the low power objective is about two or three centimeters from the stage.

FIGURE 1–14. Always carry a microscope with both hands (a). Use the coarse adjustment to focus with the low power lens (b). Turn the nosepiece to change from the low power to the high power lens (c).

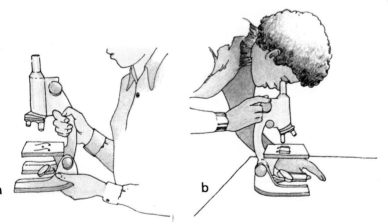

a   b   c

Making Sure

12. The eyepiece lens of a certain microscope has a power of $10\times$. This microscope has a $10\times$ (low power) objective lens and a $25\times$ (high power) objective lens. Calculate the low power magnification of the microscope. Calculate the high power magnification of the microscope.
13. What is one way an electron microscope differs from a light microscope?
14. Draw a diagram of a microscope and label its parts.
15. What could you use a microscope to study?
16. Why do you think a microscope always must be stored with the low power objective in place over the stage?

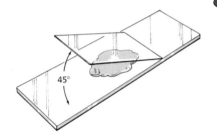

FIGURE 1–15.

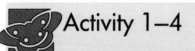

Activity 1–4   Using a Microscope

Problem: How does the microscope help you observe?

Materials   microscope, microscope slide, coverslip, newspaper, scissors, water, dropper, forceps

Procedure   (1) Place a drop of water in the center of a microscope slide. (2) Cut a letter e from a newspaper. (3) Hold the letter e with forceps and place it in the drop of water. (4) Hold a coverslip at one edge of the drop of water and gently lower the coverslip on to the drop of water. This is called a wet mount slide. (5) Place the slide on the microscope stage so the letter is over the hole in the stage. Use the stage clips to hold the slide in place. (6) View the microscope from the side and lower the low power objective with the coarse adjustment until it is near the coverslip. **CAUTION:** *Never focus down toward the stage with the coarse adjustment when you are viewing through the eyepiece. You could break the slide or the objective.* (7) Look through the eyepiece and raise the body tube until you can see the letter. Then focus with the *fine* adjustment. (8) Gently move the slide to the right and then to the left. (9) Move the slide toward you and then away from you. (10) Rotate the nosepiece to bring the high power objective into position over the coverslip and focus with the fine adjustment only.

Questions   (1) How does the letter e appear under low power? (2) What happens when you move the slide to the right? to the left? (3) What happens when you move the slide toward you? away from you? (4) How does the letter e appear under high power? (5) How does a microscope help you observe?

Technology

The New Tools in Life Science

New scientific instruments and computers are making it easier for scientists to study the mysteries of life. One study is the structure of genes. Genes are made of DNA, which is a code that tells the cell which proteins to make. Scientists worked for many months trying to make or synthesize pieces of DNA or genes. Now genes can be made within a few hours by a new machine called a DNA Synthesizer. Scientists type the genetic code for a desired gene onto the machine's computer keyboard. Synthetic genes are used to make proteins such as insulin and growth hormone. The new genes can also be used to detect inherited diseases like sickle-cell anemia.

Another computerized instrument is the Protein Sequencer. Amino acids are chemicals that make up proteins. Scientists need to know the sequence or order of the amino acids in a protein. The machine uses a sample of a protein to print out the kinds of amino acids present and the order in which they occur. Information from the Protein Sequencer can be used with the DNA Synthesizer to make unlimited amounts of protein for research.

Computerized microscope and video systems used with fluorescent dyes and lasers allow scientists to look into living cells. The computer provides a clear image and analyzes functions of the cell.

Computerized technology helps scientists make more accurate measurements, analyze data more thoroughly, and solve many problems in life science.

FIGURE 1–16. Fluorescence microscopy shows how rat muscle cells take up a protein. At the same time, the computer prints out a graph to record the changes.

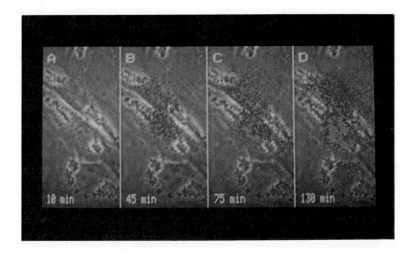

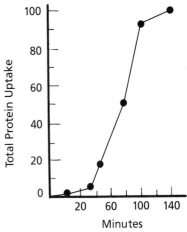

FOCUS ON
Skills

Making the Most of Each Chapter

You can get the most out of your textbook if you know how. There are several techniques that can help you read and understand this text.

First, you must learn the meanings of new words. There are several ways to do this:

1. Use context clues.
2. Use word analysis skills.
3. Use the glossary.
4. Use a dictionary.

This textbook is designed for you to figure out word meanings from *clues* within the *context* surrounding the word. New words are printed in boldface type. They are defined in the sentence or paragraph where they are first used. Sometimes, a pronunciation key is also given. For example, technology (tek NAHL uh jee) is respelled in parentheses. The respelling tells how the word sounds. The Glossary on page 562 further explains how to use respellings and provides a pronunciation key. To practice using context clues, look at question 3 in Section 1:2, which contains the following information:

3. *Form a hypothesis* (hi PAHTH uh sus). A **hypothesis** is a proposed solution to a problem. It is a prediction or "best guess" based on known facts.

As in this example, verbs such as *is, are,* and *mean(s)* often signal definitions. The respelling of hypothesis is given in parentheses to help you learn its pronunciation.

You can also use word analysis skills to determine the meanings of words. Section 1:6 deals with microscopes. "Micro-" means "small" and "scope" means "to see." What is a microscope? Verify your definition with the context clues in Section 1:6.

After being introduced to a new word, check the definition with the glossary in your textbook or a dictionary. Definitions in the glossary apply specifically to material in the textbook. Dictionary definitions may contain more information about a word or may give more than one meaning for a word. How do you know which dictionary definition to choose for a given word? All boldface terms used in each chapter are listed under Vocabulary at the end of the chapter. Use context clues in Chapter 1 to define the vocabulary words. Verify your definitions with the glossary. Compare the glossary definitions to the dictionary definitions of the words.

The second group of important words is signaled by the title of each section. These titles identify the *main ideas* of the chapter. For example, in Section 1:1, Life Science, all of the paragraphs in the passage define and give examples of life science. The first paragraph has a simple definition pointed out by a signaling verb. Questions in the margin test your understanding of the main ideas. Can you answer the margin questions about life science in Section 1:1?

The main ideas of the chapter are also summarized in Summary at the end of the chapter. Answering the questions in Making Sure at the end of some sections will help you review section material. You may need to read the sections again to locate answers. Write one sentence that summarizes the main idea for each section of this chapter.

Learning about science leaves us with many unanswered questions. New knowledge frequently leads to a desire to know more. Ideas to Explore at the end of the chapter provides you with interesting questions for further study. Readings gives you sources of related reading materials.

List two questions that you have after reading this chapter. Where might you find the answers to these questions?

CHAPTER 1
Review

Summary
1. Life science is the study of organisms using the methods of science.   1:1
2. Important steps in scientific methods are identifying and researching the problem.   1:2
3. After a hypothesis has been formed, tested, and accepted or rejected, the results are reported.   1:2
4. Experiments are used to test a hypothesis.   1:3
5. Theories are dropped or changed if observations do not support them.   1:4
6. The meter, gram, liter, and Celsius degree are useful units of measurement.   1:5
7. A light microscope contains two or more lenses that can enlarge an object hundreds of times.   1:6
8. An electron microscope uses a beam of electrons to magnify objects 100 000 times or more.   1:6
9. To use a light microscope, one must know the name and function of each microscope part.   1:7
10. A microscope must be handled carefully because microscopes are easily broken if they are not used correctly.   1:8

Vocabulary
Write a sentence using the following words or terms correctly.

conclusion	hypothesis	problem
control	liter	procedure
data	meter	technology
experiment	microscope	theory
gram	observation	variable

Questions
Do not write in this book.

A. True or False
Determine whether each of the following sentences is true or false. Rewrite the false statements to make them correct.
1. A light microscope has an eyepiece lens and an objective lens.
2. When using a microscope, always focus first with the coarse adjustment.
3. A hypothesis may be tested in an experiment.
4. In every observation, a measurement is made.

5. A scientific problem is seldom solved by one experiment.
6. Every experiment has a procedure.
7. The conclusion to an experiment comes before the procedure.
8. Your body has more mass than your textbook.
9. Life science is the study of organisms through the use of scientific methods.
10. A light microscope is more powerful than an electron microscope.

B. Multiple Choice

Choose the word or phrase that correctly completes the following sentences.
1. The magnification of the eyepiece lens in a microscope is usually about *(10×, 100×, 1000×, 40×)*.
2. A(n) *(theory, problem, observation)* is an idea that explains things or events.
3. To complete an experiment, you follow a(n) *(problem, procedure, observation, conclusion)*.
4. A(n) *(control, problem, observation)* is the part of an experiment used for comparing changes that occur.
5. A *(meter, kilogram, liter)* is a unit of length.
6. Mass is measured in *(meters, grams, liters)*.
7. The prefix *milli-* means *(0.01, 0.001)*.
8. A kilogram is *(1000, 0.001, 0.01)* gram(s).
9. Your body temperature is about *(100, 37, 21)* degrees Celsius.
10. Water boils at *(50, 100, 212, 1000)* degrees Celsius.

C. Completion

Complete each of the following sentences with the correct word or phrase.
1. Anton van Leeuwenhoek was the first to see microbes through a(n) _____ .
2. A(n) _____ is a proposed solution to a problem.
3. You make _____ through your senses.
4. What is done in an experiment is the _____.
5. L stands for a unit called the _____.
6. The freezing point of pure water is _____.
7. Facts obtained through observations are _____.
8. A hypothesis tested over and over again may become a(n) _____.
9. The _____ in an experiment is a question to be answered or hypothesis to be tested.
10. The practical application of science is _____.

D. How and Why

1. List five parts of a microscope and state the function of each part.
2. List five observations you have made today. What senses did you use?
3. How is a hypothesis tested?
4. Describe the parts of an experiment.
5. Why is a control used in many experiments?
6. Name a unit a scientist would use to measure
   a. the length of a bone.
   b. the mass of an egg.
   c. the volume of blood.

Ideas to Explore

1. **Challenge:** Consult your school or local librarian for career books and pamphlets describing jobs in life science. Make a list of careers that interest you and the preparation needed for each, such as education and experience.
2. **Challenge:** Prepare a short report on electron microscopes.
3. **Challenge:** Prepare a report on the history of lenses and the light microscope. Include descriptions of Leeuwenhoek's "wee beasties."
4. **Project:** Collect photographs of technological advances from newspapers and magazines. Display them on a bulletin board.
5. **Project:** Check grocery store items to find out what items are sold by metric measurements such as liters or grams. Make a display of some of these items.
6. **Challenge:** Write a short biography of a famous life scientist. Ask a librarian or your teacher for suggestions.

Readings

Allison, Linda and David Katz. *Gee, Wiz! How to Mix Art and Science or the Art of Thinking Scientifically*. Boston: Little, Brown, 1983.

Baird, Eva-Lee and Rose Wyler. *Going Metric: The Fun Way*. New York: Doubleday, 1980.

Kumin, Maxine. *The Microscope*. New York: Harper & Row, 1984.

Lotspeich, William D. *How Scientists Find Out*. Boston: Little, Brown, 1980.

McKie, Robin. *Technology: Science at Work*. New York: Franklin Watts, 1984.

Shapiro, Stanley J. *Exploring Careers in Science*. New York: Richard Rosens Press, 1981.

iving organisms have special characteristics that nonliving things do not have. Living organisms must be able to carry out many activities each day of their lives. What characteristics allow living organisms to perform their daily activities? How are living organisms different from nonliving things? The frog and worm are alive. How are they like other living organisms? How are they different from nonliving things?

CHAPTER 2
CHARACTERISTICS OF LIFE

2:1 Living Organisms

What does it mean to be alive? You are aware that you and your friends are alive. Plants and animals are alive. You know that things such as furniture, dishes, desks, and pencils are not alive. What is the difference between living and nonliving things?

Every living organism has special life characteristics that make it different from nonliving things. For example, all living things have a beginning and an end to their lives. During an organism's life it grows, matures, perhaps reproduces, ages, and dies. This progression of changes is its life cycle. An organism is made of one or more microscopic-size building blocks called cells. Every organism needs energy for its life activities. For instance, you use energy to walk, talk, and do math problems. Like you, most organisms obtain energy by using food and oxygen together inside their bodies. Organisms give off wastes produced by their cells. All organisms need water to stay alive. Another characteristic of a living organism is that it responds to its surroundings. How do you respond to loud noises, hot weather, and a ringing fire alarm?

GOALS:
1. You will learn the basic characteristics of living things.
2. You will learn the parts of a cell and the function of each part.
3. You will learn how cells reproduce.

What are the characteristics of living things?

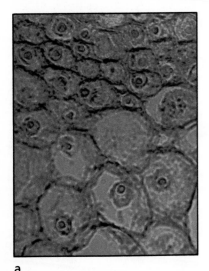

a

b

c

FIGURE 2–1. Three characteristics of organisms are cell makeup (a), response to environment (b), and reproduction (c).

Define reproduction.

An important characteristic of living things is that they can produce new organisms like themselves. This process is **reproduction** (ree pruh DUK shun). Each kind of organism has a method of reproduction. Reproduction is needed for life to continue through time. For example, if eagles did not reproduce, there would be no more eagles when all of the eagles living today die. No young eagles would hatch to replace them.

Some things have one or more of the characteristics of life, yet they are not living. For example, a burning candle uses oxygen and gives off wastes as its wax is burned. An electronic computer may appear to be alive because, like a person, it uses energy and can do calculations. However, the burning candle and computer cannot reproduce themselves.

Some nonliving things once were living. For example, the nonliving wood in a pencil, desk, and chair is made of cells. The wood was part of a living tree before it was cut down. A tomato is nonliving, but it was once part of a living tomato plant. Cotton in clothing and paper in books are two other examples of nonliving materials that once were living.

Making Sure

1. How are living and nonliving things different?
2. Tell whether each of the following things is living or non-living. Then tell whether the nonliving things are never living or once living.
   a. seed
   b. apple
   c. volcano
   d. coal

2:2 Response to Environment

Every organism behaves in certain ways. It responds to things around it. For example, a green plant grows in the direction of light. An earthworm crawls away from light. Plant roots grow down, while stems grow up. A woodchuck runs to its hole to hide. A hungry fish darts after a worm and swallows it. People put on more clothing when they are cold. How an organism responds to its environment helps it stay alive.

If the weather is cold, you dress warmly. Your intelligence is a trait that helps you survive. What might happen if you did not adapt to changes in weather?

When the environment changes, its organisms must adapt to survive. Dinosaurs lived millions of years ago in very warm climates. Today there are no dinosaurs on Earth. Many scientists believe dinosaurs could not adapt and as the climate grew colder, dinosaurs died.

An **adaptation** is a trait that helps an organism survive in its environment. Goldfish have gills with which they take oxygen from water. Hamsters have lungs for breathing air. Earthworms take in oxygen through their moist skins. Plants have roots that anchor them into the soil. Gills, lungs, roots, and moist skin are adaptations. They are major changes that have occurred over a very long time. Without these changes, different life forms would not exist. Other adaptations of organisms occur that are also helpful to their survival. These include changes in body coloring for protection from predators. Camouflage is one of nature's best examples of adaptation. What animals can you name that have camouflage as an adaptation?

Define adaptation.

How do adaptations help organisms survive?

FIGURE 2–2. When the weather turns cold, people adapt by dressing warmly.

Activity 2–1   Response to Environment

Problem: How do your eyes respond to light?

Materials   mirror, watch or clock

Procedure   (1) Write a hypothesis about the problem. (Your hypothesis should be your best guess to answer the question.) (2) Cover your left eye with your hand for two minutes. (3) Hold a mirror in front of you and remove your hand from your eye. (4) As light strikes your left eye, observe the change that occurs.

Questions   (1) When you removed your hand from your left eye, in which eye was the pupil (black area) larger? (2) To what is the pupil responding? (3) How does this response help when you go into a dark movie theater? (4) How does it help when you go outside into bright sunlight? (5) How do your eyes respond to light?

2:3 Life Substances

What are the three main life substances?

Organisms are made of many different substances. The three main life substances are carbon, hydrogen, and oxygen. Water is made of hydrogen and oxygen. Up to 70 percent or more of an organism's mass may be water. Your body is mostly water.

FIGURE 2–3. All your activities require energy.

FIGURE 2–4. Humans, like other animals, get water by drinking it or eating foods that contain water.

You and most other animals obtain water by drinking it or eating foods that contain water. Plants take in water from soil through their roots. Some organisms, such as the earthworm, get water by absorbing it through their outer coverings. Water helps circulate food and other materials through an organism's body. Water is also used to change food into substances the body can use. It is also needed for chemical changes inside an organism's cells. This change produces wastes. Water is used to remove wastes from an organism. For example, sweat and urine, two kinds of animal wastes, are mostly water.

How is water important to living organisms?

Oxygen makes up about 21 percent of air. Plants and animals living on land obtain oxygen from the air. Air enters a plant through tiny openings in its leaves. How do you get oxygen? Water-living plants and animals take in oxygen dissolved in the water around them. Organisms use oxygen inside their bodies to release energy from food.

Carbon is another life substance. All organisms contain carbon. Carbon is present in air in the form of a gas called carbon dioxide. Green plants take carbon dioxide from air and use it to make food. Animals obtain carbon from the food they eat.

Making Sure

3. Use an example to explain what would happen to an organism that is not adapted to its environment.
4. Describe three ways in which organisms obtain water.
5. Why do most plants and animals need oxygen? How do they obtain oxygen?

FIGURE 2–5. A hummingbird uses energy to hover.

2:4 Energy

Why do organisms need energy?

All organisms use energy for movement, growth, reproduction, and other life activities. Most organisms get energy from food. **Energy** is the ability to do work. You do work when you walk or move any part of your body. Your body uses energy every time you move or do something.

Energy exists in many forms. Energy in food is an example of chemical energy. Light and heat are two other forms of energy. Energy can be changed from one form to another. For example, chemical energy in food is changed to mechanical energy as you walk. The heat in your body also comes from the chemical energy in food.

By many standards, a hummingbird is probably more active than any other organism on earth. Its wings beat faster than those of any other bird. A hummingbird can hover like a helicopter. It can fly backward, forward, up, or down, with great speed. A hummingbird uses so much energy in its very active life that it must feed constantly. Suppose you were as active as a hummingbird. You would have to eat more than twice your own weight in food every day.

Making Sure

6. Define energy. List five examples of the use of energy by a living organism.

2:5 Cell Theory

Your body contains millions of cells. A **cell** is the basic unit of structure and function in an organism. Cells are like bricks that make a building. Cells are the basic building blocks of organisms. Many of life's activities take place inside cells. Most cells are too tiny to be seen without a microscope.

Robert Hooke (1635–1703), an English scientist, was the first person to see cells. He used a very simple microscope to see cells in a thin piece of cork. Cork comes from a plant. In the cork, Hook saw tiny boxlike holes. Each hole was surrounded by a wall. The cells Hooke saw were dead. They were the remains of cells that were once alive.

Every organism is made of cells and every cell comes from another cell. This idea is called the cell theory. What observations support the cell theory? Using microscopes, people have observed many times that organisms consist of cells. These repeated observations support the cell theory. It has also been observed over and over again that cells divide and form more cells. Every cell in an organism is produced by another cell.

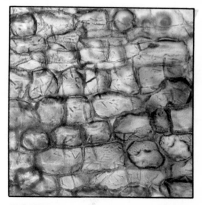

FIGURE 2–6. Using a simple microscope, Robert Hooke observed the remains of plant cells in a piece of cork.

What is the cell theory?

2:6 Cell Structure

All cells are alike in some ways. The cells of your body and the cells of a rose, puppy, tree, and mushroom have certain parts in common. For example, all cells have a cell membrane, cytoplasm, and material that controls the life of the cell. A **cell membrane** is a thin layer that surrounds and holds the parts of

FIGURE 2–7. How are the plant cells of *Elodea* (a), a cat stomach (b), and a mushroom (c) alike? How are they different?

a

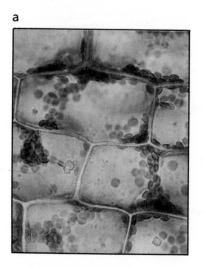

b

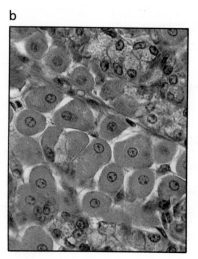

c

a cell together. It is made of proteins and fats. The cell membrane controls the movement of material into and out of a cell. Many kinds of materials can pass through a cell membrane.

In the cells of most organisms, there is a ball-shaped nucleus (NEW klee us). The nucleus contains a nucleolus and nucleoplasm. This material inside the **nucleus** controls the cell. You will usually find the nucleus in or near the center of a cell. It is surrounded by a thin nuclear membrane that separates it from the cytoplasm (SITE uh plaz um). **Cytoplasm** is the watery material of the cell. It does not contain the nucleus. The cytoplasm contains many cell materials such as proteins, enzymes, waste products, and salts.

Not every cell has a nucleus inside it. For example, a red blood cell loses its nucleus as it matures. Certain microscopic-sized organisms, such as bacteria, do not have nuclei in their cells. Nuclear material is present, but it is not separated from the cytoplasm by a nuclear membrane. Bacteria are one-celled organisms that can be seen with a microscope under high power.

Plant cells have certain features that animal cells do not have. Plant cells have a cell wall. A **cell wall** is a nonliving layer that surrounds the cell membrane of a plant cell. Water and other substances pass freely through a cell wall. Like the walls of a building, the cell wall provides shape and support for a cell. The cell walls in a plant provide support for it to stand and grow upright.

Compare the structures of a plant and an animal cell.

FIGURE 2–8. Bacteria (a) and mature red blood cells (b) contain no nuclei. Bacteria have nuclear material that is not enclosed in a nuclear membrane. Red blood cells lose their nuclei as they mature.

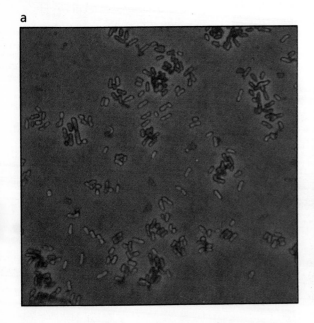

a

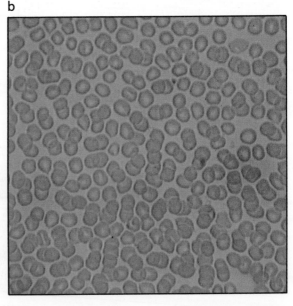

b

Activity 2–2 Comparing Cells

Problem: What do cells look like?

Materials microscope, 2 microscope slides, 2 coverslips, forceps, dropper, water, flat toothpick, methylene blue stain, *Elodea* leaf, glass-marking pencil, 15-mL dropping bottle

Procedure (1) Label one slide E for *Elodea*. (2) Remove a leaf from the tip of an Elodea plant and make a temporary wet mount slide. (3) Place the slide on the stage of the microscope with the leaf over the hole in the stage. (4) Examine the slide first under low power and then under high power. (5) Draw an *Elodea* cell. Label the cell parts that you observe. (6) Label the second slide C for cheek cell. (7) Put a drop of methylene blue on the microscope slide. (8) Use the blunt end of a toothpick to gently scrape the inside of your cheek. **CAUTION:** *Scrape lightly.* Cells will rub off on the toothpick, but you will not be able to see them. (9) Stir the end of the toothpick in the stain. Then throw the toothpick away. **CAUTION:** *Do not reuse toothpicks.* (10) Place a coverslip on the slide. (11) Examine the slide first under low power and then under high power. (12) Draw a cheek cell. Label the cell membrane, cytoplasm, and nucleus. Record any differences you notice between the *Elodea* cell and the cheek cell.

Questions (1) What parts of the *Elodea* cell did you observe? (2) What parts of the cheek cell did you observe? (3) How is the shape of the *Elodea* cell different from the shape of the cheek cell? (4) In what other ways are the cells different? (5) Why do you use high power to observe the cells? (6) What do cells look like?

FIGURE 2–9.

2:7 Cell Parts

Photographs of cells magnified 40 000 to 50 000 times show tubelike structures in the cytoplasm. The tubes form a network called the **endoplasmic reticulum** (en duh PLAZ mihk·rih TIHK yuh lum), or ER. The ER at times connects with the cell membrane or with the nuclear membrane. The ER changes constantly and is a place where many cell substances are made.

Ribosomes (RI buh sohmz) are tiny grainlike particles. They are so small they can be seen only with an electron microscope. **Ribosomes** are the sites in cells where proteins (PROH teenz) are made. Proteins are large, complex substances that are building

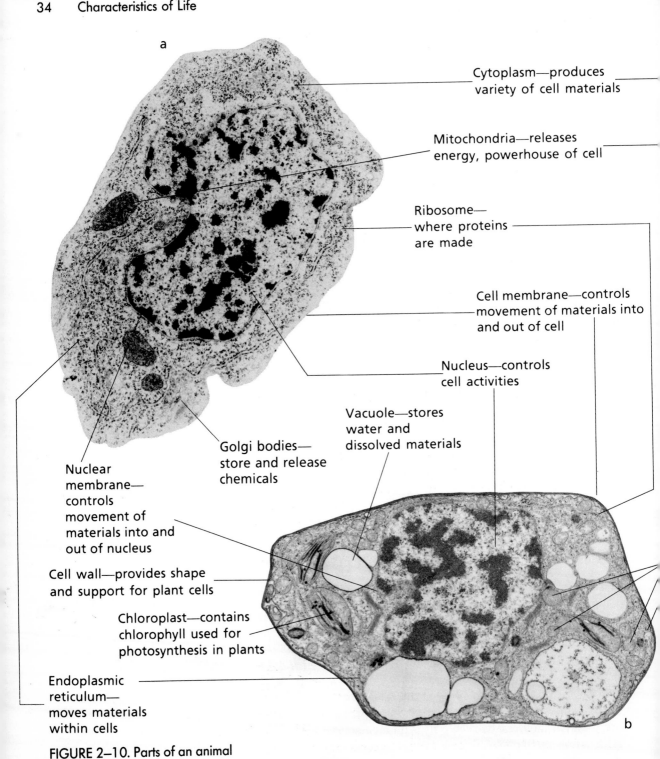

a

Cytoplasm—produces
variety of cell materials

Mitochondria—releases
energy, powerhouse of cell

Ribosome—
where proteins
are made

Cell membrane—controls
movement of materials into
and out of cell

Nucleus—controls
cell activities

Vacuole—stores
water and
dissolved materials

Nuclear
membrane—
controls
movement of
materials into and
out of nucleus

Golgi bodies—
store and release
chemicals

Cell wall—provides shape
and support for plant cells

Chloroplast—contains
chlorophyll used for
photosynthesis in plants

Endoplasmic
reticulum—
moves materials
within cells

b

FIGURE 2–10. Parts of an animal
cell (a) and a plant cell (b).

blocks of living substances. Ribosomes are made within the nucleolus in the nucleus of a cell. The ribosomes pass out of the nuclear membrane into the cytoplasm. Some ribosomes are found along the edges of the ER. Some form long strings in the cytoplasm. They both produce proteins.

Golgi (GAWL jee) bodies are found in cytoplasm, also. They are made by ER. They look like ER, but they are not connected to each other. **Golgi bodies** store and release chemicals in the cell. The chemicals affect other processes occurring in the cell.

Mitochondria (mite uh KAHN dree uh) are rod-shaped bodies in the cytoplasm. They are involved in the chemical reactions that release energy for use in the cell. For this reason, mitochondria are sometimes called the "powerhouses" of a cell.

Some cells have vacuoles (VAK yuh wohlz) and chloroplasts (KLOR uh plasts). A **vacuole** is a liquid-filled sac that stores water and dissolved materials. **Chloroplasts** are tiny disks that contain chlorophyll. Chlorophyll is a substance that makes a plant green. It traps energy from light that a plant uses to make food. Most chloroplasts are in the leaves of plants and in green stems.

Describe the parts of a plant and animal cell and their functions.

Making Sure

7. Describe what Robert Hooke saw when he first observed cells with a light microscope.
8. How is a cell wall different from a cell membrane?
9. Draw what a typical animal cell would look like. Label the parts of the cell and tell their functions.
10. What parts are found in plant cells but not in animal cells?
11. Explain how scientific methods were used to develop the cell theory.
12. If the nucleus controls a cell, how can bacteria survive with no nucleus?

2:8 Reproduction

From where do new organisms come? According to the cell theory, every cell comes from another cell. Cell division is the process in which a cell reproduces. During cell division, one cell divides to form two cells. Each of these cells divides to produce two more cells, and so on. Cell division is a form of asexual (ay SEKSH wul) reproduction. **Asexual reproduction** is the production of offspring from only one parent cell.

What is the difference between sexual and asexual reproduction?

Sexual reproduction is the production of offspring when nuclear material from two different cells combines. These different cells may be produced by two organisms of the same species or by a single organism. Sex cells are special cells produced in sex organs. Sex cells formed in the female sex organ are eggs. Sex cells formed in the male sex organ are sperm. Fertilization is the joining of an egg and sperm. The nucleus of one sperm joins with the nucleus of one egg. A single cell called a zygote is formed.

Cell division produces new cells as an organism grows in size. Also, cells that wear out and die are replaced by cell division. Every time you wash your hands or change your clothes, you rub off some dead skin cells. Cells in your skin divide and replace these cells.

How do cells reproduce?

One-celled organisms reproduce by cell division. For example, a bacterium divides into two bacteria. All plants and animals begin their lives as single cells. Repeated cell divisions produce a many-celled organism like a spider, rosebush, or whale.

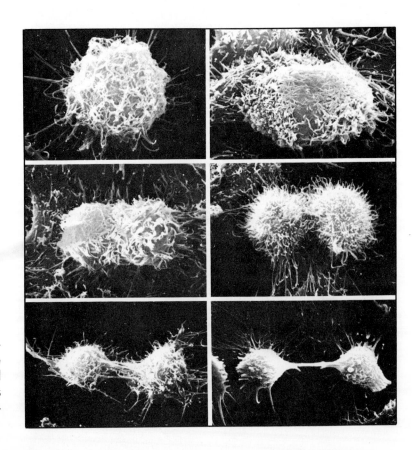

FIGURE 2–11. A scanning electron microscope was used to make these photographs of a human cell dividing. The hairlike projections on the surface of the cell are extensions of the cytoplasm.

Making Sure

13. What are female sex cells called?
14. What are male sex cells called?
15. How is a zygote formed?
16. How do one-celled organisms reproduce?

2:9 Mitosis and Cell Division

Mitosis (mi TOH sus) is the name given to the process in which the nucleus divides so that two new cells can form. During mitosis, the nucleus goes through four stages. In the first stage, nuclear material forms rodlike bodies called **chromosomes** (KROH muh sohmz). At the same time, the nuclear membrane slowly disappears. Many fine fibers appear that stretch across the cell.

In the next stage, the chromosomes line up along the middle of the cell and attach to the fibers. During the third stage, the chromosomes split apart. Two identical sets of chromosomes are formed. Each set of chromosomes is drawn away from the other by the fibers that slowly contract and pull the chromosomes apart. One set moves to each side of the cell.

In the fourth stage, the fibers disappear and two nuclei form. Each nucleus contains one set of chromosomes. Then the cell itself begins to divide as a cell membrane forms through the center of the cell. The membrane divides the cytoplasm between the two nuclei. Now the chromosomes are no longer visible. When the cell membrane is completed, two cells have been formed from one cell. Mitosis normally results in two nuclei with the same number and kinds of chromosomes. Mitosis can last five minutes to several hours, depending on the species.

The chromosomes inside the nucleus contain the life code of the cell. Because the two nuclei produced by mitosis have identical

Why does a cell have the same number of chromosomes as its parent cell?

FIGURE 2–12. The four stages of mitosis are prophase (a), metaphase (b), anaphase (c), and telophase (d).

a
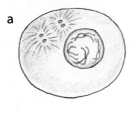

b
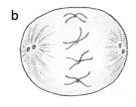

c
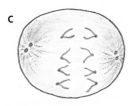

d
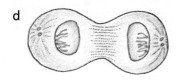

chromosomes, they have the same life code. Thus, cell activities and other features will be alike. Two cells formed by mitosis and cell division are copies of the cell from which they came.

Making Sure

17. How is mitosis important to the life of an organism?
18. Draw a series of diagrams that show what happens in mitosis. Write an explanation of each diagram.

2:10 Many-Celled Organisms

Some organisms are single cells. All of their life activities occur within one cell. Most one-celled organisms cannot be seen without a microscope. Most organisms have many cells.

The cells in complex many-celled organisms do different jobs that help keep the organisms alive. For example, a red blood cell carries oxygen. White blood cells fight disease. A green leaf cell absorbs energy from the sun. What special job is done by a muscle cell? A cell that does a certain job in a many-celled organism is called a specialized cell. You are made of billions of specialized cells.

FIGURE 2–13. Many-celled organisms in and around a pond are the conifers, shrubs, cattails, pondweed, and water lilies. A microscopic view of the pond water shows a green alga and a variety of one-celled organisms called plankton.

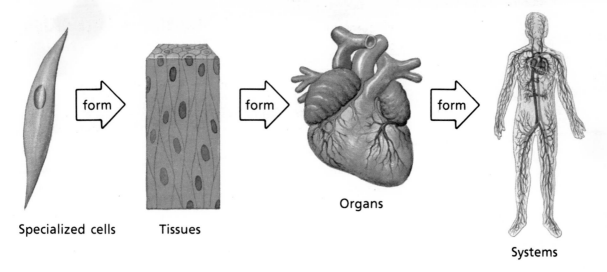

Specialized cells   Tissues   Organs   Systems

FIGURE 2–14. Complex many-celled organisms have body systems composed of organs that are made of tissues that are made of specialized cells.

Define tissue.

Define organ.

Define system.

A **tissue** is a group of similar cells that together perform a special job. Bone, muscle, blood, and nerve are kinds of tissues present in animals. Each tissue contains similar specialized cells. For example, muscle tissue contains muscle cells. Muscle cells are used to move body parts.

An **organ** is a group of tissues that work together to perform one or more life activities. Your heart is an organ that pumps blood. Lungs are organs used for breathing. The leaf of a plant is an organ that makes food. Other examples of organs are eye, ear, and nose. What life activities do these organs perform?

A **system** is a group of organs that work together to carry on life activities. Your brain is part of the nervous system in your body. Your eyes, ears, and nose are connected to your nervous system. A heart is part of the system that circulates blood in an animal. Systems in a plant circulate water, food, and minerals through the plant. Specialized cells are grouped together in tissues that make up organs, which are part of systems that keep organisms alive.

Making Sure

19. Name one system found in a plant or animal. Name some organs that are part of the system. Tell what tissues make up the organs. Tell what specialized cells make up the tissues.
20. Explain the relationship among cells, tissues, organs, systems, and organisms.

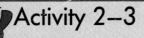

Problem: What is a tissue?

Materials

hamburger   forceps or toothpicks
3 microscope slides   pencil shavings
dropper   scissors
water   iodine stain
3 coverslips   15-mL plastic dropping bottle
microscope   glass-marking pencil
onion sections   apron
prepared slide of human blood

Procedure

1. Label three microscope slides H, P, and O.
2. Place a very small, *thin* piece of hamburger on the slide labeled H. Make a temporary wet mount slide by adding a drop of water and a coverslip.
3. Examine the cells under low power.
4. Examine the cells under high power. Draw and record your observations.
5. Place a thin part of the wood of a pencil shaving on the slide labeled P. Make a temporary wet mount slide by adding a drop of water and a coverslip.

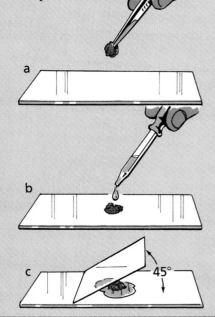

6. Examine the cells under low power.
7. Examine the cells under high power. Draw and record your observations.
8. Remove the thin membrane inside a piece of onion. **CAUTION:** *Always use scissors carefully.*
9. Place the small piece of the onion membrane on the microscope slide labeled O. Make a temporary wet mount slide by adding a drop of iodine stain and a coverslip. **CAUTION:** *Iodine stains skin and clothing.*
10. Examine under low power.
11. Examine under high power. Draw and record your observations.
12. Examine a prepared slide of human blood under low power, then switch to high power.
13. Draw and record your observations.

Data and Observations

Tissue	Observation	Description
Hamburger		
Pencil shaving		
Onion		
Blood		

Questions and Conclusions

1. What is the shape of the cells in the hamburger?
2. What is the only cell part visible in the pencil shaving cells? Why?
3. Describe the shape of the blood cells.
4. How are the onion cells, hamburger cells, and pencil shavings different from the blood cells?
5. What evidence do you have that each kind of cell makes up a different kind of tissue?
6. What is a tissue?

═══ Technology ═══
Probing Secrets of the Cell

The electron microscope is very useful in the study of the cell because of its extremely high magnification. It cannot, however, show scientists how the different parts of the cell function. Scientists use other tools to find out what the cell parts do. Different cell structures, such as the nucleus or mitochondria, have to be isolated from the cell before their functions can be studied. The two main tools that are used to isolate the different cell parts are the homogenizer and the ultracentrifuge.

The homogenizer is like a blender. It is used to break apart cells from tissue such as liver or kidney. A fluid is added to the tissue. Then the homogenizer blends the cells in a process that breaks the cell membranes. Different cell parts become suspended in the fluid that was added. This suspension of cell parts is then carefully poured into a test tube that is placed in the ultracentrifuge.

The ultracentrifuge is used for spinning solutions at very high speeds. Each cell structure has its own size, shape, and weight. When the suspensions are spun, the outward force is different for each cell structure. This causes each type of cell structure in the fluid to separate into different layers. These layers can be isolated and placed into separate test tubes. Computerized ultracentrifuges give fast results and produce clean separations. Computers are used to analyze the separate components and perform calculations on the results. The functions of the pure cell parts can then be determined. For example, the breakdown of sugar to produce carbon dioxide has been observed in isolated mitochondria. This suggests that mitochondria are the sites where energy is released in the cell.

The laser is another tool that cell biologists are using to study cell functions. Laser stands for *L*ight *A*mplification by the *S*timulated *E*mission of *R*adiation. The laser is a machine that produces a narrow beam of high-energy light. The beam can be used to make precise cuts in objects. A microscope and video system are combined and used to observe the effects of a laser beam on the cell. The laser beam is used to drill holes through the cells. Scientists can then observe how the cell functions without the parts. Their observations help researchers determine how the different parts of the cell work.

Using modern tools like the computerized ultracentrifuge and the laser, the functions of cells and their component parts can now be studied in greater detail.

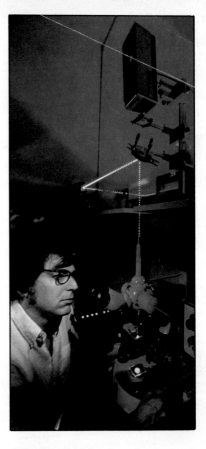

FIGURE 2–15. A microscope/video system is used to observe a human blood cell with two holes drilled by a laser beam. The reaction of the cell helps to determine the functions of the missing parts.

FOCUS ON
Skills

Understanding What You Read: Preview, Study, and Review

Preview

Previewing a chapter allows you to determine what you will learn before you actually begin to study. Basically, the preview prepares you to think about and understand the new material.

You will use three techniques for previewing a chapter. First, you should determine the scope and organization of the chapter. As you scan the chapter, note the main ideas or important points. Second, you should focus on the vocabulary. The vocabulary is a list of terms that you must understand in order to make sense out of the new information. Finally, you should determine the purpose of the chapter. Practice these three techniques as we preview Chapter 2.

Scope and Organization

1. Look at the goals for Chapter 2. Based on these goals, think of several questions that may be answered in this chapter.
2. Look at the section titles. These titles are the authors' outline. They show how the information is divided into subjects.
3. Look at Summary at the end of the chapter. Important ideas are listed here. Reading this section tells you the main ideas discussed in the chapter.
4. Quickly glance at the illustrations throughout the chapter. These illustrations suggest ideas about the information to be studied. Pictures also support the main ideas by providing examples.

Vocabulary

1. Look at the vocabulary list at the end of the chapter. How many words do you know? How could you find the meanings of the words you do not know?

2. Using context clues in this chapter, determine the meanings of each term in boldface type.

Purpose for Reading

1. Think of the purposes for reading the chapter by forming a question from each section title. Then scan the chapter. As you read, write answers to the questions you thought of when you decided the purposes for reading the chapter.
2. There are several things you should do as you read. First, write down each term that is new to you. Using context clues, write a definition for each new vocabulary word. Confirm definitions by using the glossary.

Study

After reading each section of the chapter, write the answers to Making Sure questions and to questions in the margins. Answering the questions as you go along tests your understanding of the authors' main ideas. It also gives you a written record of the main points to use in preparing for class discussions and tests.

Review

Test yourself. Have you achieved the goals stated in the beginning of the chapter? Review your vocabulary list and your answers to all questions. As a final test, complete the chapter review. Another study technique, outlining, can help you understand new information. Outlining will be discussed in a later Focus on Skills.

Remember, for each chapter, you should preview, study, and review. If you take the time to use all three steps, you will be sure to get the most out of every chapter.

Summary

1. Organisms consist of one or more cells, reproduce, have life cycles, respond to their environments, and carry on life activities.   2:1
2. Organisms grow and change throughout their lives.   2:1
3. Adaptations help organisms survive in their environment.   2:2
4. Organisms need water. Carbon dioxide and oxygen are two other important life substances.   2:3
5. Organisms need energy for life activities.   2:4
6. All organisms are made of one or more cells. Every cell is produced from another cell.   2:5
7. All cells contain cytoplasm and a cell membrane.   2:6
8. Most cells have nuclear material that controls the activities of the cell.   2:6
9. Cytoplasm contains structures that produce, store, and release substances and control their movement within cells.   2:7
10. Organisms produce offspring by sexual or asexual reproduction.   2:8
11. Mitosis is an orderly process of cell division in which the chromosome number of the cells is kept the same.   2:9
12. Tissues are grouped together to form organs that work as systems and perform complex life activities in organisms.   2:10

Vocabulary

Write a sentence using the following words or terms correctly.

adaptation	endoplasmic reticulum	reproduction
asexual reproduction	energy	ribosomes
cell	Golgi bodies	sexual
cell membrane	mitochondria	reproduction
cell wall	mitosis	system
chloroplasts	nucleus	tissue
chromosomes	organ	vacuole
cytoplasm		

Questions

Do not write in this book.

A. True or False

Determine whether each of the following sentences is true or false. Rewrite the false statements to make them correct.

1. A cell is the basic unit of structure and function in every organism.
2. Every organism has a life span.

3. You use energy when you are writing.
4. Energy can be obtained from food.
5. Water contains carbon and oxygen.
6. A cell membrane controls movement of material in and out of a cell.
7. Plant cells and animal cells have the exact same parts.
8. The gills of a fish are an adaptation for living on land.
9. The endoplasmic reticulum is sometimes connected with the membrane of the nucleus.
10. Most chloroplasts are in the stems of plants.

B. Multiple Choice
Choose the word or phase that correctly completes the following sentences.
1. The process of producing offspring is *(adaptation, reproduction, cytoplasm)*.
2. *(Light, Water, Oxygen)* is a source of energy.
3. *(Water, Carbon, Oxygen)* makes up about 70 percent of an organism's mass.
4. In organisms, food and oxygen together cause *(protein, ER, energy)* to be released.
5. The *(cell membrane, nucleus, cytoplasm)* controls the activities of a cell.
6. The cell membrane in a plant cell is surrounded by a *(vacuole, chloroplast, ribosome, cell wall)*.
7. Chloroplasts are found in *(all, plant, all animal)* cells.
8. In mitosis, the number of chromosomes in a cell is *(reduced, unchanged)*.
9. A(n) *(tissue, organ, cell)* is the basic unit of an organism.
10. All the material inside the cell membrane that is not nuclear material is *(endoplasmic reticulum, ribosomes, cytoplasm)*.

C. Completion
Complete each of the following sentences with the correct word or phrase.
1. The changes in an animal that occur from its birth to its death are part of its _____.
2. Heat in your body comes from the energy in _____.
3. Mitochondria are structures that release _____.
4. _____ are rodlike bodies that appear during mitosis.
5. A(n) _____ is a group of similar cells that perform a special task.
6. A heart is a(n) _____ that is part of a system.
7. A(n) _____ is an organ that makes food in a plant.
8. Organisms produce new organisms like themselves in a process called _____.

9. A characteristic of an organism that makes the organism suited to its environment is a(n) _____.
10. _____ traps energy from light that a plant uses to make food.

D. How and Why

1. Is a tomato seed living or nonliving? Explain.
2. Why is reproduction necessary for the survival of a kind of organism?
3. Why do living things need energy?
4. Why must an organism get rid of wastes that it produces?
5. List three responses to your environment that help keep you alive.
6. Draw a diagram of a plant cell and label its main parts.
7. How does a cell obtain energy for its life activities?
8. Describe briefly the changes that occur in mitosis.

Ideas to Explore

1. **Project:** Make a three-dimensional model of a cell and its parts.
2. **Challenge:** Write a report on the work of Matthias Schleiden and Theodor Schwann and the cell theory.
3. **Project:** Use pipe cleaners, string, cardboard, colored pens, or other materials to construct a model of a stage in mitosis. Label the parts of the model.
4. **Project:** Make a bulletin board or poster showing animal or plant adaptations. Use pictures from old magazines or make your own drawings.

Readings

Angyal, Jennifer. *Mitosis and Meiosis Illustrated*. Burlington, NC: Carolina Biological Supply, 1980.

Bantock, Cuillin. *The Story of Life*. New York: Peter Bedrick, 1984.

National Geographical Society. *Secrets of Animal Survival*. Washington, DC: National Geographic Society, 1983.

Silverstein, Alvin and Virginia B. Silverstein. *Cells: Building Blocks of Life*. Englewood Cliffs, NJ: Prentice-Hall, 1980.

The cells of organisms contain a variety of chemical compounds. The chemical compounds are involved in many cell activities. Scientists ask questions about cell chemistry in order to discover more about whole organisms. The leaf of the prayer plant (Maranta leuconeura) carries out many chemical activities that we cannot see. What kinds of chemical compounds are found in the cells of the prayer plant? What functions do the compounds perform?

CHAPTER 3
STRUCTURE OF LIFE

3:1 Matter

Every living organism is made of matter. Matter is anything that has mass and takes up space. As a young organism grows into an adult, the matter in its body increases. How much has the matter in your body increased since you were a baby?

Just as cells are the building blocks of organisms, atoms are the building blocks of matter. An **atom** is the smallest particle of an element that has the properties of the element. An **element** is a substance that cannot be broken down into simpler substances. Carbon, hydrogen, oxygen, iron, gold, and lead are examples of elements. There are more than 100 elements. Each element is composed of one kind of atom. Carbon atoms make up carbon, iron atoms make up iron, and so on.

The atoms of elements bond together to form compounds. A **compound** contains two or more different kinds of atoms bonded together. Water is a compound composed of hydrogen and oxygen atoms. Carbon dioxide is a carbon and oxygen compound. Sugar is a compound made of carbon, hydrogen, and oxygen atoms. The elements in a compound are chemically combined.

Some compounds can be broken down into molecules (MAHL uh kyewlz). A **molecule** contains two or more atoms bonded together into one particle. For example, a water molecule has two atoms of hydrogen and one atom of oxygen. A carbon dioxide molecule has one atom of carbon and two atoms of oxygen. For molecular compounds, a molecule is the smallest particle that has the properties of the compound.

GOALS:
1. You will learn the relationship of chemistry to living things.
2. You will learn to distinguish organic from inorganic compounds.
3. You will learn about processes that occur in cells.

What is the difference between an element and a compound?

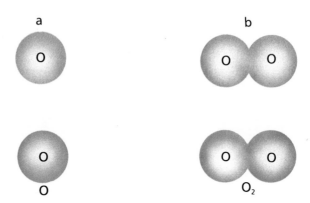

a   b

O₂

FIGURE 3–1. Oxygen is an element. Two atoms of oxygen are shown in (a). Two molecules of oxygen each containing two atoms are shown in (b).

Define matter, mixture, atom, and molecule.

Some molecules contain two or more atoms of the same element. About 78 percent of the air you breathe consists of nitrogen. One molecule of nitrogen contains two atoms of nitrogen bonded together. Another molecule in air is ozone. One molecule of ozone contains three oxygen atoms.

Have you ever used a kitchen blender to mix something? A **mixture** is two or more substances blended, but not bonded,

Activity 3-1   Chemical Changes

Problem: How can you tell if a chemical change takes place?

Materials   4 test tubes, test tube rack, graduated cylinder, glass-marking pencil, pH test paper, milk, tea, baking soda solution, vinegar, apron

Procedure   (1) Label four test tubes M for milk, T for tea, B for baking soda solution, and V for vinegar. (2) Pour 15 mL of milk into test tube M. (3) Pour 15 mL of tea into test tube T. (4) Pour 15 mL of baking soda solution into test tube B. (5) Pour 15 mL of vinegar into test tube V. (6) Test the pH of each solution and record the results. pH is a measure of the acidity of the solution. (7) Add 5 mL of vinegar to each test tube. Record your observations before adding the vinegar to the next test tube. (8) Test the pH of each solution after adding the vinegar. Record the results.

Questions   (1) How did the pH of each solution before adding vinegar compare to the pH after adding vinegar? (2) In which test tubes did a chemical change occur? (3) What evidence do you have that a chemical change occurred? (4) What was the purpose of test tube V? (5) How can you tell if a chemical change takes place?

together. The substances in a mixture are not chemically combined. The air you breathe is a mixture of gases, including nitrogen and ozone. Blood is a mixture of water, cells, and various compounds. The cytoplasm inside a cell is a mixture.

3:2 Symbols and Formulas

What states do these abbreviations represent: NM, IN, NY, TX, CA? States are represented with letter symbols. Letter symbols are used to represent elements, too. For example, C stands for carbon, H stands for hydrogen, and O stands for oxygen. Cl is the symbol for chlorine. Fe is the symbol for iron. When there are two letters in a symbol, the first letter is a capital and the second is a small letter.

Formulas are abbreviations for compounds. Examples of formulas are H_2O for water and CO_2 for carbon dioxide. The formula for table sugar is $C_{12}H_{22}O_{11}$. The small numbers in the formulas are called subscripts. In these examples, the subscripts show how many atoms of the elements are in the molecule of the compound. How many hydrogen atoms are in a water molecule? How many are in the sugar molecule?

Equations can be used to show how elements combine to form compounds. For example, $C + O_2 \rightarrow CO_2$ is an equation for the burning of carbon. It is read, "Carbon plus oxygen yields carbon dioxide." The + sign tells you that the carbon and oxygen are combined. The $\rightarrow$ means yields or produces. For the combining of hydrogen and oxygen, the equation is $2H_2 + O_2 \rightarrow 2H_2O$. It is read, "Two molecules of hydrogen plus one molecule of oxygen

What are symbols and formulas? Give two examples of each.

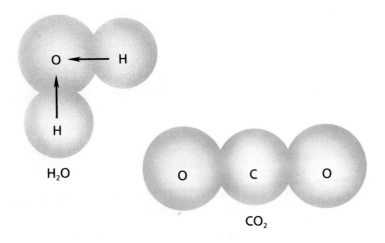

H_2O

CO_2

FIGURE 3–2. Water and carbon dioxide molecules

yields two molecules of water." Note the 2 in front of the water. This number indicates that two molecules of water are formed in the reaction.

This equation is balanced. Balanced means there is the same number of each kind of atom on both sides of the arrow. On the left side of this equation, there are four atoms of hydrogen and two atoms of oxygen. On the right side, there are two molecules of water. They contain *four* atoms of hydrogen and two atoms of oxygen. Since there are four atoms of hydrogen and two atoms of oxygen on each side of the arrow, the equation is balanced. Equations must be balanced to show that matter is not created or destroyed in a chemical reaction.

When an electric current is passed through water, the compound breaks down into hydrogen and oxygen. Here is the equation for the reaction: $2H_2O \rightarrow 2H_2 + O_2$. It is read, "Water yields hydrogen plus oxygen." Note that the two molecules of water break up to produce two molecules of hydrogen and one molecule of oxygen.

3:3 Organic Compounds

Define organic compound.

All **organic** (or GAN ihk) compounds contain the element carbon. Sugar, artificial sweeteners, and the acid in vinegar are examples of organic compounds. Most organic compounds contain hydrogen. Many have oxygen as well. Petroleum is a liquid formed from the remains of organisms that lived long ago. It is a mixture of organic compounds.

FIGURE 3–3. Many common household products contain organic compounds.

Important organic compounds in organisms are sugar, starch, fats, proteins, and vitamins. Sugar is produced in the leaves of green plants. Both plant and animal cells obtain their energy from sugar. Starch is made by bonding sugar molecules together to form larger starch molecules. Plants store starch in their fruits, seeds, stems, and roots. Many foods that animals eat contain starch. All of these organic compounds contain carbon, hydrogen, and oxygen. Blood sugar, for instance, has the formula $C_6H_{12}O_6$. Chlorophyll has the formula $C_{55}H_{72}MgN_4O_5$.

Protein contains nitrogen as well as carbon, hydrogen, and oxygen. Some proteins also contain sulfur and phosphorus. A protein molecule is made of smaller units called amino (uh MEE noh) acids. Amino acids are the building blocks of protein. Plants take in nitrogen from the soil in which they grow and use it to make protein. You obtain protein from foods you eat. For example, egg white is rich in protein.

Cells contain nucleic acids, which are organic compounds. Nucleic acids contain a life code that controls and regulates the activities of a cell. Vitamins are complex organic compounds cells use in carrying on their life processes. Animals obtain certain vitamins from the foods they eat. Other vitamins are made inside their bodies.

Cellulose (SEL yuh lohs) is an important organic compound in the cell walls of plants. Cellulose accounts for 50 percent or more of all the carbon in plants. Wood is about one-half cellulose. Cotton is at least 90 percent cellulose.

FIGURE 3—4. Cotton is mostly cellulose.

What elements are present in sugar, protein, and cellulose?

Making Sure

1. What are the building blocks of matter?
2. Is O_2 an atom or a molecule? Explain.
3. Name five organic compounds. What elements are present in each?
4. What are nucleic acids and what is their function?
5. What are the building blocks of protein?

3:4 Cell Processes

Cells use certain substances to carry on the activities that keep them alive. These substances, dissolved in water, enter the cell. A mixture of water and some substance dissolved in it is a water solution. The particles of the substance in solution are so small you cannot see them. Have you ever put a small amount of salt in water? The salt dissolves and forms a solution.

Some solutions are more concentrated than others. This means that there are more particles of the substance dissolved in a certain volume. Suppose you fill two cups with water. In one cup, you add one spoonful of salt. The salt dissolves in the water and forms a solution. In the second cup, you dissolve two spoonfuls of salt. The concentration of salt is greater in the second cup. It has twice as much salt per unit of volume as the first cup. The greater the number of particles in a given volume, the greater the concentration.

Particles of substances in solution move by diffusion (dihf YEW zhun) through a cell membrane according to their concentration. **Diffusion** is the movement of particles from where they are more concentrated to where they are less concentrated. Diffusion results in the spreading out of particles. The particles spread out evenly in all the available space.

Cells may move substances in a direction opposite to the way they would move by diffusion. **Active transport** is the movement of materials by living cells from areas of low concentration to areas of high concentration. For example, many organisms that live in the ocean have a higher concentration of iodine than the water around them. Iodine is an element in solution in ocean water. Certain small marine plants and animals move iodine into their cells by active transport. The iodine goes directly from the ocean water into the cells of these organisms. Cells must always use energy to carry out active transport.

Define diffusion.

FIGURE 3–5. When you water a plant, water becomes more concentrated in soil than in the plant roots. Water diffuses into the roots by osmosis from greater to lesser concentration (a). Some minerals are more concentrated in plant roots than in the soil. When you fertilize a plant, the minerals still move into the plant roots by active transport, from lesser to greater concentration (b).

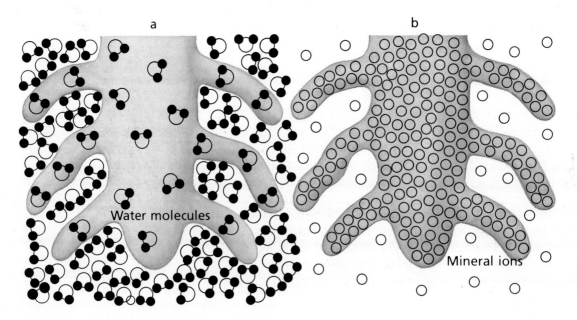

a   b

Water molecules

Mineral ions

FIGURE 3–6. Water enters the roots of plants by osmosis.

3:5 Osmosis

Osmosis (ahs MOH sus) is the diffusion of water through a membrane. The water diffuses from the side of the membrane where it is more concentrated to the opposite side. Water enters and leaves a cell by osmosis. For example, cells in the roots of a plant get water from the soil by osmosis. The water you drink enters your blood and all your body cells by osmosis.

Diffusion of water into a cell by osmosis builds up pressure in the cell. This pressure is called osmotic (ahs MAHT ihk) pressure. It pushes outward on the cell membrane and gives the cell shape. Osmotic pressure is similar to air pressure inside a balloon filled with air. Also, it is like water pressure inside a plastic bag filled with water. Osmotic pressure inside a normal cell is greater than the pressure in most automobile and bicycle tires.

Water can move out of a cell as well as into a cell by osmosis. If a cell is placed in a concentrated saltwater solution, water diffuses out of the cell. Loss of water causes the cells to shrink and become limp. For example, living plant cells can be placed in salt water and observed with a microscope. What does the observer see? The cytoplasm shrivels and pulls away from the cell walls. The change is caused by water diffusing out of the cells. The shrinking of cytoplasm caused by the loss of water is called **plasmolysis** (plaz MAHL uh sus). Plasmolysis can cause the cells to die. A very large water loss from many cells can cause an organism to die.

Define osmosis.

How is osmotic pressure produced in a cell?

Define plasmolysis.

Making Sure

6. How is diffusion different from active transport?
7. How is the concentration of a solution determined?
8. Why is osmosis an important process for organisms?
9. What happens to a cell when too much water moves out of it by osmosis?

Activity 3-2

Diffusion and Osmosis

Problem: How does osmosis occur?

Materials

3 150-mL beakers   starch solution
2 250-mL beakers   10% salt solution
dropper   2 15 cm lengths of dialysis tubing
water   string
graduated cylinder   test tube
iodine solution   2 raw potato slices
apron

Procedure

Part A

1. Label three 150-mL beakers A, B, and C.
2. Put 60 mL of iodine solution in beaker A and beaker C. **CAUTION:** *Iodine solution is poisonous and can cause stains or burns.* Rinse spills with plenty of water. Put 60 mL of starch solution in beaker B.
3. Soak two 15 cm lengths of dialysis tubing in water. Tie one end of each tube with a string tightly.
4. Pour starch solution in one dialysis tube until it is about half full. Tie the other end tightly. Carefully rinse the tube with water. Place the tube in beaker A.
5. Pour iodine solution into the other dialysis tube until it is half full. Tie the other end very tightly. Carefully rinse the tube with water. Place the tube in beaker B.
6. Fill a test tube half full of starch solution. Record in the chart the color of the starch solution. Place the test tube upright in beaker C.
7. Allow the beakers to stand 20 minutes. (Go on to Part B.)
8. Record in the chart the colors of the solutions after 20 minutes.

Part B

1. Label two 250-mL beakers 1 and 2.
2. Put a raw potato slice in each beaker. Record in the chart your observations of the potato slices.
3. Add 200 mL of water to beaker 1. Add 200 mL of salt solution to beaker 2.
4. Allow the beakers to stand for 20 minutes.
5. Remove the potato slices.
6. Record in the chart your observations of the potato slices.

Data and Observations

Part A

Apparatus	Color of starch solution	
	At beginning	After 20 minutes
bag in beaker A		
beaker B		
test tube in beaker C		

Part B

Beaker	Observations of potato slice	
	At beginning	After 20 minutes
1		
2		

Questions and Conclusions

1. What substance diffuses through the dialysis tube? What substance does not? Explain how you know.
2. What does the dialysis tube in Part A represent?
3. What is the purpose of the test tube in beaker C?
4. How does a potato slice change in salt water?
5. Explain the process that causes the potato slice to change. What is this process called?
6. What is the purpose of the potato slice placed in beaker 1?
7. Why can some molecules pass through the membrane and not others?
8. How does osmosis occur?

3:6 Cell Enzymes

Cells contain many different compounds. Some of these compounds diffuse into a cell through the cell membrane. Others are produced from simpler substances that enter the cell by diffusion. These substances are combined through chemical changes to form compounds used by the cell.

A **chemical change** occurs when a substance changes into a new and different substance. The combining of carbon and oxygen to form carbon dioxide is an example of a chemical change. Chemical changes that go on inside a cell control the life of the cell. For instance, all of a cell's energy is produced by chemical changes.

What is a chemical change?

For most chemical changes that occur inside a cell, there are enzymes (EN zimez) that control the changes. An **enzyme** is an organic compound produced by a cell that regulates the rate of a chemical change. For example, an enzyme in saliva controls the breakdown of starch in the mouth. It is estimated that a single cell may contain a thousand different enzymes. Enzymes are made according to the life code in a cell's nucleic acid.

What is an enzyme?

Metabolism (muh TAB uhl iz um) is the sum total of the chemical changes that keep an organism alive. For example, organisms use food and oxygen to obtain energy. Chemical changes involved in the growth, repair, and division of cells are also part of metabolism. The rate of an organism's metabolism may vary. For example, the rate of metabolism is high in a young, rapidly growing animal or plant. When an animal is resting or asleep, its rate of metabolism is lower than when it is active. An organism dies when metabolism ceases.

Define metabolism.

FIGURE 3–7. During sleep, the rate of metabolism decreases.

Activity 3–3

Enzyme Activity

Problem: What affects enzyme activity?

Materials

3% hydrogen peroxide ($2H_2O_2$)
11 test tubes
test tube rack
raw potato
raw turnip
raw liver
raw hamburger
yeast culture
apron
granulated cylinder
cooked potato
cooked turnip
cooked liver
cooked hamburger
boiled yeast culture
glass-marking pencil

Data and Observations

Test Tube	Food	Observation
1	raw potato	
2	raw turnip	
3	raw liver	
4	raw hamburger	
5	yeast culture	
1A	cooked potato	
2A	cooked turnip	
3A	cooked liver	
4A	cooked hamburger	
5A	boiled yeast culture	

Procedure

1. Label 5 test tubes 1 through 5. Label 5 test tubes 1A, 2A, 3A, 4A, and 5A. Label one more test tube C for control.
2. Pour 10 mL of 3% hydrogen peroxide into each test tube. **CAUTION:** *Avoid spilling hydrogen peroxide.*
3. To test tube 1, add a small piece of raw potato. To test tube 2, add a small piece of raw turnip. To test tube 3, add a small piece of liver. To test tube 4, add a small amount of hamburger. To test tube 5, add some yeast culture.
4. Observe each test tube and record your observations in a data table.
5. Predict what will happen when you add each cooked item to a test tube.
6. To test tube 1A, add cooked potato. To test tube 2A, add cooked turnip. To test tube 3A, add cooked liver. To test tube 4A, add cooked hamburger. To test tube 5A, add boiled yeast culture.
7. Observe each test tube and record your observations.

Questions and Conclusions

1. Catalase is an enzyme found in many foods. Catalase causes a chemical reaction in hydrogen peroxide: $2H_2O_2 \rightarrow 2H_2O + O_2$. Which foods contain catalase? Why do you think so?
2. What effect does cooking have on the enzyme activity of the foods? Explain.
3. What is the purpose of tube C?
4. What affects enzyme activity?

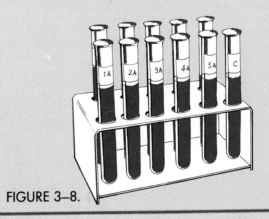

FIGURE 3–8.

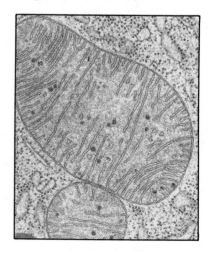

FIGURE 3–9. All of your daily activities require energy.

3:7 Cell Respiration

Growing, walking, running, swimming, flying, and thinking are all activities that require energy. What activity that you do requires the most energy? **Respiration** is the process by which cells use food and oxygen to obtain energy. Without a continuous supply of energy, a cell will die.

Cells obtain energy through aerobic (ehr ROB ihk) respiration. **Aerobic** means with oxygen. Aerobic respiration is a chemical change in which a food such as glucose is broken down with the help of oxygen. In this reaction, water and carbon dioxide are produced. Energy is released in the reaction. The equation below shows the change.

$$\underset{\text{glucose (food)}}{C_6H_{12}O_6} + \underset{\text{oxygen}}{6\ O_2} \rightarrow \underset{\substack{\text{carbon}\\\text{dioxide}}}{6\ CO_2} + \underset{\text{water}}{6\ H_2O} + \text{energy}$$

Some kinds of cells can release energy from organic compounds through anaerobic respiration. **Anaerobic** means without oxygen. In anaerobic respiration, energy is released in a chemical change that occurs in the cytoplasm without oxygen. For example, yeast cells convert sugar to alcohol through anaerobic respiration. Vinegar is produced by anaerobic respiration in a certain kind of bacteria. Energy is released in both cases. During strenuous exercise, muscle cells may lack enough oxygen. At this time, energy is released by anaerobic respiration.

All aerobic respiration is dependent upon mitochondria. The mitochondria in a cell's cytoplasm contain the enzymes needed for respiration. A muscle cell may contain more than one thousand mitochondria.

FIGURE 3–10. Most of a cell's energy is released by respiration in which the mitochondria play a major role. This mitochondrion is magnified 64 000 times.

3:8 Homeostasis

Systems of feedback regulate the metabolism of an organism. You know about other systems of feedback. One example is a thermostat that controls the temperature of a room. If the room gets too cold, the thermostat turns the heater on. When the room gets too warm, the thermostat turns the heater off. Another example of feedback is a switch that turns streetlights on at night and off again at daybreak. Feedback is a signal to a device that controls an activity. In the thermostat example, the temperature is feedback that signals the thermostat to increase or decrease the heat. In the streetlight example, daylight is feedback that signals the switch to turn the streetlights on or off. In an organism, **feedback** is a signal to decrease, increase, or maintain a life activity.

Every organism has systems of feedback that help it maintain a balanced state. For example, if you become too warm from exercise, you begin to sweat. The evaporation of sweat cools your body. If body temperature falls too low, the blood vessels in the skin contract to reduce heat loss. When you exercise, you breathe faster and as a result, the supply of oxygen to your muscles increases. On a hot day, the pores in the leaves of a plant may close to prevent loss of moisture.

FIGURE 3–11. A street light contains a switch that is sensitive to light. At dusk, the switch turns on the light (a). At daybreak, the switch turns off the light (b).

a

b

FIGURE 3–12. Deciduous trees respond to changes in day length. A feedback mechanism controls growth and development. When day length begins to decrease, cell production decreases. When day length begins to increase, cell production increases and flowering occurs.

Homeostasis (hoh mee oh STAY sus) is the tendency of an organism to maintain a balanced state. The balanced state is maintained through the careful and constant control of chemical changes inside cells. When an organism needs more energy, respiration is increased inside its cells. The removal of wastes produced in respiration is also increased. If a cell is low in raw materials for growth or repair of cell parts, diffusion and active transport into the cell are increased. When enough of a cell substance is produced, its production is decreased or stopped.

Homeostasis helps an organism survive. It enables it to adjust to daily and seasonal changes in its surroundings. For example, organisms adjust to daily changes in temperature and sunlight. Changes in the weather and hours of daylight also occur from season to season. At times, the food or water supply may be low. Feedback mechanisms involved in homeostasis help an organism adapt to these and other changes in its environment.

Give an example of homeostasis.

Making Sure

10. How do enzymes control cells?
11. What kinds of chemical changes are part of metabolism?
12. How is oxygen involved in cell respiration?
13. Compare aerobic and anaerobic respiration.
14. How does feedback control cell activities?

Petroleum Geologists

What do gasoline, a polyester shirt, and petroleum jelly have in common? They are all products of petroleum, a fossil fuel formed by the decay of marine organisms over millions of years. Fossil fuels are organic compounds made of carbon, hydrogen, and other elements.

Oil companies constantly experiment with ways to improve the efficiency of fossil fuels. The performance level of a fossil fuel depends largely on the purity of its catalyst. A catalyst is a substance that speeds up a reaction. Debbie Hsieh is a laboratory technician for a major oil company. She conducts experiments to determine the purity of different catalysts. For example, the element sulfur is highly undesirable in a catalyst because it slows the combustion reaction. Ms. Hsieh must make sure that the sulfur content of a catalyst is below a certain level.

Ms. Hsieh follows a careful routine for her tests. First, the test materials are weighed and sealed into small capsules. Then the samples are arranged on a tray to be burned. Ms. Hsieh tests for the amount of carbon, hydrogen, nitrogen, and sulfur present in each sample.

Although her major in college was in another field, Ms. Hsieh took courses in chemistry, calculus, and computer programming to prepare her for her present job. As a change of pace from her lab work, she conducts tours of the facilities.

Another kind of oil research is done by Lien-Chu Yang, a micropaleontologist (my kroh pay lee ahn TAHL uh jist). Ms. Yang studies microscopic fossils to determine the age of the rocks in which they are found. These fossils are also clues to the environment in which the enclosing rocks formed. Ms. Yang earned a bachelor's degree in biology and a master's degree in geology. After college, Ms. Yang worked as a lab technician and a research assistant. During this time, she gained experience in processing samples and conducting research projects.

In a typical day, Ms. Yang examines rock samples from both oil well cuttings and outcrops. Well cuttings are rock fragments that are obtained from deep drilling. Outcrops are rock layers exposed at Earth's surface. Ms. Yang examines the samples with a microscope and records data such as the type and age of fossils present, the environment in which the rock formed, and other geologic data. She enters this information into the computer and then determines whether or not an oil drilling project should begin or continue.

Ms. Yang says, "I would also like to improve my background in computer science." She believes this would enhance the learning process by decreasing the time spent doing calculations and analyses by hand.

CHAPTER 3
Review

Summary

1. Living things are made of matter composed of elements and compounds.   3:1
2. Equations containing symbols and formulas are used to show chemical changes.   3:2
3. Important organic compounds found in cells are sugar, starch, fat, protein, and cellulose.   3:3
4. Diffusion and active transport move substances in and out of cells.   3:4
5. Water enters or leaves a cell by moving through the cell membrane to the side where it is least concentrated.   3:5
6. Chemical changes regulated by enzymes control the processes inside a cell.   3:6
7. Cells obtain energy through aerobic respiration in the mitochondria and anaerobic respiration in the cytoplasm.   3:7
8. Feedback mechanisms maintain homeostasis by regulating the metabolism of an organism.   3:8

Vocabulary

Write a sentence using the following words or terms correctly.

active transport	diffusion	molecule
aerobic	enzyme	mixture
anaerobic	element	organic compound
atom	feedback	osmosis
chemical change	homeostasis	plasmolysis
compound	metabolism	respiration

Questions

Do not write in this book.

A. True or False

Determine whether each of the following sentences is true or false. Rewrite the false statements to make them correct.

1. Molecules are made of atoms.
2. New substances are formed in a chemical change.
3. Cl is the formula for chlorine.
4. $C_6H_{12}O_6$ is an organic compound.
5. Starch contains nitrogen.
6. Blood sugar is made of carbon, hydrogen, and oxygen.

7. Substances move from where they are most concentrated to where they are least concentrated.
8. Loss of water by osmosis causes the pressure in a cell to increase.
9. Your rate of metabolism is highest when you are sleeping.
10. In aerobic respiration, wastes are produced.

B. Multiple Choice
Choose the word or phrase that correctly completes the following statements.
1. Every organic compound contains *(carbon, oxygen, phosphorus, nitrogen)*.
2. *(Sugar, Water)* is an organic compound.
3. A(n) *(element, compound, organic compound)* cannot be broken down into simpler substances.
4. When sugar breaks down with the help of oxygen in a cell, *(carbon, protein, carbon dioxide)* is formed.
5. Chemical changes inside cells are controlled by *(diffusion, osmosis, enzymes, the cell membrane)*.
6. *(Nucleic acids, Enzymes, Sugars, Ribosomes)* contain a life code that regulates a cell.
7. A *(sugar, starch, protein, cellulose)* molecule is made of smaller units called amino acids.
8. The greater the number of particles in a given volume, the *(greater, lesser, more soluble)* the concentration of the solution.
9. *(Aerobic, Anaerobic, Active transport)* means without oxygen.
10. *(Osmosis, Feedback, Plasmolysis, Homeostasis)* is the tendency of an organism to maintain a balanced state.

C. Completion
Complete each of the following sentences with the correct word or phrase.
1. A substance diffuses from an area of _____ concentration to an area of _____ concentration.
2. An element is made of particles called _____.
3. Osmosis is the diffusion of water through a(n) _____.
4. Inside an organism, food breaks down with the help of _____.
5. Equations must be balanced because matter cannot be _____ in a reaction.
6. In an organism, feedback is a signal to _____ a life activity.
7. $C_6H_{12}O_6 + 6\ O_2 \rightarrow 6\ CO_2 + 6\ H_2O +$ _____.
8. _____ is the sum total of the chemical changes that keep an organism alive.

9. Protein contains _____ as well as carbon, hydrogen, and oxygen.

10. _____ are used to show how elements combine to form compounds.

D. How and Why

1. What are nucleic acids and what are their functions?
2. What would you expect to happen to a raw carrot stored in salt water? Why?
3. How does osmosis affect the size and shape of a cell?
4. Write the formulas for table sugar, blood sugar, carbon dioxide, oxygen, and water. What elements are in each compound?
5. Name five organic compounds found in cells and tell the function of each compound.
6. Explain how feedback mechanisms maintain homeostasis. Give three examples.

Ideas to Explore

1. **Project:** To observe osmotic pressure, cut a core out of the top of a carrot. Fill the hole with corn syrup and insert a cork that has a length of glass tubing inserted through it. Seal the edge between the cork and carrot with hot paraffin. Place the carrot in a beaker of hot water and support the tube with a clamp and stand. How high does the syrup rise in the tube?
2. **Project:** Place 25 or 30 bean seeds in a beaker. Cover with water. Mark the water level with a glass marking pencil. Observe the water level after several hours. Explain your observations.
3. **Challenge:** Make a list of organic compounds found in your kitchen.
4. **Challenge:** Prepare a list of examples of diffusion and osmosis in everyday life. For example, you might list the smell of foods cooking and the reason for keeping vegetables in a special part of the refrigerator.

Readings

Asimov, Isaac. *How Did We Find Out About Atoms?* New York: Avon, 1982.

Baker, J.J. and G.E. Allen. *Matter, Energy, and Life: An Introduction to Chemical Concepts.* Reading, MA: Addison-Wesley, 1981.

Cusumano, James A. "Designer Catalysts." *Science 85.* November, 1985, pp. 120–122.

Walters, Derek. *Chemistry.* New York: Franklin Watts, 1983.

There are thousands of kinds of organisms on Earth. How can we know them all? Organisms with similar characteristics are classified into the same group. How many ways can you group an organism? You may look at the whole organism or only a part of it. Plants can be grouped by their fruits or type of seeds. How are some of these fruits alike? How are they different? How many different types of plants do you see?

CHAPTER 4
CLASSIFICATION

4:1 Classification

Scientists use classification in solving problems in life science. Classification means to put things into groups. Classifying organisms makes it easier to study and learn about them. The groups are based on the ways in which the things are alike and different from each other.

Items sold in a supermarket are grouped so customers can find them easily. Foods that are alike are usually put together. For example, canned soups are grouped in one section. Cereals are shelved together in another. Canned vegetables are stocked separately from canned fruits. What is the basis for classifying food in a supermarket? The grouping may be based on the kind of food. The grouping might also be based on packaging, or whether the food must be kept in a refrigerator or freezer. Do all supermarkets group their foods in the exact same way? How do they differ?

Classification is used in many different ways. Books in a library are classified according to subject or author. How is this classification helpful?

GOALS:
1. You will learn how and why scientists classify organisms.
2. You will learn main features of the five kingdoms.
3. You will learn theories of the origin of life on Earth.

a

b

c

d

FIGURE 4–1. In what ways can you classify the art of "Haystacks: Autumn" by Millet (a), a wooden, spotted leopard mask from Africa (b), "Red Poppy" by O'Keefe (c), and American Indian pottery (d)?

Art can be classified, also. Look at the artworks above. How could you divide these works of art into groups? What characteristics that you observe would you use to classify the art?

You might classify the art according to whether it features plants. Then the two paintings (a, c) would be in one group. The pottery and mask show no plants. They would be in another group.

You could classify the art according to whether it shows a landscape or features animals. What other ways can you think of to classify the art?

Life characteristics are used to divide all things into two groups: nonliving and living. The ability to grow, reproduce, use energy, and respond to the environment are some life characteristics. Rocks, metal, furniture, and plastic toys are examples of things in the nonliving group. Horses, trees, and dogs are examples of things in the living group. The science of classifying living things is **taxonomy** (tak SAHN uh mee).

Define taxonomy.

4:2 Five Kingdoms

Scientists classify organisms based on their similarities and differences. As with all classification, there are different ways of grouping organisms. One accepted classification is the division of organisms into five main groups. Each group is called a **kingdom.** The five kingdoms are the animal kingdom, the plant kingdom, the fungus kingdom, the protist kingdom, and the moneran kingdom.

In the classification of organisms, more than one characteristic is always used. What characteristics are used to classify organisms? Size, shape, color, body structure, and method of food-getting are examples of such characteristics. What others can you think of?

Organisms in the animal kingdom have some characteristics that make them different from organisms in the other kingdoms. Most animals can move about. For instance, some animals fly, some swim, and others walk on the ground. Animals cannot make their own food. They eat other organisms for food.

Plants have characteristics different from animals and organisms in the other kingdoms. Plants usually have a green substance called **chlorophyll** (KLOR uh fill). They use chlorophyll to make food. A plant usually spends its whole life in one place.

How do scientists classify organisms?

Table 4–1

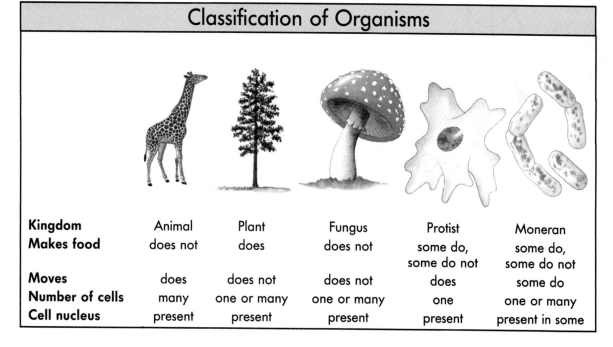

Classification of Organisms				
Kingdom	Animal	Plant	Fungus	Protist	Moneran
Makes food	does not	does	does not	some do, some do not	some do, some do not
Moves	does	does not	does not	does	some do
Number of cells	many	one or many	one or many	one	one or many
Cell nucleus	present	present	present	present	present in some

Organisms in the **fungus** kingdom, such as yeasts, molds, and mushrooms, do not move around as animals do. They do not have chlorophyll as plants do. They obtain food from the materials on which they grow.

Organisms in the **protist** and **moneran** kingdoms are simple and very tiny. Many are single cells. Some can move and some cannot. Some can make food and some cannot. They are classified according to their similarities and differences. Many organisms do not have all the characteristics of the kingdom in which they are placed. Organisms are placed into the group with which they share the most characteristics.

Making Sure

1. Select the two objects in each group that are most closely related. Explain how you decided on your selections.
   a. bicycle, car, motorcycle
   b. notebook, magazine, diary
   c. chisel, screwdriver, hatchet
   d. chair, couch, stool
   e. grasshopper, horse, cow
   f. tree, mushroom, ivy
2. Name the five kingdoms scientists use to classify organisms. Name the characteristics of the organisms in each kingdom.

FIGURE 4–2. In which of the five kingdoms would you classify each organism?

Activity 4–1   Classifying Seeds

Problem: What characteristics can be used to classify seeds?

Materials

packet of 10 seeds
hand lens
metric ruler
2 sheets of paper

Procedure

1. Empty the packet of seeds on a sheet of paper. Examine each seed carefully.
2. Divide the 10 seeds into two groups, I and II. The seeds in each group must have at least one thing in common. For example, you could classify white seeds in Group I and seeds that are not white in Group II. Record the characteristic that Group I seeds have in common in a chart like the one under Data and Observations. Record the characteristic that Group II seeds have in common.
3. Now, divide the Group I seeds into two groups. Again, the seeds in a group must have something in common. Record in the chart the characteristic that each group has in common.
4. Divide the seeds into two groups again. Record the characteristic that the seeds in each group have in common.
5. Repeat step 4 two more times.
6. Repeat steps 3 through 5 with the Group II seeds.
7. Give the seed packet and chart to another person. Ask that person to identify each seed using your classification system.

Questions and Conclusions

1. Is there more than one way to classify the seeds?
2. How is classifying helpful?
3. What characteristics can be used to identify seeds?

Data and Observations

FIGURE 4–3.

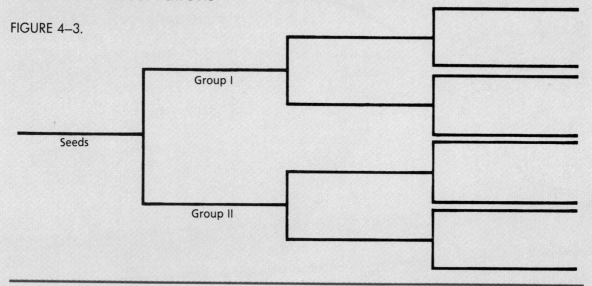

4:3 Groups in a Kingdom

Scientists divide organisms in kingdoms into smaller groups. The categories are based on the presence of very specific characteristics. Most scientists agree about the classification of organisms. However, sometimes there are differences in the ways scientists classify organisms. Sometimes different traits are used as a basis for classification.

What is a phylum?

Each kingdom is divided into groups called phyla (FI luh). A **phylum** is the largest category in a kingdom. All of the organisms in a kingdom are similar in some ways, but they are not exactly alike. People and fish are kinds of animals, but they are not the same. People and fish are classified in the same phylum in the animal kingdom. Phyla are divided into still smaller groups called classes. Each class is divided into orders. Each order is divided into families. Cats and dogs are in the same kingdom, phylum, class, and order, but they are classified in two separate families.

Each family is also divided into smaller groups. Each of these smaller groups is called a genus (JEE nus). A **genus** is divided into even smaller groups called species (SPEE seez).

A **species** is the smallest category in a kingdom. Organisms of the same species may produce more organisms of the same kind. For instance, cottontail rabbits are a species. They can produce more cottontail rabbits. They cannot produce elephants or any other species, only cottontail rabbits.

Altogether, there are seven main categories in the classification system of living things. Figure 4–4 shows the categories from largest to smallest.

Classification indicates the relationships among species. Two species that are very closely related are classified in the same phylum, class, order, family, and genus. Species that are not closely related are classified in fewer of the same groups. Which two of the three animals in Table 4–2 are more alike?

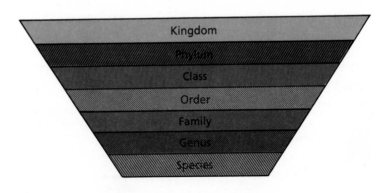

FIGURE 4–4. There are seven main categories in the classification system.

Table 4–2

Classification of Three Organisms

Organism	Steller's sea lion	Walrus	Northern fur seal
Kingdom	Animal	Animal	Animal
Phylum	Chordata	Chordata	Chordata
Class	Mammalia	Mammalia	Mammalia
Order	Pinnipedia	Pinnipedia	Pinnipedia
Family	Otariidae	Odobenidae	Otariidae
Genus	*Eumetopias*	*Odobenus*	*Callorhinus*
Species	*jubatus*	*rosmarus*	*ursinus*

All three animals are in the same kingdom, phylum, class, and order. Steller's sea lion and the northern fur seal are in the same family, too. The walrus is in a different family. So, Steller's sea lion and the northern fur seal are more like each other than they are like the walrus. This means the sea lion and fur seal have many of the same traits, body parts, and structures. Since the walrus is in a different family, it does not share as many characteristics.

Making Sure

3. List in order the six subdivisions of a kingdom.
4. How is a phylum different from a species?
5. What is the purpose of classifying organisms?

a   b

FIGURE 4–5. A jaguar (a) and a lion (b) are different species of the genus *Panthera*.

4:4 Scientific Names

A plant or animal may have several common or popular names. For example, a certain member of the cat family is known as mountain lion, cougar, puma, and panther in various parts of the United States. Several different plants are known by the name daisy. In different countries, the same organism may have different names because of the various languages. It might be hard to identify an organism when there are several common names. To avoid this problem, a system is used in which all organisms have scientific names. All scientists around the world use these names rather than using common or popular names.

How are organisms given scientific names?

The system of naming used today began over 200 years ago. It was first developed by the Swedish naturalist, Carolus Linnaeus (luh NAY us). Linnaeus gave each known plant or animal a name with two parts. The first part of the name is the genus name. The last part of the name is the species name. What are the scientific names of the three organisms listed in Table 4–2?

Panthera is the name of the genus having the species of cats such as the lion and tiger. Although alike in many ways, each member of the genus *Panthera* has certain special features of its own. The different members of the genus *Panthera* are classified into species.

Give two examples of scientific names.

A lion belongs to the species *leo*. Therefore, its scientific name is *Panthera leo*. Other scientific names in genus *Panthera* are: *Panthera tigris*, and *Panthera pardus*. The species name is never used by itself. It is always used with the genus name. The genus name is spelled with a capital letter. The species name is spelled with a small letter. When in print, both names are in italic. When written, a scientific name is underlined.

Linnaeus used the Latin language when he named plants and animals. He chose Latin because, in his time, Latin was used by scientists in all countries. Latin is still used today in scientific naming.

Sometimes the species name tells us something about an organism. The name *domesticus,* in *Felis domesticus,* means the organism is raised and cared for by people—it is domesticated. *Felis domesticus* is the scientific name of the house cat.

Who names the different species of plants and animals? The first person to describe an organism in print has this right. However, the new name must follow an international code of rules for scientific naming. The largest group of organisms described is in the Class Insecta. There are over 800 000 known insects. Not all animals or plants have been discovered. Over 1000 new species of plants and animals are found, identified, described, and named each year. Most of the new species now come from the tropics.

Making Sure

6. Which two organisms in each group are most closely related? Explain.
   a. *Canis familiaris, Mephitis mephitis, Canis lupis*
   b. *Quercus alba, Trifolium alba, Trifolium pratense*
   c. *Equus caballus, Equus zebra, Camelus dromedarius*

FIGURE 4–6. A house cat, *Felis domesticus,* has the genus name *Felis* and the species name *domesticus.*

a

No maggots
developed.

Sealed jar

b

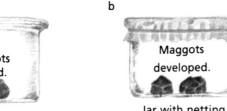

Maggots
developed.

Jar with netting

c

Maggots
developed.

Open jar

FIGURE 4–7. In Redi's experiment, flies laid eggs on the meat (c) and the netting (b). Maggots hatched from the eggs.

4:5 Spontaneous Generation

One problem of interest to scientists is how life first began on Earth. Long ago many people believed that some organisms could come from dead matter. The idea was called **spontaneous generation** (spahn TAY nee us · jen uh RAY shun). Because of their observations, people thought that frogs and eels came from mud. They also believed that decaying meat turned to maggots. Maggots are small, white wormlike organisms that develop into flies.

In 1668 an Italian doctor and biologist, Francesco Redi, decided to test the theory of spontaneous generation. He formed a hypothesis that maggots come from other organisms. He had noticed adult flies on decaying meat. He hypothesized that the flies produced the maggots. He thought that if the flies were kept away from the meat, no maggots would appear.

To test the hypothesis, Redi put meat into three separate jars. One jar was sealed. A second jar was covered with netting. The third jar was left open. The open jar served as a control for the experiment. Redi could compare the changes in the sealed and net-covered jars with changes in the open jar. Maggots appeared on the meat in the open jar, Figure 4–7 (c). They also appeared on the netting of the second jar (b). Redi observed flies laying eggs on the meat in the open jar (c). He also observed flies laying eggs on the netting of the second jar (b). Maggots emerged from the eggs. Redi concluded that flies could not get to the meat in the sealed jar (a). No eggs were laid, so no maggots appeared in that jar. Redi concluded that decaying meat does not turn into maggots and that maggots are produced from the eggs of flies. He began to help other people question spontaneous generation. Redi was the first to use scientific methods to test his hypothesis about spontaneous generation.

Analyze Redi's experiment to determine its hypothesis, control, procedures, and conclusion.

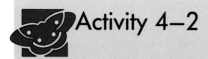

Activity 4–2   Drawing Conclusions

Problem: How do scientists make accurate conclusions?

Materials pencil, paper

Procedure (1) Study the two descriptions and Figure 4–8.

Description 1 Scientists on an archeological dig find fossils of webbed dinosaur footprints.

Description 2 A student put corn and an old shirt in a low, wooden box in a field overnight. When the student checked the box early the next day, many mice scurried away from it.

(2) Then answer the questions based on what you read and observe.

Questions (1) Does the evidence found in Description 1 support a hypothesis that these dinosaurs were water dwellers? (2) Does this evidence support a hypothesis that the area where the fossil footprints were found was formerly water-covered? (3) What hypothesis can the student in Description 2 make? (4) The person in Figure 4–8 could make what hypothesis about a bird? (5) How do scientists make accurate conclusions?

FIGURE 4–8.

4:6 Spallanzani

In 1767, Lazzaro Spallanzani (spah lahn ZAH nee), an Italian scientist, tested the hypothesis that microbes were formed by spontaneous generation. In his experiments, Spallanzani used broth, which is water in which meat has been boiled. Broth was thought to turn into microbes because microbes are found in decaying broth.

Spallanzani placed broth in several glass flasks. He divided these into four groups. In one group, he boiled the broth for over

Boiled   Not boiled

Control

a   b   c   d

FIGURE 4–9. In Spallanzani's experiment, microbes were found in flasks that were not boiled (c, d) and in flasks that were not sealed (b, d). No microbes were found in flasks boiled and sealed (a).

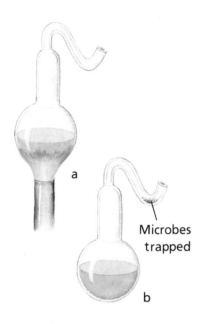

a

Microbes
trapped

b

FIGURE 4–10. In Pasteur's experiment, broth was boiled in S-shaped flasks to kill microbes (a). Although the flasks were not sealed, no microbes grew in the broth because they were trapped in the necks of the flasks (b).

Analyze Pasteur's experiment to determine his hypothesis, procedures, and conclusion.

an hour and then sealed the flasks. In one group, he boiled the broth and left the flasks open to the air. In the other two groups, he did not boil the broth. Some of these he sealed. Some were left open to the air, and these were the control, Figure 4–9. Spallanzani believed that microbes were everywhere. He thought that boiling the broth would kill the microbes. Sealing the flasks would keep out microbes in the air.

The flasks were allowed to stand for several months. Then the broth was examined with a microscope. The results were that microbes were present in the flasks that were not boiled (c, d). Microbes were also in the flasks that were not sealed (b, d). No microbes were found in the boiled flasks that were sealed (a). Spallanzani concluded that microbes that might be in broth are killed by boiling. In the unsealed flasks, microbes came into the broth from the air. He believed that microbes produce other microbes through reproduction.

4:7 Pasteur

Louis Pasteur, a French scientist, did not believe in spontaneous generation. Pasteur believed that microbes came from cells of organisms on dust particles in the air. He thought if the cells had food, they would grow into new organisms.

In 1864, Pasteur experimented to test his hypothesis. He used flasks that had S-shaped necks. Broth was put in the flasks and boiled to kill any microbes that were present, Figure 4–10. Then the flasks were allowed to stand for several months. Since the flasks were not sealed, air could enter the flasks. However, the S-shaped necks trapped any microbes that were in the air. No microbes ever appeared on the broth inside the flasks.

Pasteur's experiment showed that microbes, like other organisms, did not come from nonliving things. It also showed that spontaneous generation did not occur even though air was present. Pasteur's experiment and the work of Redi and Spallanzani were evidence that modern forms of life probably do not arise spontaneously.

Making Sure

7. Describe Redi's and Spallanzani's experiments and conclusions.
8. Why did Pasteur boil the broth in the flasks?

Activity 4–3

Problem: How can you test a hypothesis?

Materials

reference books
2 glass jars (0.5L)
cotton
bean seeds
2 thermometers
water

Procedure

1. Look up respiration in reference books and the index of your textbook. Find out what respiration in plants is and what occurs during plant respiration. Record what you learn.
2. Predict an answer to the question, "Do seeds carry on respiration as they grow?" Record your hypothesis.
3. Do the following steps to find out if your prediction is correct.
4. Label two jars I and II.
5. Fill each jar half full of bean seeds. The amounts in the jars should be about equal.
6. Cover the bean seeds in jar I with water. The bean seeds in jar II are to remain dry.

FIGURE 4–11.

7. Place a thermometer in each jar. The bulbs of the thermometers should be halfway into the seed layers.
8. Pack the top half of each jar with cotton.
9. Take thermometer readings every day at the same time for five days.
10. Record the temperature readings in a data table.

Data and Observations

Day	Temperature (°C)	
	Jar I	Jar II
1		
2		
3		
4		
5		

Questions and Conclusions

1. What is the problem in your experiment?
2. How did you research the problem before you began experimenting?
3. What was the hypothesis you were testing?
4. How did you test your hypothesis?
5. What was the control?
6. What was the variable?
7. What data was recorded?
8. On what was the data based?
9. Did you accept or reject your hypothesis? Why?
10. What was your conclusion?
11. How did you report your results?
12. Why is reporting your results important?
13. Did this experiment lead to any more questions or problems to be investigated?
14. How can you test a hypothesis?

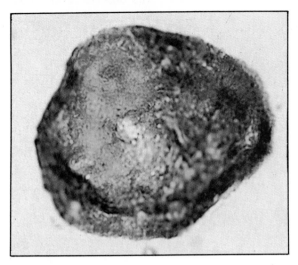

a

b

FIGURE 4–12. A fossil of a simple cell 700 million years old (a) and the Murchison meteorite (b) may provide clues about the origin of life.

4:8 Origins of Life

Scientists have no evidence that modern organisms arise from nonliving matter through spontaneous generation. All the organisms alive on Earth came from their parents through reproduction. However, at some time in Earth's long history, life had to begin. The origin of life on Earth occurred billions of years ago. At this time conditions on Earth were different from those today.

Just how did the first life begin on Earth? The main scientific theory that tries to answer this question is based on 30 years of experiments and observations. Remember that a theory is an idea that explains things. This theory states that chemical elements and compounds in the atmosphere joined billions of years ago. They formed compounds found in living organisms. These compounds could then form simple cell-like structures. The structures could eventually become like the cells found in organisms today.

In one experiment, electrical sparks were sent through a mixture of chemicals. The chemicals were substances scientists believe were present on Earth in large amounts millions of years ago. These chemicals contained elements found in living matter. New and different substances were formed in the experiment. When these substances were tested, they were found to be organic compounds. Similar organic compounds are the basic building blocks of all living organisms. Actually, the experiment does not prove or disprove that life was produced this way. It shows that the same substances present in living things could be made from nonliving substances in the environment if certain conditions exist.

What is a theory that may explain how life on Earth began?

Scientists are testing whether life on Earth could have begun from organic matter in meteorites. A meteorite is a metallic or mineral mass that has fallen to Earth from outer space. Some meteorites contain amino acids and other kinds of organic matter. The Murchison meteorite was found in Australia in 1969. Analysis of samples from the meteorite showed that it contains five basic parts of nucleic acids. Amino acids and nucleic acids are present in cells. Perhaps organic matter brought to Earth by meteorites billions of years ago formed cell-like structures. These cell-like structures may have then developed into the first living organisms.

FIGURE 4–13. Photographs of Mars show a rocky, barren surface.

What does analysis of the Murchison meteorite show?

4:9 Life Beyond Earth

Another great scientific question is: Does life exist beyond Earth? If life exists on other planets, it may be similar to life we know on Earth. There are three things needed for the kind of life we know.

1. *There must be a life substance.* All living things on Earth have the element carbon. Thus, carbon is a life substance on Earth.
2. *Living things must carry on chemical changes needed to keep them alive.* For example, there must be a chemical change that provides energy for the organism.
3. *Life must be able to reproduce itself.*

Some scientists have concluded that life could exist on Mars. An atmosphere like the one on Mars was set up in a laboratory. Pieces of soil containing microbes were kept in this atmosphere. Many microbes survived. Perhaps similar forms of life could exist on Mars.

Equipment for detecting life was carried on the Viking spacecraft that landed on Mars in 1976. Experiments were done to see if microbes were in the soil or "air." Results of these experiments were not conclusive. Organic molecules, the building blocks for life as we know it, were not found at the Viking landing sites. So far, there are no facts to show that life exists anywhere except on Earth.

What do experiments on soil and air from Mars show?

Making Sure

9. Describe an experiment that scientists did to attempt to explain how life on Earth may have begun.
10. List three things that make life as we know it possible on Earth.

FOCUS ON
Skills

Using the Scientific Method to Solve Problems

The scientific method can be used to solve a science problem and many other kinds of problems as well. Because this approach is based on common sense, you probably use it quite often without realizing it.

Have you ever tried to organize the clothes in your closet? The problem of a disorganized, messy closet is identified. You study the problem in order to formulate a hypothesis—a proposed solution to a problem based on known facts. You collect data about the problem in several ways. First, you ask friends how they organize their closets. You may also observe that you have shirts, sweaters, and pants. Then, you form a hypothesis that the closet will be more organized if clothes are arranged according to type of garment. To test your hypothesis, you arrange your clothes according to type. The way you have thought about the problem and the steps you have followed are also used in the scientific method. Let's use the scientific method to solve the problem of how to classify an organism.

1. *Identify the problem.*
   How do we classify an organism?
2. *Collect information about the problem.* Scientists classify organisms based on similarities and differences in their characteristics. Characteristics include: size, color, body structure, (for example, kind of outer covering or limbs), methods of getting food, reproduction, respiration, and control of body temperature.
3. *Form a hypothesis.* Based on the collected information, organisms can be classified using different characteristics. Therefore, selecting a few characteristics and then answering questions about an organism based on those characteristics should help to classify the organism.
4. *Test the hypothesis.* Look at the table and notice the characteristics of the different organisms. The table shows characteristics of the frog and hagfish. Both have slimy skin. But, the hagfish has no limbs and the frog has two pairs of legs. The hagfish is classified in the group Agnatha, and the frog is classified in the group Amphibia.

Characteristics			
Organism	Outer Covering	Limb Structure	Classification
hagfish	slimy skin	no paired limbs	Agnatha
shark	scales	2 pairs of fins	Chondrichthyes
trout	scales and slimy skin	2 pairs of fins	Osteichthyes
frog	slimy skin	2 pairs of legs	Amphibia

Use the scientific method to classify a group of items that you use every day, such as sports equipment, kitchen items, sewing aids, books, or tools. Follow the examples of organizing a closet and classifying animals to do your classification.

As it does in offering a way to determine how animals are alike and different, the scientific method solves many kinds of problems. First, define the problem. Then collect information by making observations, talking to people, and reading. Think of some ways to solve the problem by forming a hypothesis. Test your hypothesis by trying out your ideas for solving the problem.

CHAPTER 4
Review

Summary

1. Classification of things is based on the ways in which they are alike and different.   4:1

2. Organisms are divided into five main groups. These are the animal kingdom, the plant kingdom, the fungus kingdom, the protist kingdom, and the moneran kingdom.   4:2

3. An organism is classified by kingdom, phylum, class, order, family, genus, and species.   4:3

4. A species is the smallest division in a kingdom. Organisms of the same species can produce more organisms of the same kind.   4:3

5. The scientific name of an organism is the genus and species name of the organism.   4:4

6. The idea that some organisms come from dead matter is called spontaneous generation. Francesco Redi was the first to use scientific methods to test the theory of spontaneous generation.   4:5

7. Lazzaro Spallanzani concluded that microbes produce other microbes by reproduction.   4:6

8. Louis Pasteur's experiment showed that microbes did not come from nonliving things.   4:7

9. Modern scientific theory explains that spontaneous generation probably occurred long ago when elements combined to form compounds that formed simple cell-like structures.   4:8

10. Life is known to exist only on Earth, although some scientists think life may exist on other planets.   4:9

Vocabulary

Write a sentence using the following words or terms correctly.

chlorophyll	moneran	species
fungus	phylum	spontaneous generation
genus	protist	taxonomy
kingdom		

Questions

Do not write in this book.

A. True or False
Determine whether each of the following sentences is true or false. Rewrite the false statements to make them correct.

1. Animals and plants are classified in the same kingdom.

2. Dogs and cats belong to the same species.

3. *Felis domesticus* is the scientific name for the house cat.

4. Classification is based upon the similarities and differences of organisms.

5. Yeasts, molds, and mushrooms are organisms in the moneran kingdom.

6. A genus is the smallest division in a kingdom.

7. Scientists have evidence that modern organisms arise from nonliving matter through spontaneous generation.

8. All living things on Earth contain the element carbon.

9. The origin of life occurred billions of years ago.

10. Evidence shows that life exists on Mars.

B. Multiple Choice

Choose the word or phrase that correctly completes the following sentences.

1. The groups containing the greatest variety of organisms are *(kingdoms, phyla, classes, families)*.

2. An organism that has chlorophyll and spends its whole life in one place is a *(protist, fungus, plant)*.

3. Many scientists classify organisms into five *(species, kingdoms, phyla)*.

4. If two animals are closely related, they will be in *(fewer, more)* of the same classification groups.

5. The two-part scientific naming system used today was developed by *(Redi, Linnaeus, Pasteur)*.

6. Spallanzani tested the hypothesis that *(maggots, microbes)* were formed by spontaneous generation.

7. Pasteur's experiment shows that microbes did not come from *(living, non-living)* things.

8. Living things must carry on *(chemical, physical)* changes needed to keep them alive.

9. *(Classification, Taxonomy, Spontaneous generation)* is the idea that organisms come from dead matter.

10. Scientists have conducted experiments on *(Mars, Saturn, Jupiter)* to see if life is present.

C. Completion

Complete each of the following sentences with the correct word or phrase.

1. _____ means to put things into groups.

2. A(n) _____ name has both the genus and species names for an organism.

3. An organism may have more than one _____ name.

4. *Panthera* is the name of a genus in the _____ kingdom.

5. The life substance on Earth is _____.

6. The science of classifying living things is _____.
7. Organisms in the _____ kingdom obtain food from the materials on which they grow and do not have chlorophyll or move about.
8. Maggots come from _____.
9. Three scientists who experimented with the idea of spontaneous generation were Redi, Spallanzani, and _____.
10. When electrical sparks were sent through a mixture of _____, organic compounds were formed.

D. How and Why
1. How are organisms classified?
2. What is the advantage in using scientific names for organisms?
3. Describe one experiment that was done to test the theory of spontaneous generation.
4. What is needed for life to exist?
5. Why do some scientists believe life may exist on Mars?

Ideas to Explore
1. **Challenge:** Do you have a favorite animal or plant? Prepare a report on an animal or plant that lists all the characteristics that make the animal or plant different from other organisms.
2. **Challenge:** Based on library research, write a short biography of Louis Pasteur that lists his major contributions to life science.
3. **Project:** Visit a museum of natural history. Find how the collection of plants and animals is organized.
4. **Project:** If photography is your hobby, you may want to make a "parade of the animal kingdom." You can locate many subjects for your photos in a zoo. Learn the genus and species name for each animal. Catalog your slides according to the scientific system of classification.

Readings
Branley, Franklyn M. *Is There Life in Outer Space?* New York: T.Y. Crowell, 1984.

Margulis, L. and Karlene Schwartz. *Five Kingdoms: An illustrated Guide to the Phyla of Life on Earth.* New York: W.H. Freeman, 1982.

Toon, Owen B. and Steve Olson. "The Warm Earth." *Science 85.* October, 1985, pp. 50–57.

Scientific Measurement
Background Data

Welcome to the first of many interactions among you, your computer, and the material you have studied in class. Look for a computer feature at the end of each unit of *Focus on Life Science*.

This feature deals with scientific measurement. You studied measurement in Chapter 1, and will continue to use this information throughout the rest of the course as well as in other science courses you take. Length is a measure of distance. Length is measured in meters. The symbol for meter is m. Length can also be measured in kilometers (km), centimeters (cm), or millimeters (mm). The size of the object being measured determines which unit is most appropriate. Volume is a measure of the amount of space an object occupies. The basic unit of volume is the liter (L). Mass is the amount of matter in an object. The basic unit of mass is the gram (g).

The same prefixes are used for expressing measurements of length, volume, and mass. The prefixes that will be used in this program are listed below.

milli	(m)	0.001
centi	(c)	0.01
kilo	(k)	1000.

Input/Output

Enter the program into your computer exactly as it is printed. After you enter the entire program, type RUN. If there is a problem, type LIST, and check that you have entered the program exactly as it is printed. Remember, symbols and punctuation are important and must be typed as printed here. REM statements are provided in the program to help you. They do not need to be entered in order for the program to run. When all corrections have been made, be sure to save the program by typing SAVE MEASUREMENT, or whatever name you wish to give the program.

Once the program is running, the computer will ask you to enter your name. The computer will refer to you by name throughout the rest of the program. It will then remind you how to convert among three different units of length in the International System of Units. You will be asked to make a conversion from one unit of length to another unit of length. If you answer correctly, the computer will tell you that you did a good job and give you another conversion to make. If you do not answer correctly, you will be given a clue and two more chances to answer correctly. After the third try, you will be given another conversion. The computer will ask you a total of 12 questions. At several points during the program, the computer will give your score expressed as a percent.

Programming Notes

The computer reads each line of the program and executes the command listed there. Line 10 clears the screen. Some computers use the command CLS, others use HOME. Use the command your computer recognizes to clear the screen.

The variables used in this program are listed below.

N$ user's name
Q$ false variable that stops the program
T   part of the loop that repeats the program
A   reads data
W   converts meters to centimeters
X   converts centimeters to meters
Y   converts centimeters to millimeters
B   user answer
Q   counts incorrect answers
I   counts correct answers
P   calculates percentage of correct answers

The user's name is asked for and entered in lines 20 and 30. Lines 40 through 70 outline the general examples that will be examined. Line 80 stops the program until the user is ready to start. The loop started in line 90 causes the main program to repeat four times. Data are read and correct answers are calculated in line 100. Answers are checked in line 120, and the value of I is increased by one if the answer is correct. If the answer is not correct, line 130 provides the user with a clue and two addi-

tional chances to correctly answer the question. Line 140 provides the answer and records incorrect answers after the third try. The main program then repeats two more times. The number of correct responses is given in line 230, and the percent of correct responses is calculated in line 240. Line 250 returns the program to line 90 for another set of three questions. Data are contained in line 260.

Program

```
10   HOME : REM  MAY BE DIFFERENT
     ON YOUR COMPUTER
20   PRINT "WHAT NAME SHOULD I US
     E FOR YOU ";: INPUT N$
30   PRINT "VERY GOOD ";N$
40   PRINT "WE WILL BE STUDYING T
     HE FOLLOWING ": PRINT : PRINT
50   PRINT "METERS -> CENTIMETERS
     <MULTIPLY BY 100>"
60   PRINT "CENTIMETERS -> METERS
     <DIVIDE BY 100>"
70   PRINT "CENTIMETERS->MILLIMET
     ERS <MULTIPLY BY 10>"
80   PRINT : PRINT "ENTER WHEN RE
     ADY TO START ";: INPUT Q$
90   FOR T = 1 to 4
100  READ A:W = A * 100:X = A /
     100:Y = A * 10
110  PRINT : PRINT "HOW MANY CEN
     TIMETERS IS ";A;" METERS": INPUT
     B
120  IF B = W THEN I = I + 1: PRINT
     : PRINT "VERY GOOD ";N$: GOTO
     150
130  Q = Q + 1: IF Q < 3 THEN  PRINT
     : PRINT "SORRY ";N$;" YOU MU
     ST MULTIPLY BY 100.": GOTO 1
     10
140  Q = 0; PRINT : PRINT "THE AN
     SWER IS ";W;" CENTIMETERS"
150  PRINT : PRINT "HOW MANY MET
     ERS IS ";A;" CENTIMETERS": INPUT
     B
160  IF B = X THEN I = I + 1: PRINT
     : PRINT "THAT'S GOOD": GOTO
     190
170  Q = Q + 1: IF Q < 3 THEN  PRINT
     : PRINT "SORRY YOU MUST DIVI
     DE BY 100. TRY AGAIN.": GOTO
     150
180  Q = 0: PRINT : PRINT "THE AN
     SWER ";N$;" IS ";X;" METERS"
190  PRINT : PRINT N$;" DO YOU K
     NOW HOW MANY MILLIMETERS IN
     ";A;" CENTIMETERS?": INPUT B
200  IF B = Y THEN I = I + 1: PRINT
     : PRINT "GOOD.  NOW WE'LL GI
     VE YOU A SCORE.": GOTO 230
210  Q = Q + 1: IF Q < 3 THEN  PRINT
     : PRINT "THAT IS WRONG.  YOU
     MUST MULTIPLY BY 10.": GOTO
     190
220  Q = 0: PRINT : PRINT "THE CO
     RRECT ANSWER IS ";Y;" MILLIM
     ETERS."
230  PRINT : PRINT "YOU HAVE ";I
     ;" QUESTIONS CORRECT OUT OF
     ";T * 3
240  P =  INT ((I / (T * 3)) * 10
     0): PRINT "FOR A ";P;" PERCE
     NT  ";N$
250  NEXT T
260  DATA  10,125,30,5
```

Challenge: On Your Own

There are many ways for you to change or extend this program. Because you may be able to memorize the answers to the questions, you might want to change the numbers in DATA line 260. Make sure there are four numbers in this line or you will get an error statement when running the program.

If you enjoy programming, you might change the questions in line 100 to calculate other conversions. You would also have to ask different questions in lines 110, 150, and 190.

SIMPLE ORGANISMS

Club fungus

A club fungus has a familiar mushroom form, but the main body of a fungus is hidden in the soil or in the tissues of a host. Fungi are put into their own kingdom because of body structure. Unlike plants, which have tissues, fungi have hyphae. A microscopic view of the sporangium fungus Penicillium shows a network of hyphae. How do fungi obtain food? What other simple organisms lack chlorophyll?

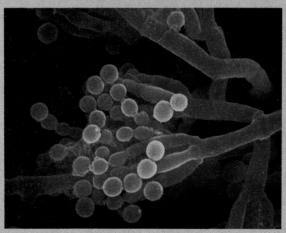

Penicillium

Viruses can grow and reproduce only inside living cells. Viruses need a host for survival. This African green monkey has AIDS. Scientists have discovered that African green monkeys are carriers of the AIDS virus. Scientists are currently doing research on these monkeys to determine how the AIDS virus is transmitted. This virus is new to the human population. It has been present in green monkeys for a long time. How might scientists use this knowledge to learn about the effects of the AIDS virus on humans?

CHAPTER 5
VIRUSES AND MONERANS

5:1 Viruses

Have you ever had a cold or the flu? Both the common cold and flu are caused by viruses. A **virus** is a complex organic compound that has some living and some nonliving characteristics. Viruses are not made of cells. A virus has a center or core composed of nucleic acid. Around the core is a coat of protein.

Viruses are so small that bacteria seem huge in comparison. They are so small they can only be seen with an electron microscope. Pictures of viruses enlarged more than 100 000 times have been made. These pictures show that viruses can be rodlike, spherical, or many-sided. A many-sided virus has a tail or stalk. Because of their unique characteristics, viruses are not classified in any of the five kingdoms.

Because viruses have some living and some nonliving characteristics, scientists debate whether viruses are alive. Outside a living cell, viruses do not grow, carry on respiration, or respond to changes in their environment. Growing and reproducing are life activities that viruses can do only inside cells. Yet, crystals of viruses taken from cells can be stored in bottles for many years. These crystals do not grow or produce more viruses until they are inside living cells again.

GOALS:
1. You will learn the characteristics of viruses and monerans.
2. You will learn about the diseases caused by viruses and monerans.
3. You will learn the helpful and harmful effects of bacteria and blue-green algae.

What is the structure of a virus?

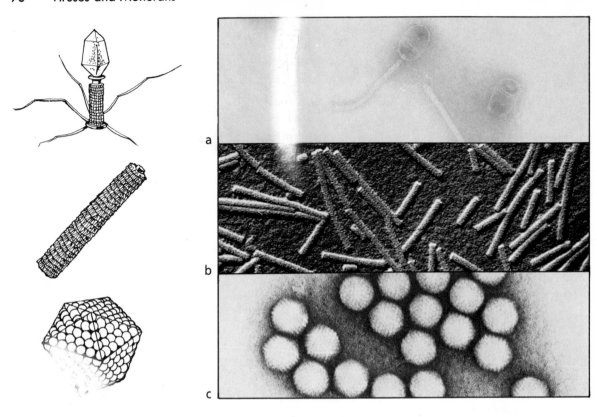

FIGURE 5–1. Viruses have different shapes. A bacteriophage (300 000X) has many parts (a). A tobacco mosaic virus (220 000X) is spiral (b). Adenovirus is many-sided (c).

Inside a cell, a virus may take control and change the normal activities of the cell. In effect, the virus becomes the "master" and the cell becomes a "slave." The viruses seem to direct the cell to make new viruses. After some time, the cell bursts. It releases the new viruses that have been formed. The new viruses then enter other cells and interfere with their life activities.

5:2 Viruses and Disease

Viruses cause disease by changing the chemistry of cells. Some of the diseases caused by viruses in humans are polio, flu, colds, measles, and mumps. In other animals, viruses cause foot and mouth disease, rabies, or distemper. Viruses may be spread from a diseased organism to another organism. Viruses are spread among people by insects, air, water, food, and other people.

How are viruses spread among people?

Some viruses can remain in cells for a long time without reproducing. Later, the viruses begin reproducing and interfering with other cells' activities. For example, cold sores are blisters that appear in or around the mouth. They are caused by a virus. Although a person may get rid of cold sores, the virus may remain in the body. As long as the virus does not reproduce, no cold sores appear. When the virus begins reproducing again, the cold sores will reappear. Viruses are difficult to get rid of completely. For example, scientists have not been able to develop a cure for the common cold. This problem has not been solved because viruses have the ability to change to different forms.

There are no known drugs that destroy viruses. Drugs can be used to treat the symptoms of diseases caused by viruses. Vaccines, substances made from weakened viruses, can be used to treat certain viral diseases. The body reacts to the vaccine viruses by producing substances to protect against the disease.

The human body has a natural defense against viruses. Cells first attacked by a virus may produce a protein called interferon. **Interferon** interferes with the reproduction of viruses. This prevents the spread of viruses to other cells in the body.

How does interferon work?

Making Sure

1. Are viruses alive? Explain.
2. Why is there no cure for the common cold?

Activity 5–1 Diseases Caused by Viruses

Problem: Which diseases are caused by viruses?
Materials   reference books, paper, pencil
Procedure   **(1)** Copy the diseases listed below. **(2)** Use reference books to look up each disease. **(3)** After reading about the disease, determine the cause of the disease. Write the cause beside the disease. **(4)** Make a table listing the diseases by cause.

athlete's foot	foot and mouth	rabies
blood poisoning	disease in cattle	ringworm
bushy stunt in	herpes simplex	smallpox
tomatoes	influenza	sore throat
chicken pox	malaria	swine influenza
diphtheria	measles	tobacco mosaic
distemper	mumps	disease
Dutch elm disease	polio	warts

Questions   **(1)** How many of the diseases caused by viruses affect humans? **(2)** How many of the diseases affect plants? **(3)** Which diseases are caused by viruses?

5:3 Moneran Classification

List the main characteristics of monerans.

Two kinds of organisms are classified in the **moneran** kingdom: bacteria and blue-green algae. These tiny organisms are the simplest of all living creatures. No one knew about them until 300 years ago when microscopes were invented. When the electron microscope was developed in the 1930s, it was found that monerans have no nuclei inside their cells. Instead of a nucleus, a moneran cell has nuclear material that contains nucleic acid and is not surrounded by a membrane.

Monerans do have cell walls. Chlorophyll may be present in the cells, but there are no chloroplasts. Some monerans make their own food; others do not. Blue-green algae and bacteria are the two phyla of the moneran kingdom. Appendix C on page 556 shows characteristics and examples of organisms in these phyla.

5:4 Blue-Green Algae

Where are blue-green algae found?

Blue-green algae cells contain chlorophyll particles that are used to make food. A blue pigment in the cells, together with the green chlorophyll, give many of these algae their blue-green color. In some species, a red pigment is present. It causes the cells to have a purple-black color.

Blue-green algae are common in ponds, lakes, puddles, streams, and moist land areas. They are important food producers for aquatic life. However, in hot weather, they can reproduce so fast that they cause the bad odor of stagnant water. Sometimes the overgrowth of algae kills other organisms in the water. Because drinking or swimming in such polluted water is a safety hazard, public water supplies are checked and treated often.

Species of blue-green algae are many-celled or one-celled organisms. They are usually microscopic. Some species are simple round or oval cells. Others consist of cells joined together in chains, filaments, or colonies. Sometimes these organisms are enclosed in a jellylike layer. Some forms can move, but how they move is not known.

FIGURE 5–2. Blue-green algae can grow rapidly and cover the entire surface of a pond.

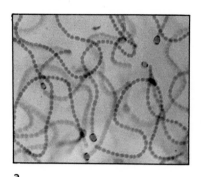

a

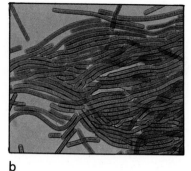

b

FIGURE 5–3. Blue-green algae, such as *Nostoc* (a) and *Oscillatoria* (b), are classified as monerans.

Blue-green algae lack many cell parts. They do not have nuclei and other cell parts such as mitochondria. However, blue-green algae do have the materials in their cells needed to carry on respiration and reproduction. They reproduce by simple cell division into two equal-sized algae.

Making Sure

3. Name the two phyla in the moneran kingdom.
4. How is the nuclear material in monerans different from other organisms?
5. List the major characteristics of blue-green algae.
6. How are blue-green algae different from plants?

Activity 5–2   Characteristics of Blue-Green Algae

Problem: What are some characteristics of blue-green algae?

Materials microscope, prepared slide of *Anabaena*

Procedure (1) Examine the algae under low and high power. (2) Draw the *Anabaena* cells that you see and record your observations.

Questions (1) Is chlorophyll present? How does it appear? (2) Can *Anabaena* make its own food? (3) Do the cells have nuclei? (4) Are the cells enclosed in a jellylike layer? (5) To what kingdom does *Anabaena* belong? (6) How does it reproduce? (7) What are some characteristics of blue-green algae?

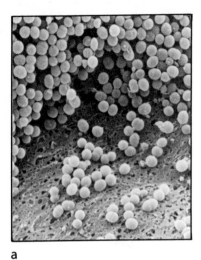

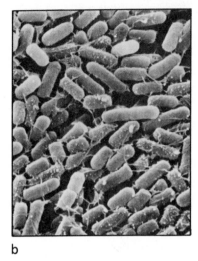

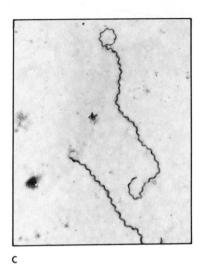

a b c

FIGURE 5–4. The three basic shapes of bacteria are cocci, spherical (a); bacilli, rod-shaped (b); and spirilla, spiral-shaped (c).

What are the three basic shapes of bacteria?

Describe the cell parts of bacteria.

What is the difference between aerobic and anaerobic bacteria?

5:5 Kinds of Bacteria

Anton van Leeuwenhoek first observed bacteria in the year 1676. **Bacteria** (bak TIHR ee uh) are one-celled monerans, most of which have no chlorophyll. There are many kinds of bacteria but only three basic shapes. Cocci (KAHK si) bacteria are spherical, bacilli (buh SIHL i) bacteria are rod-shaped, and spirilla (spi RIHL uh) bacteria are spiral-shaped. From these three shapes, other forms are possible. Pairs, groups of four or eight, chains, or large clumps are not uncommon. Each cell of such a group is an organism. Bacteria are so small that a chain of 10 000 of them would be only about one centimeter long.

A bacterial cell does not have a nucleus. It also lacks most cell parts that other cells have. Most bacterial cells do have a cell wall. The cell wall provides protection for the cell. Also, the cell wall maintains the balance of water between the bacterium and its environment. Often an outer slime capsule surrounds and protects the cell. Some bacteria have a whiplike tail and can move by "wiggling."

Bacteria live within the widest temperature range of all organisms. Some species live at ocean depths of 2743 meters where the temperature is close to 350°C. They have been found growing in Arctic ice and high in the atmosphere. Bacteria are present in your nose, intestines, skin, and in the air you breathe. One reason bacteria can survive in so many environments is that some bacteria do not require oxygen. Most species of bacteria need oxygen to live. They are called aerobic bacteria. Bacteria that do not need oxygen to live are called anaerobic (an uh ROH bihk).

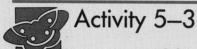

Activity 5–3   Observing and Finding Bacteria

Problem: What do bacteria look like, and where are they found?

Materials

prepared slide of bacteria types
microscope
4 petri dishes with sterile nutrient agar
glass-marking pencil
soap and water

Procedure

1. Observe the bacteria slide under low and high power. Draw what you see.
2. Label the petri dishes containing the sterile nutrient agar 1 through 4.
3. Open dish 1 and leave it open to the air for two or three hours. Then close the dish.
4. Open dish 2 and lightly rub a finger over the surface of the agar. Then close the dish.
5. Wash your hands thoroughly. Open dish 3 and rub a finger over the surface of the agar. Replace the cover.
6. Do not open dish 4.
7. Place all four dishes upside down in a warm, dark place for three days.
8. Record a hypothesis of the results you expect to observe in three days.
9. After three days, examine the dishes.
10. Count and record the number of bacteria colonies in each dish.
11. Return the dishes to your teacher. Your teacher will dispose of the bacteria.

Questions and Conclusions

1. Do any of the bacteria on the slide appear to be in clumps or chains?
2. Why were the petri dishes and agar sterilized before the activity?
3. Which dish was the control?
4. Which dish showed the greatest number of colonies? Conclude where the bacteria came from.
5. Which of the dishes you touched with your fingers contained the greater number of colonies? How can you explain this?
6. What do bacteria look like, and where are they found?

Data and Observations

Dish	Number of bacteria colonies
1	
2	
3	
4	

FIGURE 5–5.

5:6 Processes in Bacteria

Bacteria lack a nucleus and most cell parts usually found in other cells. Still, they carry out the same processes as other cells. Most bacteria need oxygen, warmth, food, and water to grow. Growth of bacteria means an increase in their number by cell division.

What conditions are necessary for the growth of bacteria?

Most bacteria obtain their food from living or dead organisms. If the water is taken out of milk through a process called dehydration, powdered milk is formed. Without water, bacteria cannot grow in the powdered milk or any other dried food. Freezing, refrigeration, and canning also prevent spoilage of food by bacteria. The high temperatures of the canning process kill all bacteria present in a food. Exposing food to high-energy radiation is another method of food preservation that kills bacteria. Pasteurization is the heating of milk to a temperature below boiling that kills harmful, but not all bacteria. Not heating the milk to boiling maintains the milk's flavor. Can you explain why unopened pasteurized milk will eventually spoil?

How do bacteria get energy?

Bacteria that have chlorophyll can make their own food from carbon dioxide and water. Bacteria lacking chlorophyll live on dead organic matter. These bacteria are saprophytes (SAP ruh fitez). A **saprophyte** is an organism that obtains its food from dead organisms or from the waste products of living organisms. Bacteria that feed on fallen leaves and dead animals are examples of saprophytes. Compounds produced in the decay of dead plants and animals enrich the soil and increase its fertility.

Some bacteria, such as those that cause sore throats in humans, are parasites. A **parasite** is an organism that gains food and protection from another living organism called a host.

a

b

FIGURE 5–6. High temperatures used in the canning process (a) kill most bacteria. When water is removed from foods (b), bacteria cannot grow on the food.

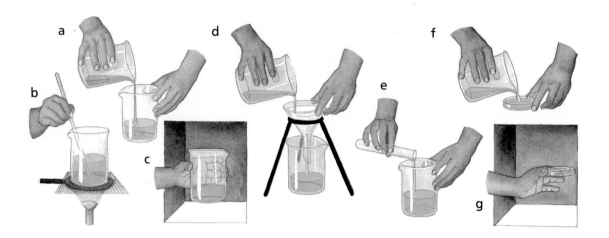

Other bacteria live in plants or animals. The bacteria help the plant or animal in some way. **Mutualism** (MEW chul ihz um) is a relationship between two different organisms that live together. Both organisms benefit from this kind of relationship. An example of mutualism is the bacteria living on waste material in the human digestive system. The bacteria prevent the growth of harmful bacteria and thus prevent infection. These bacteria receive "room and board" from the human. Both organisms benefit from the relationship.

Bacteria for study are grown in or on a special organic material, called a medium, in controlled conditions. A medium with a growing organism is called a **culture**. Soil, milk, blood, beef extract, and yeast extract may be used as food sources in cultures. They are mixed with agar (AH gur) to form a firm medium. Agar is an organic compound obtained from seaweed.

If conditions are not right for bacteria to grow, they may still survive by forming endospores. An **endospore** is a very compact cell with a wall around it that protects the cell. The wall shields the bacterium against harmful conditions. When conditions return to normal, an endospore develops into a bacterium.

FIGURE 5–7. A medium for a bacterial culture can be made by dissolving powdered sugar in meat broth (a, b). The solution is sterilized in an autoclave (c). After filtering (d) and balancing the pH (e), the solution is poured into culture dishes (f). Then it is sterilized again (g) and becomes firm.

Making Sure

7. How do endospores help a bacteria species survive?
8. How can food be stored to prevent spoilage by bacteria?
9. What do you think is the shape of a *Streptococcus* bacterium?

a   b

FIGURE 5–8. Some bacteria cause plant diseases. A squash with bacterial wilt (a) and a tomato with bacterial spot (b) are examples.

5:7 Helpful and Harmful Bacteria

Some species of bacteria are harmful. For example, some bacteria cause diseases in plants and animals and some spoil food. Most kinds of bacteria, however, are helpful. For example, bacteria that cause decay help cleanse the environment of dead plant and animal material. Decay in topsoil produces nutrients for farm crops. Bacteria in the human lungs and digestive system help protect against infection. Some bacteria make vitamins needed for good health. Bacteria in the stomachs of cows and sheep break down cellulose in the grass and hay the animals eat. Without the action of the bacteria, this plant material would have little food value. Cows and sheep raised on grass and hay are an important source of human food.

Why are bacteria of decay important?

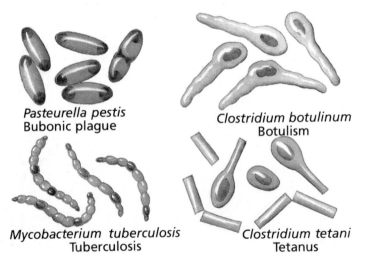

Pasteurella pestis
Bubonic plague

Clostridium botulinum
Botulism

Mycobacterium tuberculosis
Tuberculosis

Clostridium tetani
Tetanus

FIGURE 5–9. Some bacteria cause diseases. Four such organisms are shown with the disease each causes below it.

Bacteria are of major economic importance. For example, cheese, butter, and yogurt are made from milk soured by bacteria. Cheesemakers use dozens of different kinds of bacteria to produce flavorful cheeses. Sauerkraut is produced by the action of bacteria on chopped cabbage. The acid produced by the bacteria is a preservative that prevents the sauerkraut from spoiling. Vinegar produced by the action of bacteria in cider is used to pickle and preserve vegetables. Tetracyclines (teh truh sɪ kleenz), drugs used to treat infections, are produced by a species of bacteria.

Name two ways bacteria can be used to preserve food.

Bacteria are important in the growing field of biotechnology. **Biotechnology** is the use of living organisms to solve practical problems. For example, natural gas for heating and cooking can be produced through the action of anaerobic bacteria on plant and animal wastes. Protein-digesting enzymes extracted from bacteria are used in detergents for cleaning. Various bacterial enzymes have been used to treat leukemia, break down blood clots, and help aid digestion. Developing new forms of bacteria that produce useful products is a major part of the rapidly growing field of biotechnology.

Define biotechnology.

Making Sure

10. Name two ways bacteria are harmful.
11. Name five ways bacteria are helpful.

FIGURE 5–10. In the cheese-making industry, bacteria cause milk products to turn to solids (a). Aerobic bacteria break down sewage at a sewage treatment plant (b).

a   b

Understanding Magnification

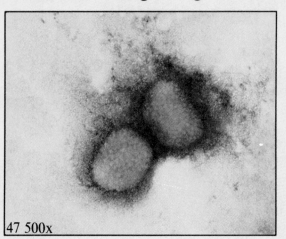

47 500x

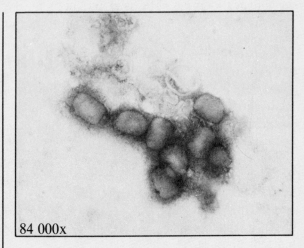

84 000x

Pictures are an important part of your textbook. Illustrations and photographs aid in a student's learning of a subject as well as help to make a book attractive and interesting. Pictures can summarize the meaning of many words. Pictures may help explain and support the authors' ideas. To get the most from this text, you should analyze and interpret pictures as you read.

Pictures in life science books often show organisms many times larger than their actual size. For instance, viruses are so small they can only be seen with an electron microscope. But pictures of viruses can be enlarged more than 100 000 times to make the viruses easily visible. The pictures above are magnified views of viruses.

The smallpox virus on the left has been enlarged 47 500 times. Enlarging 47 500× means that the virus has been magnified 47 500 times or that the virus in the picture is shown 47 500 times larger than its actual size. How many times larger than its actual size is the virus cell on the right?

When an object is magnified, the size that is seen is larger than the actual object. The amount of magnification is limited by the resolving power. The resolving power is the ability of a lens to form clear images of separate objects. The systems used for magnifying range from the simple hand lens, to the highly complex electron microscope. Magnification is the number of times the linear dimensions of an object are increased. If an object that is 5 mm long is magnified to appear 1 cm long, then the magnification is two times the original, written as 2×. Magnification with a hand lens is usually 5× or 10×.

Magnifying organisms helps scientists to understand every life process and many diseases. Biologists can even see normal cells changing into cancerous cells.

Select five pictures from this chapter and explain how each picture aids in the understanding of the text. Study each picture in a chapter as you read it. Ask yourself what the picture says. Read the words that describe the picture. Determine whether the object in the picture has been magnified, and if so, how much. Use the words to understand the picture and use the picture to understand the words.

CHAPTER 5
Review

Summary

1. Viruses are rodlike, spherical, or many-sided with a tail or stalk. A virus is composed of a nucleic acid core surrounded by a coat of protein.   5:1
2. A virus reproduces itself only when in a living cell.   5:1
3. It is difficult to treat diseases caused by viruses because drugs do not destroy viruses.   5:2
4. Blue-green algae and bacteria make up the moneran kingdom.   5:3
5. Blue-green algae and bacteria are the simplest of all organisms and lack a cell nucleus.   5:3
6. Bacteria exist in three shapes—cocci, bacilli, and spirilla.   5:5
7. Most bacteria are parasites or saprophytes. Some species can make their own food.   5:6
8. Endospores enable bacteria to survive dryness, changes in temperature, and certain chemicals.   5:6
9. Bacteria that cause decay cleanse the environment of dead plant and animal material.   5:7
10. Bacteria have many practical uses such as making cheese, preserving food, and producing natural gas.   5:7

Vocabulary

Write a sentence using the following words or terms correctly.

bacterium	endospore	parasite
biotechnology	interferon	saprophyte
blue-green algae	moneran	virus
culture	mutualism	

Questions

Do not write in this book.

A. True or False
Determine whether each of the following sentences is true or false. Rewrite the false statements to make them correct.
1. Bacteria are made of cells.
2. A medium with a growing organism is an endospore.
3. Bacteria do not need energy to live.
4. Bacteria that cause decay are saprophytes.
5. A virus is made of cells.
6. Chlorophyll is present in blue-green algae.

7. Monerans reproduce by cell division.
8. Only harmful bacteria enter the human body.
9. Bacteria can grow to form colonies.
10. Monerans have large cell nuclei.

B. Multiple Choice

Choose the word or phrase that correctly completes the following sentences.
1. Bacilli bacteria are *(rodlike, spherical, spiral)* in shape.
2. Bacteria are classified in the *(protist, fungi, moneran)* kingdom.
3. Bacteria that cause sore throats are *(saprophytes, parasites, mutualists)*.
4. *(Bacteria, Viruses, Blue-green algae)* are not monerans.
5. The core of a virus is *(sugar, protein, nucleic acid)*.
6. Interferon is produced by some *(viruses, blue-green algae, human cells)*.
7. You are most likely to find blue-green algae growing *(on a window, in a pond, on a sidewalk)*.
8. To observe viruses, a(n) *(magnifying glass, electron microscope, light microscope)* is needed.
9. The green color in blue-green algae is due to the presence of *(chlorophyll, cytoplasm, cell nuclei)*.
10. Most species of bacteria need *(soil, oxygen, sunlight)* to live.

C. Completion

Complete each of the following sentences with the correct word or phrase.
1. Blue-green algae reproduce by _____.
2. During unfavorable conditions, bacteria survive by forming _____.
3. _____ of bacteria means an increase in their numbers.
4. Bacteria that are _____ obtain food from living plants or animals without benefiting the hosts.
5. _____ are smaller than bacteria and grow only inside living cells.
6. _____ cause the souring of milk.
7. _____, butter, and _____ are made from milk soured by bacteria.
8. _____ is produced by the action of bacteria on apple cider.
9. _____ is a fuel produced by anaerobic bacteria living on plant and animal wastes.
10. _____ is the modern technological use of living organisms.

D. How and Why

1. Describe the major features of the moneran kingdom and the phyla that make up this group.

2. What is the difference between aerobic and anaerobic bacteria?
3. Is a virus alive? Give a reason for your answer.
4. Draw and label diagrams showing the three kinds of bacteria.
5. How is a parasite different from a saprophyte?
6. What are the best conditions for the growth of bacteria?
7. Explain why bacteria have major economic importance.

Ideas to Explore

1. **Project:** Visit a hospital medical laboratory to learn how technicians carry out tests for disease-causing microbes.
2. **Challenge:** Prepare a report on how food is prepared and preserved to prevent spoilage by bacteria.
3. **Challenge:** Through library research, obtain information about the electron microscope. Prepare a report for your class.
4. **Project:** Design an activity to investigate the growth of bacteria on different foods under different conditions. Plan the procedure, including materials, and have your teacher check it before you begin. Keep careful records of your work.
5. **Project:** Make a model of a virus from cardboard and wire. Use Figure 5–1 and library references as a guide.
6. **Challenge:** Prepare a report on the uses of bacteria in the food industry.
7. **Challenge:** Make a list of household products designed to kill bacteria.

Readings

Murphy, Wendy. *Coping with the Common Cold*. Alexandria, VA: Time-Life Books, 1981.

Nourse, Alan E. *Viruses*. New York: Franklin Watts, 1983.

Patent, Dorothy Hinshaw. *Bacteria: How They Affect Other Living Things*. New York: Holiday House, 1980.

Preuss, Paul. "Industry in Ferment." *Science 85*. July/August, 1985, pp. 42–46.

Silverstein, Alvin and Virginia Silverstein. *Germfree Life: A New Field in Biological Research*. New York: Lothrop, Lee and Shepard, 1980.

Simpson, Lance L. "Deadly Botulism." *Natural History*. January, 1980, pp. 12–24.

*M*any simple organisms are one-celled and microscopic. An example is this radiolarian, an ocean-dwelling organism. The structure shown is the skeleton of a radiolarian. It was found in the Indian Ocean. Other simple organisms are multicellular and visible without a microscope. Fungi are an example. What are the characteristics of fungi? What are the characteristics of a radiolarian? How are radiolarians and fungi alike and different from each other?

CHAPTER 6
PROTISTS AND FUNGI

6:1 Protist Classification

Most of the species in the protist kingdom are microscopic, one-celled organisms. Some form colonies of many cells. Protists are more complex than monerans. Protists have characteristics that are similar to plants and animals. Like plant and animal cells, each protist cell has a nucleus. Protist cells also have specialized parts that perform certain life functions.

Some protists move about to obtain food like animals do. One-celled protists that have characteristics similar to animals are called **protozoans** (proh tuh ZOH unz). Other protists have chlorophyll and make their own food as plants do. These are simple algae. Some protists are parasites that live in or on animals and plants. Other protists, such as slime molds, are saprophytes. They obtain food from dead organic material.

Because several protist characteristics differ from the characteristics of plants and animals, they are classified in a separate kingdom. The protist kingdom is divided into eight phyla. Appendix D on page 557 lists and describes the phyla in the protist kingdom.

GOALS:
1. You will learn characteristics of protists and how they are classified.
2. You will learn characteristics of fungi and how they are classified.
3. You will learn the economic importance of protists and fungi.

What is a protozoan?

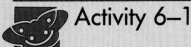

Activity 6–1   Observing Protists

Problem: How do protists compare?

Materials

Euglena culture
Amoeba culture
Stentor culture
Peridinium culture
Synedra culture
Trypanosoma prepared slide
Plasmodium prepared slide

5 microscope slides
5 coverslips
dropper
microscope

Procedure

1. Make seven charts similar to the one shown.
2. Make a wet mount from the *Euglena* culture.
3. Observe *Euglena* under low and high power.
4. Record your observations in one of your charts. (See Data and Observations.)
5. Repeat steps 1 through 3 with the *Amoeba, Stentor, Peridinium,* and *Synedra* cultures.
6. Observe the prepared slide of *Trypanosoma* under low and high power.
7. Record your observations in a chart.
8. Observe the prepared slide of *Plasmodium* under low and high power.
9. Record your observations in a chart.

Data and Observations

Organism *Euglena*	Observations
Classification (phylum)	
Cell wall (√ if present)	
Cell membrane (√ if present)	
Nucleus (√ if present)	
Color	
Method of movement	
Vacuoles (√ if present)	
Chloroplasts (√ if present)	
Shape	

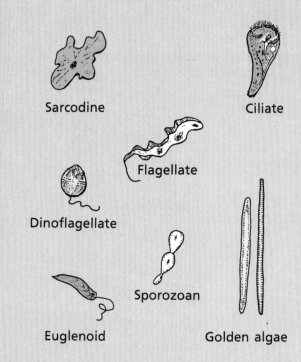

Sarcodine

Ciliate

Flagellate

Dinoflagellate

Sporozoan

Euglenoid

Golden algae

FIGURE 6–1.

Questions and Conclusions

1. Describe the structure that enables *Stentor* to move.
2. Describe the structure that enables *Euglena, Peridinium,* and *Trypanosoma* to move.
3. Describe the movement of *Amoeba.*
4. Which protists can make their own food (have chloroplasts)?
5. Which protists cannot make their own food (do not have chloroplasts)?
6. Which protists are unicellular?
7. Are any of the protists multicellular?
8. Which protists are like plants? Explain.
9. Which protists are like animals? Explain.
10. How do the protists compare?

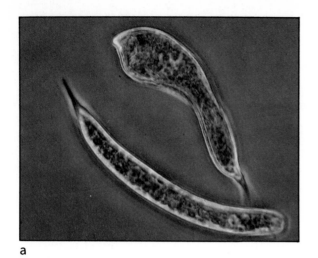

a

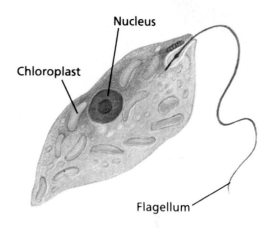

b

Nucleus

Chloroplast

Flagellum

FIGURE 6–2. Euglenoids have a flagellum for movement (a). Their structure includes chloroplasts with chlorophyll for foodmaking (b).

What are the characteristics of algae classified as protists?

6:2 Algae

Species of algae in the protist kingdom are one-celled organisms with cell walls. Their colors vary from yellow-green to golden-brown. Most protist algae live in water. However, a few species are found in soil, on damp surfaces, and in the digestive tracts of certain animals. Algae contain chlorophyll and make their own food. They are part of the vast number of tiny organisms called plankton, that float in water. Plankton provide food for many animals.

Euglenoids are a type of alga classified in the protist kingdom. A major genus of this group is *Euglena* (yew GLEE nuh), which occurs mainly in fresh water. Euglenoids are like animals in that they lack cell walls and can move about. They are plantlike in that most have chlorophyll and can make their own food. At one end of a *Euglena* is a whiplike tail called a **flagellum** (fluh JEL um). The flagellum is used for movement. Most euglenoids live in fresh water and use flagella for "swimming." *Euglena* reproduces asexually by cell division.

Diatoms are another example of algae in the protist kingdom. They can reproduce asexually and sexually. Species of diatoms vary in shape and color. Diatoms are marine species. A diatom cell has an outer shell with two parts. One part fits over the other part like a lid on a box. The shell is made of a glasslike material. The empty shells of dead diatoms collect on the ocean bottom, forming large deposits. This glassy material is called diatomaceous (di uh tuh MAY shus) earth. Diatomaceous earth has practical uses. For example, it is used to make swimming pool water filters and scouring powders, toothpastes, and cosmetics. Because it glows in the dark, diatomaceous earth is used in highway paints.

Describe the structure of a diatom.

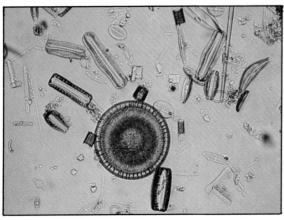

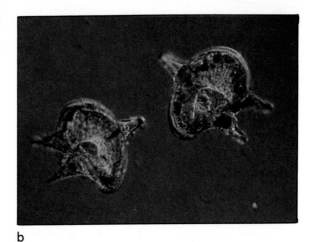

a   b

FIGURE 6–3. Diatoms (a) are golden algae. *Peridinium* (b) is a member of a phylum of algae with two flagella.

Making Sure

1. Why are protists classified in a separate kingdom from plants and animals?
2. What are the phyla in the protist kingdom?
3. What are plankton? Why are they important?
4. List three examples of protists.
5. Where do protist algae live?
6. For what is diatomaceous earth used?

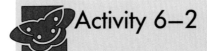

Activity 6–2   Observing Plankton

Problem: How can you determine what organisms are plankton?

Materials   plankton sample, dropper, microscope, microscope slide, coverslip

Procedure   (1) Place one or two drops of water from the plankton sample onto a clean microscope slide. (2) Add a coverslip. (3) Focus the slide on low power and draw the organisms you see. (4) Use Appendix D on page 557 to identify the organisms.

Questions   Answer the following questions for each organism you observe. (1) What shape is the organism? (2) Does the organism have a cell membrane? (3) Does it have a nucleus? (4) What color is the organism? (5) Does it have chlorophyll? (6) Does the organism move? If so, how? (7) How can you determine what organisms are plankton?

6:3 Protozoans

Animallike protists that have no chlorophyll are called protozoans. Protozoans are one-celled protists. They live in water, soil, and on decaying organic matter. Some protozoans are parasites. Malaria and African sleeping sickness are diseases caused by protozoan parasites. Protozoans are classified according to the ways they move. All reproduce asexually by cell division. Some can reproduce sexually by exchanging nuclear material.

An **amoeba** (uh MEE buh) is an example of one type of protozoan. Amoebas are always changing shape. In fact, the genus name *Amoeba* comes from a Greek word that means "change." Amoebas move with pseudopods (SYEWD uh pahdz). **Pseudopods** are slender, fingerlike projections of cytoplasm, sometimes called "false feet." Pseudopods can form in any direction. The cytoplasm inside an amoeba flows in the direction of the pseudopods. Thus, the amoeba moves in that direction.

Compare how amoebas, paramecia, and flagellates move.

Amoebas also use pseudopods to obtain food, which may be other microbes, algae, or bits of dead matter. When an amoeba comes in contact with a food particle, its pseudopods surround and trap the food and some water inside the cell. The trapped food and water form a food vacuole. Food inside a food vacuole is broken down to provide energy and materials for growth. Material that cannot be digested remains in the food vacuole. The vacuole moves toward the cell membrane, which opens and releases the waste material to the outside of the cell. The amoeba flows away from the waste.

Another protozoan is the slipper-shaped *Paramecium* (par uh MEE see um). A **paramecium** is a single cell that has two nuclei. The large nucleus, called a macronucleus, controls cell activities. The micronucleus, or smaller nucleus, is involved in reproduction.

FIGURE 6–4. Pseudopods of an amoeba flow around a food particle. The trapped food particle and water form a food vacuole.

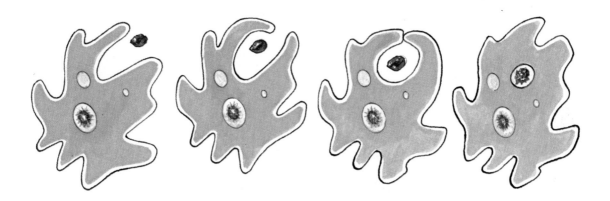

The cell is covered with **cilia** (SIHL ee uh), which are short, hairlike parts on the outside of a cell. A paramecium moves through water by beating its cilia. Cilia are also useful in obtaining food.

Along one side of a paramecium is a depression called the oral groove. When a paramecium swims forward, the oral groove funnels food into the cell, Figure 6–5(a). A food vacuole forms around food that enters the cell. Digestion and circulation take place in food vacuoles. A contractile vacuole removes excess water from the cell by contracting and pushing its contents out through the cell membrane. Ciliates are usually much larger than flagellates or amoebas.

Flagellates (FLAJ uh layts) are one-celled protozoans that have one or more flagella. Flagellates move through water by beating their flagella. Most flagellates are parasites that cause diseases in other organisms. African sleeping sickness is caused by a flagellate that reproduces within the body of a tsetse (SEET see) fly. These bloodsucking tsetse flies inject the flagellates into the human bloodstream. Sleeping sickness is a serious disease in Africa where the number of tsetse flies is uncontrolled.

Certain species of flagellates live in the digestive tracts of termites. Termites chew wood, but they cannot digest the cellulose it contains. The flagellates digest the cellulose, providing food for the termites. Since the flagellates do not feed on the termite's tissues, they are not parasites. The termites cannot survive without

What are the main characteristics of flagellates?

FIGURE 6–5. Structures (a) of a paramecium (b).

a

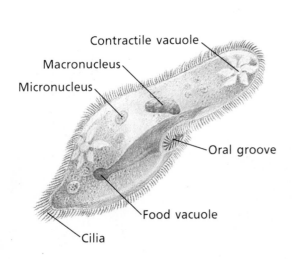

Contractile vacuole
Macronucleus
Micronucleus
Oral groove
Food vacuole
Cilia

b

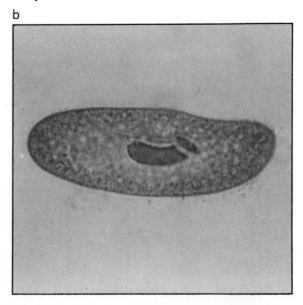

the flagellates. The flagellates receive "room and board" from the termite. The relationship between termites and flagellates living inside them is an example of mutualism. **Sporozoans** (spor uh ZOH unz) are small protozoans that reproduce by forming spores. Unlike other protozoans, sporozoans cannot move around to obtain food. They are parasites. Sporozoans obtain food from the hosts in which they live. Many have life cycles in which some stages occur in one host organism. Other stages occur in a different organism. Malaria is caused by a sporozoan. The sporozoan that causes malaria has a life cycle that involves both a vertebrate host and a mosquito. The sporozoans are carried by a certain species of mosquito. When a female mosquito bites a person who has malaria, the sporozoans are taken into the mosquito. The sporozoans grow and reproduce inside the mosquito. When the mosquito bites a healthy person, some of the sporozoans enter the person's blood. As the parasites grow, the person develops malaria.

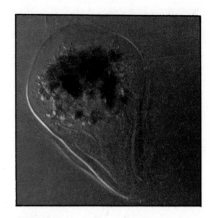

FIGURE 6–6. Flagellates are protozoans that have one or more flagella.

Making Sure

7. How do amoebas and paramecia get food?
8. What are some diseases caused by protozoans?
9. Explain how a termite and its flagellates are an example of mutualism.
10. What are the three types of movement in protozoans?
11. How do sporozoans get food and reproduce?

FIGURE 6–7. The sporozoan *Plasmodium* is carried by the female *Anopheles* mosquito.

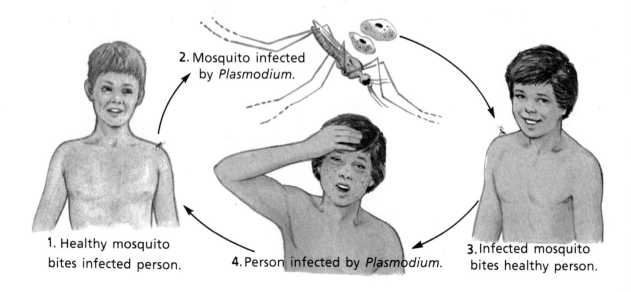

2. Mosquito infected by *Plasmodium*.

1. Healthy mosquito bites infected person.

4. Person infected by *Plasmodium*.

3. Infected mosquito bites healthy person.

Activity 6-3

Observing a Paramecium

Problem: What effects do chemicals have on the movement of *Paramecium?*

Materials

prepared slide of a *Paramecium*
Paramecium culture
acetic acid solution
methyl cellulose
microscope slide
carmine red solution
microscope
coverslip
dropper

Procedure

Part A

1. Examine a prepared slide of a paramecium under low and high power.
2. Note the cilia of the prepared specimen.
3. Locate the micronucleus and macronucleus.
4. Look for clear circles with canals leading to them at either end of the cell. These are contractile vacuoles.
5. Locate the oral groove. (Refer to Figure 6–5(a) on page 110.)
6. Draw and label the parts of a paramecium.

Part B

1. Place a drop of *Paramecium* culture on a clean slide.
2. Add a coverslip.
3. Examine the movement of the paramecia under low power.
4. Draw arrows to show the direction of movement of a paramecium.
5. Add a drop of methyl cellulose at the edge of the coverslip.
6. Examine the paramecia under high power. Record your observations of the paramecias' movements.
7. Locate a nucleus.
8. Locate a contractile vacuole.
9. Add a drop of carmine red solution to the slide.
10. Locate the oral groove and the cilia that line it.
11. Locate a food vacuole with carmine red particles. Observe the food vacuoles for a few minutes. Record your observations.
12. Add a drop of acetic acid solution at the edge of the coverslip and observe what happens. Record your observations.

Data and Observations

Solution	Effect on Movement
Methyl cellulose	
Carmine red	
Acetic acid	

Questions and Conclusions

1. Which end seems to be the front end of the paramecium?
2. Does the paramecium change shape?
3. How does a paramecium move?
4. What happens when a paramecium bumps into something?
5. What happens when carmine red solution is added at the edge of the coverslip?
6. What is the function of the cilia that line the oral groove?
7. In what direction do food vacuoles move?
8. What is the function of contractile vacuoles?
9. What happens when acetic acid is added to the edge of the coverslip?
10. How many nuclei does a paramecium have?
11. How many nuclei did you observe in Part B?
12. What effects do chemicals have on the movement of a paramecium?

6:4 Slime Molds

A slime mold is a protist with a life cycle in which there are three stages. During these stages, a slime mold resembles three different kinds of organisms. Slime molds live in damp places, such as the floor of a forest, where they feed as saprophytes on dead, decaying matter. A few species are parasitic.

One stage in the life cycle of a slime mold is a slimy mass of material having many cell nuclei, but no cell walls. By forming pseudopods, this stage can flow slowly along a decaying branch, log, or other moist surface. In this slimy mass stage, a slime mold is like an amoeba. The slimy body of the mold may be colorless, red, yellowish, violet, or some other color.

At some point in its life cycle, a slime mold stops moving and grows reproductive parts. These reproductive parts, called sporangia, produce spores. The sporangium is also colored. In some slime molds the sporangia are on stalks. In others, they are stalkless. In this second stage, spore production of slime molds is similar to that of fungi.

The spores develop into cells that can fuse together and form new individuals with flagella. In this third stage, the slime molds are like flagellate organisms. These new individuals later lose the flagella and grow to form another slimy mass stage.

Where are slime molds likely to be found?

Making Sure

12. Describe three stages in the life of a slime mold. Tell how each stage is similar to that of other organisms.
13. At what stage of its life does a slime mold grow reproductive parts?

FIGURE 6–8. A brown slime mold in the reproductive stage resembles a fungus, but it is actually classified as a protist.

6:5 Fungus Classification

Have you ever observed mold growing on bread? Mold is one kind of fungus. Two other kinds of fungi are mushrooms and yeasts. A fungus is a plantlike organism that feeds on living organisms or dead organic matter. Like plant cells, fungus cells have cell walls. Also, like plants, fungi cannot move about. However, fungi are different from plants in that fungi do not make their own food.

Fungi cannot make their own food because they do not have chlorophyll in their cells. Fungi that get food from other living things are parasites. For example, the fungus that causes athlete's foot is a parasite. Fungi that live on dead organic matter are saprophytes. A mushroom that grows on a rotting log is a saprophyte.

Most fungi are many-celled and are therefore more complex than protists. Fungi can reproduce by spore formation. They are divided into three main phyla in the fungi kingdom. These phyla are the sporangium fungi, club fungi, and sac fungi. This division is based on the different kinds of spore-forming structures produced by the fungi. Appendix C on page 556 shows the classes of fungi, their characteristics, and some examples.

Fungi can be both helpful and harmful. Table 6–1 gives examples of how fungi are economically important. The table also details the harm that fungi can cause.

Table 6–1

Helpful and Harmful Fungi	
Helpful fungi	**Harmful fungi**
1. used directly as food—mushrooms	1. cause food spoilage such as sour milk and moldy bread
2. used to flavor blue and Roquefort cheese	2. cause plant diseases such as rusts, smuts, Dutch elm disease, and mildew
3. used to make alcohol—yeasts	3. cause human diseases such as athlete's foot and ringworm
4. used to make bread rise—yeast	
5. used to make soy sauce from soybeans	4. cause animal diseases such as lung infections
6. used to make certain drugs such as penicillin	5. destroy leather, fabrics, plastic articles
7. help to decompose dead organisms and return valuable materials to the soil and atmosphere	6. cause poisoning and sometimes death in humans

FIGURE 6–9. Bread is food for Rhizopus molds.

6:6 Sporangium Fungi

Over 1.5 million people moved from Ireland to the United States because of a sporangium fungus. The migration started when the fungus killed off Ireland's potato crop in the late 1840s. Almost a million Irish died of starvation as a result of this potato blight.

A common sporangium fungus is the mold that grows on old bread. Another is the cottony fungus that grows on aquarium fish. Sporangium fungi produce spores in spore cases called **sporangia** (spuh RAN jee uh). The species are either parasites or saprophytes and grow in warm, moist places. Threadlike structures called **hyphae** (HI fee) are produced by the fungus. The hyphae grow on and in a food source, absorbing water, minerals, and food. Enzymes released from the hyphae break down the food so it can be used by the fungus.

Growth of molds can be prevented through cleanliness, drying, and chemicals. Chemical preservatives are added to some breads to retard the growth of mold. Fruits such as raisins and dates are dried to preserve them. However, fungi can grow in concentrated salt or sugar solutions such as jelly in which bacteria would normally not grow. Even refrigerated fruits are not protected from the growth of molds.

Sporangium fungi reproduce asexually by spores from the sporangia that grow on the ends of hyphae. When a mature sporangium bursts open, thousands of spores are released. Hyphae of new fungi grow from these spores when conditions are suitable. Sporangium fungi also reproduce sexually by spores formed by the fusion of two cells in two different hyphae. The nuclei of the two cells join and then divide many times. Each nucleus, with a bit of cytoplasm and a protective cell wall, becomes a thick-walled spore.

What are the characteristics of sporangium fungi?

FIGURE 6–10. A magnified spore case of a bread mold.

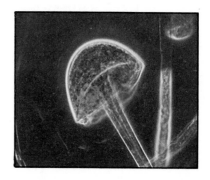

Making Sure

14. What are the phyla in the fungi kingdom?
15. Give an example of a sporangium fungus and tell how it reproduces and gets food.

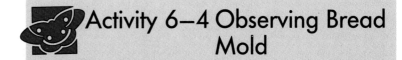

Activity 6–4 Observing Bread Mold

Problem: How long does it take bread to mold?

Materials   bread, container with cover, dropper, hand lens, forceps, microscope, microscope slide, coverslip, water

Procedure   (1) Hypothesize how many days it will take a piece of bread to mold. Record your hypothesis. (2) Place a piece of bread in a small container. Add a few drops of water to the bread. (3) Leave the bread uncovered for about an hour. (4) Cover the container and place it in a dark place at room temperature. (5) Observe the bread daily. Record your observations. Add water as needed to keep the bread moist. (6) When mold begins to grow, examine the bread with a hand lens. (7) Use forceps to prepare a wet mount slide with some of the bread mold. (8) Observe the slide under low power of the microscope. (9) Draw and label the hyphae, sporangia, and spores.

Questions   (1) What was the purpose of adding water to the bread? (2) What was the purpose of leaving the dish uncovered? (3) Where did the mold come from? (4) What provided food for the mold? (5) What conditions are necessary for mold spores to grow? (6) What do the hyphae look like? (7) Where are the hyphae located? (8) Describe the sporangia. (9) Where are the sporangia located? (10) How long does it take bread to mold?

FIGURE 6–11.

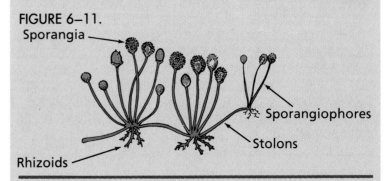

FIGURE 6–12. The visible parts of mushrooms are caps on top of thick stalks called stipes.

6:7 Club Fungi

Mushrooms, puffballs, and bracket fungi are examples of club fungi. **Club fungi** are fungi that produce spores in club-shaped structures. Some club fungi are parasites that damage crops. Others are important saprophytes that decompose organic matter. Some club fungi are good to eat; others are extremely poisonous.

Mushrooms are large club fungi that are well known to most people because of their shape. They grow in orchards, fields, and forests where there is moisture and organic matter. Most of a mushroom consists of hyphae. The hyphae grow and spread through soil or decaying logs and tree stumps. Enzymes released from the hyphae digest organic matter. The digested material is absorbed into the hyphae and used for food.

What are the characteristics of club fungi?

The visible part of a mushroom is a mass of hyphae and is used for sexual reproduction. It is a cap on top of a thick stalk called a stipe. Most mushrooms contain many platelike gills on the underside of the cap. The gills consist of many hyphae fused together. They extend out from the stipe like the spokes of a wheel. Thousands of spores are produced on the gills. They fall off and are carried away by air currents. Those that land in a favorable environment may develop hyphae to form new mushrooms. Only a few manage to survive.

How do club fungi reproduce?

Although many species of mushroom are edible, some mushrooms are poisonous. Never eat wild mushrooms unless you are certain they are safe.

Puffballs are fungi similar to mushrooms. The reproductive part of a puffball is round, or pear-shaped. Spores are produced inside the puffball. When a puffball dries out, it splits open and releases its spores. Puffballs are good to eat when they are young. No poisonous puffball species is known.

FIGURE 6–13. Puffballs have a round or pear-shaped reproductive structure.

FIGURE 6–14. Bracket fungi living on dead wood are saprophytes.

Bracket fungi are the flat, shelflike fungi that grow on stumps and tree trunks. As with mushrooms and puffballs, most of the bracket fungus is not visible. It consists of hyphae growing inside the tree or stump. The hyphae digest the wood in the tree or stump. Bracket fungi reproduce by spores formed on the inside of the shelf. The spores are released through tiny openings in the underside of the bracket.

Making Sure

16. Name three examples of club fungi. Tell how they are alike and different.
17. How do mushrooms obtain food?

6:8 Sac Fungi

Sac fungi are so named because they produce spores in an ascus which is a little sac. Yeasts, powdery mildews, edible morels and truffles, and most molds that spoil food belong to this group. One kind of sac fungus, a blue green mold, is used to produce penicillin. Enzymes produced by another kind of mold give cheeses their flavors. *Neurospora* is an important mold scientists have used to study inheritance.

Plant diseases caused by sac fungi include rye plant ergot, Dutch elm disease, and chestnut blight. Since it was first observed in 1904, chestnut blight has destroyed most of the millions of

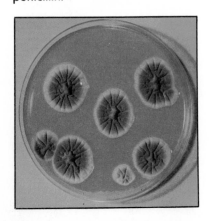

FIGURE 6–15. *Penicillium* mold, growing here in a culture, is a sac fungus that produces the antibiotic penicillin.

American chestnut trees once growing in the United States. Spores of the deadly fungus enter cracks in the tree's bark where the fungus begins to grow. Eventually, fungus kills the tree by cutting off its supply of nutrients.

Likewise, Dutch elm disease has also been responsible for the death of millions of elm trees. The fungus is carried by bark beetles. Bacteria that can stop the growth of the fungus are used to control the disease. Also, scientists are using biological chemicals to trap the beetles.

Most yeasts are one-celled fungi. They are spherical or egg-shaped. A yeast cell contains a nucleus, vacuole, and cytoplasm surrounded by a cell wall. Yeasts form spores when conditions are not favorable for growth. The spores are produced by divisions of the cell nucleus. A spore is formed when a protective cell wall grows around each nucleus and a small amount of cytoplasm. Each yeast cell usually produces four spores. Each spore becomes a yeast cell when conditions are favorable again.

Yeasts also reproduce asexually by budding. In budding, a new cell grows out from the side of a yeast cell. The new cell, called a bud, grows and separates from the old cell. The new cell is called a daughter cell. A yeast cell may produce as many as 24 generations of daughter cells in a 12-hour time period.

Yeast cells obtain energy from food in two ways, respiration and fermentation. When oxygen is present, respiration occurs in yeast cells. Sugar and oxygen are used to produce carbon dioxide, water, and energy. Fermentation, a process similar to respiration, occurs in the absence of oxygen. In **fermentation,** energy is released when sugar is changed to ethyl alcohol and carbon dioxide. The carbon dioxide formed in the process can be used in the baking industry to make dough rise. Alcoholic beverages are also produced by the fermentation of grain or fruit. Yeast cells are present as a ''bloom'' on the skin of grapes.

What are the main characteristics of sac fungi? List two examples.

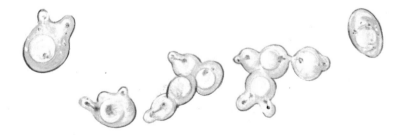

FIGURE 6–16. Yeast reproduce by budding.

6:9 Lichens

Perhaps you have seen lichens (LI kunz) growing on rocks, soil, tree branches, or tree trunks. Lichens may look like leathery leaves or slender branches. They are usually dull gray-green, bright yellow, or orange. Many lichens are able to grow in places where few plants grow such as on bare rock or on arctic ice. Reindeer "moss" is a lichen that grows in arctic regions and provides food for animals. Although they can withstand extreme temperatures, lichens are very sensitive to air pollution and acid rain. The disappearance of lichens from an area gives scientists warning of harmful air pollution.

A lichen is not one organism. A **lichen** is a fungus and an alga living in mutualism. The algae in lichens are either green or blue-green algae. The alga contains chlorophyll and makes food which is used by the fungus. The fungus supplies water and minerals to the alga. It prevents the alga from drying out. The fungus secretes acid to begin the breakdown of rock into soil.

What is the structure of a lichen?

How is lichen an example of mutualism?

FIGURE 6–17. Lichens may be called "pioneers" because they are often the first organisms to grow on the surface of a rock. Some lichens look like scales (a). Others, such as British soldier lichen (b), are colorful.

Making Sure

18. Why is fruit juice a good place for yeast to grow?
19. Is the yeast that grows in grape juice a parasite or saprophyte? Why?
20. How does a yeast cell obtain energy and reproduce?
21. How do you think scientists classify lichens?

a

b

Technology

Microbes at Work

Scientists have found ways to change the genetic information in bacteria to make them produce insulin, vitamins, and hormones for medical purposes. Bacteria have been engineered to make other products including enzymes, gasoline additives, aspirin substitutes, and the raw materials for the manufacture of plastics and rubber.

By the techniques of genetic engineering, scientists can produce strains of microbes that are programmed to make a variety of valuable chemicals. The programming is usually done by a process called splicing. Within bacteria are special rings of genetic material called plasmids. These rings can be removed from a bacterium and a desired genetic trait can be added to the ring. This process is carried out with the use of special enzymes. The programmed plasmid is then reinserted into the bacterium or new host cell. The newly inserted genes may control the production of insulin or a particular vitamin. The microbe and its new genetic trait can then be cloned.

Cloning is a process that makes large numbers of identical organisms. Genetically engineered microbes are cloned in large, liquid-filled, fermentation chambers called bioreactors. The microbes grow and reproduce within the bioreactors. At the same time, the new genetic trait is being reproduced within the microbial cells. As they grow, they manufacture the new product they are programmed to make. The product, which may be a hormone, vitamin, or some other special chemical, is then separated and purified.

The technology for purification includes centrifugation and High Pressure Liquid Chromatography or HPLC. Chromatography separates molecules based on their sizes. Liquid from the bioreactor is passed through HPLC columns under high pressure. HPLC columns are filled with resin beads that have holes to trap different-sized molecules. As the liquid in the bioreactor is filtered through the column and beads, the product is separated and isolated from the microbial cells. This liquid chromatography is fast and produces a very pure product.

The use of genetic engineering in the manufacture of drugs and valuable chemicals may provide answers to many of the world's health problems. For example, in the past a rare medicine could be used to help only a few persons. Now, large quantities can be made to help many who are ill.

FIGURE 6–18. A plasmid is isolated from bacterium (a). A new gene such as that for insulin is placed into the nuclear material (b). The altered plasmid is reinserted into a bacterium (c). This bacterium is reproduced (d), and insulin is manufactured.

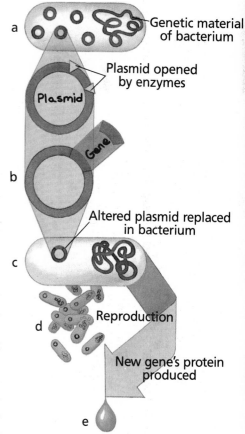

a — Genetic material of bacterium

Plasmid

Plasmid opened by enzymes

Gene

b

Altered plasmid replaced in bacterium

c

Reproduction

d

New gene's protein produced

e

FOCUS ON
People and Careers

Cheese Makers

Bacteria are important in nature and in the human economy as well. Bacteria are used in many processes in the dairy industry. Production of cheese depends on bacteria that cause the milk products to solidify.

William Knudsen is the vice president of a cheese factory founded by his grandfather. In order to carry on and improve the family business, Mr. Knudsen earned a university degree in dairy and food technology, and took additional courses necessary for certification in grading milk and dairy products.

As the company's vice president, Mr. Knudsen has many responsibilities. These include laboratory testing of milk and cheese samples, technical assistance, purchasing, bookkeeping, inventory, counter and telephone sales, and delivery supervision. In addition to observing local and state regulations, the Knudsens' cheese factory must meet standards set by the Food and Drug Administration and the United States Department of Agriculture. There are periodic inspections of the plant and its processing techniques, but Mr. Knudsen says that the most important test is customer approval.

According to Mr. Knudsen, family-owned cheese factories are becoming a thing of the past. A few large companies produce most of the cheese eaten today. These companies are looking for employees with college degrees in chemistry or business, as well as vocational or technical school graduates who are specialists in areas such as food processing or refrigeration.

Some small companies, however, still depend on employees like Kenneth Johnson. After earning his General Equivalency Diploma, he was hired by Knudsen. In the past 10 years, Mr. Johnson has been trained in all phases of cheese making. Now, he has some supervisory responsibilities with newer employees.

Mr. Johnson's workday is made up of almost anything that needs to be done in the cheesemaking process. This includes running the pasteurizer, filling the vats, monitoring the temperature and time, and operating the mill. At other times, he may assist in loading and unloading trucks. There are only seven other employees at the factory, and at peak workload times, everyone assists each other with various tasks.

Mr. Johnson says that cheesemakers must be physically fit because they must lift heavy containers. They must also be able to work in a warm environment. Awareness of safety is important when running the mill to cut the large curd blocks. Although Mr. Johnson has been a cheese maker for 10 years, he has not grown tired of the factory's product. "I still eat cheese every day," he says.

Summary

1. Most protists are microscopic, one-celled organisms that have characteristics similar to plants and animals.   6:1
2. Protists include protozoans, slime molds, and several types of algae.   6:1
3. Euglenoids and diatoms are examples of algae classified as protists.   6:2
4. Plankton include microscopic species of algae that float in water.   6:2
5. Protozoans are protists that are classified by their methods of movement.   6:3
6. Amoebas, paramecia, and flagellates are protozoans that move about.   6:3
7. Sporozoans are protozoans that cannot move about.   6:3
8. Slime molds change form several times during their life cycles.   6:4
9. Fungi do not contain chlorophyll. They are parasites or saprophytes.   6:5
10. Fungi are divided into three main phyla: sporangium fungi, club fungi, and sac fungi.   6:5
11. Sporangium fungi produce spores in sporangia.   6:6
12. Mushrooms and puffballs are two kinds of club fungi that live on dead organic matter.   6:7
13. Yeasts are sac fungi that can obtain energy through a chemical change called fermentation.   6:8
14. A lichen contains algae and fungi living together for mutual benefit.   6:9

Vocabulary

Write a sentence using the following words or terms correctly.

amoeba	flagellate	protozoan
cilia	flagellum	pseudopod
diatom	hyphae	sporangia
euglenoid	lichen	sporozoan
fermentation	paramecium	

Questions

Do not write in this book.

A. True or False

Determine whether each of the following sentences is true or false. Rewrite the false statements to make them correct.

1. All protists are parasites.
2. A euglena has a flagellum.
3. Plankton are food for ocean fish.
4. An amoeba uses cilia to obtain food.
5. There are two nuclei in a paramecium.

6. Most slime molds live in dry places.
7. All fungi contain chlorophyll.
8. Yeast cells obtain energy from sugar.
9. Mold can reproduce with spores.
10. A lichen is a fungus and an alga living in mutualism.

B. Multiple Choice

Choose the word or phrase that correctly completes the following sentences.
1. In an amoeba, food is digested in a *(nucleus, pseudopod, vacuole)*.
2. *(Slime molds, Sporozoans, Amoebas)* have three different stages in their life cycles.
3. Protozoans are *(one-, two-, many-)* celled protists.
4. A *(flagellate, paramecium, sporozoan)* causes malaria.
5. *(Sporozoans, Paramecia, Amoebas)* are organisms that cannot move under their own power.
6. Yeasts are *(one-celled, many-celled)* organisms.
7. Bread mold is an example of a *(parasite, saprophyte, lichen)*.
8. *(Algae, Yeast, Puffballs)* are similar to mushrooms.
9. A bracket fungus living on a dead log is a *(saprophyte, parasite, lichen)*.
10. A lichen is made of a fungus and a(n) *(alga, bacterium, virus)*.

C. Completion

Complete each of the following sentences with the correct word or phrase.
1. The protist kingdom is divided into _____ phyla.
2. A(n) _____ is a golden algae with a cell like a box with a lid.
3. Paramecia swim by moving their _____.
4. Fruiting bodies in slime molds produce _____ for reproduction.
5. An amoeba is composed of _____ cell(s).
6. Three kinds of fungi are _____, _____, and _____.
7. Yeast is used in the baking industry because it releases carbon dioxide by _____.
8. _____ that digest food are released by molds.
9. _____ that reproduce mushrooms are in the mushroom's cap.
10. Cells in the _____ part of a lichen contain chlorophyll.

How and Why

1. Name the phyla in the protist kingdom. List one characteristic of each phylum that makes it different from the other phyla.
2. Draw a diagram of an organism from each protist phylum.

3. Draw a diagram of an amoeba and label its parts.
4. Name three ways in which an amoeba and a paramecium are alike.
5. How are slime molds like other protists?
6. How are fungi classified?
7. How do yeasts and molds obtain food?
8. How is a saprophyte different from a parasite? Name one example of each.
9. How do the two species that live in a lichen benefit by living together?

Ideas to Explore

1. **Challenge:** Obtain information and prepare a report on fungi that infect fish. Find out how the growth of fungi on tropical fish in aquariums is controlled and prevented.
2. **Project:** Design an activity to investigate the growth of molds and bacteria on different foods under different conditions. Plan the procedure, including materials, and have your teacher check it before you begin. Keep careful records of your work.
3. **Project:** Design an activity to determine the relative effectiveness of preservatives added to different breads. Plan the procedure, including materials, and have your teacher check it before you begin. Keep careful records of your work.
4. **Challenge:** Obtain information and prepare a report on slime molds. Learn how and why scientists investigate their life activities.
5. **Project:** Make a flip book of an amoeba extending its pseudopods around a food particle and then digesting it.
6. **Project:** Make spore prints of two different kinds of mushrooms. Carefully cut off the stalk of the mushroom near the cap. Place the cap, gills down on a sheet of light-colored paper. Allow the cap to remain overnight. Compare the two spore prints.

Readings

Blonston, Gary. "The Biochemistry of Bacchus." *Science 85*. October, 1985, pp. 68–75.

Johnson, Sylvia. *Mushrooms*. Minneapolis: Lerner, 1982.

Monmany, Terence. "Yeast at Work." *Science 85*. July/August, 1985, pp. 30–35.

Whitten, Richard H. and William R. Pendergrass. *Carolina Protozoa and Invertebrates Manual*. Burlington, NC: Carolina Biological Supply, 1980.

Bacteria
Background Data

Bacteria are among the smallest single-celled organisms found in nature. They are approximately 0.001 to 0.005 cm in size. Bacteria are members of the Moneran kingdom and usually are classified into three general groups based on shape: rod-shaped, spherical, and spiral-shaped.

Bacteria are widely known for the harm they cause through disease. They are responsible for the spoilage of foods. Heat, X rays, and ultraviolet light can be used to kill bacteria. Most common types of harmful bacteria in milk are killed by pasteurization. During pasteurization, milk is heated to a temperature of 63 degrees Celsius for 30 minutes.

Bacteria also can be helpful. They are involved in the decay of dead organic matter. Through this process, many different elements are recycled. Nitrogen-fixing bacteria are found in the nodules on the roots of legumes. These bacteria take nitrogen from the air and convert it into a form plants can use. Also, bacteria are used in the production of dairy products such as butter and cheese, and are essential to the digestive processes of most animals.

Input/Output

Enter the program into your computer exactly as it is printed. After you enter the entire program, type RUN. If there is a problem, type LIST and check that you have entered the program exactly as it is printed. Remember, symbols and punctuation are important and must be typed as printed here. REM statements are provided in the program to help you. They do not need to be entered in order for the program to run. When all corrections have been made, be sure to save the program by typing SAVE BACTERIA, or whatever name you wish to give the program.

Once the program is running, the computer will tell you that the program simulates the way bacteria respond to changes in temperature. You will be given 1000 "good" bacteria and 1000 "bad" bacteria. You will be able to choose whether to increase the temperature or to decrease the temperature. The amount of the change will be determined by the computer. With each change in temperature, you should note the effect on the number of each kind of bacteria. As the program continues, try to answer these questions. At what temperature does maximum growth occur? Do all types of bacteria experience maximum growth at the same temperature? The simulation will end when all of the data are used or when one strain of bacteria is reduced to a population of zero.

Programming Notes

The computer reads each line of the program and executes the command listed there. Line 20 is used several times to clear the screen. Some computers use the command CLS, others use HOME. Use the command your computer recognizes to clear the screen.

The variables used in this program are listed below.

T   temperature
G   "good" bacteria
B   "bad" bacteria
Q   clears the screen
C$ temperature change + or −
R   reads data

The beginning value for each variable is set in line 10. Lines 30 and 40 use PRINT statements to produce the introduction to the simulation on the screen. The data are read and you are asked to input temperature change in line 50. Line 50 utilizes the first of a series of IF/THEN statements to manipulate the data. If the change is positive, the program moves to line 80 where a new temperature is calculated and the absolute value of R is checked. An absolute value of 999 ends the program. If the change is negative, line 60 changes the value of R to a negative number. The screen is cleared in line 90, and a new temperature is printed in line 100. Lines 110 through 150 use a series of IF/THEN statements to check the temperature and print the effect the temperature change will have on both types of bacteria. The number of bacteria remaining is checked in lines 160 and 170. If the number is zero, the program ends. If the number is greater than zero, the program returns to line 50 and repeats.

Program

```
10  T = 24:G = 1000:B = 1000
20  HOME : IF Q = 1 THEN 100: REM
    MAY BE DIFFERENT ON YOUR CO
    MPUTER
30  PRINT "THIS IS A SIMULATION
    OF BACTERIA GROWTH.": PRINT
    "THERE ARE TWO KINDS OF TEMP
    ERATURE": PRINT "SENSITIVE B
    ACTERIA.  ONE IS HELPFUL"
40  PRINT "BACTERIA, WHILE THE O
    THER IS HARMFUL.": PRINT "YO
    UR JOB IS TO TRY TO ELIMINAT
    E THE": PRINT "HARMFUL ONE A
    ND PRESERVE THE GOOD ONE"
50  PRINT : PRINT : READ R: PRINT
    "TEMPERATURE CHANGE < - >  O
    R  < + >";: INPUT C$: IF C$ =
    "+" THEN 80
60  IF C$ = "-" THEN R =  - R: GOTO
    80
70  GOTO 50
80  T = T + (R * .2): IF  ABS (R)
    = 999 THEN  PRINT : PRINT :
    PRINT "YOU HAVE RUN OUT OF
    TIME IN": PRINT "YOUR BATTLE
    WITH THE HARMFUL BACTERIA."
    : END
90  Q = 1: GOTO 20
100 PRINT "TEMPERATURE IS  ";T;
    "  DEGREES CELSIUS"
110 IF T > 27 THEN T = 27: PRINT
    : PRINT : PRINT "HIGH TEMPER
    ATURE CRITICAL TO BACTERIA":
    G = G - ((T - 10) * (T - 10)
    ):B = B - ((T - 14) * (T - 1
    4)):A$ = "DOWN":B$ = A$
120 IF T < 27 AND T > 25.1 THEN
    G = G - ((T - 10) * (T - 10)
    ):B = B + ((T - 10) * (T - 1
    0)):A$ = "DOWN":B$ = "UP"
130 IF T < 25 AND T > 22.5 THEN
    G = G - ((T - 10) * (T - 10)
    ):B = B + ((T - 6) * (T - 6)
    ):A$ = "UP":B$ = A$
140 IF T < 22.6 AND T > 21.1 THEN
    G = G + ((T - 10) * (T - 10)
    ):B = B - ((T - 10) * (T - 1
    0)):A$ = "UP":B$ = "DOWN"
150 IF T < 21 THEN T = 21: PRINT
    : PRINT : PRINT "LOW TEMPERA
    TURE CRITICAL TO BACTERIA":G
    = G - ((T - 10) * (T - 10))
    :B = B - ((T - 14) * (T - 14
    )):A$ = "DOWN":B$ = A$
160 IF G < 0 THEN G = 0: PRINT
    : PRINT : PRINT "YOU HAVE LO
    ST THE BATTLE TO HARMFUL BAC
    TERIA":Q = 2
170 IF B < 0 THEN B = 0: PRINT
    : PRINT : PRINT "YOU HAVE WO
    N THE BATTLE AGAINST HARMFUL
    BACTERIA":Q = 2
180 PRINT : PRINT : PRINT "THE
    HELPFUL (GOOD) BACTERIA COUN
    T": PRINT "IS  ";A$;"  AT  "
    ; INT (G);"  PER UNIT AREA"
190 PRINT : PRINT : PRINT "THE
    HARMFUL (BAD) BACTERIA COUNT
    ": PRINT "IS  ";B$;"  AT  ";
    INT (B);"  PER UNIT AREA": IF
    Q = 2 THEN  END
200 GOTO 50
210 DATA 4,5,3,6,4,6,3,4,6,5,5,
    4,6,3,4,5,4,5,5,4,5,6,6,4,99
    9
```

Challenge: On Your Own

An easy way to modify this program is to change the data found in line 210. Larger numbers will cause more extreme changes in temperature when the program is run. Fewer numbers will shorten the simulation. Adding more numbers will lengthen the simulation. If you change the data, be sure that all numbers are separated by a comma and that the last number is 999. The number 999 acts as a flag to the computer that the simulation should be ended.

PLANTS

Students identifying plants

UNIT 3

An important part of science is exploration of the outdoors. There are two good ways to learn how to recognize plants. You can ask a teacher for the names of plants, or you can find out by yourself with books. A Flora is a book with keys or pictures to help you identify plants. Students are using a Flora in the photo to identify a cactus. When a cactus flowers, it is easier to identify. Why? What other parts of a plant help in identification?

Flowering cactus

There are three unrelated groups of pitcher plants. In all of
these plants, the leaves have evolved into specialized structures
in which insects are trapped. Once inside, the insects slip
down onto a pool of juices in which they drown and are digested.
The Sarracenia of North America, shown below, has an umbrella-shaped
flower. The flowers of the other two groups are different. What
use is the trapping of insects to a plant? How do we know
that the pitchers are leaves?

CHAPTER 7
PLANT LIFE

7:1 Plant Classification

Over 300 000 species are classified in the plant kingdom. Each species has certain characteristics that distinguish it from other species. Plants are more complex than fungi, protists, and monerans. Most plant species are many-celled, containing tissues and organs. Plants contain chlorophyll and can make their own food. They cannot move about as do animals. Also, unlike animal cells, a plant cell has a cell wall surrounding the cell membrane.

Some plants absorb water through roots. Extending from the roots up through the plant are tubelike structures called vessels that move water to the stem and leaves. The system is similar to pipes carrying water from a well to different rooms in a house. Plants with these vessels are called **vascular** (VAS kyuh lur) **plants.** Ferns, conifers, and flowering plants are examples of vascular plants.

Some plants such as mosses and brown algae do not have true roots, stems, and leaves. They lack the vessels needed to move water. These plants are called **nonvascular plants.**

Five divisions make up the plant kingdom. The major subgroups of the animal kingdom are called phyla. In the plant kingdom, they are called divisions. Green, brown, and red algae make up three of these divisions. Mosses are classified in the division Bryophyta. The fifth division, Tracheophyta, includes all species of vascular plants. Each division is divided into classes. Appendix E on pages 558–559 lists some of the divisions in the plant kingdom and the characteristics of plants in each division.

GOALS:
1. You will learn the functions of roots, stems, and leaves.
2. You will learn the life activities of plants.
3. You will learn how the environment affects plant behavior.

Define vascular plants.

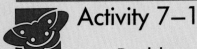

Activity 7–1

Making a Terrarium

Problem: How do you make a terrarium?

Materials

large glass container with cover
soil
metric ruler
pebbles
small plants and lichens
spoon
scissors
water

Data and Observations

Plant	
Date planted	
Height when planted	
Growth in 4 weeks	
Growth in 8 weeks	

Procedure

1. Place a layer of pebbles about 2 cm deep in the bottom of the container.
2. Slowly add water to the soil and mix thoroughly. Keep adding water until the soil feels moist, not wet.
3. Put about 6 cm of moist soil in the container, on top of the pebbles.
4. Slope the surface of the soil slightly from the rear of the terrarium to the front.
5. Observe, measure, and record the characteristics of the plants you have selected.
6. Use a spoon to scoop out shallow holes large enough for the plant root systems.
7. Place the tallest plants toward the back. Place the shorter ones in the foreground. Fill in soil around the roots, and press the soil down lightly.
8. After the planting is complete, add mosses and other ground cover plants.
9. Cover the terrarium and place it in indirect sunlight. For each plant, make a chart similar to the one shown.
10. Keep a record of your observations of the growth of the plants. If water drops form on the inside, open the terrarium for a short period of time. If the plants grow too large, cut them back with scissors. **CAUTION:** *Always use scissors carefully.*

Questions and Conclusions

1. What are some nonliving things in the terrarium?
2. What are some living things in the terrarium?
3. What do the living things in the terrarium need for life?
4. How do the living things in the terrarium get what they need for life?
5. What is the purpose of the pebble layer?
6. Why should the terrarium not be placed in direct sunlight?
7. Why should the terrarium be covered?
8. Why should you remove the cover when excess water forms on the inside?
9. How do you make a terrarium?

FIGURE 7–1.

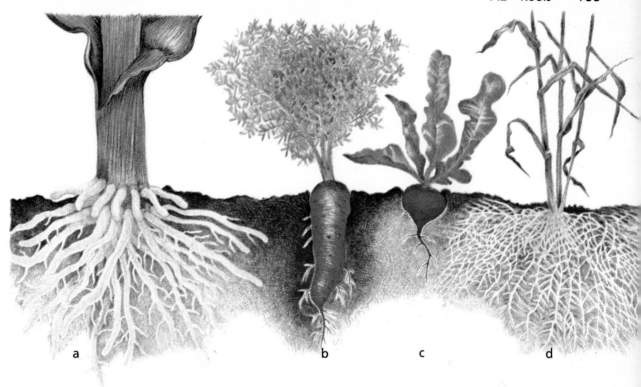

a   b   c   d

FIGURE 7–2. Roots absorb, store, and transport water and minerals. Some plants have taproots (b, c). Some have fibrous roots (a, d).

7:2 Roots

Have you ever tried to pull a plant out of the ground? Most plants are well anchored. If they were not, they could be carried away by wind or washed away in a rainstorm. Most land plants have as much root growth below ground as they have stem and leaf growth above ground. The long, slender roots of alfalfa may grow 4.5 meters down into the soil. Plant roots absorb, store, and transport water and minerals.

Roots have very small threadlike parts called **root hairs** growing from them. Each root hair is a single cell. Root hairs absorb water and minerals from the soil. Water and dissolved minerals travel through the root hairs into xylem (ZI lum) tissue that contains xylem cells. **Xylem** cells make up the tubes that transport water and dissolved minerals to all parts of plants. Another tissue in roots is phloem (FLOH em) tissue that is composed of phloem cells. **Phloem** cells make up the tubes that transport food made by the plant.

What are the functions of roots?

Compare xylem and phloem.

There are two basic types of root systems. Plants such as turnips, beets, and dandelions have a taproot system. In these plants, food is stored in a large, long main root. Other plants, such as most trees and grasses, have a fibrous (FI brus) root system. Fibrous root systems have many branches and help hold soil in place, preventing wind and water erosion.

Making Sure

1. Describe the difference between vascular and nonvascular plants. Give an example of each.
2. How do plants get water and minerals from the soil?

7:3 Stems

Stems support the leaves of a seed plant and connect these parts to the roots. Stems also move water, minerals, and food through the plant. Some stems produce and store food. Bamboo, asparagus, and rhubarb stems produce and store food. Ginger and potato are underground stems that store food produced in the above-ground parts of the plant.

Describe the two types of plant stems.

There are two types of plant stems—herbaceous (her BAY shus) and woody. **Herbaceous stems** are soft, green, and flexible. The stems of tomato, bean, pea, and corn plants are herbaceous. **Woody stems** are harder and more rigid than herbaceous stems because they contain woody tissue. Woody stems are usually not green. Trees and shrubs have woody stems.

Most herbaceous stems live for only one growing season. They die in the fall or winter. Since they live during only a single year,

FIGURE 7–3. Trees have woody stems. Tulips have herbaceous stems.

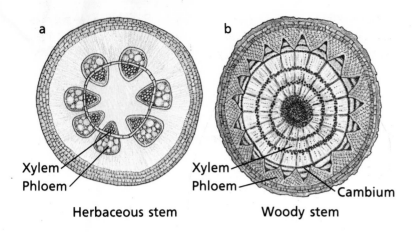

a

b

Xylem
Phloem

Xylem
Phloem

Cambium

Herbaceous stem

Woody stem

FIGURE 7—4. Cross sections of herbaceous (a) and woody (b) stems

these plants are called annuals. An annual is a plant that grows, reproduces, and dies within one growing season. Peas, beans, tomatoes, and radishes are examples of annuals. A biennial produces leaves and food in one year, and in a second year, reproduces and dies. Carrots, sugar beets, and onions are examples of biennials.

A **perennial** (puh REN ee ul) is a plant that lives from one growing season to another. All woody plants are perennials. Each year during the growing season, the thickness of a woody stem increases. The new growth forms a circle of wood called an annual growth ring. The age of a woody plant may be found by counting the annual growth rings. The thickness of annual growth rings in a tree depends upon the weather. Annual growth rings are broad in wet years and narrow in dry years.

Stems provide us with many useful products. One product is wood that is used to make furniture, pencils, heating fuel, lumber for construction, and many other things. Medicines, tannin for the leather industry, and dyes for artwork come from wood. The procedure of tapping stems removes liquids that are useful. Rubber, materials for making chewing gum, and turpentine are made from liquids tapped from tree stems. Maple syrup is another liquid tapped from tree stems.

Stems contain several kinds of tissues such as xylem, phloem, and cambium (KAM bee um). Xylem tissue transports water and dissolved minerals upward through the stem. Xylem is the major part of woody stems. Wood used in construction actually was the xylem of a tree. Phloem tissue transports food. Between the xylem and phloem is a growth tissue, cambium. **Cambium** produces new xylem and phloem cells. This growth makes the plant stem

How are annuals and perennials different?

What tissue produces new xylem and phloem cells?

larger in diameter. In a herbaceous plant, the xylem and phloem are arranged in bundles. In a woody plant, these tissues are in separate rings with the phloem outside the xylem.

Making Sure

3. What are two kinds of cells in plant roots?
4. What are the functions of these tissues in plant stems?
    a. xylem
    b. phloem
    c. cambium
5. How are woody stems different from herbaceous stems?

FIGURE 7–5.

Activity 7–2 Observing Stem Tissues

Problem: What plant tissue carries water?

Materials   water, 200-mL beaker, dropper, blue food coloring, stirring rod or spoon, stalk of celery, scalpel, 2 microscope slides, 2 coverslips, microscope

Procedure   (1) Fill a 200-mL beaker half full of water. (2) Add 10 drops of blue food coloring to the water and stir (3) With a scalpel, cut off the end of a stalk of celery. **CAUTION:** *Always be careful handling a scalpel. Direct the edge of the blade away from yourself.* (4) Place the stalk upright in the beaker. Let it stand for 24 hours. (5) Remove the celery from the water and observe the top leaves of the stalk. (6) Examine the cut end of the stalk section. (7) Cut a piece of the stalk lengthwise. (8) Carefully remove one of the colored tubes from the slice. (9) With the scalpel, cut a very thin cross-section from the tube and make a temporary wet mount slide. (10) Examine the cross-section under low power of the microscope and then turn to high power. (11) Remove another colored tube from the celery stalk. (12) Split the tube lengthwise. Make a temporary wet mount slide with a small part of the tube. Observe the slide under low power and then switch to high power.

Questions   (1) Draw a cross section of the celery stem. (2) Draw a cross section of the colored tube as it appears under high power. (3) Draw several cells from the lengthwise part of the colored tube under high power. (4) Are the tubes in the celery made of cells? (5) Do the cells have thick or thin walls? (6) What plant tissue carries water?

7:4 Leaves

Leaves are special parts of a plant that produce food and oxygen. Some are used for food by humans and other animals. Lettuce, spinach, and cabbage are leaves that humans eat. Grazing animals eat the leaves and stems of grasses and other kinds of plants. Leaves such as parsley, sage, and bay are used for food flavorings and spices.

Leaves vary in size, shape, structure, and arrangement. The shape of a leaf is an important clue in identifying a plant. For example, you may be able to tell the name of a tree by the shape of its leaves. How is the shape of an oak leaf different from a maple leaf or a white pine leaf? A leaf is made up of a blade and a stalk. The blade is the plant's major organ for capturing light. The stalk is called the petiole. The petiole attaches the leaf blade to the stem. Some leaves, such as grass, do not have petioles. Leaves can be simple or compound. A compound leaf has many leaflets. These provide the plant with a greater surface area for receiving sunlight. An oak leaf is simple. A hickory leaf is compound.

Like stems and roots, leaves also have tissues and cells. The epidermis (ep uh DUR mus) is a thin protective layer of flattened cells that covers the surface of a leaf. The top surface is called the upper epidermis; the bottom surface is called the lower epidermis. These two surface layers protect the inner parts of the leaf. A waxy cuticle (KYEWT ih kul) covers the epidermis of some leaves. It is similar to the waxy covering that makes an apple

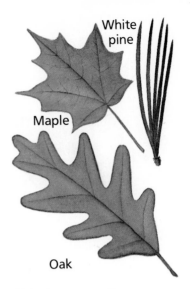

FIGURE 7–6. Differences in leaf shapes provide important clues in identifying plants.

Describe the structure of a leaf.

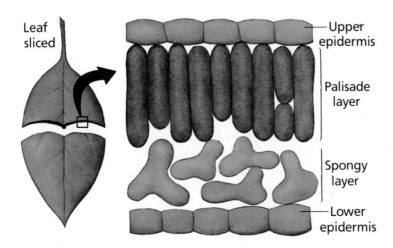

FIGURE 7–7. A leaf has four layers of cells.

a

b

FIGURE 7–8. Leaves of deciduous trees change and fall in autumn (a). Evergreens remain green throughout the year (b).

Why do some leaves change colors in autumn?

Compare deciduous and evergreen leaves.

shine. The cuticle reduces loss of water from leaves. This helps protect a plant from wilting and drying out during dry weather.

Inside the leaf are cells with relatively thin cell walls. These cells form two layers: the palisade (pal uh SAYD) layer and the spongy layer. The palisade layer has rows of cylinder-shaped cells just under the upper surface layer. Spongy cells are located between the palisade layer and the lower surface layer of cells. They have irregular shapes. Many of the palisade and spongy cells contain chlorophyll, a green compound that gives leaves their color. Food is produced in cells that contain chlorophyll. Other cells in the leaf form veins that transport food and water through the leaf.

Many trees have leaves that change color in autumn. The color of leaves is due to pigments. Pigments are substances that color the tissues of organisms. The pigment chlorophyll colors leaves green. Other pigments color leaves yellow, orange, or red. In autumn, when chlorophyll disappears from the leaves, the other colors can be seen. Less chlorophyll is made in autumn because of the shorter daylight hours. Trees that lose their leaves every autumn are called **deciduous** (dih SIHJ uh wus). Throughout winter, deciduous trees are without leaves. In spring, new leaves grow. Then the cycle repeats itself. Trees whose leaves remain green throughout each year are called **evergreen.** Evergreens lose their leaves in the same way you lose hair from your head. Evergreens do not lose all their leaves at the same time, so evergreens always appear green. Some examples of evergreens are wintergreen, pine, and holly.

7:5 Gas Exchange

In the epidermis of a leaf are many openings. Each opening is called a **stoma** (STOH muh). Usually there are more stomata (STOH maht uh) on the lower epidermis than the upper epidermis of a leaf. A leaf may have from 9000 to 70 000 stomata per square centimeter of surface area. A stoma is a slitlike opening or pore. A stoma opens into an air space within the leaf. A stoma is very tiny. It would take 20 stomata placed end to end to equal the thickness of this page.

Each stoma is surrounded by two guard cells. **Guard cells** can swell and relax, thereby changing the size of the stoma. When guard cells absorb water, they swell and the stoma opens. When guard cells lose water, they relax and the stoma closes. Stomata are usually closed at night and open during the day.

Gases such as oxygen, carbon dioxide, and water vapor enter and leave a leaf through the stomata. These gases move in and out of the leaf by diffusion. During a sunny day, the stomata in a leaf are open. Carbon dioxide enters the leaf and oxygen exits the leaf through the stomata. Water vapor also escapes through the stomata. At night, the stomata are only partially opened or completely closed. At this time, less water escapes from the leaf.

Loss of water vapor through the stomata of a leaf is called **transpiration** (trans puh RAY shun). Much of the water taken in by the roots moves up the xylem in the stem to the leaves and is lost by transpiration. An apple tree loses as much as 15 liters of water per hour on a hot, sunny day. A corn plant transpires about 200 liters of water during its growing season.

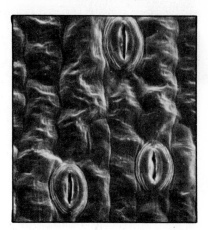

FIGURE 7–9. The enlargement of the surface of a leaf 455 times makes stomata clearly visible. The slit-shaped openings are the stomata. Guard cells surround the stomata. The ridged area is epidermal cell.

Describe the structure of a stoma.

Making Sure

6. What are the four layers in a leaf?
7. How does a stoma control gas exchange in a leaf?
8. What is transpiration?

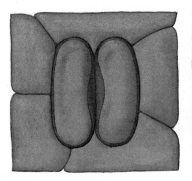
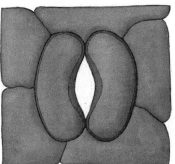

FIGURE 7–10. Guard cells swell with water, opening the stoma. The stoma closes when guard cells lose water.

Activity 7–3   Gas Exchange in Plants

Problem: How do gases enter and leave a plant?

Materials

2 geranium plants
forceps
dropper
scissors
4 small jars
2 pieces cardboard (10 cm square with a small hole
   in center)
clay
microscope
microscope slide
coverslip
glass-marking pencil
graduated cylinder
water

Procedure

Part A

1. Label two jars A and B. Measure 400 mL of water
   into each jar.
2. Place one plant in the hole of a cardboard square.
   Seal the hole with clay.
3. Place a cardboard square over the jar marked A.
   Make sure the roots of the plant are in the water.
4. Remove the leaves from the second plant and save
   a leaf for Part B. Place the plant in the hole in
   the cardboard square. Seal the hole with clay.
5. Place a cardboard square over the jar marked B.
   Make sure the roots of the plant are in the water.
6. Place the jars in a well-lighted area.
7. Cover the plants in jars A and B with the remaining two jars.
8. Observe the inside of the top jars after 24 hours.
   Record your observations in a data table.
9. Measure the amount of water remaining in jars
   A and B after 24 hours. Record your observations
   in a data table.

Part B

1. Fold a geranium leaf in half until it cracks. Peel
   a section of the colorless part from the underside
   of the leaf. This is the epidermis. Carefully remove a small piece of the epidermis with forceps.

2. Prepare a temporary wet mount using the epidermis tissue.
3. Examine the epidermis tissue under low power.
   Observe the shape and arrangement of the cells.
   Locate the guard cells on either side of a stoma.
   Observe the walls of the guard cells.
4. Draw the shape and arrangement of the cells you
   observe in the leaf epidermis. Label the guard
   cells and stoma on your drawing.

Data and Observations

	Jar A	Jar B
Observations of top jar		
mL water at start		
mL water after 24 hr		

Questions and Conclusions

1. What did you observe inside the top of Jar A after
   24 hours?
2. How does Jar A after 24 hours compare with Jar
   B after 24 hours?
3. Compare the amount of water after 24 hours in
   Jar A and Jar B.
4. What was the purpose of the plant in Jar B?
5. What evidence do you have that water passed
   from the bottom jar through the geranium leaf in
   Part A?
6. What is the function of the guard cells?
7. What is the purpose of the stomata?
8. How does a plant lose water?
9. Conclude from your observations whether water
   loss in plants is greater during the day or at night?
10. How do gases enter and leave a plant?

FIGURE 7–11. Plants use light energy for photosynthesis. The energy stored in plants is used by all living things.

7:6 Photosynthesis

Green plants are different from animals in an important way. Plants make their own food. Animals get their food by eating plants or other animals that eat plants. Green plants can make their own food because they contain chlorophyll. **Chlorophyll** is a green pigment that traps energy in light.

Photosynthesis (foht oh SIHN thuh sus) is the chemical change in which sunlight is used to produce food. Light is necessary for photosynthesis because it provides the energy for the chemical change. In photosynthesis, carbon dioxide gas and water are combined to produce sugar and oxygen. The energy supplied by the light becomes locked in sugar molecules.

Here is the equation for photosynthesis.

Describe the chemical change that occurs in photosynthesis.

$$6\,CO_2 \;+\; 6\,H_2O \;\xrightarrow[\text{chlorophyll}]{\text{light energy}}\; C_6H_{12}O_6 \;+\; 6\,O_2$$

carbon dioxide   water   chlorophyll   sugar   oxygen

Note in the equation above that oxygen is produced in photosynthesis. Without oxygen, plants and animals could not live on earth. Through photosynthesis, plants recycle air by taking out carbon dioxide and adding oxygen. Most of the oxygen in our atmosphere comes from the photosynthesis occurring in simple ocean plants.

Light Reactions of Photosynthesis

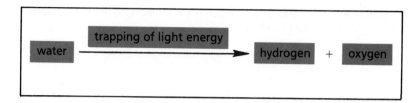

Dark Reactions of Photosynthesis

FIGURE 7–12. Photosynthesis can be divided into light and dark reactions. The dark reactions use the hydrogen from the light reactions to make sugar.

What are the light reactions of photosynthesis?

What happens in the dark reactions?

The changes that occur in photosynthesis can be classified into light reactions and dark reactions. Light reactions are those that will occur only in light. The first part of the light reactions is the trapping of light energy. Another part of the light reactions is the use of this energy to separate water (H_2O) into hydrogen and oxygen. The hydrogen is used later in the dark reactions. The oxygen is given off as gas (O_2).

The dark reactions do not have to occur in the dark. They simply do not require light to occur. In the dark reactions, hydrogen from the light reactions combines with carbon dioxide, forming sugar.

Plants use energy from the food they make to build and repair their cells, tissues, and organs. Also, sugar is used to make cellulose that forms the wall of a plant cell. Cellulose in grass can be digested and used as food by animals such as cows, goats, and sheep. Wood from a tree is mostly cellulose. Cotton used to make clothing is a form of cellulose produced by a cotton plant. Sugar is also produced by plants to be stored as a food in roots, stems, fruits, and seeds.

Making Sure

9. How does a plant capture and use the sun's energy?
10. How does photosynthesis change the air around a plant?
11. List uses for the food plants make.

7:7   Respiration

Cells need energy for growth and other life activities. In plants, this energy is obtained from the food they make. During the early 19th century, scientists were studying steam engines. They began to see similarities in how organisms get energy to do work and how fuel is used to do work in steam engines. Scientists noticed that when wood or coal was burned, heat was produced. Water and carbon dioxide were given off as wastes. The heat could be used to push a piston in an engine or do other work. Scientists also observed that organisms took in fuel (food), produced heat, and gave off carbon dioxide and water. As a result of this reaction, energy is released in a cell to do work.

In plants and animals, the energy to do work is obtained by using sugar and oxygen in a chemical change called **respiration.** Here is the equation for respiration.

$$\underset{\text{sugar}}{C_6H_{12}O_6} \; + \; \underset{\text{oxygen}}{6\,O_2} \;\xrightarrow{\text{energy}}\; \underset{\text{carbon dioxide}}{6\,CO_2} \; + \; \underset{\text{water}}{6\,H_2O}$$

Table 7–1 compares the process of respiration with the process of photosynthesis. Note that the two chemical changes are opposite to each other. Carbon dioxide and water are used to make food in photosynthesis. In respiration, both of these substances are produced. During photosynthesis, energy is stored in the food that is made. In respiration, energy is released from food for use by a cell. Photosynthesis occurs in plant cells that contain chlorophyll. Respiration occurs in all plant and animal cells.

How is the use of food by a plant like the use of fuel in an engine?

How is energy obtained in respiration?

FIGURE 7–13. Steam engines and organisms both use fuel to transfer energy as heat or work.

Table 7–1

A Comparison of Photosynthesis and Respiration		
	Photosynthesis	**Respiration**
Energy	Stored	Released
Materials	Water, carbon dioxide	Sugar, oxygen
Products	Sugar, oxygen	Water, carbon dioxide
Location	Cells with chlorophyll	All cells

7:8 Plant Behavior

Plants respond to stimuli (STIHM yuh li) in their environment. A **stimulus** is something in the environment that causes a response by an organism. Touch the leaves of a sensitive plant and they will fold up. The touch is the stimulus; the folding of the leaves is the response. A Venus's-flytrap catches insects by folding its leaves around them. Folding of the leaves in these plants is caused by a drop in pressure inside cells due to a sudden loss of water. The action is somewhat like a car sagging to the ground when a tire is punctured.

Define stimulus.

FIGURE 7–14. The stimulus of touch (a) causes *Mimosa* leaves to fold up in response (b).

a

b

FIGURE 7–15. Poinsettias are short-day plants.

One important stimulus is light. A geranium growing toward sunlight coming in through a window is an example of a response to this stimulus. Gravity and water are two stimuli that affect the growth of roots. Roots grow down in response to gravity, and they also grow toward water. Plant vines wrap around poles and other objects that serve as stimuli for the winding growth pattern. Other plants, such as the prayer plant, respond to darkness at nightfall by curling their leaves. Unlike animals, most plants usually respond slowly to stimuli in their environment.

Different kinds of seed plants produce flowers at different times during the year. In some plants, flowering depends on the amount of daylight. The flowering response of a plant to the number of daylight hours per day is called **photoperiodism.** Some species of plants are short-day plants. They will not produce flowers if the hours of daylight are too long. Some short-day plants are soybeans, poinsettias, and violets. Short-day plants normally flower in spring or fall. Other plant species are long-day plants. They require long days, ranging from 12 to 16 hours of daylight. Some long-day plants are spinach, clover, corn, and gladiolus. Dandelions, sunflowers, cotton, and tomatoes are examples of day-neutral plants. Their flowering is not much affected by the amount of daylight. Temperature, moisture, and soil nutrients are also factors affecting the time of flowering.

What is photoperiodism? Give two examples.

FIGURE 7–16. Plant roots show positive geotropism. Plant stems show negative geotropism.

Explain how a chemical controls a tropism.

7:9 Tropisms and Auxins

Does it matter in what position a seed is placed when it is planted? No, it does not. Regardless of its position, the roots of the new plant grow down and the stem grows up. Gravity is the stimulus for this behavior. The response of a plant to a stimulus is called a **tropism** (TROH pihz um). Response toward a stimulus is a positive tropism. Response away from a stimulus is a negative tropism. Growth of roots down into the earth is an example of a positive geotropism. Upward growth of a stem away from the earth is a negative geotropism. The response of a plant's growth to light is phototropism. Would plants growing toward light show a positive phototropism?

Tropisms are controlled by chemical compounds in plants called hormones. An **auxin** (AHK sihn) is one kind of plant hormone. Auxins produced in one part of a plant can cause changes in another part of a plant. One kind of auxin stimulates the growth of cells. If a plant has light on one side, the auxin moves away from the lighted side of the stem. The amount of auxin increases on the shaded side. It causes the cells to grow faster on the shaded side than on the lighted side. The unequal growth rates cause the stem to bend toward the light.

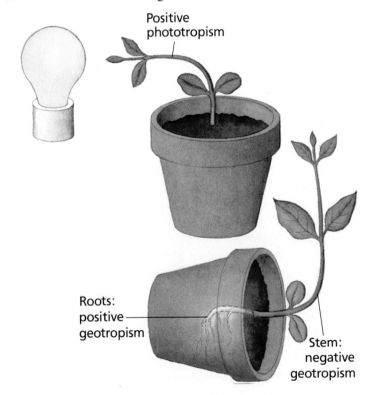

Positive phototropism

Roots: positive geotropism

Stem: negative geotropism

FIGURE 7–17. A stem shows negative geotropism and positive phototropism. A root shows positive geotropism.

FIGURE 7–18. Auxins are hormones that can be sprayed on trees to prevent falling of undeveloped fruit.

Artificial auxins such as 2–4D are used to kill weeds. When 2–4D is sprayed on a lawn, it is absorbed by broad-leafed weeds. The auxin increases the rate of growth of the weeds, causing them to use up their reserve food supply and die. The narrow-leafed grasses are resistant to the chemical. Other auxins are used to stimulate the growth of roots when cuttings are made for reproducing the plants. Auxins can also be sprayed on fruit trees to prevent the falling of undeveloped fruit.

A simple chemical that acts like an auxin is a gas called ethylene (ETH uh leen). Large amounts of ethylene are made by ripening fruit. Many important fruit crops such as oranges, tomatoes, grapes, and bananas are picked when green. The fruit is stored in, or later sprayed with ethylene. By the time the fruit arrives at the marketplace, it has ripened.

Gibberellic (jihb uh REL ik) acid is a plant hormone mostly produced in the chloroplasts of leaves. Gibberellic acid stimulates plant growth. When treated with gibberellic acid, some dwarf varieties of plants grow to normal height. The hormone is also applied to some plants to stimulate flowering. Other plant hormones control the seasonal loss of leaves and the opening and closing of stomata.

Making Sure

12. How does energy compare in the processes of photosynthesis and respiration?
13. Describe four examples of plant behavior.
14. How does an auxin cause a stem to grow toward light?

FOCUS ON
People and Careers

Horticulturists

Georgia Ann Muenzler is a landscape architect who, in addition to working with private clients, teaches landscape design and graphics at a state technical school. She describes her job as making things in nature beautiful for people to see.

Ms. Muenzler plans ways to use available space, whether it is a courtyard for a home, a plaza at a shopping mall, a park, or a housing development. Her tools are a drawing table, triangles, a calculator, templates, computers, cameras, blueprint machines, a measuring tape, and survey equipment.

She begins an assignment by visiting a site to study its characteristics. She measures the space and studies plants already growing there. Then she takes photographs and makes sketches. Following meetings with her client, Ms. Muenzler draws up the final plan, estimates the cost, and begins the planting. Ms. Muenzler supervises the job to its end.

Among the courses Ms. Muenzler took to qualify for landscape work were algebra, trigonometry, surveying, and freehand drawing. She earned a master's degree in horticulture with an emphasis on landscape architecture. To earn her license, she worked full-time for a landscape architect for two years and passed a national test. She believes that artistic ability and an aptitude in math are helpful to a person who wants to be a landscape architect.

Jerry Howard is a plant propagator. His specialty is geraniums. In his job at a large nursery, he helps grow thousands of plants each year for retail sales outlets.

Early in the spring a list is made of the kinds of geranium cuttings needed. Only about a thousand cuttings from healthy plants are ordered. During the next few months, enough cuttings will be taken from them to grow the nursery's whole stock of geraniums for the months to come.

Mr. Howard covers the joint end of each geranium cutting with a rooting compound. Then he sets the cutting in a small pot filled with soil. The pots are packed into trays and stored on shelves. The trays are easy to carry so nursery employees can work with at least a dozen plants at a time.

Mr. Howard graduated from a vocational-technical school where he majored in horticulture classes. Mr. Howard also has taken courses at a state technical institute, but he believes that on-the-job training has been the most important part of his education.

Mr. Howard also owns his own small wholesale business. In a greenhouse in his backyard, he propagates geraniums, which he sells to stores. He has a city and state license to sell flowers and tropical plants.

CHAPTER 7
Review

Summary

1. Vascular plants have tubelike structures through which food and water move.   7:1
2. Roots anchor plants in soil and absorb water and minerals from the soil.   7:2
3. Xylem transports water and minerals. Phloem transports food.   7:2
4. There are two main kinds of stems—woody and herbaceous.   7:3
5. A leaf is composed of four layers of cells: upper epidermis, palisade, spongy, and lower epidermis.   7:4
6. Plants lose water by transpiration.   7:5
7. Food production takes place in plants by photosynthesis.   7:6
8. Respiration occurs in every cell.   7:7
9. Plant behavior occurs in response to stimuli in the environment.   7:8
10. Geotropism and phototropism are examples of plant behavior.   7:9

Vocabulary

Write a sentence using the following words or terms correctly.

auxin	nonvascular plant	stimulus
cambium	perennial	stoma
chlorophyll	phloem	transpiration
deciduous	photoperiodism	tropism
evergreen	photosynthesis	vascular plant
guard cell	respiration	woody stem
herbaceous	root hair	xylem

Questions for Review

Do not write in this book.

A. True or False

Determine whether each of the following sentences is true or false. Rewrite the false statements to make them correct.

1. All seed plants have roots, stems, and leaves.
2. The shape of the leaf is one key to identifying a seed plant.
3. Plants obtain water and minerals through their roots.
4. Food is produced in leaves.
5. The downward growth of roots is a positive geotropism.
6. Stomata are usually closed on a sunny day.
7. A plant takes in carbon dioxide through its leaves.
8. Wood contains cellulose.
9. Carbon dioxide and water are produced in photosynthesis.
10. Photosynthesis occurs inside all plant cells.

CHAPTER 7
Review

B. Multiple Choice
Choose the word or phrase that correctly completes the following sentences.
1. Plants absorb water from soil through *(guard cells, root hairs, annual rings, stomata)*.
2. The green substance in leaf cells is *(chlorophyll, xylem, phloem, cambium)*.
3. *(Xylem, Phloem, Cambium)* is the growth tissue of a plant.
4. A maple tree is a(n) *(annual, perennial, herbaceous)* plant.
5. Growth of a plant toward light is an example of a *(positive, negative)* tropism.
6. *(Woody, Herbaceous)* stems are hard and rigid.
7. A(n) *(annual, perennial)* is a plant that lives its life during one year.
8. *(Carbon dioxide, Sugar, Energy)* is produced in photosynthesis.
9. Transpiration is the loss of water from a plant through its *(root hairs, stomata, tropisms)*.
10. Food is produced in plant cells that have *(chlorophyll, root hairs, cambium)*.

C. Completion
Complete each of the following sentences with the correct word or phrase.
1. A perennial plant lives for _____ years.
2. _____ is the part of the stem that carries water.
3. _____ enters a leaf through an opening called a stoma.
4. Energy is released inside cells in a change called _____.
5. Photosynthesis occurs inside plant cells that contain _____.
6. Respiration occurs in _____ plant cells.
7. A(n) _____ is a plant hormone.
8. _____ is the plant tissue that transports food.
9. The lettuce and spinach that people eat are the _____ of these plants.
10. Changes that occur in photosynthesis can be classified as _____ reactions and _____ reactions.

D. How and Why
1. Why is it incorrect to say that plants obtain food from soil?
2. Why does a tree die if the cambium is cut off in a circle around the truck of a tree?
3. Stomata in a plant may close during very dry weather. Why?
4. How could you tell the age of a tree that is cut down?
5. How is respiration different from photosynthesis?
6. Make a list of the main parts of a seed plant. What is the function of each part?
7. Name two plant tropisms and identify the stimulus and response for each.
8. What is a vascular system and how is it important to the classification of plants?

CHAPTER 7
Review

Ideas to Explore

1. **Project:** Collect 10 different tree leaves and learn to identify these trees by their leaves.
2. **Project:** Obtain information on hydroponics. Prepare a written report describing the procedure and its importance. Try growing plants hydroponically.
3. **Project:** Find out how different colors of light are involved in photosynthesis. Design and do an experiment that demonstrates how colored light affects photosynthesis in a green plant.
4. **Project:** Design an experiment to investigate the effect of various factors on the growth or behavior of plants. For example, you might investigate factors such as sound, magnetism, infrared or ultraviolet light, and waste. Use scientific methods of problem solving as described in Chapter 1.
5. **Challenge:** Make an illustrated report on insectivorous plants. Discuss how each type of plant captures its prey.
6. **Challenge:** Make a report on plant auxins, their effects, and how they are important to us.
7. **Project:** Find out about chromatography. Try to separate plant pigments found in plants such as spinach and blueberries.
8. **Challenge:** Make a bulletin board display called "Little Known Facts About Plants."

Readings

Cork, Barbara. *Mysteries and Marvels of Plant Life*. Tulsa: Educational Development Corp., 1984.

Holmes, Anita. *Cactus: The All-American Plant*. New York: Four Winds, 1982.

Lerner, Carol. *Pitcher Plants: The Elegant Insect Traps*. New York: William Morrow, 1983.

Wilson, Ron. *How Plants Grow*. New York: Larousse, 1980.

A desmid is a simple kind of plant. Does a desmid look like a plant? It is actually a one-celled green alga. Desmids live in moist environments. They either inhabit fresh water or they live in the ocean. Desmids have characteristics similar to those of other plants. What plant characteristics does a desmid possess? What other kinds of simple plants exist? What do they have in common? How are they different?

CHAPTER 8
SIMPLE PLANTS

8:1 Plants Without Seeds

Algae, mosses, and ferns are simple plants. Simple plants do not produce seeds. Algae and mosses are nonvascular. They do not have vessels in the roots, stems, or leaves. Some simple plants have parts that look like roots, stems, or leaves. However, these parts do not contain vascular structures for transporting water and other materials. Therefore, they are not *true* roots, stems, or leaves. Ferns are vascular plants. They have true roots, stems, and leaves, but they do not produce seeds.

The simplest plants are **algae.** Algae are simple organisms that contain chlorophyll, which is used to make food. Three kinds of algae—green, brown, and red algae—are classified as plants. The other kinds of algae are classified in the protist and moneran kingdoms.

Remember, scientific classification is based on the structures and functions of organisms. Green, brown, and red algae have structures and functions similar to other plants. Like other plants, these kinds of algae have chloroplasts. The chlorophyll in green,

GOALS:
1. You will learn the characteristics of simple plants.
2. You will learn how simple plants are classified.
3. You will learn how simple plants reproduce.

Name the three kinds of algae classified in the plant kingdom.

153

a   b

FIGURE 8–1. Green algae species such as *Protococcus* (a) can live on land. Some types of seaweed (b) are also green algae.

red, and brown algae is contained in these chloroplasts. Some species of algae are one-celled and some are many-celled. Algae are found almost everywhere.

An example of a species of green alga is *Protococcus*. *Protococcus* forms a green coating as it grows on tree trunks and other objects. This species is so tiny that millions of the organisms cover only a few square centimeters. The "moss" that some people say grows on the north side of trees is really *Protococcus*, the alga.

Seaweeds are examples of brown algae. Most of the species in this phylum live in the oceans. All brown algae species are many-celled. Some grow as long as 50 meters or more. A brown pigment in the cells gives the organisms a brownish color.

Most red algae, like the brown algae, are seaweeds that live in the oceans. Most species of red algae are many-celled and live at greater depths than brown algae. They contain pigments that trap light in deep ocean water. Red algae are not always red! Many are black. Agar, a jellylike substance used in laboratories for growing bacteria, is made from red algae.

a   b

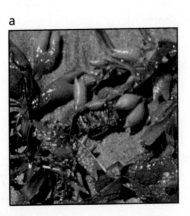

FIGURE 8–2. Most brown (a) and red (b) algae live in the oceans.

Activity 8–1

Investigating Algae

Problem: How do algae differ?

Materials

Protococcus on bark
Spirogyra culture
brown algae, preserved
red algae, preserved
microscope
2 microscope slides
2 coverslips
hand lens
dropper
toothpick
forceps
water

Data and Observations

| Kind of algae: |
| Species: |

| Kind of algae: |
| Species: |

| Kind of algae: |
| Species: |

| Kind of algae: |
| Species: |

Procedure

1. Divide a sheet of paper into four sections for recording your observations. Label each section as shown in Data and Observations. Leave space for drawings.
2. Examine a growth of *Protococcus* on a piece of bark with a hand lens.
3. Place a drop of water on a clean slide.
4. Use a toothpick to scrape some of the *Protococcus* from the bark into the drop of water. Add a coverslip.
5. Observe the algae under low and high power.
6. Draw a single *Protococcus* cell in your data table. Label the cell wall, chloroplast, and nucleus.
7. Place some *Spirogyra* filaments into a drop of water on a clean slide. Add a coverslip.
8. Observe the algae under low and high power.
9. Draw a single *Spirogyra* cell in your data table. Label the cell wall, chloroplast, and nucleus.
10. Examine a red alga sample with the hand lens.
11. Draw the red alga in your data table.
12. Examine a brown alga sample with the hand lens.
13. Draw the brown alga in your data table.

Questions and Conclusions

1. Does the *Protococcus* on the bark appear to be made up of single cells when you view it with the hand lens?
2. How do the groups of *Protococcus* cells differ from the groups of *Spirogyra* cells?
3. What kind of alga is *Spirogyra*?
4. How did you identify the chloroplasts in the algae cells?
5. How are the chloroplasts of the *Spirogyra* different from those of the *Protococcus*?
6. List two ways that the red and brown algae differ from the green algae.
7. How are the brown and red algae different?
8. What is responsible for the color of the green algae?
9. What is responsible for the color of the red and brown algae?

FIGURE 8–3. A form of sexual reproduction called conjugation occurs in *Spirogyra*. Tubes of cytoplasm form between cells in two strands of the alga. Cell material moves through the tubes from one strand to the other.

Describe examples of asexual and sexual reproduction in algae.

8:2 Reproduction in Algae

Recall that in order for a species to survive, over time it must reproduce. Both asexual and sexual reproduction occur in algae. In asexual reproduction, an offspring has only one parent. Brown and red algae reproduce asexually when parts of the parent plant break off and form new individuals.

Protococcus is a green alga that reproduces asexually by mitosis. One *protococcus* cell divides to form two *Protocooccus* cells. From a single cell, through many cell divisions, a colony of *Protococcus* organisms may be formed. All green algae can reproduce asexually by mitosis.

Many species of green alga also reproduce sexually. In sexual reproduction, materials from two different cells combine. **Conjugation** (kahn juh GAY shun) is a method of sexual reproduction.

Spirogyra is a green algae that reproduces asexually by mitosis and sexually by conjugation. *Spirogyra* consists of strands of cells arranged end to end. Long strands of *Spirogyra* cells often form dense mats in ponds. Each strand is surrounded by a slimy coating. There are one or more ribbonlike chloroplasts arranged spirally in each cell. During conjugation, a tube of cytoplasm grows from a cell in one strand to a cell in a second strand. Then cell material moves from one cell through the tube into the other cell. Material from both cells combines together. The two cell nuclei, one from each cell, fuse to form one nucleus. A hard case forms around the new cell, which is called a **zygospore.** Then the zygospore breaks away from the other cells.

Formation of zygospores through conjugation occurs when living conditions are not good for *Spirogyra*. For example, zygospores may form when a pond is drying up in summer. A zygospore can live through dryness and very hot or cold temperatures. When conditions become right for growth to occur, the zygospores form *Spirogyra* cells. Kelp, *Laminaria,* is a large brown alga that grows along the coasts of the Pacific Ocean. It is important commercially as a source of iodine. In Japan the cultivation of a red alga, *Porphyra,* for food is a major industry. In Hawaii about 40 different species of algae are eaten.

Making Sure

1. How are green, brown, and red algae like other plants? How are they different?
2. How do brown and red algae reproduce?
3. When might conjugation be likely to occur in green algae?

Activity 8—2   Conjugation

Problem: How does *Spirogyra* reproduce?

Materials   microscope, prepared slide of *Spirogyra* conjugation

Procedure   **(1)** Examine a prepared slide of *Spirogyra* conjugation under low and high power. Notice that each strand is made up of individual cells arranged in single file. **(2)** Locate two strands side by side with small projections growing toward each other. These projections meet and form tubes of cytoplasm. **(3)** Draw a section of the two strands showing the projections. **(4)** Locate two cells in which the contents of one cell have passed through the tube to the second cell. **(5)** Draw and label the new cell.

Questions   **(1)** What is the new cell called? **(2)** Is the spiral chloroplast visible? **(3)** What kind of reproduction is conjugation? **(4)** How do you think *Spirogyra* got its name? **(5)** How does *Spirogyra* reproduce?

8:3 Liverworts and Mosses

Liverworts and mosses are nonvascular plants. They do not have true roots, stems, or leaves. How are liverworts and mosses different? A **moss** grows a stemlike organ to which a circular group of leaflike structures are attached. **Liverworts** are simpler in structure. They grow as flat, ribbonlike structures that lie on the ground.

Liverworts are held in the ground by rhizoids (RI zoydz). A **rhizoid** is a thin, threadlike structure that grows out from the body of the plant. Through rhizoids, liverworts absorb water from

List the main characteristics of a liverwort and of a moss.

FIGURE 8—4. Liverworts, such as *Marchantia* (a), grow close to the ground. Some species such as *Ricciocarpus* (b) grow on water.

a

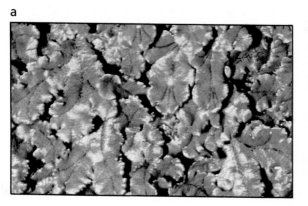

b

FIGURE 8–5. *Sphagnum* is a moss that grows in bogs and marshes. Dried *Sphagnum* moss can absorb and hold a lot of water. For this reason it is used as a packing material for live plants.

the soil by osmosis. Water and food move through a liverwort by diffusion. Because diffusion is slow, liverworts always remain small in size. Water cannot move fast enough from cell to cell by diffusion to supply all the parts of a large plant. *Marchantia* (mahr SHAN tee uh), Figure 8–6a, is one example of a liverwort.

Most mosses are green and grow in moist, shaded areas. Moss plants appear to have "stems" with many "leaves." These are not true stems and leaves because they lack vessels for moving water and food. A moss has rhizoids at the base of the "stem." Rhizoids absorb water by osmosis. *Sphagnum,* Figure 8–5, is one example of a moss.

Mosses perform an important job in nature. The rhizoids produce chemicals that break down rocks into tiny soil particles. These rock particles build up for many years. Together with the remains of dead and decaying organisms, the rock particles form soil. Peat, used as planting material or as fuel, is the remains of *Sphagnum* moss that lived long ago.

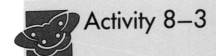

Activity 8–3   Comparing Liverworts and Mosses

Problem: How are liverworts and mosses similar?

Materials   liverwort, moss, hand lens

Procedure   (1) Examine a liverwort with a hand lens. Look closely at the leaflike part. (2) Notice the slender, hairlike structures on the underside. (3) You may find reproductive structures growing up from the plant surface. (4) Examine a moss plant that has a long stalk and a capsule attached to it. (5) Pull a leaflike part from the plant and examine it with the hand lens. (6) Locate the stemlike part of the moss plant. (7) Use the hand lens to look closely at the rhizoids.

Questions   (1) How is the leaflike part of a liverwort shaped? (2) What are the hairlike structures? (3) Does the liverwort have a stemlike part? (4) Describe the reproductive structures of a liverwort. (5) What does a moss plant produce in the capsule at the end of the long stalk? (6) Describe the leaflike and stemlike parts of the moss. (7) Describe the moss rhizoids. (8) How are liverworts and mosses different? (9) How are liverworts and mosses similar?

8:4   Reproduction in Liverworts and Mosses

Mosses, liverworts, and ferns reproduce sexually by gametes and spores. A moss develops both male and female sex organs. Mosses do not have true stems, but have structures that look like stems. Sperm are produced in the male sex organ located in the tip of a moss "stem." Eggs are produced in the female sex organ located in the tip of another moss "stem." Sperm and eggs are the plant's sex cells and are called gametes. Sperm swim from the male sex organ through moisture to the eggs in the female sex organ. When a sperm fuses with an egg, **fertilization** occurs. When fertilized, an egg becomes a **zygote.**

The zygote grows a long, thin stalk. This stalk grows out and up from the tip of the "stem." A capsule is formed at the tip of the stalk. Spores are produced inside this capsule. A **spore** is a special kind of reproductive cell that is very small, like dust. When mature, the spores are released into the air. If a spore lands in a place suitable for growth, it develops into another moss plant.

Sexual reproduction in a liverwort is similar to a moss. Asexual reproduction can also occur in cuplike structures located in the upper surface of a liverwort. Special cells produced in these structures detach from the parent plant. These cells can grow into new liverworts. Mosses also can reproduce asexually by small groups of cells breaking away from the parent body.

What is a spore?

Where are spores found in a moss?

FIGURE 8–6. Liverworts like *Marchantia* form umbrella-shaped reproductive structures (a). Mosses produce spores inside capsules at the tops of long stalks (b).

a

b

Making Sure

4. Describe how reproduction occurs in liverworts and mosses.
5. Give an example of a liverwort and a moss.

8:5 Club Mosses and Horsetails

Club mosses and horsetails are vascular plants. They have true roots, stems, and leaves. **Club mosses** look a lot like mosses. They have a creeping stem that grows close to the ground. From this stem grow upright stems with thin, flat, spirals of leaves. Roots grow down into the ground from the creeping stem. *Lycopodium,* commonly called ground pine, is an example of a club moss. Club mosses grow in the tropics and moist temperate areas. They are usually less than 30 centimeters high. Many species that lived long ago were treelike, as much as a meter thick and 20 meters or more tall.

Horsetails are branched and bushy like a horse's tail. Most of these plants are less than 40 centimeters tall. They grow in moist and dry places from the tropics to the Arctic. The stem of a horsetail has a hollow center surrounded by vascular tissue. Their leaves are small and scalelike in shape. Horsetails reproduce by producing spores.

Describe club mosses and horsetails.

FIGURE 8–7. Club mosses, such as *Lycopodium* (a), and horsetails, such as *Equisetum* (b), are vascular plants. They have true roots, stems, and leaves.

a

b

One species of horsetail native to the United States and Canada is *Equisetum,* the scouring rush. Its name comes from the fact that it has a harsh, scratchy quality. Before steel wool and scouring powder were developed, people used scouring rushes to clean pots and pans.

Most species of club mosses and horsetails lived long ago. Only a few species are living today. Horsetails that lived in ancient times were treelike plants and grew as much as 30 meters tall. The remains of these giant horsetails, along with other plants, formed Earth's coal deposits.

Give an example of a club moss and a horsetail.

a

b

c

8:6 Ferns

Ferns grow in forests, swamps, and gardens where the moisture content is high. Ferns also make good houseplants because they require little light. Most ferns grow larger than liverworts and mosses, but few grow more than two meters tall. Some tree ferns in the tropics reach a height of 16 meters.

A **fern** is a vascular plant containing xylem and phloem tissues that transport water and other substances. Ferns have true roots, stems, and leaves. A fern leaf is called a **frond** (FRAHND). In some ferns, the fronds are divided into many tiny leaflets that give the fronds a feathery appearance. Ferns also have **rhizomes** (RHI zohmz), stems that grow underground. From the rhizome grow hairlike roots through which a fern absorbs water and minerals from soil.

Ferns differ from liverworts and club mosses in the structure of their leaves and stems. The stem and root of a fern are similar

FIGURE 8–8. Tree ferns (a) may grow to be more than 10 meters tall in tropical rain forests. Other tropical ferns (b) grow near the ground. Ferns also grow in temperate climates, such as the walking fern (c) that grows in woodlands.

List the main characteristics of a fern.

in structure to those of a seed plant. Fern leaves have veins like seed plants. However, the water transporting xylem of ferns is somewhat different from the xylem in seed plants.

Millions of years ago, large forests of giant-sized ferns, club mosses, and horsetails covered parts of the earth. Most of the land was wet and marshy. In time, the forests were buried by shallow seas that covered the land. Sand and gravel carried into the seas by runoff water buried the plants. The weight of the sand and gravel produced great pressure and heat. Over millions of years, the pressure and heat changed the ferns and other plants into coal.

How was coal formed from ferns and other plants?

8:7 Reproduction in Ferns

Describe reproduction in ferns.

Ferns reproduce through the production of gametes and spores. If you examine the underside of a fern leaf, you may find tiny brown or orange dots. The dots are round spore cases called sporangia. Each sporangium contains many spores. When the spores are released, they fall to the ground. Some are carried away by wind or water. When a spore lands in favorable conditions, such as in moist soil or on a dead log, it will begin to grow. It develops into a green, flat, heart-shaped plant. Rhizoids grow down from the plant into the soil to obtain water and minerals and anchor the plant.

On the underside of the plant grow male and female sex organs that produce the gametes. An egg cell is produced in the female part, and the male part produces sperm cells. Sperm cells have flagella that enable them to swim through water. After a rainstorm,

FIGURE 8–9. Sori on the underside of fern leaves contain spores that are catapulted into the air. The spores absorb water, which causes them to break open.

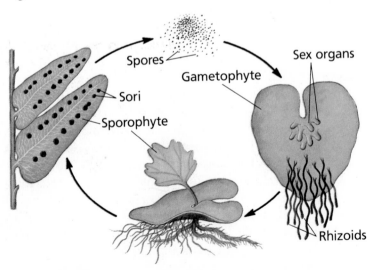

sperm are released. They swim through the water on the underside of the plant to the female part. One sperm combines with the egg forming a single cell. This fusion of the sperm and egg is fertilization. From this single cell, a new fern plant with roots, stems, and leaves develops. Many species of ferns also reproduce asexually. New plants grow from rhizomes that spread through the ground.

All plants have life cycles that include sexual reproduction. Sexual reproduction is the union of two gametes, the sperm and the egg, from different plants. The part of the plant that produces the gametes is called the gametophyte. Fused gametes form a zygote that grows and eventually produces spores. This part of the plant is called the sporophyte. Spores disperse the new plants away from the parent plants. The life cycle is completed by the growth of a spore into a new gametophyte.

Mosses and liverworts have a sporophyte that develops from and lives on the gametophyte, which is usually the major part of the life cycle. In ferns, the leafy plant is the sporophyte, which grows from a small gametophyte. The sporophyte is the major part of a fern's life cycle.

Making Sure

6. Why can ferns grow much larger than liverworts or mosses?
7. How do you think club mosses and horsetails got their names?
8. Why is reproduction in liverworts, mosses, club mosses, horsetails, and ferns called sexual reproduction?

8:8 Soils

Soil originates from solid rock. Rain, wind, snow, and ice wear rock down, breaking it into tiny particles. Lichens and mosses growing on bare rock aid in the process. They release chemicals that dissolve the rock. The pressure of plant roots growing through cracks in rocks also helps break up rocks. Over time, plants and the animals that live on them die and decompose. Remains of the dead matter mix with particles of rock, forming soil.

Soil is made up of two layers above the rock. The upper layer of soil in which most plants grow is called **topsoil.** It contains tiny rock particles and many kinds of microbes. There may be a million microbes in a spoonful of topsoil. Microbes cause the decay of plant and animal material. The decayed organic matter in soil is called **humus** (HYEW mus). The layer of soil beneath topsoil is called **subsoil.** Subsoil contains little humus. The rock particles in subsoil are larger than in topsoil.

FIGURE 8–10. The dark top layer of soil is topsoil. The layers beneath are subsoil.

Minerals used by plants come from both the humus and rock particles in soil. The three minerals that plants take from soil in largest amounts are nitrogen, phosphorus, and potassium. Nitrogen is important for the growth of stems and leaves. Many important compounds in a plant cell contain phosphorus. For example, phosphorus compounds are used in changes that release energy. Potassium is needed for the overall health and growth of a plant.

Humus increases the water-holding capacity of soil. Some soils are very sandy. The sand allows water to run through easily. Therefore, most plants do not grow well in sandy soil. Desert soils are sandy and contain little humus. Cactus and other desert plants can grow in sandy soil because they can store water.

Clay soils contain very fine rock particles. The particles cling tightly together making it hard for water and air to enter the soil. Clay soils are not good for growing most crops.

A soil that is ideal for gardening and farming is loam. Loam is a mixture of sand, clay, and humus. About 30 percent of loam soil is water and air. Loam soils are said to be fertile. Fertile soils are rich in humus and minerals needed by plants.

Fertilizers are materials added to soil to make it better for growing plants. Organic fertilizers contain plant and animal material, such as decayed leaves and manure. They add humus to the soil. Chemical fertilizers are inorganic compounds that contain minerals. The right kinds and amounts of fertilizers help plants grow better. Farmers and gardeners may add fertilizers to soil to increase their crop yields.

Define humus.

What are fertilizers and how are they used?

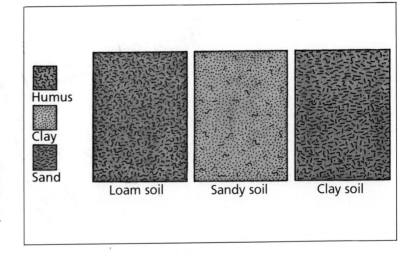

FIGURE 8–11. Loam soil is a mixture of clay, sand, and humus. Sandy soil is mostly sand with little or no humus or clay. Clay soil is mostly clay, which is fine rock particles, with little or no sand or humus.

Activity 8–4   Soil Testing

Problem: What minerals are present in the soil from your school environment?

Materials

3 250-mL beakers
trowel
metric ruler
soil test kit
spoon
hand lens
glass-marking pencil
reference books

Procedure

1. Collect soil samples from three different places around your school.
2. Use the spade to remove the soil from a depth of about 10 cm.
3. Place each sample in a clean beaker and number the beakers 1, 2, and 3.
4. For each sample, record the kind of vegetation growing in the soil, the kind and amount of dead plant material lying on the ground, and any soil organisms that are found in the sample.
5. Break up each sample using a spoon. Remove any small stones and unwanted organic material, such as grass roots. Mix the sample thoroughly. Allow it to dry naturally.
6. Use reference books to find out more about the importance of nitrogen, phosphorus, and potassium in soil.
7. Using this information, predict whether each sample will be high, medium, or low in nitrogen, phosphorus, and potassium.
8. Follow the directions in the soil test kit and test each sample for nitrogen, phosphorus, and potassium.
9. Compare the test results with the nitrogen reading chart, the phosphorus reading chart, and the potassium reading chart.
10. Clean the glassware from the kit and replace the reading charts before returning the kit.

Data and Observations

Sample	1	2	3
Soil description			
Nitrogen			
Phosphorus			
Potassium			

Questions and Conclusions

1. Why is nitrogen in soil important?
2. How are phosphorus compounds used by plants?
3. Why is potassium needed by plants?
4. Why are soil tests useful to people who grow plants?
5. How are nitrogen, phosphorus, and potassium replaced in the soil other than by fertilizing?
6. What minerals are present in the soil from your school environment?

FIGURE 8–12.

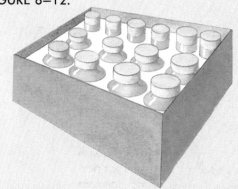

8:9 Natural Cycles

Nitrogen is important to the growth and development of plants and animals. Nitrogen is the most plentiful gas in the air. But plants and animals cannot use the nitrogen in air. Nitrogen is removed from air by certain kinds of bacteria. The nitrogen removed from air is combined with oxygen to form compounds in the soil. Plants use the nitrogen compounds in the soil. Animals take in nitrogen compounds when they eat the plants. Nitrogen compounds are returned to soil when plants and animals decay. Bacteria in the soil break down nitrogen compounds and return nitrogen to the air. These processes are part of the nitrogen cycle.

Plants and other living organisms need certain substances like nitrogen, to live. Many of these substances are part of natural cycles. Carbon dioxide and oxygen are two important gases that organisms need. They are part of the carbon dioxide–oxygen cycle. About 0.03 percent of air is carbon dioxide. About 21 percent of air is oxygen. Animals and plants take in oxygen and give off carbon dioxide as they respire. Plants also remove carbon dioxide from air and add oxygen during photosynthesis. About 90 percent of the oxygen in air comes from algae that live in the oceans. Burning fuels, forest fires, and eruptions of volcanoes also remove oxygen from air and add carbon dioxide. The ongoing exchange of oxygen and carbon dioxide in air make up the carbon dioxide–oxygen cycle.

Organisms also need water. They are part of the water cycle. Oceans, lakes, and streams are part of the water cycle, too. Water evaporates from their surfaces. Water also evaporates from soil,

Explain the water cycle, carbon dioxide–oxygen cycle, and nitrogen cycle.

FIGURE 8–13. The water cycle (a), the carbon dioxide-oxygen cycle (b).

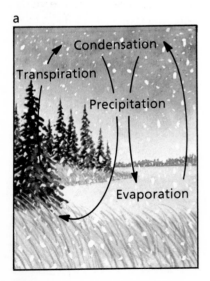

a

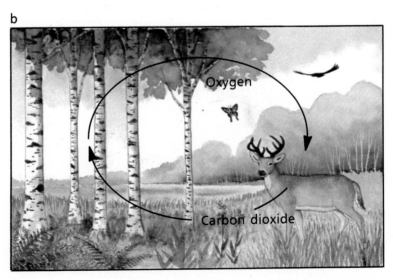

b

plants, and animals. Water vapor in the air rises to high altitudes. Here the water vapor cools and condenses to liquid water droplets that form clouds. The water vapor may also freeze to form ice crystals. The water returns to earth in liquid form as rain or in solid form as snow, sleet, or hail. Then the water cycle starts over again.

Making Sure

9. Why are plants important to soil? Why is soil important to plants?
10. Draw diagrams of the water cycle and the CO_2–O_2 cycle.

Technology

Hydroponics Today

In 1860, Julius Sachs, a German botanist, discovered that certain minerals were required for the healthy growth of plants. He grew plants in pure water to which he added minerals. He was then able to observe the individual effects of the different minerals on plant growth. This "plant water culture" became known as hydroponics. Hydroponics is not a new idea. In the 16th century the Aztecs of Mexico grew a water plant as a crop to dry and use as a fertilizer for their land crops. Hydroponics today refers to plants grown in water or any soil-free medium.

Hydroponics is used extensively today to test the effects of various environmental factors on plants. For example, soybean seedlings can be grown in a special liquid containing polyethylene glycol-600 (PEG-600). The PEG-600 provides an environment that simulates drought. The effect of high salt concentrations may also be determined with the hydroponic growth of seedlings. Certain strains of barley have been found that are tolerant to high salt concentrations. This type of research is useful to crop production in countries with poor soils and food shortages.

Hydroponics has also been used to grow crop plants. Seedlings are placed in styrofoam rafts that are floated in large containers filled with water and nutrients. Pumps are used to circulate and put air into the water so that roots can respire and will not rot. Computers determine the time to add more nutrients to the water. Hydroponic growth is so rapid that a hydroponic farmer can produce up to 20 000 heads of lettuce weekly. As the world's food requirements steadily rise, research such as this will be increasingly important.

FIGURE 8–14. Sachs grew plants in water. He used a cork to suspend a corn seedling. The roots were in a known nutrient solution.

FOCUS ON
Skills

Organizing Information

In science class you obtain information from lectures, readings, demonstrations, films, laboratory experiments, and field trips. A key to success in science class is organizing that information.

Keeping a written summary of all information is an excellent study technique. Taking good notes helps you to learn.

During a lecture you cannot record everything that is discussed. Listen carefully and concentrate on the main idea and how it is supported.

Note Taking for Lectures		
Before Class	**During Class**	**After Class**
Review notes	Listen critically	Summarize notes
Read assignments	Determine main ideas and supporting details	Frequently review notes
	Record information	

You will take better lecture notes if you are prepared. Before class, review your notes and make sure you understand everything covered in the previous lecture. Then you can focus your attention on the new lecture. Read text assignments before class to get an idea of what will be covered.

During class, determine the main topic of the lecture. Decide what details support the topic. Write notes in your own words to be sure that you understand the material.

After class, summarize the notes and be sure you understand them. Also take notes during oral presentations, films, demonstrations, and field trips. Good notes are your most valuable resource when studying for tests.

Take notes while reading text assignments. Determine the main idea and how it is supported. After each paragraph, decide what subject is being discussed. Key words should refer to the topic. If they do not, you should reread the paragraph to determine the most important topic. Look at the second paragraph in Section 8:2, Reproduction in Algae. What is the main idea?

An outline shows the relationship between main ideas and supporting details. The main ideas of the book are indicated by section titles. You can use the titles to outline the chapter.

The beginning of an outline for Chapter 8 follows. Finish the outline with the main ideas and supporting details of each section and paragraph in the chapter.

I. Simple Plants (Section 8:1)
   A. Simple plants do not produce seeds (main idea of paragraph one).
      1. Nonvascular plants have no vessels in stems or leaves (supporting detail).
      2. Vascular plants have vessels in stems and leaves (supporting detail).

You will have notes from many sources, including handouts, lab reports, worksheets, and answers to Making Sure or Chapter Review questions. This information should be easy to retrieve when it is time to study. Therefore, you should organize your notes properly. Tabbed dividers will separate notes from different sources. You may prefer to use pocket folders for notes from different sources.

Date all forms of information. Each time you take notes, put the date at the top of your paper. Also, date worksheets, questions answered from the text, lab reports, and handouts.

Keeping information organized means being prepared for class, taking notes carefully, writing an outline, and keeping notes sorted. Using this approach will help you succeed in all aspects of learning science.

Review

Summary

1. Green, brown, and red algae are classified as plants.   8:1
2. Algae reproduce by sexual and asexual reproduction.   8:2
3. Liverworts and mosses absorb water through rhizoids by osmosis.   8:3
4. Liverworts and mosses reproduce by spores.   8:4
5. Club mosses and horsetails are vascular plants. Most species of these plants are now extinct.   8:5
6. Ferns are vascular plants. They do not produce seeds.   8:6, 8:7
7. Lichens, mosses, and other plants are important in the formation of soil.   8:8
8. Humus and rocks in soil provide minerals used by plants for healthy growth.   8:8
9. Water is cycled through the environment and living organisms.   8:9
10. In natural cycles, water vapor, nitrogen, oxygen, and carbon dioxide are added to and removed from the air.   8:9

Vocabulary

Write a sentence using the following words or terms correctly.

algae	horsetail	spore
club moss	humus	subsoil
conjugation	liverwort	topsoil
fern	moss	zygospore
fertilization	rhizoid	zygote
frond	rhizome	

Questions

Do not write in this book.

A. True or False

Determine whether each of the following sentences is true or false. Rewrite the false statements to make them correct.

1. Conjugation is a method of asexual reproduction.
2. Moisture is needed for moss plants to reproduce.
3. *Spirogyra* is a species of green alga.
4. Moss plants have rhizoids.
5. Ferns grow in moist places.
6. Algae reproduce only by sexual reproduction.
7. A spore is a reproductive cell.
8. Most species of club mosses and horsetails are alive today.
9. Ferns have vascular tissue in their roots, stems, and leaves.
10. Fertilization occurs in sexual reproduction.

CHAPTER 8
Review

B. Multiple Choice
Choose the word or phrase that correctly completes the following sentences.
1. A rhizoid is part of a *(moss, leaf, stem)*.
2. A moss obtains water through *(roots, stems, rhizoids)*.
3. Moss would most likely be found growing *(in a desert, under water, under a shade tree)*.
4. Millions of years ago, large *(fern, liverwort, moss)* forests grew on earth.
5. Coal is formed from dead *(animal, plant)* material.
6. *Spirogyra* reproduces by *(spores, mitosis only, conjugation)*.
7. Spores are produced by *(algae, ferns, kelp)*.
8. A horsetail is most like a *(moss, fern, club moss)*.
9. Humus is *(mineral, organic, mineral and organic)* material.
10. *(Loam, Sandy, Clay)* soil is made of very fine rock particles.

C. Completion
Complete each of the following sentences with the correct word or phrase.
1. Mosses and _____ are examples of nonvascular plants.
2. Water moves through a liverwort by _____.
3. Tree ferns grow in the region of the earth called the _____.
4. The color of green algae cells is due to the presence of _____.
5. Protococcus is an example of a(n) _____ algae.
6. *Spirogyra* form _____ through conjugation.
7. Horsetails reproduce by producing _____.
8. _____ is the upper layer of soil that contains a lot of humus.
9. Fusion of an egg and sperm is called _____.
10. _____ are added to soil to help plants grow better.

D. How and Why
1. Compare sexual and asexual reproduction in green algae.
2. Why are all liverworts and mosses small plants?
3. How is soil formed?
4. Why are algae called simple plants?
5. Make a table that lists the characteristics of the nonvascular and vascular plants discussed in this chapter.
6. Explain why ferns are not classified in the same phylum as liverworts and mosses.
7. How would you increase the fertility of soil to be used for growing a garden?
8. Explain how a plant is part of the water cycle and carbon dioxide–oxygen cycle.

CHAPTER 8
Review

Ideas to Explore

1. **Challenge:** Prepare a report on how and where bogs form. Include the characteristics of mosses that allow them to grow in bogs and the other types of plants that grow in bogs.
2. **Project:** Obtain algae from a health food store. Find a recipe with algae as an ingredient. Follow the recipe and report the results to your class.
3. **Project:** Survey the items in your local supermarket. Make a list of the items that contain products from algae.
4. **Project:** Collect soil samples from different areas. Compare the color, texture, particle size, and capacity to absorb water for each of the soils. Determine in which soils seeds will grow best.
5. **Challenge:** Make an illustrated report on the life cycle of a fern.
6. **Project:** Visit a library and do research on spikemosses. Obtain a resurrection plant from a garden store and make a report on this plant to the class.
7. **Project:** Collect ripe fern spores. Fill a clear, sterile container that has an airtight lid with sterile African violet soil mix. Water it with boiled water. Sow the fern spores sparsely over the surface and cover the container immediately with the seal. High humidity will be maintained and no further watering is necessary. Set the container in a well-lit area. Observe the growth of the spores over several weeks. The heart-shaped gametophyte may take up to three months to fully develop.

Readings

Frankel, Edward. *Ferns: A Natural History*. Brattleboro, VT: Greene, 1981.

Kavaler, Lucy. *Green Magic: Algae Rediscovered*. New York: Cromwell, 1983.

Marcus, Elizabeth. *Amazing World of Plants*. Mahwah, NJ: Troll, 1984.

Milne, Lorus J. and Margery. *Nature's Great Carbon Cycle*. New York: Atheneum, 1983.

There are over 250 000 known species of seed plants. They vary greatly in size and shape. They are suited to many different environments. Water-loving plants may live in wet areas, such as this swamp. What kinds of seed plants do you see? What specialized structures do seed plants have? The young saplings in the photo will grow into mature trees. How do plants grow and reproduce?

CHAPTER 9
SEED PLANTS

9:1 Kinds of Seed Plants

Most of the plants you know are seed plants. For example, dandelion, spinach, grass, corn, and strawberry are seed plants. Plants that produce showy flowers like the rose, aster, lily, and geranium are also seed plants. The fruit and vegetables you eat come from seed plants. Pine, palm, oak, and redwood trees are other examples of seed plants.

Seed plants are vascular plants classified in the division Tracheophyta. They have roots, stems, and leaves, and special tissues that transport water, food, and minerals. Unlike ferns, which are also classified in this division, seed plants produce seeds for dispersal. Ferns produce spores. More than 250 000 species of seed plants have been identified. Some are tiny, like duckweed. Others are large, like oak trees.

Seed plants are divided into two main classes: gymnosperms (JIHM nuh spurmz) and angiosperms (AN jee uh spurmz). **Gymnosperms** are seed plants that do not produce flowers. The seeds of a gymnosperm are not enclosed in a fruit. Cone bearers such as pine and spruce are examples of gymnosperms. Plants that produce flowers make up the **angiosperm** group. Their seeds are completely enclosed by a fruit wall that can be dry or fleshy. Although both gymnosperms and angiosperms produce seeds, the method of reproduction in these two kinds of plants is different.

GOALS:
1. You will learn the characteristics of seed plants.
2. You will learn how seed plants are classified.
3. You will learn how seed plants reproduce.

How are seed plants different from ferns?

What are the two main kinds of seed plants?

9:2 Gymnosperms

Describe the characteristics of a gymnosperm.

A common example of a gymnosperm plant is a pine tree. Hemlock, yew, fir, cypress, and cedar are other gymnosperm species. The name "gymnosperm" comes from the Greek words "gymnos" meaning naked and "sperma" meaning seed. Gymnosperms are vascular plants that reproduce by seeds not enclosed by a fruit wall. Redwood trees are gymnosperms. Some of the oldest and tallest trees in the world are redwoods growing in California. They often reach a height of 60 to 80 meters with trunks two to four meters across. Over 500 species of gymnosperms have been discovered.

Included in the gymnosperm group are the cycads, ginkgo tree, and conifers (KAHN uh furz) such as the pine and redwood. Cycads grow in the tropics and semitropical regions. Many of this group look like small palm trees. Ginkgos are grown as shade trees because of their broad, fan-shaped leaves. Ginkgos are sometimes called "living fossils." They are the only living species of a group of gymnosperms that were plentiful millions of years ago.

Conifers, the cone bearers, are the largest group of gymnosperms. Although most conifers are trees, some are shrubs. Most have needle-shaped leaves. **Conifers,** like other gymnosperms, do not bear flowers. The seeds produced by conifers are on the inner sides of scalelike leaves arranged in spirals along a short stalk forming a cone. Most conifers are evergreen. They retain their leaves through the winter, not losing them all in the fall. A

FIGURE 9–1. Cycads (a) and ginkgos (b) are two kinds of gymnosperms. About 100 species of cycads but only one species of ginkgo, *Gingko biloba*, is alive today.

a

b

a   b

few such as larches and bald cypress are deciduous and lose their leaves in the fall.

Conifers are important commercially. They supply more than three-fourths of the wood used in the construction of buildings. Wood from conifers is used to make paper, plastics, rayon, lacquer, photographic film, and explosives. Turpentine, various tars, and oils used to flavor beverages are obtained from conifers. Farmers plant rows of evergreen conifers as windbreaks and to help prevent soil from blowing away.

FIGURE 9–2. Redwoods (a) and yews (b) are conifers.

What are three practical uses of conifers?

9:3 Angiosperms

Do you have a favorite flower? Many of the plants you are familiar with are flowering plants. More than half of the known species of plants are flowering plants. Many such plants produce food for people. Many others beautify gardens and landscapes. Angiosperms are flowering plants that produce seeds within fruits. The name "angiosperm" comes from the Greek words "angeion" meaning an enclosing vessel and "sperma" meaning seed. Apple and maple trees, daisies, tomato plants, and grasses are examples of angiosperms. In the temperate regions, most angiosperm trees are deciduous. They lose their leaves in the autumn. In areas where winters are mild, or in the tropics, angiosperm trees are evergreen.

What are the main characteristics of an angiosperm?

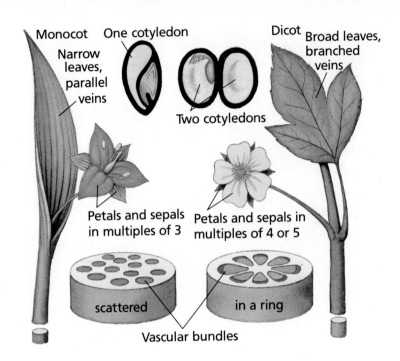

FIGURE 9–3. Compare the characteristics of a monocot and a dicot.

How is a monocot different from a dicot? Give an example of each.

Angiosperms are divided into two groups: monocots (MAHN uh kahtz) and dicots (DI kahtz). There are differences in the seeds and stems of these two groups. **Monocots** have one seed leaf. **Dicots** have two seed leaves (Section 9:8). Bundles of xylem and phloem tissue are arranged differently in the two stem types. In monocots, the bundles are scattered throughout the stem. In dicots, the bundles are arranged in a circle.

In addition, there are other differences in structure that separate monocots from dicots. For example, monocots have leaves with parallel veins. Dicots have leaves with a network of branched veins. The parts of monocot flowers are arranged in threes or multiples of three. The parts of dicot flowers are arranged in fours or fives or multiples of four or five. Examples of monocots are grass, corn, orchids, daffodils, and palms. Examples of dicots are oak trees, roses, beans, clovers, and dandelions.

Making Sure

1. How are seed plants different from simpler plants?
2. Name five examples of conifers.
3. Name two important differences between a conifer and an angiosperm.

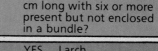

Activity 9–1

Classifying Plants

Problem: How can you use a key to classify plants?

Materials numbered angiosperm plants and gymnosperm twigs

Procedure (1) Write down a prediction of whether each plant is an angiosperm or gymnosperm. If it is an angiosperm, predict if it is a monocot or dicot. If it is a gymnosperm, guess the name of the plant. (2) Use the key to check your predictions.

Questions (1) How can you tell a gymnosperm from an angiosperm? (2) How is a monocot different from a dicot? (3) How can you tell a pine from a spruce? (4) How can you use a key to classify plants?

1. Does the plant have flowers?

| YES | Go to 2. |

| NO | Go to 3. |

2. Does the plant have flower parts in fours or fives and netted veins in the leaf?

| YES | Dicot |

| NO | Monocot |

3. Does the plant have leaves that look like needles?

| YES | Go to 4. |

| NO | Go to 11. |

4. Are the needles in groups of two or more?

| YES | Go to 5. |

| NO | Go to 7. |

5. Are the needles at least 5 cm long with two to five enclosed in a bundle?

| YES | Pine |

| NO | Go to 6. |

6. Are the needles at least 5 cm long with six or more present but not enclosed in a bundle?

| YES | Larch |

| NO | Go to 7. |

7. Do the needles have four sides and grow in a spiral pattern?

| YES | Spruce |

| NO | Go to 8. |

8. Do the needles grow straight and side by side in two rows as shown?

| YES | Go to 9. |

| NO | Go to 10. |

9. Are the needles light colored and featherlike?

| YES | Bald Cypress |

| NO | Go to 10. |

10. Do the needles have gray stripes on the bottom and are they attached to the stem by a short woody stalk?

| YES | Hemlock |

| NO | Fir |

11. Does the plant have leaves that look like overlapping scales as shown?

| YES | Cedar |

| NO | Go to 12. |

12. Does the plant have two kinds of leaves, overlapping scales, and needles?

| YES | Juniper |

| NO | Go back to 1 again. |

177

9:4 Reproduction in Seed Plants

Seed plants reproduce sexually. They have male and female reproductive organs that produce egg and sperm cells. In conifers the reproductive organs are in cones. In angiosperms the reproductive organs are in flowers. **Eggs** are female reproductive cells. They form in female reproductive organs called **ovules. Sperm** are male reproductive cells. Sperm form inside **pollen grains** which are produced by male reproductive organs.

Define pollen grain, sperm, egg, and ovule.

The transfer of pollen grains from male reproductive organs to ovules is called **pollination.** Within an ovule, a sperm joins with an egg. The joining of a sperm and an egg is fertilization. A zygote is formed by fertilization. Inside the ovule, mitosis occurs many times as the zygote develops into an embryo (EM bree oh). The ovule becomes a seed. An **embryo** is a young growing plant within the seed.

Describe the development of a seed.

For most species of seed plants, male and female reproductive organs are on the same plant. In some species, the male and female reproductive organs are on separate plants. For reproduction to occur in these species, both male and female plants must be present. One example is holly. There are male and female holly trees. Male and female trees must be planted near each other or seeds will not be produced. Only the female tree produces seeds. Other examples are the gingkos and cycads.

FIGURE 9—4. Male reproductive organs in plants produce pollen grains that contain sperm.

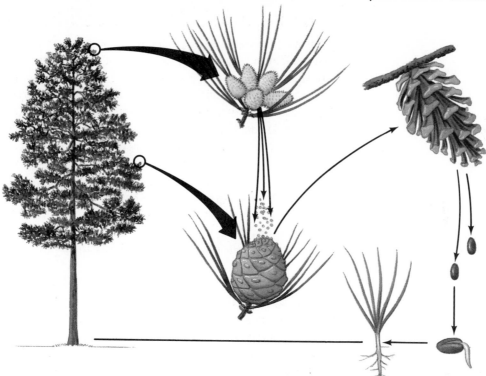

FIGURE 9–5. Pollen grains are produced in male cones of pine. Wind carries the pollen to female cones. Sperm in the pollen grains fertilize eggs in the ovules of the female cones. The ovules become pine seeds that fall out of female cones.

9:5 Reproduction in Conifers

Pine trees provide a good example of reproduction in conifers. Have you ever noticed that two different kinds of cones grow on a pine tree? A pine tree produces male and female cones. Each cone is a spiral of scales on a short stem. The male cones are small and produce pollen grains. Female cones are larger than male cones and produce eggs.

Mature pollen grains are released from male cones. A single cone may release millions of pollen grains. After the pollen grains are released, the male cones fall off the tree.

The pollen grains may be carried far away by wind. In this method of pollination, most of these pollen grains fail to reach a female pine cone, but some do. They sift down between the scales of the cone. Here a pollen grain grows a tube into an ovule at the base of a scale. The ovule contains an egg. A sperm nucleus in the pollen grain enters the egg through the tube and unites with the egg nucleus. This fertilization process forms a zygote. The zygote grows into a tiny embryo inside the ovule. The ovule becomes a pine seed.

Describe how seeds are formed in a conifer.

The seed produced in the female pine cone contains the embryo plant and stored food. Around the stored food and embryo is a layer called the seed coat. The seed coat protects the embryo and stored food.

Each seed is attached to the base of the scale in the cone. In the fall and winter, the female cones fall off the pine tree. The cones break open, and the seeds may be carried away. If the seeds are transported to a place where the soil is moist and rich, they may grow into new pine trees.

Making Sure

4. Where are the reproductive organs of conifers and angiosperms located?
5. How is fertilization different from pollination?

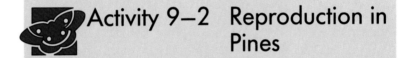 Activity 9–2   Reproduction in Pines

Problem: How are pine seeds fertilized?

Materials   mature 2-year-old female pine cone, one-year-old female pine cone, male pine cone, forceps, hand lens, knife, coverslip, microscope, microscope slide, dropper, water

Procedure   (1) Examine a mature 2-year-old female pine cone. Observe the arrangement of scales on the cone. (2) Remove a scale from the female cone. **CAUTION:** *Always be careful when using a knife. Direct the edge of the blade away from you.* Use a hand lens to look for seeds on the scale. Count the number of seeds on a scale. (3) Examine a one-year-old female pine cone. (4) Examine a male pine cone. (5) Cut the male cone lengthwise and remove one of the cone scales. (6) Examine the sacs of pollen with a hand lens. Gently crush one of the sacs. (7) Make a wet mount of the pollen grains. Examine under low and high power.

Questions   (1) How are female and male pine cones different? (2) How are the 2-year-old female pine cone and the one-year-old female pine cone different? (3) How are female cones adapted to catch pollen? (4) What differences or similarities in structure do you observe between pollen grains and seeds? (5) How are pine seeds fertilized?

FIGURE 9–6. Parts of a flower

9:6 Parts of a Flower

Flowers contain the reproductive parts of angiosperms. Seeds are produced inside a fruit that is formed from part of the flower. Complete flowers have the following parts—stamens, pistils, petals, and sepals. **Stamens** are the male reproductive organs of angiosperms. They have a stalk or filament, and an anther where the pollen is produced. **Pistils** are the female reproductive organs. They have an ovary that produces the ovules, and a stigma on a stalk or style where pollen is received. The stamen and pistil are in the center of a flower. They are surrounded by the petals. Petals are like leaves in their structure. Sepals are leaflike structures of the flower. Sepals surround and cover the other parts before the flower opens. A rose is an example of a complete flower.

Some angiosperms produce incomplete flowers. An incomplete flower has one or more parts missing. For example, the flowers of some trees do not have petals or sepals. Some plants, such as corn, produce two different incomplete flowers. Male flowers with stamens are in the tassel at the top of the plant. Female flowers with pistils are in the ears of corn. In some species of plants, male and female flowers are produced on separate plants.

How are complete and incomplete flowers different?

Problem: What are the parts of a flower?

Materials

gladiolus flower   microscope slide
scissors   coverslip
scalpel   toothpick
hand lens   dropper
black paper   water
microscope

Procedure

1. Remove the sepals from the flower. The sepals are colored leaflike structures around the outside of the flower. Notice their arrangement on the flower. Record the number and color of sepals in a data table.
2. The leaflike structures inside the sepals are the petals. Remove the petals. How were they arranged on the flower? Record the number and color.
3. Locate the stamens and remove them. Look at one of the stamens with a hand lens. Identify the anther and the filament. The top part of the stamen is the anther. The stalklike part is the filament. Record the number of stamens.
4. Gently tap the anther against a piece of black paper. What falls onto the paper? Examine some of the pollen grains with a hand lens.
5. Make a temporary wet mount with some of the pollen grains. Make simple drawings of your observations.
6. The structure in the center attached to the top of the flower stem is the pistil. It is made up of three parts. Identify the stigma, style, and ovary.
7. Remove the pistil from the flower. Examine it with a hand lens. The stigma is the top part of the pistil. The stalklike part of the pistil is the style. The ovary is the base of the pistil. Record the number of pistils.

8. Use a scalpel to split the pistil lengthwise. **CAUTION:** *Always be careful with sharp instruments.* Use a hand lens to look at the inside of the ovary. The structures that you see are ovules. The fertilized ovules will become seeds. Record your observations.

Data and Observations

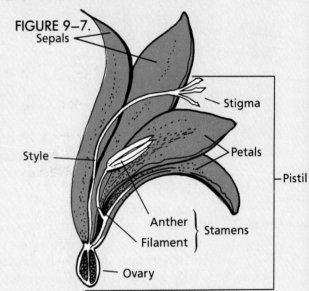

FIGURE 9–7.

Questions and Conclusions

1. How does the number of stamens compare to the number of petals and sepals?
2. Are there more pollen cells produced by one anther than ovules produced by one ovary?
3. Draw the pistil and label the stigma, style, and ovary.
4. Describe the stigma.
5. How are the ovules arranged in the ovary?
6. Is a gladiolus flower a complete flower or an incomplete flower? Explain.
7. Is a gladiolus a monocot or a dicot? Explain.
8. What are the parts of a flower?

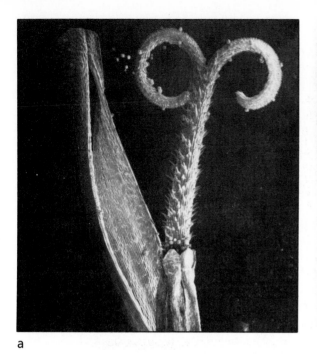

a

b

9:7 Reproduction in Flowering Plants

For sexual reproduction to occur in a flowering plant, pollination and fertilization must take place. Pollen grains are produced by the stamens. In pollination, pollen grains are moved from the stamens to the top part or stigma of the pistil. A sugary fluid makes the stigma sticky. This keeps the pollen grains from falling off or blowing away once they have landed.

Pollination may be aided by wind, water, or insects. Grasses are pollinated by wind. Wind carries pollen from the stamens to the pistils. A raindrop falling on a flower may carry pollen from a stamen to a pistil. Perhaps you have seen bees or butterflies flying from flower to flower in a garden. Bees pollinate many kinds of flowers as they obtain nectar. Pollen grains collect on the hairs of bees' legs and are transferred from stamens to pistils.

Complete flowers have both stamens and pistils. Therefore, they produce both pollen grains and eggs. Transfer of pollen grains from stamens to pistils within flowers is called **self-pollination.** In incomplete flowers, one flower may produce the pollen grains and another flower may produce the eggs. Pollination between two flowers is called **cross-pollination.**

FIGURE 9–8. A 38X magnification of a dandelion makes the stigma and pollen grains clearly visible (a). Bees aid in the pollination of many flowers. As bees move from flower to flower, they distribute pollen that has collected on their legs (b).

Name three ways pollination of an angiosperm may occur.

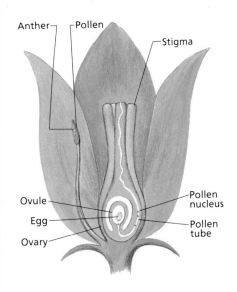

Anther — Pollen

Stigma

Ovule

Egg

Ovary

Pollen nucleus

Pollen tube

FIGURE 9–9. Pollination and fertilization in an angiosperm.

After pollination the pollen grain grows a thin-walled tube down through the pistil. This pollen tube grows until it reaches an ovule. Ovules are in the **ovary,** the bottom, rounded part of the pistil. Eggs, the female reproductive cells, are produced inside the ovules. After reaching an ovule, the pollen tube enters the ovule. Then the sperm in the pollen grain moves into the ovule through the pollen tube and fuses with the egg. The zygote that is formed by this fertilization grows by cell division into an embryo. Meanwhile, the ovule becomes a seed containing the embryo. The ovary that surrounds the ovule swells and grows to form a fruit. For example, an ovary in the pistil of a grape flower becomes the grape. The ovules inside the ovary become the grape seeds.

Making Sure

6. Draw a diagram and label the parts of a complete flower. What is the function of each part?
7. How many ovules are in a peach, plum, and avocado pistil?
8. How is reproduction in conifers different from reproduction in angiosperms?

9:8 Seeds

You have learned that after a zygote is formed, cell division produces an embryo within a seed. Then seeds become dormant for awhile. Dormancy is a period of time when the embryo is not actively growing. Chemical changes occur that prepare the embryo for further growth.

When fruits and cones drop from seed plants, the seeds grow into new plants if conditions are right. The early growth of a plant from a seed is called **germination** (jur muh NAY shun). Moisture, oxygen, and a favorable temperature must be present for germination to occur. Then the embryo within the seed begins to develop.

Every seed contains a seed coat and an embryo. Angiosperm seeds have seed leaves called **cotyledons** (kaht ul EED uns). Seeds with one cotyledon are monocots. Seeds with two cotyledons are dicots. Cotyledons contain food that the embryo uses during its early growth.

Few seeds would produce new plants if they all began to grow in the same spot. There would be too much competition for water, minerals, and sunlight. Seed dispersal increases the chances of a seed growing into a new plant. Seed dispersal means seeds are

How are seeds formed in an angiosperm?

Why is seed dispersal important in plant reproduction?

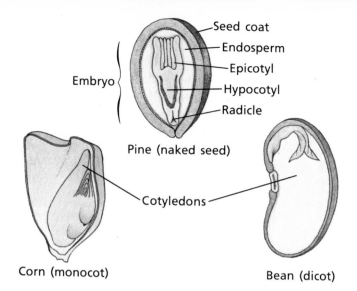

Seed coat
Endosperm
Epicotyl
Hypocotyl
Radicle

Embryo {

Pine (naked seed)

Cotyledons

Corn (monocot)

Bean (dicot)

FIGURE 9–10. A plant embryo has three main parts. The radicle becomes the root of the plant. The hypocotyl becomes the lower stem. The epicotyl grows into an upper stem and leaves. Monocots have one cotyledon. Dicots have two cotyledons.

carried away from the plant that produced them. Animals, wind, and water aid in seed dispersal.

Seeds eaten by animals may be carried great distances away from a plant. Many plant fruits have tiny hooks that cling to the fur or feathers of animals. Milkweed seeds have silky hairs that cause them to be carried by wind. A coconut may be carried far from a coconut palm tree by ocean currents.

9:9 Growing Plants

Some garden plants such as beans and tomatoes are raised from seeds. Others are grown by vegetative propagation (VEJ uh tayt ihv · prahp uh GAY shun). Vegetative propagation is a kind of asexual reproduction in which a new plant is grown from part of another plant. Perhaps you have grown tulips from bulbs, which are a kind of short underground stem. Plants such as ivy or geranium can be grown from pieces of stems or leaves. Grafting is an artificial method of vegetative propagation. A cutting from one plant is bound to the root or stem of another plant. By new growth at the point of attachment, the cutting becomes part of the plant onto which it was grafted.

Light, correct temperature, air, water, and minerals are needed for the healthy growth of plants. Plants grown indoors are usually set near a window so they receive light. Many flowering plants need several hours of direct light each day. Most plants grow best in a moderate temperature of 16° to 21°C. The air must also contain some moisture. Sometimes the air in a heated room during the winter may be too dry for the good health of plants. To grow well, plants also need the right amount of water in the soil in

FIGURE 9–11. With proper care, a variety of plants can be grown indoors in pots.

which they grow. A lack of water causes plants to wilt and die. Too much water results in disease or the rotting of roots. Fertilizer may be used to provide the minerals that plants need.

Plants such as mosses, liverworts, and most ferns need a moist environment and grow well in terrariums. Small cacti may be grown in a desert terrarium. The bottom layers of a desert terrarium should be sand and gravel. No cover should be placed on top, and it should be kept in bright sunlight. The sand should be watered about once every three weeks.

Making Sure

9. Describe the development of a seed into a mature, healthy plant.
10. What do plants need in order to grow well?

Activity 9–4   Growing Plants

Problem: How can you grow plants from seeds, stems, roots, and leaves?

Materials   fresh orange seeds, carrot, wandering jew plant, *Coleus,* warm water, jars and dishes, peat moss, potting soil, metric ruler, scissors, toothpicks, sweet potato

Procedure   (1) Soak orange seeds in warm water overnight. Plant the seeds in a mixture of peat moss and potting soil. Keep them in a warm place but out of direct sunlight until the sprouts begin to grow. Keep the soil moist but not wet. (2) Cut off the top of a carrot. Set the top in a dish of water. Watch for new shoots to grow. (3) Cut a healthy stem about 15 cm long from a wandering jew plant. Place the stem in a container of water and watch for roots to appear. When roots appear, plant the stem in a container of potting soil. (4) Place healthy *Coleus* leaves in small containers of water. Watch for roots to appear on the leaf stalks. When roots appear, plant the leaves in a container of potting soil. Place in indirect light. (5) Submerge the tapered end only of a fresh sweet potato in a small-mouthed jar filled with water. You may have to insert three toothpicks to suspend the potato. Put the jar in a sunny window. Keep the water level constant. Record the number of days it takes roots and leaves to grow.

Questions   (1) Why were the orange seeds soaked overnight? (2) Why was the tapered end of the potato suspended in water and not the whole potato? (3) Why must the plants that root in water be placed in soil? (4) Why are young plants placed in the light? (5) What do seeds, stems, roots, and leaves need in order to reproduce? (6) How can you grow plants from seeds, stems, roots, and leaves?

FIGURE 9–12.

Technology

The New Gardens

From the beginning of agriculture, about 10 000 BC, humans have sought to improve crop plants. For thousands of years, new varieties have been produced by the method of cross-pollination. New breeds of crop plants were selected for their hardier, tastier, and more nutritious traits. Cross-pollination is most successful when plants of the same species are used. Often it takes many years to develop a new plant variety. The time-consuming method may now be replaced by two new techniques—genetic engineering and protoplast fusion. These modern methods may make it possible for scientists to develop new and improved plant varieties in a matter of weeks.

Genetic engineering involves the transfer of a desired trait into a plant. For example, the trait for resistance to a disease could be transferred from one variety of tomato plant to another. Scientists use a bacterium to introduce the new trait into the plant cells. The plant cells with the new trait are then grown in a test tube or culture dish containing nutrients for the growth of plant tissue. Genetic engineers have already shown how completely unrelated species can be crossed by this technique. They created a new plant called the sunbean by transferring a trait from a bean plant into a sunflower plant.

Protoplast fusion is the latest development in plant tissue culture. Protoplasts are plant cells whose cell walls have been dissolved by an enzyme. With the cell walls removed, the protoplasts from two different plants can then be fused. The genetic material of the two cells is then combined into one cell. Next, the protoplasts are cultured until they grow into a new plant. Scientists have successfully fused protoplasts from potato and tomato species. This fusion resulted in varieties of potatoes that are more resistant to certain diseases.

A promising method for the rapid improvement of crop plants is called direct gene transfer. This combines the techniques of genetic engineering and protoplast fusion. The desired genetic trait is isolated by genetic engineering and is then cultured with plant protoplasts. The genetic material is transferred without the use of bacteria. This new technology will allow scientists to combine beneficial traits of different species of plants that normally could not be crossed. Compared with the traditional crossing methods, this new technique will also allow for relatively rapid production of new and improved varieties. The new gardens may become an important source of the world's future food.

FIGURE 9–13. Two types of protoplasts (clear and green) from different plants can be fused to make a hybrid protoplast (center).

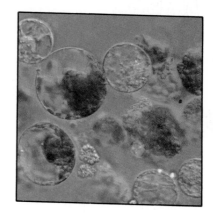

Seeds of Tomorrow

Breeding has reduced the genetic diversity of crop plants over the past twenty years. Growers have continually selected crop plants that are uniform in size and development. This selective breeding has eliminated some genetic traits in the crops, including differences among them. As a result, our domestic crops have become less resistant to insect pests and diseases. In 1970, a fungus destroyed 15 percent of the national corn crop. Because much of the corn planted that year had identical genetic makeup, it was equally susceptible to that particular fungus.

Such problems can be helped by creating greater variety among strains of the same crop. Genetic diversity is vital to developing new and better crops. There is an enormous natural supply of genetic characters available in the world's seeds. Some of these seeds may have the genetic information for new or improved crop plants. They may be resistant to disease, drought, and pests. Seeds can be collected as an insurance against a major crop loss in the future and in order to study their characteristics. Seed banks have been established to ensure a ready supply of diverse strains. These seed banks try to maintain as many varieties of seed as possible. The seeds are stored until needed by professional breeders or researchers. Some seed banks are conducting research on how to make seeds live longer by storing them at very low temperatures.

The latest advances in plant breeding and genetic engineering also are important to the creation of new and improved plants that grow in adverse conditions. Food plants often originate in areas of poor soil, where large roots and seeds give the plant an advantage for survival. An example of such a plant is the winged bean. Although this is a little-known plant, it is being advertised as "the soybean of the tropics." The seeds of this plant are similar to soybeans, but have a better flavor. Even the leaves and roots are edible. The leaves taste like spinach, and the roots are like potatoes. This plant has the ability to grow in nutrient-poor soils. The winged bean, like other beans, can be grown without nitrogen fertilizer.

Through searching nature and through research and development of plants from seed banks, scientists continue to explore ways to guarantee the world's future supply of healthy plants.

The largest national seed bank in the United States is at Fort Collins in Colorado. The collection includes more than 200 000 different seed samples of wild and domesticated crop varieties from around the world. The seeds are kept in dark, refrigerated rooms, packaged in small sacks for long-term storage.

CHAPTER 9
Review

Summary

1. There are two kinds of plants that produce seeds: gymnosperms and angiosperms. 9:1
2. Gymnosperms are "naked seed" plants. 9:2
3. Conifers are seed plants that produce seeds in cones and have needles or scales. 9:2
4. Angiosperms are flowering plants that produce seeds enclosed in fruits. 9:3
5. Angiosperms are classified into monocots and dicots. 9:4
6. Seed plants produce eggs and sperm for sexual reproduction. 9:5
7. Pollination, fertilization, and seed formation are part of the reproduction of seed plants. 9:6, 9:7, 9:8
8. Complete flowers contain sepals, petals, stamens, and pistils. Incomplete flowers lack one or more of these parts. 9:7
9. A zygote develops into an embryo. A seed develops from an ovule. A fruit develops from an ovary. 9:6, 9:7, 9:8
10. Cotyledons contain stored food, which is used by an embryo during germination. 9:8
11. Seed dispersal aids survival of a plant species. Seeds may be dispersed by animals, wind, or water. 9:8
12. Moisture, oxygen, and favorable temperatures are required for germination. 9:9

Vocabulary

Write a sentence using each of the following words or terms correctly.

angiosperm	embryo	pistil
conifer	germination	pollen grain
cotyledon	gymnosperm	pollination
cross-pollination	monocot	self-pollination
dicot	ovary	sperm
egg	ovule	stamen

Questions

Do not write in this book.

A. True or False
Determine whether each of the following sentences is true or false. Rewrite the false statements to make them correct.

1. Most plants living today are seed plants.
2. A pine tree is a flowering plant.
3. A grape grows from part of a flower.

4. A tomato plant is an example of an angiosperm.
5. A ginkgo belongs to the gymnosperm group.
6. Pollen is produced in the stamens.
7. Flowers in the corn plant are complete flowers.
8. Pollination is the transfer of pollen from male to female reproductive organs of a plant.
9. A lima bean develops from an ovary.
10. Seeds contain stored food.

B. Multiple Choice
Choose the word or phrase that correctly completes the following sentences.
1. Seeds are produced by *(all plants, flowering plants only, gymnosperms and angiosperms).*
2. *(Corn, Grass, Bean, Palm)* is an example of a dicot.
3. *(Pistils, Stamens, Cotyledons)* contain stored food.
4. Seed plants are *(vascular, nonvascular).*
5. The *(stamen, sepal, pistil, petal)* is the female reproductive organ of a flower.
6. Fusion of sperm and egg is called *(pollination, germination, fertilization).*
7. Seed dispersal *(increases, decreases, does not affect)* the chance for a greater number of plants to grow to maturity from seeds.
8. Seeds form inside the *(ovary, stamen, sepal)* of a flowering plant.
9. *(Stigmas, Stamens, Ovules)* produce a sticky fluid that traps pollen grains.
10. Both conifers and angiosperms produce *(cones, flowers, pollen).*

C. Completion
Complete each of the following sentences with the correct word or phrase.
1. Animals, wind, and _____ aid seed dispersal.
2. Vegetative propagation is one kind of _____ reproduction.
3. The female reproductive cell in a plant is a(n) _____ .
4. Conifers produce their seeds in _____.
5. The early growth of an embryo plant from a seed is called _____.
6. _____ -pollination may occur when a flower contains both stamens and pistils.
7. A tomato seed develops from the _____ in a tomato flower.
8. Favorable temperature, moisture, and _____ are required for germination.
9. The sex cells formed by stamens are called _____.
10. _____ is growing a new plant from part of another plant.

D. How and Why

1. How are seed plants classified?
2. Compare reproduction in conifers to reproduction in flowering plants.
3. Draw a diagram of a complete flower and label its parts.
4. Why is pollination necessary for fertilization to occur?
5. Where does fertilization occur in a flower? How?
6. Why do some farmers keep beehives in their orchards?
7. Why is seed dispersal important to the survival of plant species?
8. What conditions are necessary for germination?
9. How is a fruit different from a seed?

Ideas to Explore

1. **Challenge:** Obtain a seed or garden catalog. Make a list of the plants you would select for planting around a building or in a public park. Prepare a short report that gives the reasons for your selection.
2. **Project:** Visit a nursery or garden store and find out what kinds of plants are sold there. Find out what a landscape designer does and why this work requires a good knowledge of plants.
3. **Challenge:** Find out what kinds of plants grow around your school or home. Make a list of their common and scientific names.
4. **Project:** Do germinating seeds produce heat? Test your hypothesis by placing some moist absorbent cotton in the bottom of a pint vacuum bottle. Fill the bottle to 3 cm from the top with germinating bean seeds. Seal the vacuum bottle with a one-hole stopper containing a thermometer. The seal should be airtight. Record the temperature at the beginning of the experiment and at the end of a 24-hour period. Repeat the procedure with germinating corn, peas, wheat, and oats and compare your results.
5. **Project:** Find out if seeds will germinate in an acid solution. Place a paper towel soaked with dilute vinegar solution into a glass jar. Add ten corn seeds. Make a control using a paper towel soaked in water. Place both jars in a warm area. Observe and record any changes in the seeds after several days.

Readings

Lambert, Mark. *Plant Life*. New York: Warwick Press, 1983.

Selsam, Millicent E. *The Plants We Eat*. New York: William Morrow, 1981.

Selsam, Millicent and Jerome Wexler. *Eat the Fruit, Plant the Seed*. New York: William Morrow, 1980.

Verey, Rosemary. *The Herb Growing Book*. Boston: Little, Brown, 1980.

Verey, Rosemary. *The Potted Plant Book*. Boston: Little, Brown, 1980.

Photosynthesis
Background Data

In green plants, photosynthesis occurs in chloroplasts that contain chlorophyll. During photosynthesis, carbon dioxide gas is absorbed from the air, and water is picked up by the root system. They are combined in the presence of sunlight and chlorophyll to produce water vapor, oxygen, and glucose, a simple sugar.

The rate of photosynthesis is controlled by temperature, light intensity, and concentration of carbon dioxide in the air. In general, the higher the value of each variable, the faster the rate.

Input/Output

Enter the program into your computer exactly as it is printed. After you enter the entire program, type RUN. If there is a problem, type LIST and check that you have entered the program exactly as it is printed. Remember, symbols and punctuation are important and must be typed as printed here. REM statements are provided in the program to help you. They do not need to be entered in order for the program to run. When all corrections have been made, be sure to save the program by typing SAVE PHOTOSYNTHESIS, or whatever name you wish to give the program.

Once the program is running, the computer will ask you to make changes in the intensity of light, the air temperature, and the percentage of carbon dioxide gas in the air. You may increase or decrease any of these variables. A change in any variable changes the amount of oxygen produced during photosynthesis. The new amount produced is printed on the screen. You may only change one variable at a time. However, because any change you make in a variable remains in effect until you change it again, it is possible to see the effect of changes in all three variables.

Programming Notes

The computer reads each line of the program and executes the command listed there. Line 20 clears the screen. Some computers use the command CLS, others use HOME. Use the command your computer recognizes to clear the screen.

The variables used are listed below.

L	light intensity
T	temperature
M	carbon dioxide level
Q	clears the screen
C	category for change
X\$,Y\$,Z\$	statements about plant conditions
X,Y,Z	multipliers of oxygen production
P	change in light intensity
D	amount of temperature change
N	change in carbon dioxide level
A	total amount of oxygen produced

The commands in lines 50 through 80 generate a data chart on the screen. Student input is checked in lines 90 through 180 to determine if it is between the upper and lower limits. Equations contained in lines 190 through 240 calculate the effect changes in the variables have on oxygen production. The program will end if the variables have been changed beyond acceptable limits. PRINT statements in lines 260 through 280 print the results of changes made in the variables.

Challenge: On Your Own

You may wish to change the limits on the variables that cause the program to end. For example, in line 190, the upper limit of light is set at 250 units, with a warning message printed if the value entered is greater than 200 units. By changing 200 to 220, the warning will print at 220 units. The maximum of 250 units could be changed to another number, thus extending the simulation. You also would need to change statements in X\$ and line 260.

Program

```
10  L = 100:T = 15:M = 100
20  HOME : IF Q = 1 OR Q = 2 THEN
    260: REM  MAY BE DIFFERENT O
    N YOUR COMPUTER
30  PRINT "PHOTOSYNTHESIS IS DEP
    ENDENT ON SEVERAL": PRINT "T
    HINGS INCLUDING THESE THREE
    THINGS.": PRINT "YOU DECIDE
    HOW TO CHANGE THE VARIABLES.
    ": PRINT " LIGHT VARIES BY A
    TMOSPHERE CONDITION"
40  PRINT "      BETWEEN 30 AND 25
    0 PERCENT": PRINT " TEMPERAT
    URE VARIES FOR SAME REASONS"
    : PRINT "    BETWEEN 8 AND 20
    DEGREES": PRINT " CARBON DI
    OXIDE PRODUCED BY COMBUSTION
    ": PRINT "      BETWEEN 25 AND
    350 PERCENT"
50  C = 0:X$ = "":Y$ = "":Z$ = ""
    : PRINT : PRINT  TAB( 30)"IN
    C"; TAB( 35)"DEC"
60  PRINT "LIGHT INTENSITY BY %"
    ; TAB( 28)"/ 1"; TAB( 32)"/
    2 / "
70  PRINT "TEMPERATURE BY DEGREE
    S"; TAB( 28)"/ 3"; TAB( 32)"
    / 4 /"
80  PRINT "CARBON DIOXIDE BY %";
    TAB( 28)"/ 5"; TAB( 32)"/ 6
    /"
90  PRINT : PRINT "WHAT CATEGORY
    DO YOU WISH ";: INPUT C: IF
    C < 1 OR C > 6 THEN 90
100  IF C = 1 OR C = 2 THEN  PRINT
    "HOW MUCH PERCENT TO CHANGE"
    ;: INPUT P: IF C = 1 AND P >
    0 THEN 190
110  IF C = 2 and P > 0 THEN P =
    - P: GOTO 190
120  IF C = 1 OR C = 2 THEN  PRINT
    "YOU MUST USE A NUMBER BIGGE
    R THAN ZERO": GOTO 100
130  IF C = 3 OR C = 4 THEN  PRINT
    "HOW MANY DEGREES TO CHANGE"
    ;: INPUT D: IF C = 3 AND D >
    0 THEN 190
140  IF C = 4 AND D > 0 THEN D =
    - D: GOTO 190
150  IF C = 3 OR C = 4 THEN  PRINT
    "YOU MUST USE A NUMBER BIGGE
    R THAN ZERO": GOTO 130
160  IF C = 5 OR C = 6 THEN  PRINT
    "HOW MUCH PERCENT OF CHANGE"
    ;: INPUT N: IF C = 5 AND N >
    0 THEN 190
170  IF C = 6 AND N > 0 THEN N =
    - N: GOTO 190
180  IF C = 5 or C = 6 THEN  PRINT
    "YOU MUST USE A NUMBER BIGGE
    R THAN ZERO": GOTO 160
190  L = L + P:X = L: IF L > 200 THEN
    X = 1:X$ = "PLANTS DIE AT LI
    GHT OF 250 %": IF L > 250 THEN
    X$ = "ALL PLANTS HAVE DIED O
    F EXCESS LIGHT":Q = 2: GOTO
    20
200  IF L < 50 THEN X = 1:X$ = "
    PLANTS WILL DIE AT 30 % LIGH
    T LEVEL": IF L < 30 THEN X$ =
    "ALL PLANTS DEAD LACK OF LIG
    HT":Q = 2: GOTO 20
210  T = T + D:Y = T: IF T > 18 THEN
    Y = 1:Y$ = "TOO HOT! 20 IS C
    RITICAL": IF T > 20 THEN Y$ =
    "ALL PLANTS HAVE BURNED UP":
    Q = 2: GOTO 20
220  IF T < 10 THEN Y = 1:Y$ = "
    TEMPERATURE LOWER THAN 8 WIL
    L KILL": IF T < 8 THEN Y$ =
    "PLANTS HAVE DIED FROM LOW T
    EMPERATURES":Q = 2; GOTO 20
230  M = M + N:Z = M: IF M > 300 THEN
    Z = 1:Z$ = "CO2 LEVELS TOO H
    IGH 350 % CRITICAL": IF M >
    350 THEN Z$ = "PLANTS HAVE D
    IED FROM LACK OF OXYGEN":Q =
    2: GOTO 20
240  IF M < 75 THEN Z = 1:Z$ = "
    TOO LOW CO2 LEVEL 25 % IS CR
    ITICAL": IF M < 25 THEN Z$ =
    "PLANTS DIED FROM LACK CARBO
    N DIOXIDE":Q = 2: GOTO 20
250  Q = 1: GOTO 20
260  A = A + (X * 2) + (Y * 10) +
    (Z * 2): PRINT "OXYGEN PRODU
    CTION"; TAB( 23)"LEVEL"; TAB(
    30)"CRITICAL": PRINT : PRINT
    "LIGHT = ";X * 2; TAB( 23);L
    ; TAB( 30)"(30 - 250)": PRINT
    X$
270  PRINT "TEMPERATURE = ";Y *
    10; TAB( 23)T; TAB( 30)"(8 -
    20)": PRINT Y$: PRINT "CARB
    ON DIOXIDE = ";Z * 2; TAB( 2
    3)M; TAB( 30)"(25 - 350)": PRINT
    Z$
280  PRINT "TOTAL OXYGEN PRODUCE
    D IS ";A: IF Q = 2 OR A > 50
    0000 THEN  END
290  GOTO 50
```

ANIMALS

Giraffes

UNIT 4

Animals are complex organisms that show great diversity. Although many species of animals have evolved, they all possess a basic structural design that reflects a lifestyle. This is controlled by the feeding habits and methods of movement of each animal. The long neck of the giraffe allows it to feed on the shoots of very tall trees. How are long legs useful to a giraffe? Meerkats are inhabitants of the Kalahari Desert. They have very stiff tails and flat triangular heads. How are these features useful for life in the desert?

Meerkats

Turtles are an ancient group of reptiles. The newly hatched Northern Diamondback turtle will not be protected by its mother. Once the eggs are laid, the mother leaves the nest. Turtles depend heavily on their senses of sight, smell, and hearing. A turtle can see four colors. What type of eye receptor cells does a turtle have? Turtles respond well to vibrations of the ground and to high light intensity. How can a newly hatched turtle find its way back to the sea?

CHAPTER 10
ANIMAL LIFE

10:1 Behavior

Every animal responds to its environment in one way or another. Moving, resting, fighting, hunting, and eating are examples of animal behavior. **Behavior** is the way an organism acts. Something in the environment that causes a behavior is called a stimulus. Food, odors, sounds, light, heat, gravity, and water can each be a stimulus. The action of an organism as a result of a stimulus is a **response.** Simple responses are movements toward or away from something. An example is a bird flying away from a cat.

One type of behavior is inborn behavior. **Inborn behavior** means the behavior is inherited from parents. The organism responds naturally to certain stimuli. Inborn behavior is not learned. Examples are a cat drinking milk, a duck swimming, and a baby crying. The killdeer, a small bird commonly found in fields, displays an inborn behavior when its nest is threatened. If a dog comes near the nest, the killdeer pretends to be injured by dragging its wing and moving away from the nest. Following the killdeer, the dog is led far from the nest before the killdeer flies away. What was the stimulus for the killdeer's behavior? What was the response?

GOALS:
1. You will learn to identify inborn and acquired behaviors and to explain the difference.
2. You will learn the characteristics of social behavior.
3. You will learn how sense organs function.

a   b

FIGURE 10–1. In dim light, pupils become large (a). In bright light, they become small (b). The response of the pupils to light is a reflex act.

One type of inborn behavior is a reflex act. A **reflex act** is a quick action that does not involve the brain. The behavior is an automatic response to a stimulus. Examples of reflexes are a hand jerking away from a hot stove or lifting a bare foot quickly off a sharp object. During a reflex act, an animal's sense organ detects a stimulus such as a hot stove. The response, jerking away fast, is very swift, taking only a fraction of a second. A reflex act does not involve thinking.

Spiders use a web as a home and to trap smaller insects for food. Spinning a web is a very complex behavior. Yet a spider does not learn to spin a web. A spider does not take lessons and it needs no practice. Spiders spin webs correctly on the very first try. Different species of spiders have different web structures. Web spinning is an instinct in spiders. An **instinct** is an inborn behavior that involves complex responses to a stimulus.

Name two kinds of inborn behaviors.

Birds flying south in winter is another example of an instinct. Studies show that young birds do not follow older birds when migrating. In some species, young birds raised apart from older birds can find their way even if they have never migrated before. Scientists have evidence that some birds may be able to use the earth's magnetic field to find their way. Also, birds may use the sun or stars and the horizon to guide them in finding their way.

Making Sure
1. Compare a reflex act with an instinct.
2. How is behavior related to the survival of an organism?

10:2 Acquired Behavior

Another major type of behavior is acquired behavior. **Acquired behavior** must be learned. Dogs trained as guides for persons who are visually or hearing impaired are trained to behave in certain ways. Then they are rewarded for the behavior. The rewards are usually a pat on the head and praise from the trainer. Training requires practice. The behavior and rewards have to be repeated over and over until the behavior is learned.

Ivan Pavlov, a Russian biologist, was the first scientist to experiment with a type of learning called conditioning. **Conditioning** occurs in response to a stimulus that does not normally cause the response. Pavlov knew that when a hungry dog sees food, its mouth waters. This behavior is a reflex act. Food is the stimulus. Increased saliva in the mouth is the response. Pavlov began to ring a bell every time a dog was shown food. After a while, the ringing of the bell alone, without the appearance of food, caused the dog's mouth to water. The dog's mouth watered when the bell was rung because its brain associated the sound of the bell with food. The dog's mouth would water even though there was no food. The bell stimulus had replaced the food stimulus, and the response remained the same. This is an example of conditioning because the dog's mouth watered in response to the bell ringing.

Define acquired behavior. Give an example.

Describe an experiment that demonstrates conditioning.

FIGURE 10–2. Ivan Pavlov, a Russian scientist, conducted his famous conditioned response experiment in the 1890s. Each time a dog was fed, Pavlov rang a bell (a). In time, the dog began to associate the ringing of the bell with food. The dog began to salivate when the bell was rung, even when no food was served (b).

a

b

FIGURE 10-3. The chimpanzee tries to reach the bananas by jumping (a). Then, it stacks boxes (b) and solves the problem by climbing on top of the boxes (c).

Describe an example of trial and error learning.

Learning is a change in behavior that results from experience. In **trial and error** learning, an animal develops a behavior based on avoiding mistakes. It is another kind of conditioning. For instance, a hungry rat eats a small amount of poisoned food that makes it ill. Because of this error, the rat never eats the poisoned food again. The rat's behavior changes because of the experience. In one experiment, a pigeon was placed in a cage containing five levers. Each lever was a different color. When the red lever was pressed, pigeon food was released into the cage. No food was released when the other levers were pressed. After many lever-pecking trials, the pigeon learned how to get its food. Each peck at a lever that did not release food was an error. The pigeon, through trial and error, learned to peck the red lever to get food.

Reasoning is the ability to remember past experience and use it to solve a new problem. Simple forms of reasoning have been observed in monkeys and apes. In one case, a banana was hung out of the reach of a chimpanzee. In the chimp's cage were several boxes. No matter how high the animal jumped, it could not reach the banana. How did the chimp solve the problem? It stacked the boxes on top of each other, climbed to the top of the stack, and grabbed the banana. A major characteristic that distinguishes humans from other animals is that humans have a higher developed level of reasoning.

Making Sure

3. How are inborn and acquired behavior different?
4. Describe how you would train a dog to sit and lie down on command. What rewards would you use?

Activity 10–1   Conditioning

Problem: How can you demonstrate conditioning?

Materials

aquarium	food for guppies
glass cover for aquarium	dip net
thermometer	guppies
coarse sand	snails
tap water aged three days	water plants
metric ruler	aquarium light–optional
dish	

Procedure

1. Wash and rinse the aquarium thoroughly.
2. Place the aquarium on a flat surface. Select an area that will receive indirect sunlight or use an aquarium light.
3. Wash the sand until the water is clear. Place sand on the bottom of the aquarium. Place a dish on the sand. Pour aged tap water on the dish so you do not stir up the sand. Add enough water to bring the level 5 cm above the sand.
4. Place rooted plants near the back corners of the aquarium. Anchor the plants by pushing the roots into the sand. Do not heap sand above the roots. Plants should be placed about 5 cm apart to allow room for growth.
5. Add aged tap water slowly to fill the aquarium. Let it stand one day to allow the plants to begin photosynthesizing.
6. Add the guppies and snails. One guppy and one snail per four liters of water works well.
7. Cover the aquarium to reduce evaporation and to keep out dust.
8. Maintain a water temperature of 24°C. Add aged tap water to replace water that evaporates. Keep the plants pruned so that they do not fill the tank. Remove yellowed stems and leaves.
9. Observe the movements of the snails and the way they get food. Record your observations.
10. Feed the fish at the same time each day. They should get the same amount and the same kind of food. Before you feed the fish, tap *gently* on the side of the aquarium where you are going to place the food. Feed the fish this way for 3 weeks.

11. Observe the fish feed. Note the characteristics of the fish. Observe the gill cover movements. Record your observations.
12. After 3 weeks, at the normal feeding time, tap gently on the side of the aquarium where the food is usually placed. Do not put any food in the water this time. Observe the behavior of the fish. Feed the fish when you have finished observing.

FIGURE 10–4.

Data and Observations

Date	Organism	Observations

Questions and Conclusions

1. What are the characteristics of snails?
2. To what phylum of animals do snails belong?
3. What are characteristics of guppies?
4. In what phylum and class are guppies classified?
5. How are guppies and snails different?
6. How do snails help keep the aquarium clean?
7. How does a fish get oxygen?
8. Why is the aquarium kept covered?
9. What happened when you tapped on the aquarium without putting in food? What is the name for this type of behavior?
10. How can you demonstrate conditioning?

FIGURE 10–5. By hunting in a pack, wolves are more likely to catch prey than if they each hunt alone.

Name five examples of social animals.

10:3 Social Behavior

Many species of animals live in groups instead of alone. Examples of social animals are schools of fish, flocks of birds, insect colonies, wolf packs, and prides of lions. By living together, the animals are better able to survive than if they lived alone. For instance, forming flocks enables birds to better defend themselves against enemies such as hawks. Wolves hunting in a pack are more likely to obtain food then if they each hunt alone. Also, social organization, because of its order, helps species survive by reducing fighting over food and mates.

Ants, wasps, and termites are social insects that live in colonies. Another example of an insect colony is the honeybee hive. In its social order, there are three kinds of bees. These are the adult queen, female workers, and male drones. Each kind of bee has a special job to do in the hive. A male drone fertilizes the queen bee. The queen produces eggs that develop into new bees. Worker bees produce wax and build the comb in which honey is stored. Workers also leave the hive to bring back nectar and pollen to make the honey. The youngest workers serve as "nurse bees," feeding bees that have not yet developed into adults. Division of labor within a beehive is similar to the organization of a school, business, or army. Each individual has a certain job. The labors of each contribute to the working of the whole unit.

Another example of social behavior is courtship behavior. In their selection of mates for reproduction, male and female animals act in ways that attract each other and signal their desire for mating. The behaviors of each sex are stimuli for the other. One vivid example of courtship is shown by the male prairie grouse. It courts females during the mating season by raising its neck feathers, spreading its tail feathers, and moving around in tight circles several times. The male also makes a hollow, booming sound by inflating two air pouches on the sides of his throat. A male American goldeneye duck performs a courtship display in which he throws his head back and kicks up water. The male in one species of fiddler crab signals its desire to mate by moving its large right claw in a certain pattern. The males in each species of firefly have a different courtship pattern of light flashes. These and all other courtship behaviors are instincts.

What is courtship behavior? Describe three examples.

Courtship ensures that mating will occur only between members of the same species. In many species, males compete with one another for females. Large size, strength, bright colors, and particular patterns of behavior have an advantage in the competition. Finally, it is the female in most species that selects the male for mating.

Making Sure

5. How does organizing into societies help some species survive?
6. How does the division of labor in a school compare with that of a honeybee hive?
7. How does courtship behavior help a species survive?

FIGURE 10–6. The male prairie grouse displays courtship behavior during the mating season. It raises its neck feathers, spreads its tail feathers, and moves around in tight circles. The male inflates two air pouches. The sacs go down as the air rushes out, and a booming sound echoes across the prairies.

Activity 10–2

Social Behavior in Ants

Problem: How do ants interact in a colony?

Materials

coffee can with lid
glass tubing
dropper
bread crumbs, lettuce, carrots
masking tape
soil

ants
muslin
string
newspaper
large spoon
small water dish
black construction paper

2 widemouthed jars or beakers (one must fit inside the other one with a space of about 1.5 cm between the two)

Procedure

1. Place the small container inside the larger one.
2. Fill the space between the containers with soil as shown in Figure 10–7.
3. Insert a glass tube into the soil. Push the tube down to the bottom of the soil. Drop water down the tube to keep the soil at the bottom moist but not wet. The top of the soil should always be dry.
4. Anchor a piece of string in the soil and let it hang down into the inner jar.
5. Find the entrance to an ant nest. With a spoon, dig down into the soil and place the loose soil on a newspaper. Look for ants, small white ant eggs, ant cocoons, and wriggling larvae. Spoon these into the empty coffee can and put on the lid. A colony with a queen will last much longer than a colony without a queen. If your collection includes a larger ant, this may be the queen. Do not mix ants from different nests.
6. Place the ants in the refrigerator for about 5 minutes to quiet them. Then gently place the ants in the space between the two jars. Fasten a piece of muslin over the top of the containers to prevent their escape.
7. Tape a piece of black construction paper around the outside jar. Remove the paper when you wish to observe the ants.
8. Place food inside the inner jar three times each week. Small pieces of lettuce, bread crumbs and

carrots may be used for food. Remove leftover food so that it does not spoil. A small water dish may be placed in the inner jar.
9. Observe the ants at least twice a week.
10. Make a sketch of the tunnels the ants build.

Data and Observations

Date	Number of ants visible	Other observations

Questions and Conclusions

1. Does the ant colony have a queen? What is the job of the queen?
2. How do members of the colony differ? Do these differences benefit the colony?
3. What characteristics of ants are common to all insects?
4. How long does it take the ants to build tunnels?
5. How do ants interact in a colony?

FIGURE 10–7.

FIGURE 10–8. Animals tend to maintain a certain distance from each other.

10:4 Territoriality

Have you ever watched a flock of birds sitting on a power line? They all space themselves out evenly. Animals tend to maintain a certain distance from each other.

Territoriality (tair uh TOHR ee al uh tee) is a behavior in which an animal defends a particular area. The space the animal defends against others is its territory. Territories vary in size from species to species. The territory of a mountain lion is large. In highly social animals, such as nesting gulls, it is quite small.

Aggressive behaviors are used by animals to warn others to stay out of their territories. For example, a male bird will sing loudly as a warning to other male birds to stay out of his space. Birds flap their wings excitedly when a stranger invades their territories. Geese make hissing sounds when aroused. A dog will bark and growl, and the hair on its back will rise if its territory is threatened.

Territoriality promotes the survival of animals. Because it spaces animals out, it reduces the competition for food and mates. This results in less fighting. Territoriality can affect the size of an animal population. If the population becomes too large, the size of each individual's territory decreases. When territories become too small, the rate of reproduction decreases, thereby decreasing the number of animals in the population.

Define territoriality.

10:5 Communication

When a bird sees an enemy and gives an alarm call, it communicates the danger to other birds. Communication occurs when an animal performs an act that changes the behavior of another animal. Courtship, for example, involves communication between a male and female that leads to mating. Animal communication can take the form of sounds, body movements, odors, coloration, and touch. Its purpose is to aid in locating food, defending against enemies, and reproducing a species.

Honeybees communicate through a series of body movements called a dance. When a worker bee locates a rich source of nectar, it returns to the hive and dances. Through the dance, the bee tells the other bees in the hive what it has found. If the food is nearby, it does a round dance. If the food is far away, the bee does a waggle dance, stepping through a figure-eight pattern that indicates the direction of the source. In the waggle dance, the bee emits sounds and waggles its body. The amount of nectar it has found and its sugar content is communicated by the sounds and speed of dancing.

Animals also communicate through pheromones (FAIR uh monez). A **pheromone** is a chemical with an odor that conveys information to other members of a species. Pheromones are used in the attraction of mates, location of food, and for defense or marking of territories. A female gypsy moth releases a pheromone whose scent can attract male gypsy moths up to three kilometers

What forms can animal communication take?

Define pheromone and give one example.

FIGURE 10–9. A bee that has found a source of nectar communicates the location of the source in a wagging dance. The center line in the figure indicates to the other bees the direction of the flowers in relation to the direction of the sun at that time of day.

a

b

away. Ants leave a trail of pheromones that other ants can follow to a food supply. If foreign termites from another nest enter a termite colony, the resident termites release an alarm pheromone. The odor of the chemical attracts soldier termites that fight off the invaders. In many species, females secrete pheromones when they are ready for mating. Dogs and many other mammals mark their territories by pheromones in their urine. Synthetic pheromones are used in insect control to lure male insects into traps.

Another more advanced kind of learned animal behavior is the use of language. Language consists of sounds and symbols that communicate information. When you talk with a friend, you express your thoughts in a language you have learned. By reading the symbols—printed words—on this page, you gain information. Can animals other than humans learn and use language to communicate? Research has been done with dolphins, whales, and chimps to study this question. These species have large brains and complex nervous systems. Scientists find that the animals have special sounds they use in locating food, finding mates, and avoiding enemies. Scientists have taught chimps to communicate in simple sign language. However, much remains to be learned about the ability of animals to communicate. A major feature that separates humans from other animals is our complex language and its use in recording knowledge.

FIGURE 10–10. Using a trail of pheromones, ants communicate the location of a food supply (a). An animal trainer communicates with a dolphin by using hand signals (b). The trainer's eyes are covered to eliminate visual cues.

a

b

FIGURE 10—11. Most living clocks are on 24-hour cycles. Four o'clock flowers close in the morning (a) and open at mid or late afternoon (b).

What is a living clock? Give one example.

10:6 Living Clocks

Many life activities occur over and over again. Most of these activities occur in 24-hour cycles. For example, many flowers open and close at certain times of the day. Human body temperatures and enzyme activity vary with the time of day.

Fiddler crabs change their skin color on a daily schedule. Their color becomes black about daybreak and turns pale about sunset. The changes are the same even if a fiddler crab is taken from the ocean and kept in an aquarium in total darkness.

Probably the best known example of a living clock is hibernation in animals. Several small mammals, such as chipmunks and bats, as well as some types of bears, hibernate through the winter. When they hibernate, the animals' normal rates of body functions slow down, and their body temperatures become lower. The condition produced is similar to a deep sleep. Hibernation enables these animals to survive very cold winter weather.

Organisms may reset their clocks in response to light, temperature, and other factors. This reset ability is important to survival. Without it, an animal or plant would be unable to adjust to slight changes in its environment. People who have flown across many time zones may experience "jet lag." For several days, the travelers may get hungry or sleepy at the time they would normally be hungry or sleepy at home. Gradually their living clocks are reset, and their activities adjust to local time.

Making Sure

8. What advantages does having a territory give to an animal species?
9. In what ways does communication help an animal species survive?

10:7 Sensing Sound

Behavior of animals depends on their ability to detect stimuli. Their response or lack of response will depend on the kinds of sense organs they have. Each kind detects certain stimuli.

Sound can be detected by ears. An ear contains a thin, tightly stretched membrane called an **eardrum.** A sound creates a sound wave. A sound wave is a vibration (vi BRAY shun) that moves through air or other matter. The sound wave causes an eardrum to vibrate. The vibrating eardrum causes the ear to send nerve impulses to the brain. The animal hears the sound.

Mammals have eardrums inside their heads. A mammal's ear contains three main parts. They are the outer ear, the middle ear, and the inner ear. The outer ear is the fleshy part on the head that collects sound waves. These waves are carried through a tube called the auditory canal to the eardrum. The eardrum separates the outer ear from the middle ear. The sound waves cause the eardrum at the end of the auditory canal to vibrate. Three tiny bones in the middle ear connect the eardrum to a structure in the inner ear called the **cochlea** (CAHK lee uh). The vibrations produce impulses in the nerves of the cochlea. These nerve impulses are carried by the auditory nerve to the brain.

Some animals have eardrums on the surfaces of their bodies. For example, the eardrums of grasshoppers are located on both sides of the abdomen, or hind region of their bodies. The eardrums in a frog are located in the skin just behind the eyes.

Animals have different abilities to hear. Some species of animals hear very well. Some moths can hear sounds that you cannot hear. Other species of animals hear poorly. Worms and snails cannot hear at all. Hearing in humans is poor compared to some other animals. You may be familiar with whistles that emit very high pitched sounds that dogs can hear but people cannot. Perhaps

FIGURE 10–12. The circular area behind the eye is the tympanic membrane, part of a frog's organ for sensing sound.

How do animals with ears hear?

Describe the structure of a mammal's ear.

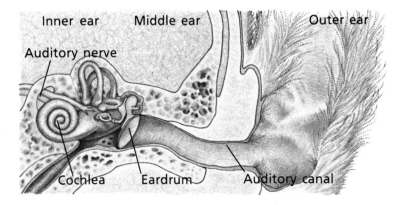

Inner ear   Middle ear   Outer ear

Auditory nerve

Cochlea   Eardrum   Auditory canal

FIGURE 10–13. A mammal's ear has three main parts: the outer, middle, and inner ear. Sound waves are converted to nerve impulses in the ear and carried to the brain by the auditory nerve.

you have played a game in which one person must guess another player's location by hearing voices and movements and not by seeing the person. Part of the fun results from the difficulty the players have in locating things with their ears rather than their eyes.

10:8 Sensing Light and Color

How does an animal see color? Light from the sun is white light. White light is a mixture of colored lights. The colors in white light are red, orange, yellow, green, blue, and violet. Objects appear to have colors because they reflect light of different colors. You see an object when light strikes it and then is reflected into your eyes. For example, when the object reflects only blue light, the object appears blue. When all the colors are reflected and mixed together, the object appears white. An object appears black when all colors are absorbed and not reflected.

An eye is an organ that detects light and produces sight. Although some animals do not have eyes, they can still detect light. An earthworm has cells on its skin that detect light. Most of the cells are at the head. A planarian also has cells that detect light. Planaria can detect the direction from which light comes.

Vertebrates have two eyes. Each eye contains an iris (I rus), pupil, lens, fluid, and a retina (RET nuh). The **iris** is the colored part of the eye. It controls the amount of light that enters the eye through the **pupil,** or opening. The lens is behind the pupil and acts like the lens of a camera. The **lens** forms an image on the back of the eye called the **retina** like the image formed on film. In bright light the pupil gets smaller. In dim light, it gets larger to let more light into the eye. Nerve impulses are produced in the retina by the image. These impulses travel along the optic

Why do objects have color?

FIGURE 10–14. The lens of a single eye focuses an image on the retina. The image creates a nerve impulse. The optic nerve carries the nerve impulse to the brain.

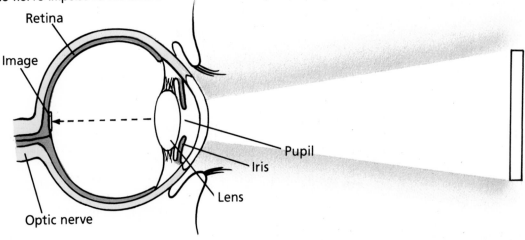

Retina

Image

Pupil

Iris

Lens

Optic nerve

nerve to the brain. As impulses enter an animal's brain, the animal sees things around it.

The eyes of insects are compound eyes. A compound eye contains many small lenses packed together. The surface of each small lens is a tiny plate. Under the plate, a cone is connected to a nerve that can detect light. Light passes through the plate and the cone to the nerve. The nerve sends impulses to the brain. The dragonfly has an especially large number of lenses, more than 30 000, in each of its compound eyes.

A compound eye produces an image in a special way. Each small eye in a compound eye looks in a different direction than the other small eyes. Each receives some of the light entering the whole eye. As a result, each small eye forms a part of the image. Many parts together form the image seen by the animal. Have you ever seen a picture made of small tiles? A tile picture is like the image formed by a compound eye. Each tile is a part. The combined parts form a picture. Another example is the picture on your television screen. If you look at it closely, you can see that it is composed of many small dots. The combined dots form a picture.

Some animals have cones and rods in their retinas. Cones and rods are two kinds of nerve cells. Cones detect color and bright light. Rods detect dim light. Most animals with cones and rods in their retinas have color vision. Fishes, reptiles, most birds, and some mammals have color vision. Most nocturnal animals do not see colors. They see only black, white, and shades of gray as in a black-and-white photograph. Cats do not have color vision.

Can insects see colors with their compound eyes? Experiments show that insects do have color vision. Yet the colors seen by an insect are not always the same as those you see. It has been found that bees cannot see the difference between red and black. However, bees can see ultraviolet light, which is not detected by our eyes. What color does a bee see when its eyes detect ultraviolet light? This is one of many questions in science that is difficult to answer. By exposing a film that is sensitive to ultraviolet light, scientists learn what some insects may see.

a

b

FIGURE 10–15. Animals that have no cones in their eyes would see scene b as it appears in scene a.

What are the functions of cones and rods in an animal's eyes?

Making Sure

10. Draw a diagram of a mammal's ear. Label the structures.
11. How is an eye like a camera? How is it different?
12. Name the parts of a cat's eye, Figure 10–14. What is the function of each part?

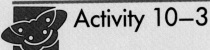

Activity 10–3   The Effect of Light on Animals

Problem: Do different animals react to light in the same ways?

Materials

dissecting pan	flashlight
moist paper towel	red cellophane
aluminum pie pan	fruit flies
culture containers for fruit flies	mealworms
black cloth	earthworm
loosely woven dishcloth	rubber band
tape	

Procedure

Part A

1. Tap the fruit flies to the bottom of the culture container. Remove the top of the container and immediately cover it with a second container. Tape the two containers together.
2. Place the containers horizontally on a table.
3. Observe where the fruit flies locate themselves. Record your observations in the "Fruit flies, No cloth" section of the data table.
4. Cover the end and sides of one culture container with the black cloth.
5. After a few minutes, observe the location of the fruit flies. Record your observations in the data table across from "Fruit flies, Black cloth."

Part B

1. Stretch the cloth over an aluminum pie pan and secure it with a rubber band.

FIGURE 10–16.

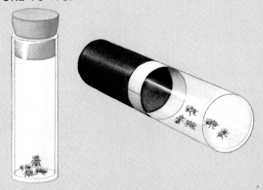

2. Place several mealworms on the cloth and observe the mealworms. Record your observations.

Part C

1. Place an earthworm on a moist paper towel in a dissecting pan. Shine a flashlight on the anterior end of the worm. Shine the flashlight on other areas of the earthworm's body.
2. Record your observations.
3. Make a red light by placing red cellophane over a flashlight.
4. Shine the red light on the anterior end of the earthworm. Record your observations.

Data and Observations

Organism	Observations
Fruit flies No cloth	
Fruit flies Black cloth	
Mealworms	
Earthworm in light	
Earthworm in red light	

Questions and Conclusions

1. What is the stimulus in each part of the activity?
2. Is the response the same in each part? If not, how can you explain the different responses?
3. How does each animal's behavior help it survive?
4. At what time of day are you most likely to find an earthworm crawling on the surface of soil?
5. Do different animals react to light in the same ways?

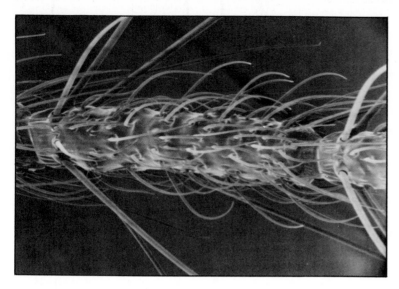

FIGURE 10–17. A mosquito antenna magnified 515 times shows many spines. The spines are sensory structures responsible for smell and touch.

10:9 Taste, Smell, and Touch

Have you ever noticed that when you have a cold and your nose is clogged, food has little flavor? Taste and smell are connected. Odors that pass from the mouth to the nose are detected and become part of a food's flavor. Taste is affected by the texture and temperature of a food. The organs of human taste are the taste buds located throughout the mouth and throat. Nerve endings in the taste buds are sensitive to chemicals in food and send messages to the brain. Four taste regions are located on the tongue. Each of these areas contains nerve endings that are sensitive to a particular taste or chemical. The four different tastes are sour, salty, sweet, and bitter.

Insects such as the fly, butterfly, and moth have taste hairs. Located on the insect's legs and mouthparts, taste hairs contain nerve cells sensitive to water, sugar, and salt. Insects use them to recognize food and water, and to avoid harmful substances.

Nerve cells responsible for the sense of smell are in the upper part of the human nose. When stimulated by chemicals in the air, they send messages to the brain. The organs for smell are much more sensitive than taste buds. For example, a person can detect the odor of violets when it is present in only one part of 30 billion parts of air. Some animals, such as the dog, have a highly developed sense of smell. Human noses have about five million cells to sense odors. Dogs have between 125 and 300 million cells sensitive to smells.

Name three things that affect a food's taste.

FIGURE 10–18. Nerve endings in the taste buds are sensitive to chemicals in food.

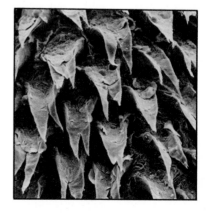

Name the five different kinds of nerve cells involved in the sense of touch.

Nerve endings in the skin provide the sense of touch. They are stimulated by things with which they come in contact. Five different types of nerve endings detect pain, pressure, heat, cold, and touch. Some areas of the body, such as the fingertips and lips, are more responsive to touch. They contain more touch sensitive nerve endings per unit area. Differences also exist in detecting pain. A small area on the forehead has about four times as many nerves for detecting pain as the same size on your thumb.

Insects have antennae that are sensitive to touch. Rats and cats rely on sensors in their whiskers when hunting and moving around. They find their way easily in the dark and can function well even if blinded. Mosquitoes can sense a warm-blooded target because they are able to detect heat. For some time, scientists wondered how rattlesnakes sense and locate their prey. Snakes that were blinded had no trouble catching other animals for food. The same thing was true if their noses were blocked. A rattlesnake has two pits above its mouth just below its eyes. Scientists learned that these pits are sensitive to heat. They can detect differences of a few tenths of a degree Celsius. Humans have about three heat-sensitive points per square centimeter on their skin. A rattlesnake has more than 150 000 points in its pit organ. Using the pit organ, a rattlesnake can detect a nearby animal by its body heat. Even motionless lizards that look like leaves are not safe from these snakes.

Making Sure

13. How do insects use taste hairs?
14. How do mosquitoes sense their targets?

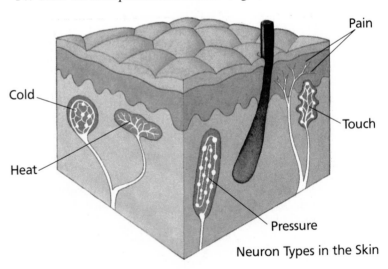

Pain

Cold

Touch

Heat

Pressure

Neuron Types in the Skin

FIGURE 10–19. Five different types of nerve endings detect pain, pressure, heat, cold, and touch.

Technology
Shark Sense

Studies of sharks have revealed that they possess remarkable sensory systems. Three sensory systems of sharks have been investigated: their detection of electric fields; their vision; and their detection of underwater vibrations.

Using underwater electrodes, scientists have shown that sharks can detect extremely weak electric fields. The electrical fields are detected by tiny pitlike openings in the underside of the sharks' heads. One type of shark, the smooth dogfish, can detect an electric field 25 million times weaker than the faintest level felt by humans. There are no records of any other animal capable of this level of sensitivity. All living things produce a bioelectric field. The shark uses its ability to detect electric fields to locate its prey. Even fish buried in the sand cannot escape detection by sharks using this sense.

Shark vision is also being studied. In the brains of sharks 12 new sites that are connected to nerves of the eye have been discovered. This discovery was made by French scientists using a technique called autoradiography. They injected radioactive tracers, which are substances that emit nuclear energy, into a shark's eye. Sections of the shark's brain were then exposed to photographic film. The radioactive tracers reacted with the film to produce a picture of these areas of the brain. The tracers marked the nerves along which they traveled to the brain. The scientists could tell exactly where the nerves of the eye entered the shark's brain by examining this picture. Additional research using the electron microscope has revealed that sharks can see much better than originally hypothesized.

Sharks can also detect underwater vibrations. Recordings of the vibrations made by wounded fish, easy prey of sharks, were played underwater. From overhead in an airplane, scientists observed the distances from which sharks turned and swam for the recorder. It was estimated that sharks detected the underwater vibrations as far away as 275 meters. To detect underwater vibrations, sharks use a series of sense organs called the lateral line system. These organs are located along both sides of the head and body of the shark. The lateral line system is present in both fishes and amphibians and serves to detect movements and pressure changes in the surrounding water.

The cartilage of sharks contains a substance that inhibits the growth of cancerous tumors. Research is proving sharks to be fascinating creatures as well as potentially useful to humans.

FIGURE 10–20. A shark's lateral line system detects movements and pressure changes in the water.

FOCUS ON
Skills

Understanding Tables and Graphs

Scientific information contains many facts. This textbook uses tables and graphs to organize those facts and help you understand scientific information. Tables serve two purposes. First, they allow you to find specific information quickly. Second, they enhance information in the text. To use tables to your advantage, you need to:

1. Understand the vocabulary in the table.
2. Note the purpose of the table as indicated by its title.
3. Understand how the table is organized.
4. Read background information presented in the text.

Table 10–1 gives examples of conditioned responses. Answer the questions that follow.

Table10–1

Conditioned Responses			
Before experiment		**After experiment**	
Stimulus	Reflex act	Stimulus	Response
Food	Salivation	Bell	Salivation
Cold air	Shivering	Flashing light	Shivering

1. In which section can you find the meaning of the following words?

Conditioned Stimulus Response Reflex Act

2. How does the text help you to understand Table 10–1 better?
3. Which response does a flashing light cause?

Graphs help you to visualize what written words mean. A *line graph* shows how quantities change or the relationship between quantities. A *bar graph* is used to compare numbers of things. A *circle graph* shows parts that make up a whole. The parts look like slices of pie. Each part is expressed as a percentage. For example, 25% means 25 items out of 100 (the whole).

The graphs that follow have information about grades earned in a certain class. Answer the questions under each graph.

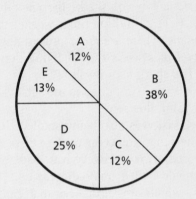

1. What does the whole represent in this circle graph?
2. Which two grades were achieved by the same percentage of students?
3. Which grade was earned by the most students?

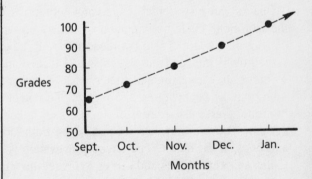

1. What type of graph is this?
2. What can you say about Amy's grades?

CHAPTER 10
Review

Summary

1. Reflex acts and instincts are types of inborn behavior.   10:1
2. Conditioning, trial and error learning, and reasoning are types of acquired behavior.   10:2
3. Many species of animals live in groups having a social organization that promotes the survival of the species.   10:3
4. Territoriality promotes the survival of animals because it reduces competition for food and mates.   10:4
5. Sounds, body movements, odors, and coloration are forms of animal communication.   10:5
6. Many animals have living clocks that control life activities.   10:6
7. Animals vary greatly in their ability to hear sounds.   10:7
8. Images produce nerve impulses that travel to the brain. As impulses enter an animal's brain, the animal sees things around it.   10:8
9. The tongue has four areas sensitive to particular tastes—sour, salty, sweet, and bitter.   10:9
10. Five different types of nerve endings detect pain, pressure, heat, cold, and touch.   10:9

Vocabulary

Write a sentence using the following words or terms correctly.

acquired behavior	instinct	reflex act
behavior	iris	response
cochlea	lens	retina
conditioning	pheromones	territoriality
eardrum	pupil	trial and error
inborn behavior	reasoning	

Questions

Do not write in this book.

A. True or False
Determine whether each of the following sentences is true or false. Rewrite the false statements to make them correct.

1. A change in the size of the pupil in an eye is a reflex act.
2. A spider spinning a web is an example of an instinct.
3. Bees can see light that people cannot see.
4. All animals with eyes can see colors.

5. A stimulus is produced by a reflex.
6. In a conditioned response, the stimulus is changed.
7. Reasoning has never been observed in chimps.
8. Ants, wasps, and termites are social insects.
9. Every animal has the same size territory.
10. Honeybees can communicate by body movements.

B. Multiple Choice
Choose the word or phrase that correctly completes the following sentences.
1. A(n) (*reflex act, instinct, conditioned response*) is one kind of acquired behavior.
2. A change in the (*stimulus, response*) produces a conditioned response.
3. The (*optic nerve, auditory nerve, spinal cord*) connects the eye to the brain.
4. (*Color, Body structure, Migration*) of birds is controlled by an internal living clock.
5. An image is produced on the (*iris, pupil, retina, brain*).
6. A (*queen, drone, worker*) produces eggs that develop into new bees.
7. If an animal population becomes too large, the size of the individuals' territories will likely (*increase, decrease, remain the same*).
8. Most living clocks are on a (*yearly, monthly, weekly, daily*) cycle.
9. The inner ear contains the (*eardrum, auditory canal, cochlea*).
10. An object that reflects (*white, black, no*) light appears black.

C. Completion
Complete each of the following sentences with the correct word or phrase.
1. Saliva produced in the mouth of a dog at the sound of a bell is a(n) _____ response.
2. The _____ is the part of an ear that first detects sound.
3. Eardrums in a grasshopper are located on the insect's _____ .
4. Training a dog to sit on command is an example of _____ behavior.
5. _____ is a change in behavior that results from experience.
6. A rat may learn not to eat a poison through trial and _____ .
7. An insect _____ is an example of social organization.
8. _____ occurs between male and female animals before mating.
9. The area an animal defends is called its _____ .
10. _____ taste regions are located in the tongue.

D. How and Why
1. How is acquired behavior different from inborn behavior?
2. Describe an experiment with trial and error learning.

3. How does social behavior aid in survival?
4. How is it possible for an animal to smell or taste something?
5. Describe three examples of sense organs in animals other than humans.
6. How do instincts and reflexes help an animal survive?
7. Draw a diagram of the parts of a vertebrate eye. Label the parts.
8. Describe two behaviors controlled by living clocks inside organisms.

Ideas to Explore

1. **Project:** Obtain a library book on training a dog. As a project, teach a dog to respond to six different commands. Write a report explaining your plan, the results, and the problems.
2. **Project:** Experiment to see if you can train a goldfish. Train the fish to come to the surface when a light is flashed. Plan the procedure for your experiment and have your teacher check it before you begin.
3. **Project:** Do an experiment to determine at what time of evening you can no longer see different colors. Put different colors of construction papers outside. Just before sunset, watch the colored papers and record the time at which you no longer see the different colors. When the colors start to disappear, turn your head slightly to see out of the side of your eye.
4. **Project:** Using tuning forks and meter sticks, experiment to determine the distance at which you can no longer hear various sounds. Plan the procedure for your experiment and have your teacher check it before you begin.
5. **Challenge:** Do library research and prepare a report on sociobiology.
6. **Challenge:** Write a report on the animal behavior studies of B.F. Skinner or Konrad Lorenz.
7. **Challenge:** Write a report on the courtship behavior of the black widow spider.

Readings

Davis, J. Michael. *What About Behavior?* Burlington, NC: Carolina Biological Supply Co., 1981.

Reidman, Sarah R. *Biological Clocks.* New York: T.Y. Crowell Junior Books, 1982.

Sattler, Helen Roney. *Fish Facts and Bird Brains: Animal Intelligence.* New York: Dutton, 1984.

Walter, Eugene J., Jr. *Why Animals Behave the Way They Do.* New York: Charles Scribner's, Sons, 1981.

The starfish is an invertebrate that belongs to the phylum Echinodermata. The starfish has internal, fluid-filled canals that connect to the tube feet on the underside of its arms. This water vascular system aids in movement, attachment, feeding, and gas exchange. Starfish are carnivores that feed on snails, clams, and other marine organisms. What characteristics enable it to be classified as a simple animal? What are other simple animals?

CHAPTER 11
SIMPLE ANIMALS

11:1 Animal Classification

What do you think of when you see the word *animal*? You may think of cats, dogs, birds, or fish. These are only a few examples of a very large kingdom. All animals have certain characteristics in common. Animals are many-celled organisms. They must obtain food to stay alive and most can move.

Animals with backbones are called **vertebrates** (VURT uh brayts). You are a vertebrate. Reach around with your hand to the center of your back. Press hard and feel your backbone. People, snakes, frogs, birds, fish, and cows have backbones. Vertebrates have skeletons of bones inside their bodies.

About 95 percent of the known species of animals do not have backbones or skeletons inside their bodies. These animals without backbones are called **invertebrates.** Many invertebrates, such as jellyfish and worms, have soft bodies. Other invertebrates, such as grasshoppers and snails, have skeletons or hard coverings on the outside of their bodies.

In the animal kingdom, animals are classified into nine main groups, or phyla, and several smaller phyla. Each phylum contains animals that are different in some ways from animals in the other phyla. All the vertebrate animals belong to one phylum of animals. Invertebrate animals are divided into eight major phyla and several smaller phyla in the animal kingdom. Appendix F on pages 560–561 summarizes the nine major phyla in the animal kingdom. It lists some characteristics, and gives examples of animals in each phylum.

GOALS:
1. You will learn the characteristics of different kinds of simple animals.
2. You will learn how the cells, tissues, and organs of simple animals function.
3. You will learn how simple animals reproduce.

How are vertebrates different from invertebrates?

FIGURE 11–1. A sponge gets food and oxygen from the water that flows through its many pores, canals, and chambers.

Why are sponges classified as animals and not plants?

Name three examples of coelenterates.

11:2 Sponges

A **sponge** is the simplest kind of animal. Sponges are classified in the phylum Porifera (puh RIHF uh ruh) of the animal kingdom. You may have used sponges for washing or cleaning. Most sponges used today are artificial sponges made from wood pulp or nylon fibers. Natural sponges are the mineral material of a sponge's body that is left after the organic cells have decomposed.

There are about 5000 different kinds of sponges. Most of them are marine. They grow attached to rocks or at the bottom of shallow seas. Scientists once thought that sponges were plants because the adults do not move about like most animals. However, sponges do not make food like most plants.

The body of a sponge is a thick sack of cells with many pores through which water flows into the sponge. The sponge filters out microscopic organisms in the water for its food. A sponge also gets oxygen from the water. The same water removes waste products produced by the sponge's cells. The water flows out through a few large openings in the sponge's body.

Sponges have two layers of cells, but no tissues. The outer layer of cells secretes the mineral material that protects the sponge. The cells of the inner layer have flagella that help draw in food and water. Some sponges have a jellylike mass of cells between the layers. Structures called spicules stick out of this mass and help support the sponge.

Making Sure

1. Name three vertebrate animals and three invertebrate animals. Explain how they are different.
2. What is the difference between a natural sponge and an artificial sponge?

11:3 Coelenterates

Jellyfish, hydra, sea anemones, and corals are examples of coelenterates (sih LENT uh raytz). Most of these species live in the oceans. One exception is the hydra found in freshwater ponds. Some coelenterates, such as the jellyfish, are free-swimming. Others, like coral, grow attached to the ocean floor and other surfaces.

A **coelenterate** has a hollow body surrounded by two layers of cells. The two layers form two kinds of tissues but no organs. At one end of the body's central cavity is a mouth with tentacles around it. A **tentacle** (TENT uh kul) is a ropelike piece of tissue.

Food enters the open, mouth end of the cavity and is digested inside the body. Wastes are excreted through the mouth. A coelenterate obtains oxygen by diffusion from the water in which it lives.

Tentacles contain stinging cells that coelenterates use to catch other animals for food. Inside each stinger is a coiled thread with spines. The thread ejects a poison that can paralyze a small fish. After the fish is stung, the tentacles pull the animal into the body cavity. Some of the largest jellyfish have tentacles 30 meters long. People who swim in the oceans should avoid jellyfish because their stings are very painful.

FIGURE 11–2. The mangrove jellyfish is one example of a coelenterate.

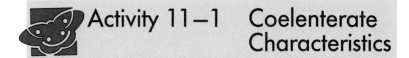

Activity 11–1   Coelenterate Characteristics

Problem: How does a hydra react to touch and food?

Materials   dropper, hydra, small dish, hand lens or stereomicroscope, camel-hair paintbrush, *Daphnia* or brine shrimp

Procedure   (1) Use a dropper to place a hydra into a small dish along with some of the water in which it is living. (2) Observe the hydra with a hand lens or under a stereomicroscope. Record the color of the hydra. Estimate the length of the hydra. (3) Observe the tentacles. Count the number of tentacles on the hydra. Do all hydra have the same number of tentacles? (4) Find the basal disk by which the hydra attaches itself to a surface. (5) A small slit between the tentacles is the mouth. Observe the mouth. (6) Locate the central cavity. (7) Describe how the hydra moves and changes its shape. (8) Predict what will occur when the hydra is touched with a camel-hair brush. Touch the hydra on the tentacles, mouth, body, and basal disk. Record the reaction of the hydra to the touch. (9) Predict how the hydra takes in food. Record what you observe. (10) Drop a *Daphnia* or a small amount of brine shrimp into the dish. Describe how the hydra takes in food.

Questions   (1) Do all hydras have the same number of tentacles? (2) When you touched the hydra, did you observe anything to suggest that the touch spreads to areas away from the touch? (3) How can you explain what you observed? (4) Is there evidence that the hydra uses stinging cells to get food? (5) What is the function of the central cavity? (6) What is the function of the tentacles? (7) What is the function of the mouth? (8) How does a hydra react to touch and food?

FIGURE 11–3.

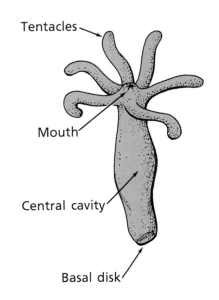

Tentacles

Mouth

Central cavity

Basal disk

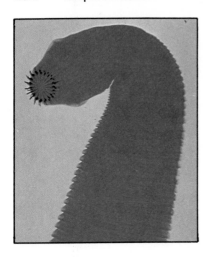

FIGURE 11—4. Tapeworms are parasitic flatworms that obtain nourishment from host organisms.

How is the body of a flatworm different from a coelenterate?

FIGURE 11—5. A planarian has a nervous system (a) and is a free-living flatworm (b).

11:4 Flatworms

A **flatworm** has a flat, legless body with a front end, or anterior, and a rear end, or posterior. Some freeliving species of flatworms live in the oceans. Others, such as *Planaria,* live in freshwater ponds. Planarians range from microscopic to about 2.5 centimeters in length. Flukes and tapeworms are flatworms that live as parasites on other animals.

Flatworms are more complex in body structure than sponges and jellyfish. Like other worms, a flatworm has body organs and three layers of tissue. The planarian, for example, has a muscular mouth it uses to take in food. Food is digested in the animal's digestive system. Undigested food is excreted through the mouth. Planaria live on tiny animals they trap in a mucous secretion. As with sponges and coelenterates, oxygen enters a flatworm by diffusion.

Flatworms have nervous systems. For example, the planarian has a simple brain, eyespots, and other sense organs in its head. Two nerve cords extend the length of the body. They are connected by other cords, like rungs in a ladder. A flatworm also has an excretory system it uses to rid itself of body wastes. A reproductive system with sex organs is present, too. Tapeworms may produce as many as 600 million eggs in a year. Planarians reproduce by both sexual and asexual reproduction.

A tapeworm is a long flatworm with a small head. Its body may grow to a length of six meters or more. Tapeworms live in the bodies of other animals as parasites. The head of a tapeworm has suckers by which it attaches itself to the wall of the animal's digestive tract. The tapeworm absorbs food, water, and oxygen from the host animal. Tapeworms from cows, pigs, and fish can infect humans. For this reason, it is important to cook meat and fish thoroughly. Cooking kills any worms that may be present.

a

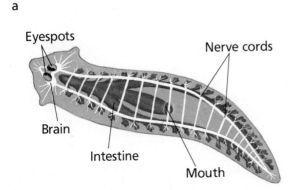

Eyespots

Nerve cords

Brain

Intestine

Mouth

b

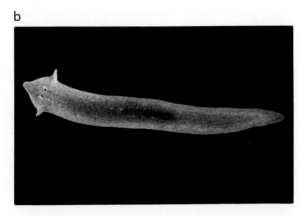

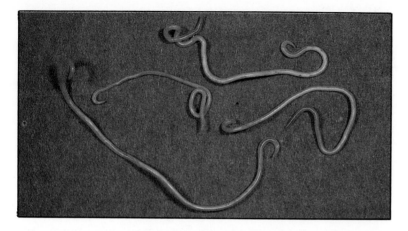

FIGURE 11–6. The hookworm is a parasite that can live in the intestine of humans.

Making Sure

3. How does a jellyfish obtain food?
4. How are sponges and coelenterates different?
5. How are flatworms different from coelenterates?

11:5 Roundworms

Roundworms live in soil, oceans, and fresh water. A **roundworm** has a round, tubelike body that tapers to a point at each end. Hookworms, hairworms, and vinegar eels are examples of roundworms. Although many roundworms are free-living, others are parasites on plants and animals.

A roundworm has a digestive tract that extends the length of its body. At the anterior end is a mouth. At the posterior end is an opening through which it excretes wastes. A nervous system with a brain and other simple sense organs is present in a roundworm. Roundworms have sex organs for reproduction. In most species, there are separate male and female sexes. A roundworm does not have a circulatory system to supply nutrients and other materials to parts of its body. Instead it has a body cavity filled with fluid.

The human hookworm and trichina worm are two roundworms that infect people. They are parasites. Adult hookworms live in the intestine of a human host. They lay eggs that develop on soil into microscopic larvae. If a person walks barefoot on soil containing the larvae, they may bore through the skin and enter the person's blood. The larvae migrate to the person's intestine where they develop into adult worms. Trichina worms live in pigs as well as humans. Humans become infected with trichina worms by eating poorly cooked, infected pork. Trichina infection can be prevented by freezing pork or cooking it well.

Compare roundworms with flatworms.

FIGURE 11–7. Trichina worms are parasitic roundworms that infect the muscle tissues of the host animal.

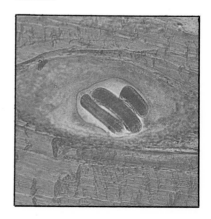

FIGURE 11–8. An earthworm is a segmented worm that breaks down organic matter and loosens the soil.

Describe a segmented worm.

11:6 Segmented Worms

When you think of worms, you probably think of earthworms. Earthworms are segmented worms. Like other segmented worms, they are invertebrate animals with soft bodies and no bones. Segmented worms are classified in phylum Annelida in the animal kingdom. **Segmented worms** have tube-shaped bodies divided into sections, or segments, that are similar in structure. Some have bristle or paddlelike structures that are used for movement. Segmented worms also have a circulatory system and a body cavity that contains organs. A nerve center, or "brain," in the head of a segmented worm is connected to a main nerve that extends the length of the animal's body.

Segmented worms are the simplest animals with circulatory systems. Five pairs of enlarged tubes act as hearts. The tubes pump blood through the major blood vessels of the worm's body. These major blood vessels branch into tiny blood vessels called capillaries. The exchange of materials between cells and blood occurs through the capillaries.

Different kinds of respiratory systems are present in segmented worms. Many species have gills and use oxygen dissolved in water. Oxygen from the air moves into the blood of an earthworm through its moist skin. Carbon dioxide moves out of the earthworm's body in the opposite direction.

Segmented worms have two body openings, one at each end of the digestive tract. A digestive tract is a long tube made up of organs through which food passes. Food enters the digestive

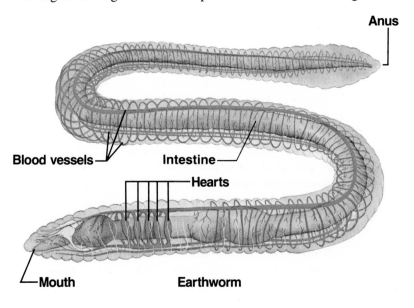

Anus

Blood vessels **Intestine**

Hearts

Mouth   **Earthworm**

FIGURE 11–9. Earthworms are the simplest animals to have a circulatory system. They have tubes or hearts that pump blood through blood vessels.

FIGURE 11—10. The leech *Pisciola* feeds on nutrients in the blood of a 3-spined stickleback.

tract through the mouth of the earthworm. An earthworm has a crop and gizzard in its digestive tract. The food is stored in the crop until it can be moved into the gizzard. In the gizzard, the food is ground up. In the intestine, digestive juices and enzymes are produced and mixed with the food. Digested food diffuses from the intestine into the animal's blood. Undigested food leaves the body through the anus, the opening at the other end of the digestive tract.

Earthworms feed on decayed plant and animal matter. They break down this organic matter and loosen the soil as they burrow through the ground. Earthworms are important to farmers and gardeners because they help aerate the soil and make it more fertile for growing plants.

Why are earthworms important in farming?

Unlike the familiar earthworm, most segmented worms live in water. Leeches are an example of segmented worms that live in water. Many leeches are parasites on plants or animals. They feed on the sap of plants or the blood of other animals.

Making Sure

6. How are roundworms different from flatworms?
7. Classify each of the following worms.
   a. Lugworm: Tube-shaped, two body openings, circulatory system, body covered with bristles.
   b. Fluke: Parasite, three tissue layers, one body opening.
   c. Sea mouse: Tube-shaped, two body openings, paddlelike structures on each segment.
   d. Hookworm: Parasite, three tissue layers, two body openings.

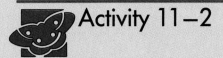

Activity 11–2

Characteristics of a Segmented Worm

Problem: What are the characteristics of an earthworm?

Materials

live earthworm
moist paper towel
shallow pan
water
hand lens
loose soil
cotton swab
vinegar

Procedure

1. Place a live earthworm on a moist paper towel in a shallow pan. Observe the earthworm closely.
2. Wet your hands. Hold the worm gently between your thumb and forefinger. Observe its movements. Lightly rub your fingers along its body. The bristles are called setae (SEE tee).
3. Examine the earthworm with a hand lens.
4. Observe the thickened area encircling the body. This area is called the clitellum.

FIGURE 11–11.

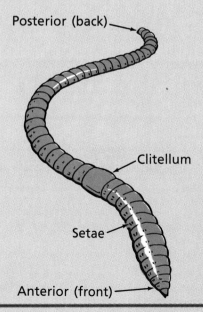

Posterior (back)

Clitellum

Setae

Anterior (front)

5. Touch the anterior and posterior areas of the body. Observe and record.
6. Dip a cotton swab in vinegar. Draw a "line of vinegar" in front of the worm. Observe and record.
7. Remove the earthworm and paper towel from the pan.
8. Cover the bottom of the pan with a thick layer of loose soil.
9. Place the worm on the surface of the soil. Observe and record its movements as it burrows into the soil.

Data and Observations

Environment/ Stimulus	Response
Moist paper towel	
Holding between fingers	
Touch—anterior	
Touch—posterior	
Vinegar	
Soil	

Questions and Conclusions

1. Does the earthworm have segments?
2. How does the anterior differ from the posterior?
3. Where are the setae located?
4. How many setae are on each segment?
5. Does your earthworm have any visible sense organs?
6. How does it respond to touch?
7. Is the worm sensitive to acid (vinegar)?
8. Describe how the earthworm lives in soil. How does it get oxygen?
9. What are the characteristics of an earthworm?

11:7 Reproduction

For a species to survive over time, reproduction must occur. Reproduction produces offspring to replace members of a species that die. Both asexual and sexual reproduction occur in animals. In asexual reproduction, there is only one parent. Sexual reproduction involves the combination of nuclear material from two different sex cells to produce offspring. The sex cells may be produced by one parent or by separate parents.

Budding in hydra or sponges is one example of asexual reproduction. The bud is a tiny piece of tissue that grows, breaks off, and develops into a new hydra or sponge. A planarian reproduces asexually by splitting in the middle to form two individuals. Each individual then grows back its missing parts.

In sexual reproduction, an egg and sperm are produced. With species such as the hydra, planarian, and earthworm, the same animal develops male and female sex organs. One organism produces both the egg and sperm. A sperm fertilizes an egg, forming a single cell. Through repeated cell division, the fertilized egg develops into a new animal. In roundworms, the sexes are usually separate, and the male is smaller than the female. When the sexes are separate, both male and female animals are needed for reproduction to occur. Self-fertilization is possible, but is not the usual method of reproduction.

Regeneration (rih jen uh RAY shun) is the regrowth of lost or damaged tissue and organs. It is common in coelenterates, worms, and sponges. A piece of sponge can grow into a complete sponge. If a hydra's body is cut into pieces, most of the pieces slowly grow back their missing parts. Some species of more complex animals can regenerate missing body parts such as arms or tails.

FIGURE 11–12. A starfish can regenerate a missing arm.

How do asexual and sexual reproduction in animals differ?

Explain how budding and regeneration occur.

FIGURE 11–13.

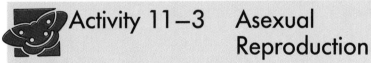

Activity 11–3   Asexual Reproduction

Problem: What is the method of asexual reproduction in hydra?

Materials dropper, hydra culture, microscope, culture slide

Procedure (1) Place a hydra in the depression of the culture slide. (2) Examine the hydra for buds beginning to form or already formed. (3) Diagram a hydra that has a bud.

Questions (1) What did you observe in the hydra culture? (2) How may hydra reproduce? (3) Why is budding considered a form of asexual reproduction? (4) What is the method of asexual reproduction found in hydra?

FOCUS ON
Skills

Roots, Prefixes, and Suffixes

Many words in our language are made up of word parts that appear over and over again in different words. Root words are basic words to which beginning or ending word parts can be added. Prefixes are word parts that can be added to the beginning of root words to change their meanings. Suffixes are word parts that can be added to the end of root words to change their meaning. Many science words are combinations of roots, prefixes, and suffixes. If you learn the meanings of a few common word parts, you will be able to take apart unfamiliar words and figure out what they mean.

Examples:

magni-	large or great	magnify
micro-	extremely small,	
scope-	see	microscope
multi-	many	multicellular
uni-	one	unicellular
bio-	life,	
logy-	science of	biology
organ-	group of tissues performing a function,	
ism	act or condition of being	organism

Some of these words had both familiar and unfamiliar parts. You should have been able to figure out their meanings once you learned the unfamiliar parts. Now try to figure out the meaning of a word with no familiar parts. Write the definition of the word after you put together the meanings of the parts of the word. Remember that sometimes a word's meaning can be figured out just by knowing what the word parts mean. But, sometimes it takes an extra step.

Example:
pseudopod
"pseudo" means "false"
"pod" means "foot"

You might guess false foot and you would be basically correct. A pseudopod is a slender projection on a one-celled animal. The pseudopod helps the animal move, just as your feet help you get around.

1. If the prefix "re" means "again" and "gen" means "birth," what does "regeneration" mean?
2. A vertebrate is an animal with a backbone. Since the prefix "in" means "not," what is an invertebrate?
3. If "spir" means breath and "ation" means the act of, what does respiration mean?
4. If "cent" means 100 and "pede" means foot, what is a "centipede?"
5. If "photo" means "light" and "syn" means "together," what is "photosynthesis?"
6. A "tropism" is a plant's response to a stimulus; what is "phototropism?"
7. If "geo" means "earth," what is "geotropism?"
8. If the prefix "anti" means against, what is an "antibody?"
9. If "exo" means "outer," what is an "exoskeleton?"
10. If the prefix "sub" means "under," where is "subsoil" found?
11. What is "topsoil?"
12. If "aerobic" means "with oxygen," and the prefix "an" means "not," what is "anaerobic?"
13. If "taxis" means arrangement and "nomy" refers to laws of distribution, what is "taxonomy?"

CHAPTER 11
Review

Summary

1. Animals with backbones are vertebrates. Animals without backbones are invertebrates. 11:1
2. All vertebrates are grouped into one phylum. Invertebrates are grouped mainly into eight different phyla. 11:1
3. Sponges are the simplest invertebrates. 11:2
4. Coelenterates are animals with central cavities and tentacles. 11:3
5. Most worms are classified according to their structure into one of three phyla. 11:4–11:6
6. Asexual reproduction produces offspring from one cell. Sexual reproduction produces offspring from two sex cells. 11:7
7. Budding is a form of asexual reproduction. 11:7
8. Animals can regenerate lost cells and tissues. Some animals can regenerate body parts. 11:7

Vocabulary

Write a sentence using the following words or terms correctly.

budding	invertebrate	segmented worm
coelenterate	regeneration	sponge
flatworm	roundworm	tentacle
		vertebrate

Questions

Do not write in this book.

A. True or False
Determine whether each of the following sentences is true or false. Rewrite the false statements to make them correct.

1. Sexual and asexual are two kinds of reproduction.
2. Budding is a form of sexual reproduction.
3. All the vertebrates belong to one phylum.
4. A worm is an example of a vertebrate.
5. Sponges and jellyfish are in the same phylum.
6. Tapeworms are parasites.
7. A trichina infection is caused by a flatworm.
8. An earthworm belongs to the roundworm phylum.
9. A roundworm has a digestive tract.
10. Hydra reproduce only by sexual reproduction.

B. Multiple Choice

Choose the word or phrase that correctly completes the following sentences.
1. Animals without backbones are (*vertebrates, invertebrates*).
2. A tapeworm is an example of a (*flatworm, roundworm, segmented worm*).
3. Tentacles are present in a (*jellyfish, flatworm, roundworm*).
4. Budding in a hydra is a form of (*asexual, sexual*) reproduction.
5. Worms are (*vertebrates, invertebrates, coelenterates*).
6. A jellyfish has (*one, two, three, four*) kinds of tissues.
7. (*Coelenterates, Flatworms, Roundworms*) have tentacles.
8. A(n) (*hydra, planarian, roundworm, earthworm*) has a circulatory system with blood.
9. The regrowth of lost or damaged tissue is called (*budding, regeneration, reproduction*).
10. A (*planarian, hydra, jellyfish, trichina worm*) is a parasite.

C. Completion

Complete each of the following sentences with the correct word or phrase.
1. All animals with backbones are called _____.
2. Growing a new body part to replace one that is lost is called _____.
3. _____ have tentacles that they use to capture other animals for food.
4. An earthworm is a(n) _____ worm.
5. A(n) _____ is an organism that lives on or in a host.
6. The _____ is an example of a flatworm that is not a parasite.
7. Animals are _____ -celled organisms.
8. Sponges are classified as animals partly because they do not _____ food.
9. Dissolved oxygen enters a roundworm's body by _____.
10. Sexual reproduction requires a(n) _____ cell and _____ cell.

D. How and Why

1. How does a sponge obtain its food?
2. Why might a swimmer be harmed if he or she came in contact with jellyfish?
3. Name three kinds of worms. Give one example of each.
4. Describe how reproduction can occur in hydra through budding.
5. How is a parasite different from a free-living animal?
6. What characteristics make an earthworm different from a roundworm?
7. Why is a sponge classified as an animal and not a plant?
8. How are invertebrates different from vertebrates?
9. Why must pork and beef be well cooked before they are eaten?
10. How do earthworms affect the soil?

CHAPTER 11
Review

Ideas to Explore

1. **Challenge:** Research the dog heartworm. Illustrate and describe the life cycle on a poster.
2. **Project:** Find a local worm farmer and learn how to grow worms. Report to the class on the equipment needed, the problems, and how profitable worm farming is.
3. **Challenge:** Make a report on the use of leeches for medical purposes in the Middle Ages.
4. **Project:** Obtain planarians from a local pond or stream. Place the planarians in a culture dish and feed them a small piece of liver (the size of a pinhead). Observe how they feed.
5. **Project:** Visit an aquarium or local pet shop and look for sea anemones. Watch the movements of these coelenterates. Find out the names of the different sea anemones and also where each type came from. Make a report for your class and include diagrams in color of each sea anemone about which you talk.
6. **Project:** Collect about six earthworms along with soil and place them into a widemouthed jar. Put some leaves on top of the soil. Keep the jar covered with dark paper until you want to observe the worms. Keep the soil moist and place small pieces of lettuce leaves on the top for food. Observe how the worms tunnel through the soil, how they move their bodies, how they eat, and how they drag leaves down into the soil.
7. **Challenge:** Make a report on the life in a coral reef. Choose one particular island's coral reef and find out how a coral reef forms and how it is affected by changes in its environment.

Readings

Chinery, Michael (ed.). *Dictionary of Animals*. New York: Arco, 1984.

Goaman, Karen and Heather Amery. *Mysteries and Marvels of the Animal World.* Tulsa: Educational Development Corp., 1984.

Jacobson, Morris K. and David R. Franz. *Wonders of Corals and Coral Reefs.* New York: Dodd, Mead and Company, 1980.

Sumich, James L. *An Introduction to the Biology of Marine Life*. Dubuque, IA: Brown, 1980.

There are thousands of kinds of invertebrate animals. Some of the largest animal groups are represented by complex invertebrates. Like other animals, complex invertebrates have special structures, functions, and behaviors that enable them to survive. What special features of the nudibranch enable it to survive? What other complex invertebrates are there? How do they compare with the nudibranch?

CHAPTER 12
COMPLEX INVERTEBRATES

12:1 Animal Symmetry

Complex invertebrates have bodies that are more complex than those of simpler organisms, such as coelenterates and worms. Examples of complex invertebrates are a snail, octopus, crayfish, grasshopper, and spider. They are more complex because they contain a greater number of different kinds of cells organized into different tissues. The body tissues are organized into organs and systems having special functions. For example, specialized systems work to take in oxygen, circulate materials, excrete wastes, and produce offspring. A nervous system regulates body functions and detects stimuli in the environment. In insects and other arthropods, muscle systems are used to enable the organism to move about.

Symmetry (SIH muh tree) means a similarity or likeness in parts. Look at your two hands and note the symmetry. The fingers on one hand are like the fingers on the other. An object with **bilateral symmetry** can be divided lengthwise into two sides, a left side and a right side, that are alike. Look in a mirror and you will see that your face has bilateral symmetry. The right half is like the left half. Most animals have bilateral symmetry. A lengthwise line between the anterior and posterior ends of an animal with bilateral symmetry divides it into two roughly equal parts. Examples of bilateral symmetry are the bodies of a dog, cat, butterfly, crab, spider, parakeet, and worm.

GOALS:
1. You will learn the characteristics of complex invertebrates.
2. You will learn how the cells, tissues, and organs of these animals function.
3. You will learn how complex invertebrates reproduce.

Define symmetry.

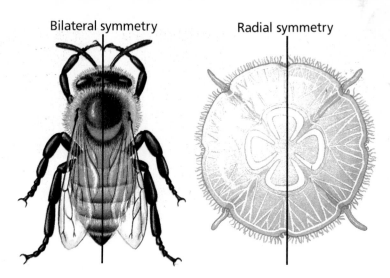

Bilateral symmetry   Radial symmetry

FIGURE 12–1. An insect has bilateral symmetry. At only one place, a line between its anterior and posterior divides it into two equal parts. The jellyfish, an animal with radial symmetry, can be cut through the center in any direction and two equal parts result.

Compare bilateral and radial symmetry.

Radial symmetry is the arrangement of similar parts around a central axis. A bicycle wheel and merry-go-round are examples of radial symmetry. Coelenterates are animals that have radial symmetry. Their body structures form a circle with an axis at its center. The hydra, jellyfish, and starfish have radial symmetry. A sponge has an irregular shape without any symmetry.

FIGURE 12–2.

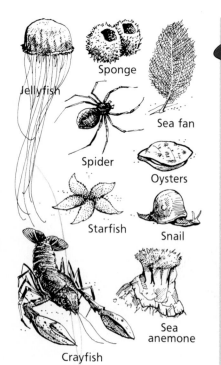

Jellyfish
Sponge
Sea fan
Spider
Oysters
Starfish
Snail
Crayfish
Sea anemone

Activity 12–1 Body Symmetry

Problem: What types of symmetry do animals have?

Materials   pencil and paper

Procedure   (1) Make a three-column chart on a sheet of paper. At the top of each column, list Animal, Type of Symmetry, and Reason. (2) In the Animal column, list the animals pictured on this page. (3) Decide whether each animal has radial symmetry, bilateral symmetry, or no symmetry. Write the type of symmetry that the animal has in the Type of Symmetry column. (4) In the Reason column, explain how you decided what type of symmetry the animal has.

Questions   (1) Which animals have radial symmetry? (2) Which animals have bilateral symmetry? (3) Which animals have no symmetry? (4) Is symmetry a phylum characteristic? Explain your answer. (5) What are the advantages of radial symmetry to an animal? (6) What are the advantages of bilateral symmetry to an animal? (7) What types of symmetry do animals have?

a

b

12:2 Mollusks

Have you ever collected shells on a beach? Shells are the remains of mollusks. **Mollusks** are invertebrate animals that have soft bodies. They are classified in phylum Mollusca. Most have a shell or a shell-like covering. Most mollusks also have a thick, muscular organ called a foot. It is used for movement. A few species of mollusks live attached to rocks or other surfaces.

There are many different kinds of mollusks. Snails, oysters, and clams are mollusks that have hard outer shells. Some mollusks, like the squid and octopus, live in water. Other mollusks, such as some slugs, live on land. Compared to other invertebrates, most mollusks are large. Most have bilateral symmetry. Even though they may look different, all mollusks have a similar internal body structure.

Mollusks have three tissue layers, like the worms. They also have a body cavity where internal organs are located. They have two body openings and a digestive system. Some mollusks, such as snails, eat plants by rubbing special mouth structures called radulas against the surface of a plant. Other mollusks, such as clams, filter food from water. Some mollusks, such as the octopus, catch other animals for food. Giant squids are the largest of all invertebrates.

Mollusks have a circulatory system with a heart. They have gills or lungs for respiration. Many have tentacles that function as sense organs. Some mollusks have eyes. The main difference between mollusks and the simpler invertebrates is the hard outer body covering. Sexual reproduction occurs in most mollusks.

FIGURE 12–3. A snail (a) is an example of a mollusk that has a hard outer shell and lives on land. An octopus (b) is a water-dwelling mollusk without an outer shell.

Describe the characteristics of a mollusk. How do mollusks compare with simpler invertebrates?

Making Sure

1. What kind of symmetry does an octopus have?
2. Name three mollusks and tell how they are similar.

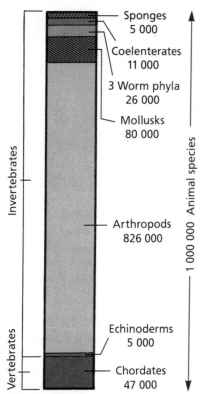

Sponges
5 000

Coelenterates
11 000

3 Worm phyla
26 000

Mollusks
80 000

Arthropods
826 000

Echinoderms
5 000

Chordates
47 000

Invertebrates

Vertebrates

1 000 000 Animal species

FIGURE 12—4. There are more arthropods than any other kind of animal on Earth.

12:3 Arthropods

What do spiders, butterflies, and lobsters have in common? Each is classified in phylum Arthropoda, meaning each has jointed legs. Phylum Arthropoda is divided into many classes. Table 12–1 shows some major classes and animals in this phylum. **Arthropods** (AHR thruh pahdz) have jointed legs, or appendages, and an exoskeleton. The body of arthropods is segmented. In many arthropods the segments are grouped into three body regions: the head, thorax, and abdomen.

Most other invertebrates crawl or float. The jointed legs of arthropods permit more movement. Compare the movement of an earthworm and a grasshopper!

The **exoskeleton** is a hard outer covering that protects the internal parts of an arthropod. It is made of protein and a hard, lightweight substance called chitin. The exoskeleton consists of sections that are "hinged" together allowing for movement. Arthropods shed their exoskeletons from time to time. This process of shedding the exoskeleton is called **molting.** Arthropods must molt in order to grow.

Arthropods have specialized mouth parts for biting, sucking, chewing, or holding food. They also have sense organs, such as antennae and eyes, that are important for their survival.

Arthropods are adapted to many different environments. They are found almost everywhere. There are more arthropods than any other kind of animal on Earth.

Table 12—1

Phylum Arthropoda		
Class	**Some characteristics**	**Examples**
Chilopoda	flat, segmented body, one pair of legs per segment	centipedes
Diplopoda	round, segmented body, two pairs of legs per segment	millipedes
Crustacea	hard, flexible exoskeleton, gills, two pairs of antennae	sowbugs, shrimps, crabs
Insecta	three body regions, one pair of antennae, three pairs of legs	grasshoppers, bees, ants, butterflies
Arachnida	two body regions, no antennae, four pairs of legs	spiders, mites, scorpions, ticks

a

b

12:4 Centipedes and Millipedes

Centipedes (SENT uh peedz) and millipedes are two classes in phylum Arthropoda. These animals live on land and are usually found in damp areas under stones or wood. They hide by day. At night they come out to search for food. Centipedes and millipedes are alike in some ways. They both have a head and a body divided into segments.

Although they are called "hundred legged," most **centipedes** have about 30 legs. In some species the number of legs is 100 or more. There is one pair of legs on each body segment. A centipede has two antennae on its head. They are organs used to detect things around it. A mouth in the animal's head contains parts that are used to bite and chew. The first segment of a centipede's body has a pair of poison claws attached to it. These claws are used to kill tiny animals for food. Food for a centipede is mainly small animals such as insects, earthworms, and slugs.

Millipede means "thousand legged." Although millipedes have many legs, none actually has 1000, and they run much slower than centipedes. A millipede has two pairs of legs on each adult body segment. The head of a millipede has simple eyes, a pair of short antennae, and a mouth. Millipedes usually eat dead plant material.

Both centipedes and millipedes have circulatory systems. Fine branching tubes carry oxygen to their body organs. The digestive system is a tube through the body where food is digested. These animals reproduce by sexual reproduction. Males fertilize females who lay eggs in damp earth. Young hatch from the eggs and go through a series of molts as they grow to adults.

FIGURE 12–5. Centipedes are arthropods with one pair of legs attached to each body segment (a). Millipedes have two pairs of legs attached to each of their body segments (b).

In what phylum are centipedes and millipedes classified? Why?

How are centipedes and millipedes alike and different?

12:5 Crustaceans

Describe and give examples of crustaceans.

Lobsters, shrimp, crabs, and crayfish are crustaceans (kruh STAY shunz). They are a class in the phylum Arthropoda. A **crustacean** has a segmented body that has two main regions. The head and thorax are usually fused to form one region. The abdomen is the other region. Attached to the body are appendages adapted for walking, swimming, or carrying eggs and young. Clawlike legs at the anterior end of the body are adapted for grabbing and holding food. The animal's exoskeleton is hard except at the joints where softness permits movement. Two pairs of antennae connected to the head are used for touch and taste. Tough, sharp parts, called mandibles (MAN duh bulz), on each side of the mouth are used for biting and chewing. Two glands in the head remove body wastes that are excreted through ducts at the bases of two antennae. Many crustaceans have eyes, sense organs that detect gravity, and sensory bristles. They obtain oxygen through gills on the base of each leg. Crustaceans can regenerate lost claws and other limbs.

Describe the development of a crustacean.

Sexual reproduction occurs in crustaceans. Sperm deposited in the female by a male of the same species fertilize the female's eggs. The fertilized eggs hatch into larvae (LAHR vee). Next, the larvae develop through a series of molts into young crustaceans that look like small adults. These young continue to grow and molt until they reach adult size. A lobster molts seven times during its first summer of life.

Crustaceans such as lobsters, shrimp, and crabs are used for food by people. These and many other crustacean species live in the oceans. Billions of microscopic crustaceans are often found in huge swarms in ocean water. They are food for fish and whales. Many species of crustaceans, including crayfish, live in freshwater ponds and streams. Crayfish hide by day under stones or in clumps of plants. Their food includes insects, worms, crustaceans, small snails, fish, and tadpoles. Crayfish are another crustacean people eat. A few species of crustaceans, such as sowbugs, live on land.

FIGURE 12–6. A freshwater crayfish (a), shrimp (b), and hermit crab (c) are examples of crustaceans.

a

b

c

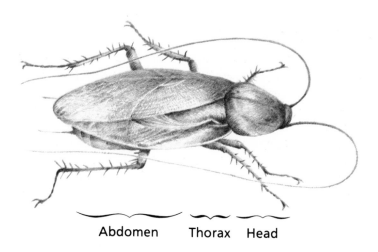

Abdomen   Thorax Head

FIGURE 12–7. The body of an insect, such as a cockroach, is divided into three regions.

12:6 Insects

Insects are the most abundant animals on Earth. There are more species of insects than all other animals combined. About 800 000 species of insects have been named and described. Grasshoppers, flies, lice, butterflies, fleas, beetles, and bees are examples of insects. Insects are found almost everywhere. Most insects live on land; some live in water. If all the insects in the world could be collected, they would weigh more than all the other land animals. Insects are a class in the phylum Arthropoda.

An **insect's** body is covered with an exoskeleton that protects its soft internal organs. The body is divided into a head, thorax, and abdomen. A pair of antennae is attached to the head. The antennae and eyes in the head are sense organs. Connected to the thorax are three pairs of jointed legs. Many insects have one or two pairs of wings. Insects are the only invertebrates that can fly. The mouth parts of some insects, such as the grasshopper, are used for chewing. In insects like the fly, mouth parts are designed for sucking and lapping. Oxygen enters an insect's body through pores in the abdomen called spiracles. The spiracles lead to a network of tubes. At the end of the tubes are air sacs. Air is pumped in and out of the air sacs by movements of the insect's body.

An insect has a heart that pumps blood into a single large blood vessel. The blood vessel empties the blood into a large cavity where it bathes the cells. Then the blood flows back into the heart. Insects have separate male and female sexes that mate and produce young through sexual reproduction.

A cockroach is an insect with a flattened body and mouth parts suited for biting. Cockroaches range in size from one to five

FIGURE 12–8. The mouth parts of grasshoppers and cockroaches are used for biting and chewing (a). The mouth parts of the fly are used for sucking and lapping (b). A mosquito has mouth parts that are used for both piercing and sucking (c).

a Grasshopper

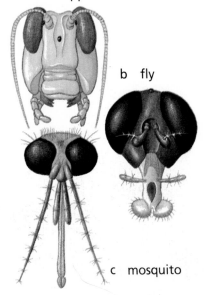

b fly

c mosquito

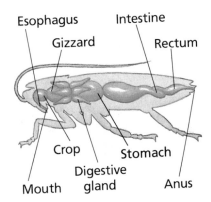

Esophagus   Intestine
Gizzard   Rectum
Crop
Stomach
Digestive
Mouth   gland   Anus

FIGURE 12–9. Cockroaches, like other insects, digest food inside a digestive tract.

FIGURE 12–10. Some insects are helpful such as ladybugs that eat aphids (a). Harmful insects include the crab louse, (b), which is a parasite on humans.

centimeters. They often live inside buildings in dark corners where they can find food. A cockroach eats dead plant and animal material. It hides by day and goes looking for food at night. Cockroaches, like other insects, digest food inside a digestive tract. Food enters the mouth and undigested food is excreted out of the body through the anus. Body wastes are collected by tiny tubes that carry the wastes into the digestive tract.

Species of insects such as cockroaches, termites, ants, flies, and mosquitoes are pests. Many kinds of insects such as aphids and weevils destroy crops. Flies, lice, fleas, and mosquitoes can spread disease. Some insects are helpful in pollinating the flowers of crops and fruit trees. Some insects eat harmful insects. For instance, a ladybug eats aphids, which are insects that eat vegetable plant leaves and stems. Insects are food for wildlife such as birds, reptiles, and fish.

12:7 Arachnids

Spiders, scorpions, mites, and ticks are arachnids (uh RAK nihdz). Like other animals in phylum Arthropoda, they have segmented bodies, jointed legs, and exoskeletons. An **arachnid** has two body regions. On the front region are two pairs of appendages near the mouth and four pairs of legs. It does not have antennae. Appendages near the mouth are used to hold and chew food and also may have sense organs for tasting food. Spiders are the largest group of arachnids and they produce silk to spin

a

b

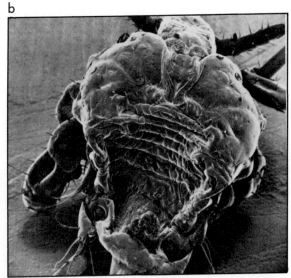

a

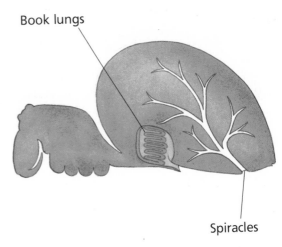

b

Book lungs

Spiracles

FIGURE 12–11. A jumping spider (a) is an example of an arachnid. Spiders get oxygen through either spiracles or book lungs or both (b).

webs. Spinning a web is an inborn behavior in spiders. Most arachnids live on land.

Many people are afraid of spiders because some species bite. They bite to obtain food. Some spiders inject poison when they bite. However, the bite of most spiders is not poisonous to people. Arachnids usually prey on small arthropods.

Arachnids obtain oxygen through either spiracles or book lungs. Some species have both kinds of structures. A book lung is an air-filled sac that has parts like the pages of a book. These parts contain tiny blood vessels. Air enters the abdomen through slits and passes into the lungs. Oxygen and carbon dioxide are exchanged between the blood and air.

Mites and ticks make up the second largest group of arachnids. Most are tiny; many are parasites. A familiar example of an arachnid is a daddy longlegs. It has long legs that are bent so that its body hangs low. Daddy longlegs live outdoors and eat small insects. They do not spin webs and are harmless to people.

Making Sure

3. What characteristics of mollusks make them different than arthropods?
4. How are millipedes different from centipedes?
5. Name five classes of arthropods and an animal in each class.
6. What characteristics of insects and spiders place them in phylum Arthropoda?
7. How are spiders different from insects?

Activity 12–2   Identifying Arthropod Classes

Problem: How is a key used to determine the class of an animal?

Materials   selected animals or pictures, paper, pencil

Procedure   (1) Make a four-column chart like the one under Data and Observations on a sheet of paper. (2) In the first column, write the name of each animal you are studying. (3) Predict the class of the animal and write your prediction in the second column. (4) Write the characteristic that your prediction was based on in the third column. (5) Use the key to determine the class of each animal. Write the class from the key in the fourth column.

1. Does the animal have more than five pairs of walking legs?

   YES   Go to 2
   NO   Go to 3

2. Does the animal have two pairs of legs for each body segment?

   YES   Diplopoda
   NO   Chilopoda

3. Does the animal have antennae?

   YES   Go to 4
   NO   Arachnida

4. Does the animal have more than one pair of antennae?

   YES   Crustacea
   NO   Insecta

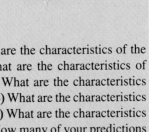

Questions   (1) What are the characteristics of the class Diplopoda? (2) What are the characteristics of the class Chilopoda? (3) What are the characteristics of the class Arachnida? (4) What are the characteristics of the class Crustacea? (5) What are the characteristics of the class Insecta? (6) How many of your predictions were correct? (7) How is a key used to determine the class of an animal?

12:8 Echinoderms

Describe an animal in phylum Echinodermata.

Even if you have never seen a starfish, you can probably guess how one looks. Starfish have radial symmetry. Most have five arms that radiate from the center of their bodies. Starfish are marine animals. Their bodies have a tough outer covering of coarse spines. Sea urchins and sand dollars are marine animals that also have "spiny skin" and radial symmetry like starfish.

They are all classified in phylum Echinodermata (ih ki nuh DUR muh tuh). All animals in this phylum live in salt water.

Echinoderms have a skeleton made of spines inside their bodies. They also have a special system for movement and obtaining food. It is called a water vascular system. On the underside of an echinoderm are rows of structures called tube feet, which work like suction cups. Most echinoderms can move slowly about by attaching an arm to the seafloor, then contracting the arm. To obtain food, starfish attach their tube feet to the shells of oysters and clams. The starfish pulls the shells of these animals apart. Starfish feed on the soft bodies of oysters, clams, and other mollusks. The starfish turns its stomach inside out, pushes it through its mouth, and surrounds the soft parts of its prey. The food is digested and taken back into the starfish's body. Lost arms of a starfish are replaced by regeneration.

FIGURE 12–12. A brittle star is an example of an echinoderm.

Making Sure

8. What are the characteristics of echinoderms?
9. How are echinoderms different from mollusks?
10. If a starfish loses an arm, how is it replaced?

12:9 Reproduction

Complex invertebrates reproduce by sexual reproduction. Males produce sperm and females produce eggs. Sperm swim to the eggs and fertilize them. In fertilization, a single sperm unites with an egg to form one cell. The nucleus of the sperm fuses with the nucleus of the egg to form one nucleus. These animals, like all others, begin life as a single cell called a zygote. Repeated cell divisions produce the new creature.

Asexual reproduction is simpler than sexual reproduction. In asexual reproduction, there is only one parent. A single cell from the parent produces the new organism by mitosis. An egg and sperm do not unite and there is no fertilization. In some insects, young develop from unfertilized eggs. For example, honeybee drones develop from unfertilized eggs produced by the queen honeybee.

In species like the spider, a male deposits sperm in a female during mating. The female then lays the fertilized eggs in a place where they will develop. Some spiders, insects, and other species lay their eggs in nests. The sperm and eggs of clams are released into the ocean water in which they live. Sperm fertilize the eggs in the water where the young develop into adults.

How do sperm and eggs produce offspring?

FIGURE 12–13. Termites lay their eggs in nests that can reach a large size such as this one in Kenya.

Explain why large numbers of off-spring benefit a species.

Because the death rate is high, invertebrates produce large numbers of offspring to replace the adults who die. Some female insects, for example, produce hundreds of eggs. Invertebrates do not take care of their young as people do. The offspring must survive on their own. Most of the young organisms do not survive to develop into adults. They become food for other animals or die because they cannot obtain sufficient food, oxygen, moisture, or warmth. Overproduction of offspring ensures that sufficient numbers will live to be adults and continue to reproduce the species.

FIGURE 12–14.

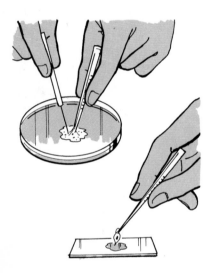

Activity 12–3　Sexual Reproduction

Problem: How do snail eggs develop?

Materials　snail egg masses, small dish, hand lens, dissecting needle, forceps, dropper, microscope slide, coverslip, microscope

Procedure　(1) Remove some snail egg masses from the classroom aquarium. Place the eggs in a dish with enough water to keep them moist. (2) Observe each egg mass with a hand lens. Record as many details as you see. (3) Use a dissecting needle and forceps to separate a single egg from the mass. (4) Place the egg in a drop of water on a microscope slide. Cover with a coverslip. Observe on low power. (5) Examine the eggs daily with both the hand lens and microscope. Record your observations.

Questions　(1) How is an egg fertilized? (2) How many cells are present immediately after fertilization? (3) How does the embryo form from the single cell? (4) What factors might prevent the development of the snail embryo? (5) How do snail eggs develop?

Define metamorphosis.

12:10　Metamorphosis

Many species of insects that reproduce sexually go through a metamorphosis (met uh MOHR fuh sus) during their lives. **Metamorphosis** is the name given to the set of stages that occur in the development of certain organisms into adults. The stages of development in complete metamorphosis of an insect are the egg, larva, pupa, and adult. The butterfly is an insect that goes through complete metamorphosis. A butterfly zygote develops into a wormlike organism called a larva or caterpillar. The larval stage is the feeding and growing stage. This stage is followed by the pupa stage when the caterpillar spins a cocoon around itself. Inside the cocoon the pupa develops into an adult butterfly. When fully developed, the adult butterfly hatches out of the cocoon. Bees, fleas, ants, moths, and flies are examples of insects that develop through complete metamorphosis.

The development of a grasshopper is an example of incomplete metamorphosis. During the first stage of development, a fertilized grasshopper egg grows into a nymph. The nymph looks like a tiny grasshopper, but it has no wings or reproductive organs. Like other insects, a nymph lives inside a tough exoskeleton that covers its body. A grasshopper nymph molts, or sheds its skeleton, five or six times as it grows larger and develops wings. At the end of these stages, the nymph has turned into an adult grasshopper. Other insects that develop through incomplete metamorphosis are locusts, dragonflies, cockroaches, and termites.

Making Sure

11. What are the stages in a butterfly's development?
12. Why is molting important in a grasshopper's development?

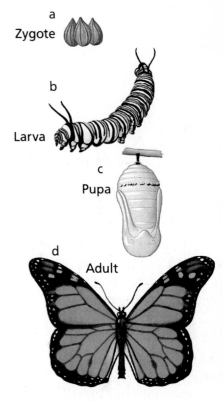

FIGURE 12–15. A butterfly goes through complete metamorphosis. The zygote (a) develops into a larva or caterpillar (b). In the pupa stage (c), a cocoon is spun. An adult butterfly (d) emerges from the cocoon.

Activity 12–4 Stages of Metamorphosis

Problem: What are the stages of metamorphosis in a mealworm?

Materials large glass jar, bran, metric ruler, mealworms, raw potato, shredded newspaper, cheesecloth, rubber band, paring knife

Procedure **(1)** Fill a large glass jar with bran to a depth of seven centimeters. **(2)** Place some mealworms in the jar. **(3)** Cut two very thick slices of raw potato. **CAUTION:** *Always be careful when using knives.* **(4)** Put the potato slices on top of the bran in the jar. The potato provides moisture. **(5)** Add shredded newspaper to a depth of 10 centimeters on top of the bran and potato slices in the jar. **(6)** Cover the top of the jar with cheesecloth. Fasten the cheesecloth on the jar with a rubber band. **(7)** Place the jar in a warm location in dim light. Observe the mealworms each day and record any changes you see.

Questions **(1)** How long does it take for each stage in metamorphosis to occur? **(2)** What stage in metamorphosis is the beetle? **(3)** What stage is the mealworm? **(4)** What are the stages of metamorphosis in a mealworm?

Marine Biologists

Jack Schneider is curator of Aquaticus, a marine aquarium. A curator is a person who is in charge of a museum, zoo, or other place of exhibit. Mr. Schneider earned degrees in biology and zoology with an emphasis on oceanography and fisheries management. As an undergraduate, he also studied business, a much-needed foundation for a curator.

Before coming to Aquaticus, Mr. Schneider served as a curator at two other marine aquariums. He designed and built exhibits, bought and cared for live specimens, tested and controlled water quality, kept records, managed the budget, and supervised the aquarium staff.

Mr. Schneider took part in the earliest planning stages of Aquaticus. He was consulted about the overall design of the aquarium and helped choose the animals that would be exhibited there. After the necessary funds were raised, building began and he started to search for the animals he wanted. He supervised their shipment to the aquarium and saw them established in their new homes.

Mr. Schneider still does much paperwork, but settling a great number of animals into a new environment is a difficult task. From time to time, Mr. Schneider enjoys putting on a wetsuit and entering a fish-filled tank to share the animals' world.

As the assistant supervisor at Aquaticus, Laura Bottaro has achieved an important goal. She had wanted to be a veterinarian until she saw her first live dolphin. From that time on, she wanted to work with marine animals.

Ms. Bottaro's associate degree in liberal arts and seven years' experience working for a veterinarian had not prepared her to care for marine animals. She applied to Moorpark College in California and was one of 60 applicants selected for a program called Exotic Animal Training and Management.

At Aquaticus, she works with crews to make display areas for the marine animals. Using her knowledge of the sea, she helps make realistic corals, sponges, and rocks from fiberglass to be used in backgrounds for fish tanks.

When shipments of live marine animals arrive, Ms. Bottaro's workday can last far into the night. Her first concern is the welfare of the animals. She encourages students interested in a zoo career to work in a junior curator program similar to the one at her zoo. Such programs give students the opportunity to work side-by-side with professionals. Students learn about animal care and day-to-day zoo work.

Career possibilities in any animal field are limited, but there is an increasing need for dedicated professionals who love animals. Ms. Bottaro is happy with her career choice, and to improve her chances for promotion and salary increases, she is taking management courses.

Summary

1. Most animals have bilateral symmetry; some have radial symmetry. 12:1
2. Mollusks are soft-bodied animals, and most have hard shells or shell-like coverings. 12:2
3. Arthropods have segmented bodies, jointed legs, and exoskeletons. 12:3
4. Centipedes, millipedes, crustaceans, insects, and arachnids are five different classes of arthropods. 12:3
5. The bodies of centipedes and millipedes have a head, antennae, segments, and legs attached to the segments. 12:4
6. Lobsters, shrimp, crabs, and crayfish are examples of crustaceans. 12:5
7. Insects are the largest group in the animal kingdom, having more than 800 000 species. 12:6
8. An insect has an exoskeleton, body with three regions, jointed legs, antennae, and eyes. Some species have wings and can fly. 12:6
9. An arachnid has four pairs of legs and a body divided into two parts. It does not have antennae. 12:7
10. Echinoderms are animals with spiny skin and water vascular systems. 12:8
11. Fertilization in which an egg and sperm are fused into a single cell occurs in sexual reproduction. 12:9
12. Metamorphosis occurs in many insect species. 12:10

Vocabulary

Write a sentence using the following words or terms correctly.

arachnid	echinoderm	mollusk
arthropod	exoskeleton	molting
bilateral symmetry	insect	radial symmetry
centipede	metamorphosis	symmetry
crustacean	millipede	

Questions

Do not write in this book.

A. True or False
Determine whether each of the following sentences is true or false. Rewrite the false statements to make them correct.

1. All animals have bilateral symmetry.
2. A starfish is a mollusk.

3. Spiders have three pairs of legs.
4. A millipede does not have antennae.
5. Crustaceans are classified in phylum Arthropoda.
6. Insects have an exoskeleton.
7. Spiders are classified in the same phylum as insects.
8. A crayfish is an example of an arachnid.
9. Insects obtain oxygen through gills.
10. Sperm can swim through water.

B. Multiple Choice
Choose the word or phrase that correctly completes the following sentences.

1. An example of a mollusk is a(n) (*jellyfish, octopus, lobster, sponge*).
2. Snails, oysters, and clams are in the (*Coelenterata, Annelida, Mollusca, Chordata*) phylum.
3. The largest group of animals is class (*Arachnida, Crustacea, Diplopoda, Insecta*).
4. A cocoon is a stage in (*complete, incomplete*) metamorphosis of an insect.
5. A snail is (*more, less*) complex than a worm.
6. A mollusk has a (*hard, soft, segmented*) body.
7. Millipede means (*many, hundred, thousand*) legged.
8. Gills are present in (*crustaceans, arachnids, insects*).
9. A (*clam, shrimp, crayfish, starfish*) is an echinoderm.
10. In fertilization, (*one, two, many*) sperm fuse(s) with an egg.

C. Completion
Complete each of the following sentences with the correct word or phrase.

1. "Thousand legged" refers to animals in the _____ class.
2. Soft-bodied animals with hard shells are _____.
3. A spider is classified in phylum _____.
4. A cockroach belongs to the _____ phylum.
5. Starfish live in _____ water.
6. A(n) _____ is an animal that lacks symmetry.
7. During molting, a lobster sheds its _____.
8. The _____ and _____ of a crayfish are fused together into one region.
9. An insect's body contains tiny pores for respiration called _____.
10. Book lungs are present in some _____.

D. How and Why

1. How are mollusks different from arthropods?
2. In what ways are all arthropods alike?
3. Why is a starfish not really a fish?
4. How would you know if an animal has bilateral symmetry?
5. How are insects harmful and helpful?
6. Draw simple diagrams of a spider and an insect that show three ways they differ.
7. Draw a diagram that shows the stages in complete metamorphosis.

Ideas to Explore

1. **Project:** Obtain a library book that explains how to make a butterfly collection. Start a collection of your own.
2. **Challenge:** Check with a local pest control service for information about insect control in your area. Prepare a report for your class.
3. **Project:** Obtain a library book about seashells. Make a collection of shells and learn the characteristics of each species in your collection.
4. **Project:** Collect pictures of animals and arrange the animals into three groups based on symmetry.
5. **Challenge:** Make a report on the farming of oysters, mussels, and clams.
6. **Challenge:** Make an illustrated report on two poisonous spiders—the black widow and brown recluse.

Readings

Arnett, Ross H. and Richard L. Jacques. *Guide to Insects*. New York: Simon & Schuster, 1981.

Cole, Joanna. *An Insect's Body*. New York: Morrow, 1984.

Dallinger, Jane. *Spiders*. Minneapolis: Lerner Publications, 1981.

Jacobson, Morris K. and David R. Franz. *Wonders of Snails and Slugs*. New York: Dodd, Mead and Company, 1980.

Jourdan, Eveline. *Butterflies and Moths Around the World*. Minneapolis: Lerner Publications, 1981.

Warner, Robert. "Metamorphosis." *Science 82*. December, 1982, pp. 42–47.

The American elk is a member of the deer family. Elk weigh up to 350 kilograms, stand 1.5 meters high at the shoulders, and can be 2.4 meters long. Males have antlers that can span over 1.5 meters. The coat is grayish brown with a white patch near the tail. What characteristics enable the elk to be classified as a mammal? How do complex vertebrates like the elk reproduce? How do mammals care for their offspring?

CHAPTER 13
VERTEBRATES

13:1 Phylum Chordata

What do you have in common with a sponge, a coelenterate, a worm, a mollusk, an arthropod, and an echinoderm? You and all of these organisms are classified in the animal kingdom. However, you have a characteristic that none of these other animals have. You have a backbone. They do not have backbones. They are invertebrates. Fish, amphibians, reptiles, birds, and mammals, including people, are vertebrates.

Vertebrates are classified in phylum **Chordata** (kohr DAHT uh). Phylum Chordata is subdivided into seven classes. Fish are grouped into three classes in phylum Chordata. Amphibians, reptiles, birds, and mammals are each a separate class in this phylum. Table 13–1 on page 258 summarizes the classes of vertebrates in phylum Chordata. It lists some characteristics and gives examples of animals in each class.

Phylum Chordata also includes two other groups of animals that are not vertebrates. One group is the tunicates (TEW nuh kayts). Tunicates live in the sea. Most grow singly or in colonies attached to rocks. They have a thick, tough body covering. They vary in size from nearly microscopic to 30 centimeters in diameter.

GOALS:
1. You will learn the characteristics of animals classified in phylum Chordata.
2. You will learn the body processes of animals classified in phylum Chordata.
3. You will learn how animals in this phylum reproduce.

What are some examples of animals classified in phylum Chordata?

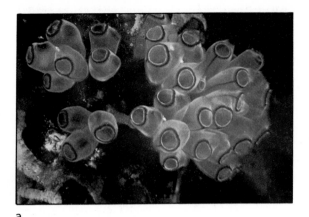

a

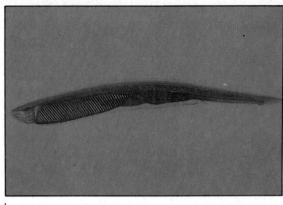

b

FIGURE 13–1. Examples of chordates that are not vertebrates are tunicates (a) and a lancelet (b).

The best known tunicates are the "sea squirts." When they are touched, sea squirts suddenly squirt water from openings in the body covering.

Lancelets are the other nonvertebrate group in phylum Chordata. One kind of small lancelet is fishlike. Its body is slender and pointed at each end. The animal burrows in the sand of shallow shore waters. At times it leaves its burrow and swims, feeding on microorganisms in the water.

All chordates at some time in their lives have a stiff cord of cartilage (KAHRT uhl ihj) that runs along their dorsal, or back, side. **Cartilage** is a tough, flexible material that does not contain all the minerals that make bone stiff. You have cartilage in your nose and ears. In vertebrates, the cord is present in young animals. Later, it becomes the backbone.

13:2 Vertebrate Characteristics

About 43 000 species of vertebrates have been identified. Inside a vertebrate animal is a skeleton that supports and protects its body parts. Lampreys, rays, and sharks have skeletons made of cartilage. Other vertebrates have skeletons made of bone. Along the length of the dorsal side of a vertebrate's body is a nerve cord. The cord is surrounded by cartilage or bony segments. At the anterior end of the animal is a brain surrounded by a braincase made of cartilage or bone. The brain is connected to the spinal cord. Both are made of nerve tissues. Together, the brain and spinal cord form the animal's central nervous system. The central nervous system is connected by nerves to other body organs it controls and regulates. Sense organs such as the eyes, ears, and nose send messages through nerves to the central nervous system.

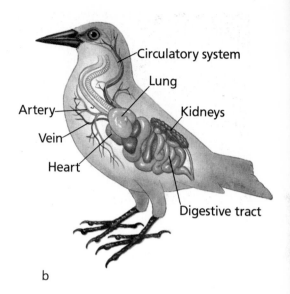

Circulatory system

Lung

Artery

Kidneys

Vein

Heart

Digestive tract

a

b

A vertebrate has a closed circulatory system composed of blood vessels. A heart with two, three, or four chambers pumps blood through the system. Three kinds of blood vessels in the system are the artery, vein, and capillary. Arteries carry blood away from the heart. Blood is carried to the heart by the veins. Capillaries connect arteries and veins, forming a closed system.

Food is digested in a vertebrate's digestive system. This system includes organs that produce digestive juices. Most food that animals eat must be made soluble before it can be used by cells. Soluble means the food dissolves in water. Digestion of food involves a chemical change that changes food from an insoluble to a soluble form. Organs such as the liver and pancreas aid in digestion. They produce digestive juices that flow through ducts into the digestive system. Digested food is absorbed and moved to cells by the blood. The food transported by the blood moves into cells by diffusion. Wastes produced by the cells are carried away by the blood.

Vertebrates need energy for their life activities. They obtain this energy from the breakdown of digested food in cells. The chemical change is respiration. Energy is released in respiration for use by cells in their life activities. Respiration also produces water, carbon dioxide, and other wastes. Wastes are removed from the blood by organs called kidneys. Water-living vertebrates like sharks and fish obtain oxygen and excrete carbon dioxide through gills. These gases are exchanged in the lungs of land-living vertebrates like reptiles, birds, and mammals.

FIGURE 13–2. Vertebrates such as a bird have skeletons (a) and circulatory and digestive systems (b).

Describe circulation in vertebrates.

Describe digestion in vertebrates.

Activity 13–1

Frog Dissection

Problem: What are the body systems of a frog?

Materials

preserved frog
dissecting pan
scissors
forceps
scalpel

probe
dissecting pins
dropper
paper towels

Procedure

1. Place a paper towel in the dissecting pan. Lay the frog on its ventral (front) side in the pan. Find the eyes, nostril, mouth, tympanic membrane, forelegs, hind legs, and feet. Compare the length of the forelegs with the length of the hind legs.

2. Make a drawing of the frog. As you proceed, draw and label each part you identify.

3. With the scissors, make a cut on both sides of the mouth. Open the mouth wide. Locate the internal nostrils, vomerine teeth, maxillary teeth, Eustachian tube openings, gullet, glottis, and tongue. Note how the tongue is attached.

4. Turn the frog over on its dorsal (back) side. Raise the skin on the front and make an incision along the midline from the lower jar to the anus. **CAUTION:** *Always be careful with scissors.* Make cuts across the top and bottom of the incision so that the skin may be pulled back like doors. Pull the skin back and pin it to the wax in the pan. Note how the skin is attached to the muscle.

5. Cut through the muscles, being careful not to cut into the organs beneath. Cut through the bone in the chest region. Pin back the muscles and expose the chest cavity.

6. Find the frog's heart. The membrane around the heart is the pericardium. Observe the chambers in the heart. Observe the blood vessels leading to body organs. Locate the lungs, liver, and gall bladder. The gall bladder is a small greenish sac beneath the liver.

7. If you have a female frog, it will have large masses of small dark eggs. Remove the egg masses.

8. Locate esophagus, stomach, small intestine, pancreas, and large intestine. These are organs of the frog's digestive system. The spleen is a round red

organ under the intestines. The membrane that holds the organs in place is called mesentery.

9. Lift up and cut out the intestines. Identify the kidneys, adrenal glands, and bladder. If you have a female frog, you have already removed the ovaries. The two long coiled white tubes are the oviducts. If you have a male frog, the round, white organs near the kidneys are the testes.

10. Turn the frog over and remove the skin from the head. Cut through the muscle and skull. Do not cut deeply. Use forceps to remove bone and expose the brain. Locate the cerebrum, olfactory lobes, optic lobes, cerebellum, medulla, and spinal cord. These are parts of the frog's nervous system.

Data and Observations

FIGURE 13–3.

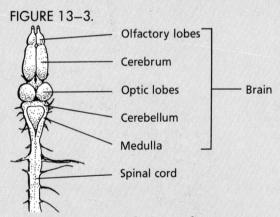

Questions and Conclusions

1. What are some characteristics of the frog that enable it to live on land?

2. What are the parts of the circulatory system?

3. How many lobes does the liver have?

4. What organs make up the digestive system?

5. What is the function of the mesentery?

6. What are the parts of the excretory system?

7. What are the parts of the nervous system?

8. How does the study of the frog contribute to the study of human biology?

9. What are the body systems of a frog?

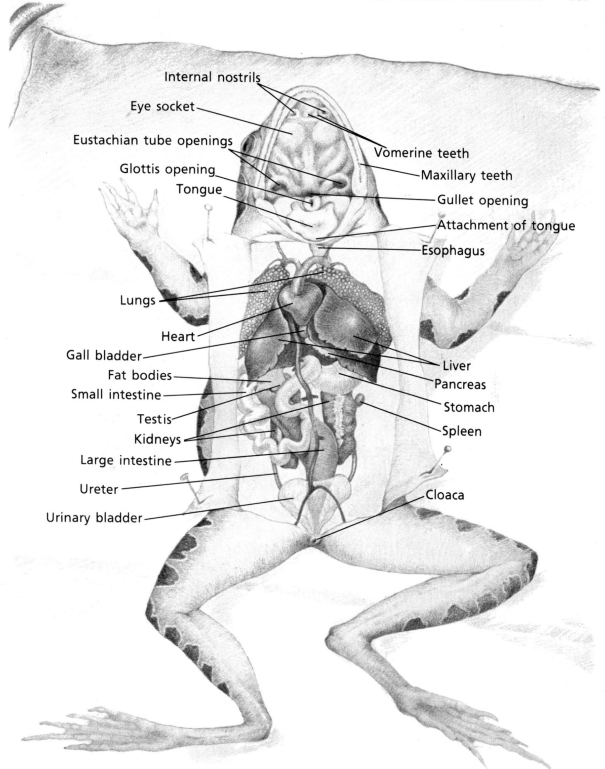

Internal nostrils
Eye socket
Eustachian tube openings
Glottis opening
Tongue
Vomerine teeth
Maxillary teeth
Gullet opening
Attachment of tongue
Esophagus
Lungs
Heart
Gall bladder
Fat bodies
Small intestine
Testis
Kidneys
Large intestine
Ureter
Urinary bladder
Liver
Pancreas
Stomach
Spleen
Cloaca

FIGURE 13–4.

Table 13—1

Vertebrates in Phylum Chordata		
Class	**Some Characteristics**	**Examples**
Agnatha	cold blooded, live in water cartilage skeleton jawless, sucker-shaped mouth, sharp teeth	Lamprey Hagfish
Chondrichthyes	cold blooded, live in water cartilage skeleton gills not covered hinged jaws, fins	Ray Shark
Osteichthyes	cold blooded, live in water bony skeleton gills covered with hard plate hinged jaws, fins, scales	Tuna Goldfish
Amphibia	cold blooded, live part of lives in water and part on land moist skin, no scales	Toad Salamander
Reptilia	cold blooded, breath air, live mainly on land dry skin with scales	Turtle Lizard
Aves	warm blooded, breathe air, live mainly on land feathers, wings, beaks	Sparrow Hawk
Mammalia	warm blooded, breathe air, live on land or in water hair feed milk to young	Kangaroo Whale

13:3 Fish

All **fish** live in fresh water or seawater. They are **cold blooded,** meaning their body temperature changes with the temperature of the environment. Fish have two chambers in their hearts.

Fish obtain oxygen from water using gills. Gills are organs that remove dissolved oxygen from water. The gills of a fish are located inside slit-shaped openings behind its head. As a fish swims, water flows over the gills and an exchange of gases is made. Dissolved oxygen is removed from the water and diffuses into the fish's blood. Another function of the gills is to remove carbon dioxide from the fish's blood. The carbon dioxide diffuses into the water that passes over the gills.

Most fish are less than one meter in size. Minnows are as small as two centimeters. Ribbon fish grow as large as six meters. There are more than 20 000 species of fish. They account for more than half of the known species of vertebrates. Sharks, salmon, eels, seahorses, and barracudas are examples of fish.

Fish are grouped into three classes in phylum Chordata. Class Agnatha (AG nuh thuh) includes the jawless fish that are the simplest in structure. These fish have sucker-shaped mouths lined with sharp teeth. Their skeletons are made of cartilage. One example of a jawless fish is the lamprey. A lamprey is a parasite. It obtains food by attaching itself to another fish by suction. It then feeds on the tissue and blood of the host fish. Lampreys occur in both fresh and salt water.

Sharks, skates, and rays are called cartilage fish because their skeletons are made of cartilage. These fish are classified in the

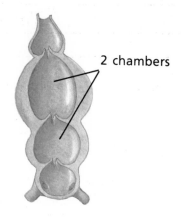

FIGURE 13–5. Fish have a two-chambered heart.

Name one fish in each class.

FIGURE 13–6. Fish have gills that remove dissolved oxygen from water. The gills of a bony fish are located inside slit-shaped openings that are covered by a hard plate.

a

b

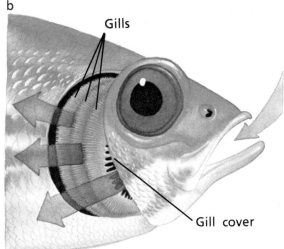

a

b

FIGURE 13–7. A skate (a) has a skeleton made of cartilage. A bluegill (b) has a skeleton made of bone.

class Chondrichthyes (kahn DRIHK thee eez) in phylum Chordata. Cartilage fish have hinged jaws that can open and close. Attached to their bodies are paired fins used for swimming. The openings to the gills are not covered. Most sharks have rows of sharp teeth on their jaws and are meat eaters. They feed on other animals in the sea. Rays and skates have bodies that are flattened. Some have poison stingers in their tails that are used for defense. Rays and skates live at the bottoms of oceans along the coasts. They usually feed on mollusks such as clams and oysters.

Tuna fish, salmon, eels, and trout are examples of the third group, bony fish. Bony fish are classified in the class Osteichthyes (ahs tee IHK thee eez) in phylum Chordata. This group has the largest number and variety of fish species. Bony fish live in both fresh and salt water. They have skeletons made of bone, jaws that are hinged, and fins. Their gills are covered with a hard plate that provides protection. Depending on the species, the bony fish eat either animal or plant material.

Making Sure

1. What are the classes of animals included in phylum Chordata?
2. Describe the main characteristics of the following.
   a. jawless fish
   b. cartilage fish
   c. bony fish
3. What two groups in phylum Chordata are not vertebrates?

Activity 13–2

Blood Circulation in a Fish

Problem: What blood vessels can be observed in the tail of a fish?

Materials

2 8-cm squares of absorbent cotton
aquarium water
petri dish half
small piece of corkboard
goldfish
thumb tacks
aquarium net
2 microscope slides
microscope
dropper
250 mL beaker

Procedure

1. Spread one square of cotton in half of a petri dish. Use aquarium water to wet the cotton.
2. Before handling the fish, wash your hands to avoid infecting the fish.
3. Wet the second square of cotton with aquarium water. Carefully wrap the fish's gills with the wet cotton. Make sure the mouth is uncovered.
4. Place the wrapped fish on a small cork board in the petri dish. Pin the cotton to the cork with thumb tacks to prevent the fish from moving. Take care not to pin the fish's fins. Use the dropper to keep the fish and cotton wet at all times.
5. Place a clean microscope slide under the tail of the fish and another clean slide on top of the tail. This will hold the tail in place. **CAUTION:** *Work quickly. Keeping the fish out of water for a long time may harm the fish.*
6. Place the petri dish on the stage of the microscope with the tail over the hole in the stage.
7. Use low power to focus on a section of the tail.
8. Locate and identify the blood vessels. Determine whether the direction of blood flow is toward the tail, away from the tail, or in both directions.
9. Draw a section of the tail showing the blood vessels.

Data and Observations

FIGURE 13–8.

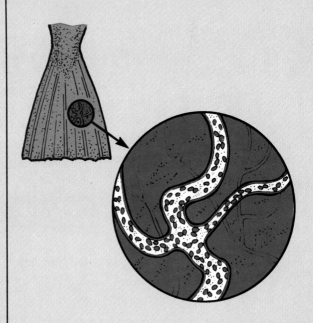

Questions and Conclusions

1. What are the smallest vessels?
2. How do blood cells travel through these vessels?
3. Which blood vessels appear to have a pulse?
4. In which blood vessels does blood move the slowest?
5. In which blood vessels does it move the fastest?
6. How can you tell the difference in an artery and a vein?
7. Does a fish have an open or closed circulatory system? Explain.
8. What blood vessels can be observed in the tail of a fish?

13:4 Amphibians

Animals that live part of their lives in water and part on land belong to the Amphibia (am FIBH ee uh) class in phylum Chordata. **Amphibians** have moist skin with no scales. Like fish, they are cold blooded, but amphibians have three-chambered hearts.

Salamanders and toads, are amphibians that live mostly in moist regions in or near fresh water or in damp places. Some toads live in desert regions like the Mexican burrowing toad of the south-western United States. These toads stay in underground burrows during the hot day and become active at night.

Frogs are amphibians, too. Adult frogs live on land and breathe air but they mate and lay eggs in water. Fertilization of eggs is usually outside the body. Tadpoles grow from frog eggs and live in water. A tadpole looks like a fish. It has a long tail for swimming. Like fish, tadpoles have gills through which they get oxygen from water. As a tadpole ages, it loses its gills. Also, the tail is absorbed into the body as the animal matures into a land-living adult frog.

Frogs and toads are similar in appearance. Frogs have smooth skin and toads have warty skin. The head of a frog or toad is attached to the trunk of the animal's body. Neither frogs nor toads have necks or tails. Their front legs are small and their hind legs are long and strong. A salamander's head is connected to its body by a neck. The body is shaped like a cylinder and there is a long tail attached. The tail is rounded in adult salamanders that are land dwellers. It is flattened in species that swim in water.

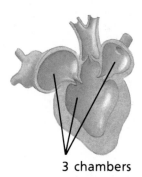

3 chambers

FIGURE 13–9. Amphibians have three-chambered hearts.

Describe the growth of a frog.

FIGURE 13–10. A Barking Tree Frog (a) and an American Toad (b) are examples of amphibians.

a

b

a   b

13:5 Reptiles

FIGURE 13–11. A snake is a reptile that sheds its outer layer of skin by molting (a). The turtle (b) can pull its head, legs, and tail into its shell for protection.

Many people think that the skin of a snake would feel wet and slimy. However, a snake's skin is dry. The skin has two layers of cells. Living cells form the inner layer. Dead cells form the outer layer of dry scales. From time to time, a snake sheds its outer layer of skin. This process, called molting, is similar to the shedding of an exoskeleton by an arthropod.

Snakes are vertebrates that are classified as reptiles. Other examples of reptiles include lizards, turtles, crocodiles, and alligators. They belong to class Reptilia (rep TIHL ee uh) in phylum Chordata. Dinosaurs, animals that lived about two hundred million years ago to 65 million years ago, were also reptiles.

Name three examples of reptiles.

All **reptiles** are cold blooded, breathe air, and live mainly on land. They have three-chambered hearts, like amphibians. Unlike snakes, most reptiles have a long body with a head, neck, trunk, tail and four legs. Fertilization occurs inside their bodies and most reproduce by laying eggs that have a leathery shell. The young hatch from the eggs. Some turtles that live in water have legs like flippers that are used for swimming. Some reptiles, such as turtles, have shells. If danger threatens, a turtle can pull its legs, head, and tail into its shell for protection. Reptiles have scales that help prevent loss of water from their bodies.

What are the main characteristics of reptiles?

The tropics and other warm regions have the greatest number of reptile species. Reptiles feed chiefly on other animals, such as insects and small vertebrates. Some species of lizards eat plants.

Making Sure

4. How is a reptile different from an amphibian?
5. How is an amphibian different from a fish?

FIGURE 13–12. Some birds use their high rates of body metabolism to produce body heat that allows them to survive in cold climates.

List five ways in which all birds are alike.

FIGURE 13–13. For lightness, many bird bones are hollow with struts strengthening them. The whole skeleton of a 1.8 Kilogram bird with a 2 meter wingspread, has a mass as little as 114 grams— less than the weight of the bird's feathers.

13:6 Birds

Birds belong to class Aves (AY vayz) in phylum chordata. They are the only animals that have feathers. Feathers are lightweight, strong, and flexible. They serve as insulation that protects a bird's body against heat and cold. Birds also have wings often used for flying. Some, such as penguins and ostriches, have reduced wings, and cannot fly. The bones of birds are strong and lightweight. Many of the bones are hollow, containing air. Birds reproduce by sexual reproduction. Fertilization of the eggs takes place inside the body. They lay eggs from which offspring hatch.

Birds are warm-blooded vertebrates. **Warm blooded** means they maintain a constant body temperature no matter what the temperature of their surroundings. A bird obtains oxygen by breathing air with its lungs. Its circulatory system has a four-chambered heart. A bird has a high rate of metabolism. This means its body processes occur at a rapid speed. This high rate of metabolism produces the huge amount of energy that birds need to fly. It also produces body heat that allows some birds to live and be active in cold climates. Because of its high rate of metabolism, a bird needs to eat often to supply its body with the necessary energy. Birds eat seeds, fruits, worms, and insects. Some, such as owls and hawks, eat small animals like field mice and rabbits. Gulls and pelicans are marine birds that catch and eat fish. Grouse and quail live in fields and eat plants.

Among birds there is a variety of form in feathers, beaks, feet, wings, and tails. The kind of beak a bird has is related to the kind of food it eats. Birds also vary in their behavior. For example, some birds migrate south in winter. Other birds do not migrate. The many differences in characteristics are used to identify and classify birds. Chickens, turkeys, ducks, and geese are an important source of food for people, providing meat and eggs.

Activity 13-3 Observing Birds

Problem: What can you learn about birds by observing them?

Materials large empty milk carton, scissors, 2 wire coat hangers, wire cutters, wild birdseed, empty mesh onion sack, suet, field guide to birds, binoculars—optional

Procedure (1) Make a bird feeder out of an empty milk carton. Wash and rinse the carton well. (2) Cut large windows in opposite sides of the carton. **CAUTION:** *Use scissors carefully.* (3) Make a wire hanger for the bird feeder from a wire coat hanger. Hang the feeder in a tree outside your classroom window. (4) Place birdseed in the feeder. (5) Fill an empty mesh onion sack with suet. Tie a firm knot in the top of the sack. (6) Make a hanger for the suet feedbag. Hang the suet feedbag on a tree branch high enough so other animals cannot reach it. (7) Watch for birds to come to your feeders. It may take two or three days. Keep a record of the kinds of birds that eat at the feeders.

Questions (1) What birds are most common at each kind of feeder? (2) What is the best time of the day for observing birds? (3) Why must you keep the feeder filled all the time, especially in winter? (4) Why is it better not to feed birds at all in winter if you do not feed them all the time? (5) What can you learn about birds by observing them?

Downy woodpecker

Chickadee

Starling

Rock dove

Grackle

Sparrow

FIGURE 13–14.

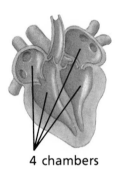

4 chambers

FIGURE 13–15. Mammals and birds have four-chambered hearts.

What are the characteristics of mammals?

13:7 Mammals

People do not always see themselves as animals because they can think and act in complex ways. For example, people can learn to speak, read, and write. Also, people can make and use tools. People are animals, though, with highly developed brains. People are classified in the class Mammalia (muh MAY lee uh) in the phylum Chordata of the animal kingdom.

Mammals are warm-blooded animals that have hair and feed milk to their young. Examples of mammals are people, whales, porpoises, bats, kangaroos, bears, rats, and mice. Some domestic (duh MES tihk) animals are mammals. For example, cats, dogs, cows, sheep, and goats are domestic animals. A domestic animal is a species that is raised and cared for by people. Domestic animals provide wool, hides, milk, meat, and other products. Species such as dogs and cats are companions for people.

A mammal has a muscle called a diaphragm that assists the lungs in breathing. A mammal's circulatory system has a separate pathway that carries blood from the heart to the lungs and back again. A mammal's heart has four chambers. The hair on a mammal acts as insulation which helps in maintaining a constant body temperature. Mammals have sweat glands that are used to excrete wastes.

Most animals hatch from eggs. However, the young of most mammals develop completely inside their mother's body before birth. One exception is the marsupial (mahr SOO pee uhl), like the kangaroo and opossum.

The young of a marsupial grow inside the mother and are not fully developed when born. After birth, they crawl into the mother's pouch where they complete their development. After birth, young mammals are fed milk produced by the mother's milk glands called mammary glands. Human babies are given much more care than the young of other animals.

FIGURE 13–16. Marsupials such as the kangaroo complete their development inside their mother's pouch.

Activity 13—4   Classifying Vertebrates

Problem: How do scientists classify vertebrates?

Materials

paper
pencil
animals or pictures of animals

Procedure

1. Copy the four column chart shown under Data and Observations.
2. Write the name of each animal you are studying in the first column.
3. Predict the class of the animal and write the predicted class in the second column.
4. Write the characteristics of the animal that helped you decide its class.
5. Use the key to find the class of each animal. Write the class name in the last column.

Data and Observations

Animal			
Predicted Class			
Characteristics			
Actual Class			

Questions and Conclusions

1. How many of your predictions were correct?
2. What characteristics of each vertebrate class are used for identifying the animals?
3. How do scientists classify vertebrates?

---

1. Does the animal have a backbone?

YES   Go to 2.

NO   Invertebrate

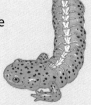

2. Does the animal have feathers?

YES   Class Aves

NO   Go to 3.

3. Does the animal have jaws?

YES   Go to 4.

NO   Class Agnatha

---

4. Does the animal have paired fins?

YES   Go to 5.

NO   Go to 6.

5. Does the animal have a bony skeleton?

YES   Osteichthyes

NO   Chondrichthyes

6. Does the animal have fur?

YES   Mammal

NO   Go to 7.

7. Does the animal have skin scales?

YES   Reptilia

NO   Amphibia

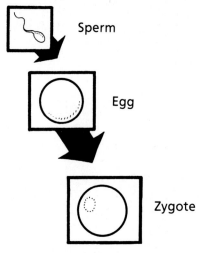

FIGURE 13–17. The female egg cell and the male sperm cell combine in sexual reproduction, forming a single cell called a zygote.

13:8 Sexual Reproduction

Sexual reproduction with male and female parents takes place in vertebrates. The male of the species produces sperm. The female produces eggs. Males and females of the same species mate.

During mating, sex cells from each parent join together. Sex cells are special cells produced in sex organs. Sex cells formed in the female sex organs, the ovaries, are called eggs. Sex cells formed in the male sex organs, the testes, are sperm.

Fertilization is the joining of an egg and a sperm. The nucleus of one sperm joins with the nucleus of one egg. A single cell called a zygote is formed. Mating usually results in one or more eggs being fertilized. The zygotes develop into embryos and eventually into young organisms that grow to be adults.

Two animals of different species cannot normally mate and reproduce sexually. For sexual reproduction to occur, an egg and a sperm from the same species must come together. The ability to sexually reproduce by mating and to produce fertile offspring are factors used to determine whether a group of animals should be classified as a species.

13:9 External Fertilization

What is external fertilization?

External fertilization means sperm fertilize eggs outside the female animal's body. External fertilization occurs in many animals that live in water. Fish and amphibians reproduce this way. These animals release eggs and sperm into water. The sperms swim to the eggs and fertilize them. Sperm can only travel in a fluid, such as water.

FIGURE 13–18. Big horn sheep are mammals that reproduce sexually.

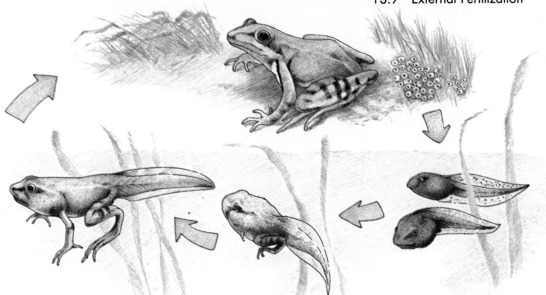

External fertilization occurs in most frogs. Eggs are produced in ovaries inside the female frog. The two ovaries are hollow sacs with thin walls located in the top of the abdomen near the kidneys. From the ovaries the eggs move through two tubes to the cloaca (kloa AY kuh), an opening at the end of the large intestine. It takes about four hours for an egg to go through the tubes. Glands in the tubes add a jellylike coating around the egg. The egg leaves the female frog through the cloaca. A large mass of eggs is dropped into a pond or stream.

Sperm are produced in the male frog's two testes. Each testis is a mass of coiled tubes attached to the frog's kidneys. When mature, sperm pass out of the testes. They leave the frog's body through the cloaca at the end of the large intestine. A male frog deposits its sperm in the water near the eggs. The sperms swim to the eggs and fertilize them. One sperm can fertilize one egg, forming a zygote.

A frog zygote develops in water. It grows into an embryo, the first stage of growth after fertilization. After some days, the embryo grows into a tiny frog larva. The frog larva, usually called a tadpole, has an oval body and a slender, compressed tail. On the surface of the larva's body are three pairs of gills. As the animal grows into a larger tadpole, these gills are lost. They are slowly replaced by internal gills within gill slits in the skin. The tail increases in length. Over weeks or months, the tadpole grows legs and develops lungs. Slowly the gills and tail are lost as they are absorbed into the body. These and other changes occur as the tadpole develops into an adult frog.

FIGURE 13–19. A female frog deposits a mass of eggs in a pond or stream. The eggs are fertilized by sperm from a male frog. Tadpoles develop from the eggs and grow into mature frogs.

Describe reproduction in a frog.

13:10 Internal Fertilization

What is internal fertilization?

Many animal species reproduce through internal fertilization. Some examples of these animals are insects, earthworms, birds, and mammals. In these species, sperm is deposited inside the female reproductive organs. Fusion of the egg and sperm occurs within the body. For instance, eggs are produced inside the ovaries of a female bird. Eggs are released from the ovaries into a tube called an oviduct. If sperm are present in the oviduct, an egg may be fertilized by a single sperm. A hard shell forms around the zygote and fluids. The female bird lays one or more eggs. The eggs are incubated, or kept warm, by the female as she sits on them. The incubation time varies with species. Inside an egg a baby bird develops. When fully developed, the young bird hatches out of the egg.

Describe reproduction in a mammal.

Mammals also reproduce by internal fertilization. Eggs are produced in the ovaries of female mammals. An important reproductive organ in female mammals is the uterus (YEWT uh rus), a sac-shaped, muscular organ. Oviducts are tubes through which eggs travel to the uterus from the ovaries.

A series of changes occur during the estrous (ES trus) cycle in the female mammal. The estrous cycle is repeated over and over again during the female's reproductive years. During the cycle, the uterus prepares for reproduction by developing a thick lining and a rich blood supply. Then an egg is released from an ovary into the oviduct. This part of the cycle is estrus. **Estrus** is the time when a female animal can mate with a male and produce offspring.

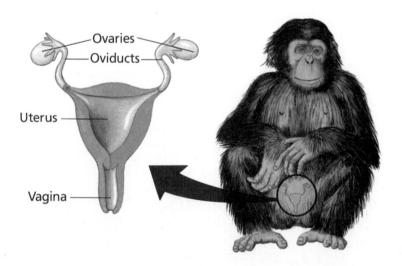

Ovaries
Oviducts
Uterus
Vagina

FIGURE 13–20. The reproductive systems in mammals are different from the reproductive systems in frogs. Fertilization is internal in mammals.

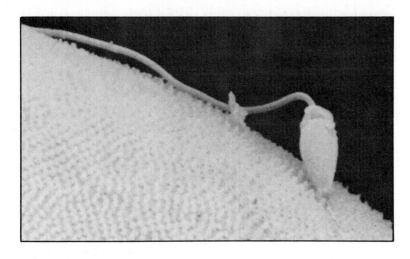

FIGURE 13–21. Sperm swim through the vagina and uterus to the oviducts. When an egg and sperm meet in the oviduct, fertilization occurs.

Sperm are produced in the testes of male mammals. During mating, sperm are deposited in the female's vagina (vuh JI nuh). The **vagina** is a canal that leads to the uterus. The sperm swim through fluid in the vagina and uterus and go into the oviducts. When an egg and sperm meet in the oviduct, fertilization occurs. An egg must be fertilized shortly after it is released from an ovary or it will die. Only one sperm fertilizes an egg. When this occurs, the cell membrane of the egg changes chemically to prevent other sperm from entering. The zygote that forms grows into an embryo that develops into the new offspring inside the uterus. There is no metamorphosis in the development of mammals and birds as there is in insects and frogs.

Making Sure

6. How does reproduction in mammals differ from reproduction in amphibians?
7. In what body structure of mammals are eggs produced?
8. In what body structure does fertilization occur in mammals?
9. What is estrous?

13:11 Development and Birth

After an egg is fertilized inside a female mammal, development of the new offspring begins. The time between fertilization and the birth of the offspring is called **gestation** (juh STAY shun). Another word for gestation is pregnancy. Gestation periods vary among animals. For a rat, the gestation period may be only about 22 days. For an elephant, it is 600 days. For people, the gestation period is 266 days, or about nine months.

Define gestation.

What changes occur in a mammal zygote as it develops?

During gestation, changes occur as a zygote develops. The zygote moves through the oviduct into the uterus where it begins to divide. Within a few hours two cells are formed. Soon each of these two cells divides, producing four cells. The four cells divide producing eight cells. The eight cells divide producing 16 cells. More and more cells are formed by repeated cell divisions.

During these early stages of development, the organism is called an embryo. Table 13-2 shows the stages in the growth of animal embryos. After an embryo develops the shape and form of its species, it is called a **fetus** (FEET us).

FIGURE 13–22. A frog zygote develops by repeated cell divisions. About five hours pass from the fertilized egg stage (a) to the 16-cell cleavage stage (f).

As the zygote develops into an embryo, membranes form around it. The membranous sac becomes filled with fluid. The sac of fluid helps protect the organism. Part of the sac grows onto the wall of the uterus. This part of the sac is called the **placenta** (pluh SENT uh). Food, oxygen, and wastes move back and forth

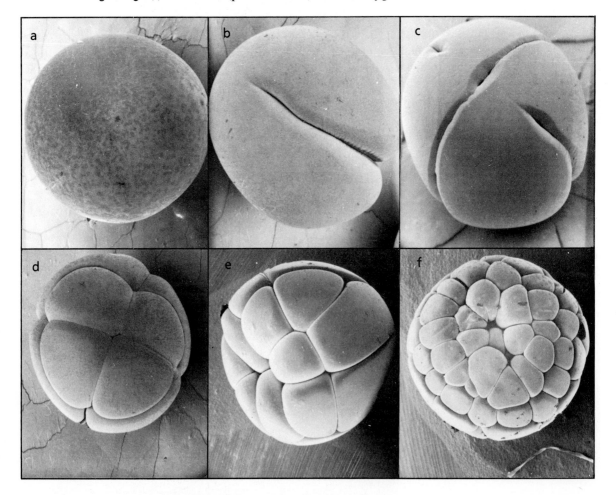

Table 13-2

Stages of Embryo Development			
Stage	Morula	Blastula	Gastrula
Structure	solid ball of cells	ball with fluid 2 layers of cells	cup-shaped 3 layers of cells

by diffusion through the placenta from the uterus to the embryo or fetus. The exchange of materials between the mother and fetus takes place without the mixing of blood. The uterus provides protection, food, and oxygen to the developing organism throughout gestation.

Mammals have milk-producing mammary glands. During gestation, the mammary glands enlarge. At birth they begin to secrete a watery fluid that contains substances that fight germs. These germ fighters protect a newborn animal from disease. The fluid continues to be produced the first days after birth. Then milk is produced.

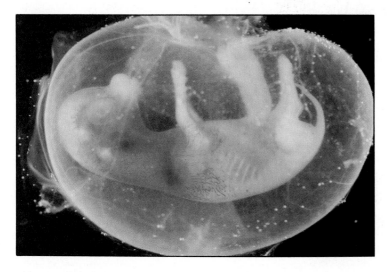

FIGURE 13-23. A mammal embryo develops inside a sack of fluid that helps protect the organism.

FIGURE 13–24. Mammals produce fewer offspring than most other animals. They care for the newborns to increase their chances for survival.

How do multiple births occur?

At birth, the fetus is forced out of the uterus by muscular movements of that organ. Soon after birth, the placenta and other membranes are expelled.

Twins and multiple births occur in many species of mammals. The offspring may be identical or different. The zygote may develop into two or more parts. Each part grows to form an embryo. In the armadillo, several identical young are always produced from a single zygote. At the beginning of its development, the zygote divides into four or more parts. Each part grows to form an armadillo embryo. The embryos grow into fetuses. Thus, females of the armadillo species always give birth to more than one offspring.

Multiple births may also result if more than one egg is released and fertilized at the same time. Each of the zygotes formed grows into an embryo. Each embryo grows into a fetus. Rabbits, cats, dogs, and pigs commonly give birth to several offspring at one time. Humans usually produce one offspring at a time.

Mammals care for their young after birth. Care of a newborn offspring increases the chances for it to live and grow into an adult. Because mammals produce fewer offspring than most other kinds of animals, care of young is important to the survival of mammal species. In animal species that produce large numbers of offspring, parents provide little or no care for the offspring. The large number of offspring increases the chances that some of the offspring will survive.

Making Sure

10. What is the difference between an embryo and a fetus?
11. How does a mammal embryo get food and remove wastes?

Technology

What Happened to the Dinosaurs?

Sixty-five million years ago, most life on Earth died. About 70 percent of all known species, including the dinosaurs, became extinct, or no longer existed. The fossil record documents this mass extinction. Remains of creatures that had ruled Earth for 140 million years vanished from the more recent fossil beds of rock. Unfortunately, the fossil record could not help scientists find a reason for the extinction.

In an attempt to explain the mass extinction of species, a theory concerning a rare element—iridium—was developed. In 1977, Luis and Walter Alvarez discovered unusual amounts of iridium in clay sediments. Since that time, iridium has been found in similar sediments in 36 different sites around the world.

To measure elements such as iridium, scientists use a technique called neutron activation analysis (NAA). Sample sediments are placed in a reactor that bombards them with neutrons. This causes the elements in the sample, such as iridium, to produce a unique pattern of colored lines on a spectrometer. The spectrometer records and interprets information from the patterns to give the amount of iridium (and other elements) present in the sample. A computer then prints out a graph showing amounts of each element present in the sample.

Iridium is normally found in very small amounts in Earth's crust. The only source known that could account for the amount of iridium found in the clay was believed to be an extraterrestrial object. Present evidence suggests that this iridium was deposited by a comet that struck Earth 65 million years ago. This is the same time that marks the period of the dinosaur extinction. The Alvarezes speculated that 65 million years ago, a comet hit Earth causing large amounts of dust to accumulate in the atmosphere. This dust may have prevented sunlight from reaching Earth for up to six months. Photosynthesis would have been impossible, and food chains would have been disrupted. Many animals, including the dinosaurs, would have died from lack of food. With no sunlight reaching Earth, temperatures may have cooled, producing an unfavorable environment for the dinosaurs. Comet impact also could have resulted in the formation of nitric oxide (NO). When combined with water, nitric acid is formed. High concentrations may have produced acid rain, polluted the water supply, and caused a lack of oxygen for animals. The combination of disrupted food chains, cooler temperatures, and pollution may have been the cause of this mass extinction.

FIGURE 13–25. Why did *Stegosaurus*, a dinosaur that roamed Earth millions of years ago, become extinct?

FOCUS ON
Frontiers

An Invasion of Land

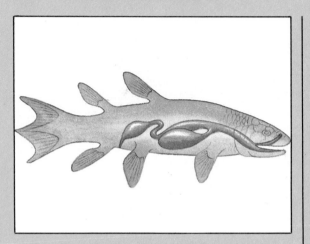

The major transition of animals from life in water to land was first realized by E.D. Cope in 1892. From his studies of fossil fish, he was able to state that this important event occurred about 350 million years ago. The fossil fish on which Dr. Cope based his research are known as coelacanths. Coelacanths are lizardlike fish with hollow fin spines. From fossil evidence, it is clear that these fish were once abundant all over the world.

Fossil coelacanths have several unique features. They have unusual limblike fins that are lobed. These lobe-fin fish were considered likely ancestors of the first land vertebrates. However, there are difficulties with the interpretation of past life forms from fossils. To understand how an animal once moved and breathed, it would be useful to know the structures of major body organs. Vital organs are usually soft and are rarely preserved. Their form can only be guessed. It was hypothesized that coelacanths possessed a lung to breathe air. They were thought to have become extinct about 60 million years ago.

The secret of the coelacanth's anatomy was dramatically revealed by the catch of an unusual fish in 1938. Fishers working in the Bay of the Chalumna River, South Africa, netted a fish that they could not identify. A curator of a museum was brought to examine the fish, which was nearly two meters long. It had powerful jaws and heavy, thick scales. The curator, convinced it was an important find, contacted Professor J. B. L. Smith, an expert on African fish. Dr. Smith recognized it to be a lobe-fin fish that was known previously only from the fossil record of coelacanths. The news of the discovery of this "living fossil" was received with excitement by the scientific community, since it revealed one more link in the history of life. The study of modern coelacanths has since confirmed the earlier hypotheses. The fins are used for support and movement, and coelacanths possess a lung to breathe air.

Another discovery of a similar fossil lobe-fin fish had leglike fins. It also had a passage linking its nostrils with the roof of its mouth. This passageway could have allowed air to pass from the nose to the lung. This is a feature of all land vertebrates. From the studies of fossil and living coelacanths, it appears likely that all land vertebrates are descended from similar lobe-fin fish.

Review

Summary

1. Vertebrates are classified in phylum Chordata.   13:1
2. The brain and spinal cord of a vertebrate make up its central nervous system.   13:2
3. Fish live in water, have gills, and are cold blooded.   13:3
4. Fish are divided into three classes: jawless fish, cartilage fish, and bony fish.   13:3
5. Amphibians live part of their lives in water and part on land. They have moist skin, no scales, and are cold blooded.   13:4
6. Reptiles are cold blooded, breathe air, and live mostly on land.   13:5
7. Birds are warm blooded and reproduce by laying eggs. They have feathers, lightweight bones, and wings.   13:6
8. Mammals are warm-blooded animals that have hair and feed their young milk.   13:7
9. Fertilization is the joining of an egg and sperm to form a zygote.   13:8
10. Fertilization occurs outside the bodies of some vertebrates.   13:9
11. Fertilization and the development of an embryo occurs inside the body of the female mammal.   13:10
12. Cell divisions change a zygote into an embryo.   13:11
13. During gestation, a mammal embryo receives nourishment from its mother's uterus.   13:11

Vocabulary

Write a sentence using the following words or terms correctly.

amphibian	estrus	placenta
bird	external fertilization	reptile
cartilage	fish	vagina
Chordata	gestation	warm blooded
cold blooded	mammal	

Questions

A. True or False
Determine whether each of the following sentences is true or false. Rewrite the false statements to make them correct.

1. Vertebrates are classified in five classes of the phylum Chordata.
2. Fish are warm-blooded animals.
3. Amphibians and reptiles are in the same class.

4. A turtle is a reptile.
5. Most reptiles and all birds lay eggs.
6. Frogs reproduce by internal fertilization.
7. The gestation time in all mammal species is the same.
8. Blood from the mother circulates through a fetus during gestation.
9. An embryo develops from a zygote.
10. Mammals feed their young on milk.

B. Multiple Choice
Choose the word or phrase that correctly completes the following sentences.
1. A *(shark, ray, tuna)* is an example of a bony fish.
2. A *(frog, toad, lizard)* is a reptile.
3. A(n) *(octopus, alligator, worm)* is a chordate.
4. A *(starfish, jellyfish, shark, frog)* is an amphibian.
5. *(Fish, Amphibians, Reptiles, Birds)* are warm blooded.
6. A salamander is a(n) *(amphibian, reptile, invertebrate)*.
7. A *(frog, fish, whale)* is a mammal.
8. After birth, a mammal feeds its young *(meat, plants, milk, water)*.
9. Internal fertilization occurs in *(starfish, frogs, chickens)*.
10. A zygote develops into a(n) *(placenta, embryo, sperm, egg)*.

C. Completion
Complete each of the following sentences with the correct word or phrase.
1. _____ are nonvertebrates in phylum Chordata.
2. The skeleton of a shark is made of _____.
3. Fish and tadpoles obtain oxygen from water through _____.
4. _____ grow and develop into frogs.
5. Many of the bones in a(n) _____ are hollow.
6. Mammals are _____ blooded.
7. During the _____ cycle a mammal's uterus is prepared for reproduction.
8. _____ is the joining together of an egg and sperm.
9. Gestation is the time from fertilization to _____ of a new offspring.
10. _____ result if two eggs are released and fertilized at the same time.

D. How and Why
1. What are the characteristics of each of the three classes of fish?
2. How are the amphibians different from fish?
3. How are cold-blooded animals different from warm-blooded animals?
4. Compare the characteristics of amphibians and reptiles.

5. How are birds different from mammals?

6. How are mammals different from other vertebrates?

7. Frogs produce many offspring. Why is the world not overpopulated with these animals?

8. The production of frog sperm is many times greater than the production of frog eggs. How does this help a frog species to survive?

9. Why does a mammal embryo have a better chance of survival than a frog embryo?

10. Why is it likely that a drug injected into the blood of a pregnant female rabbit will appear in the blood of the fetus?

Ideas to Explore

1. **Project:** Take a camera with you and visit a zoo. Make a collection of pictures of animals you observe. Learn the scientific name for each animal you photograph.

2. **Project:** Set up an aquarium of tropical fish. Prepare a key that people can use to identify the fish.

3. **Challenge:** Obtain a library book about snakes. Learn which snakes are common to your region and their identifying characteristics.

4. **Challenge:** Make a poster or bulletin board display for your classroom of drawings of animals in phylum Chordata.

5. **Challenge:** Make a chart showing the gestation periods for different animal species. Obtain this information from your school or local library.

6. **Challenge:** Prepare a report on programs for increasing the reproduction of endangered animal species such as the peregrine falcon and California condor.

7. **Challenge:** Obtain information about artificial insemination and superovulation in cows. Learn how these techniques are used to preserve sperm and eggs for later use in reproducing these animals.

8. **Project:** Observe birds around your home. Make a list of the birds you can recognize. Use a field guide to identify the birds you cannot recognize.

Readings

Hartman, Jane E. *How Animals Care for Their Young*. New York: Holiday House, 1980.

Leen, Nina. *Rare and Unusual Animals*. New York: Holt, Rinehart, and Winston, 1981.

National Geographic Society. *The Wonder of Birds*. Washington D.C.: National Geographic Society, 1983.

Olesky, Walter. *Careers in the Animal Kingdom*. New York: Messner, 1980.

Classification

Background Data

Classifying helps scientists study in an organized way the vast variety of organisms found on Earth. The classification most often used includes five major subdivisions called kingdoms. Each kingdom is subdivided into more specific groups called phyla. The distinguishing characteristics among members of a phylum are less varied than the characteristics that group organisms in a kingdom. The organisms within each phylum are separated into smaller groupings called classes. Classes are subdivided into orders that can be subdivided into families. The subdividing continues as families are divided into smaller groups. Each smaller group is a genus. Species is the smallest division of a kingdom. Members of a species, if they mate with one another, produce offspring that are capable of reproducing. Members of the same genus but different species are similar but incapable of producing fertile offspring.

Input/Output

Enter the program into your computer exactly as it is printed. After you enter the entire program, type RUN. If there is a problem, type LIST and check that you have entered the program exactly as it is printed. Remember, symbols and punctuation are important and must be typed as printed here. REM statements are provided in the program to help you. They do not need to be entered in order for the program to run. When all corrections have been made, be sure to save the program by typing SAVE CLASSIFICATION, or whatever name you wish to give the program.

Once the program is running, the computer will present you with a menu with two choices. If you select choice one, you will be asked to enter the name of a common animal. The computer will print out the animal's complete classification if it is in its memory. If the classification is not in the computer's memory, you will be given the chance to choose again from the menu. If you select choice two, the computer will present you with a list of animals in its memory and ask you to select one of them. When you make your choice, the computer will print out the complete classification of the animal.

Programming Notes

The computer reads each line of the program and executes the command listed there. Line 20 is used several times to clear the screen. Some computers use the command CLS, others use HOME. Use the command your computer recognizes to clear the screen.

The name of the animal entered is read in lines 40 and 50 and checked to see if it ends the program. Lines 80 and 90 print the menu. The input to the menu is checked in lines 100 through 120. An animal is entered and read in line 130, and checked against the data list in line 140. If the animal is present in the list, the program moves to line 170 and the classification is printed. If the animal is not present, a statement is printed by line 160. A list of animals is printed by lines 210 through 240. Line 250 is used to choose the animal desired, and the program loops back to line 170 to print the classification.

Challenge: On Your Own

If you want to change the program, the data statements can be extended to include 120 organisms. You will need to change line 10 as well as add DATA statements following line 1009. When adding additional organisms to the data list, be sure to follow the format used in the existing data statements. Also, you must end the data with a DATA END statement.

Program

```
10   DIM A$(120): DIM B$(120): DIM
     C$(120): DIM D$(120): DIM E$
     (120): DIM F$(120): DIM G$(1
     20): DIM H$(120): DIM I$(120
     )
20   HOME : IF Q = 1 THEN 80: REM
     MAY BE DIFFERENT ON YOUR CO
     MPUTER
30   IF Q = 2 THEN 180
35   IF Q = 3 THEN 210
40 I = I + 1: READ A$(I): IF A$(
     I) = "END" THEN I = I - 1: GOTO
     70
50   READ B$(I),C$(I),D$(I),E$(I)
     ,F$(I),G$(I),H$(I),I$(I)
60   PRINT I$(I): GOTO 40
70 Q = 1: GOTO 20
80   PRINT "      MENU": PRINT :
     PRINT" 1. TYPE IN NAME OF
      COMMON ANIMAL": PRINT "
     COMPUTER WILL CHECK CLASSIFI
     CATION"
90   PRINT "2.   PRINT A MENU OF T
     HE COMMON ANIMALS": PRINT "
          THAT ARE IN COMPUTER MEMO
     RY": PRINT : PRINT : PRINT "
     WHAT IS CHOICE ";
100  INPUT A: IF A = 1 THEN 130
110  IF A = 2 THEN 205
120  GOTO 100
130  PRINT : PRINT : PRINT "WHAT
     IS THE COMMON ANIMAL FORM":
     PRINT "THAT YOU ARE LOOKING
     FOR?": PRINT "SPELL PRECISE
     LY PLEASE ": INPUT J$
140  FOR X = 1 to I: IF J$ = A$(
     X) THEN 170
150   NEXT X
160  PRINT "SORRY, THAT NAME IS
     <NOT> <ONLY ONE>": PRINT "IN
     THE COMPUTER MEMORY BANK": FOR
     T = 1 to 3000: NEXT T: GOTO
     70
170 Q = 2: GOTO 20
180  PRINT "KINGDOM => ";B$(X): PRINT
     "PHYLUM => ";C$(X): PRINT "C
     LASS => ";D$(X): PRINT "ORDE
     R => ";E$(X)
190  PRINT "FAMILY => ";F$(X): PRINT
     "GENUS => ";G$(X): PRINT "SP
     ECIES => ";H$(X): PRINT : PRINT
     : PRINT "COMMON NAME => ";I$
     (X): IF A = 2 THEN  PRINT : PRINT
     "ENTER FOR MENU ";: INPUT Q$
     : GOTO 70
200  PRINT : PRINT : PRINT "ENTE
     R FOR ANOTHER ";: INPUT Q$: GOTO
     150
205 Q = 3: GOTO 20
210  FOR Y = 1 TO I: PRINT Y;"
     "A$(Y),: IF A$(Y + 15) = "" THEN
     250: PRINT Y + 15;"   ";A$(Y +
     15);
220  IF Y = 15 THEN Y = 30: PRINT
     "ENTER FOR MORE ";: INPUT Q$
230  IF Y = 45 THEN Y = 60: PRINT
     "ENTER FOR MORE ";: INPUT Q$
240  IF Y = 75 THEN Y = 90: PRINT
     "ENTER FOR MORE ";: INPUT Q$
250  PRINT : NEXT Y: PRINT "ENTE
     R NUMBER OF ANIMAL ";: INPUT
     X: GOTO 170
1000   DATA   HUMAN,ANIMAL,CHORDAT
     A,MAMMALIA,PRIMATE,HOMINIDAE
     ,HOMO,SAPIENS,MAN
1001   DATA   DOG,ANIMAL,CHORDATA,
     MAMMALIA,CARNIVORA,CANIDAE,C
     ANIS,FAMILIARIS,DOMESTIC DOG
1002   DATA   CAT,ANIMAL,CHORDATA,
     MAMMALIA,CARNIVORA,FELIDAE,F
     ELIS,DOMESTICUS,DOMESTIC CAT
1003   DATA   BEAR,ANIMAL,CHORDATA
     ,MAMMALIA,CARNIVORA,URSIDAE,
     EURARCTOS,AMERICANUS,BLACK B
     EAR
1004   DATA   BEAR,ANIMAL,CHORDATA
     ,MAMMALIA,CARNIVORA,URSIDAE,
     URSUS,HORIBILIS,GRIZZLY BEAR
1005   DATA   CHIPMUNK,ANIMAL,CHOR
     DATA,MAMMALIA,RODENTIA,SCIUR
     IDAE,TAMIAS,STRAITUS,COMMON
     CHIPMUNK
1006   DATA   DEER,ANIMAL,CHORDATA
     ,MAMMALIA,ARTIODACTYLA,CERVI
     DAE,ODOCOILEUS,VIRGINIANUS,W
     HITE TAIL DEER
1007   DATA   RABBIT,ANIMAL,CHORDA
     TA,MAMMALIA,LAGOMORPHA,LEPOR
     IDAE,LEPUS,AMERICANUS,SNOWSH
     OE RABBIT
1008   DATA   PRAYING MANTIS,ANIMA
     L,ARTHOROPODA,INSECTA,ORTHOP
     TERA,MANTIDAE,MANTIS,RELIGIO
     SA,PRAYING MANTIS
1009   DATA   CAT,ANIMAL,CHORDATA,
     MAMMALIA,CARNIVORA,FELIDAE,F
     ELIS,LEO,AFRICAN LION
2000   DATA   END
```

HUMAN LIFE

Windsurfer

UNIT 5

*P*eople who run, swim, walk, or even windsurf know the importance of physical activity. A wide variety of activities, such as dancing and aerobics, include exercise of all large muscles. The precise and fast finger work of a skilled violinist involves intense training of smaller muscles. Why does physical activity benefit your body? How do your body systems work together?

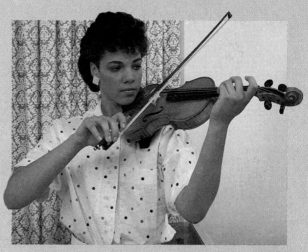

Violinist

In humans, the hand is adapted to grasping objects. This is made possible by the special position of the thumb. This adaptation makes possible our most complex manipulations. Also in humans, an object is seen with both eyes at once, and the brain perceives a three-dimensional view. How do the bones, muscles, and nerves work together to give the hand-eye coordination needed for the mastering of skills such as juggling?

CHAPTER 14
SUPPORT AND COORDINATION

14:1 Body Structure

You have probably seen drawings of body parts. Remember that they are drawn to represent a "typical" person. Your body may differ from these drawings. Most real bodies do. Each human being is a distinct and unique individual.

However, all human bodies are alike in that they are composed of cells. A cell is the basic unit of structure and function. Cells are grouped together in tissues like bricks in a brick wall. All the cells in a tissue are similar in structure and function. A tissue is a group of similar cells that perform a specific function. For example, a certain kind of cell makes up the tissue lining the digestive tract. Cells in the lining tissue make chemicals to digest food. Lining tissue also protects the inside of the digestive tract.

Different kinds of cells have different functions. Muscle cells contract. Red blood cells carry oxygen. Cells that make up your skin provide protection for the tissues under the skin.

Organs are made of tissues. An organ is a group of tissues working together to perform a special function. Tissues such as blood and nerve tissues work together in an organ. Muscle tissue is one of a group of tissues that make up an organ, the heart. The lungs, stomach, and brain are other examples of organs.

The human body is made up of many organs. Together, they form body systems. A system is a group of organs that work together to perform one or more functions. The heart is one of

GOALS:
1. You will learn the basic structures of the human body.
2. You will learn how the skeleton provides support and protection.
3. You will learn the functions of muscles and the nervous system.

Define cell, tissue, organ, and system.

the organs making up the circulatory system, the system that moves blood through the body. Other human systems include the skeletal, digestive, and nervous systems.

14:2 The Skeleton

What are the main functions of the skeleton?

A house is constructed with a wood framework that holds up the roof and walls. The skeleton inside your body is like the framework of a house. The adult human **skeleton** has 206 bones that support the body and protect internal organs. The skeleton also serves as a frame to which muscles are attached. You use

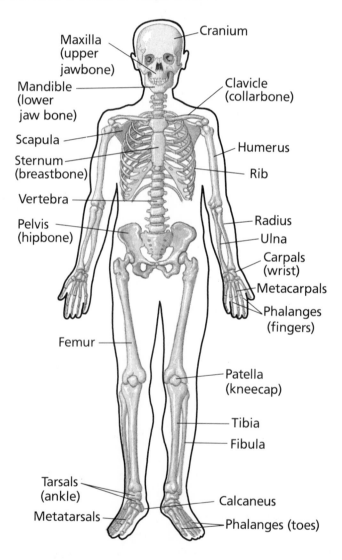

FIGURE 14–1. The human skeleton

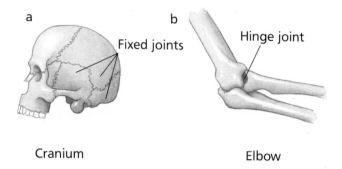

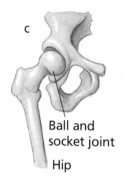

Cranium   Elbow   Hip

bones and muscles to move the parts of your body. About 18 percent of a person's weight is bone.

A skeleton is made of bones held together by strands of tough tissues called **ligaments.** Ligaments hold bones together at joints. A joint is the point at which two bones move against each other. Bones can move freely because ligaments are flexible.

Bones may move a lot or a little at joints. Your skull bones are connected together at fixed joints. A fixed joint allows very little movement. A hinge joint allows bones to move back and forth like a door on a hinge. Your knee is a hinge joint. Your shoulder is a ball and socket joint. In a ball and socket joint, one bone has a rounded end. The end fits into a socket, or hole, in the other bone. A ball and socket joint allows a bone to move in a circle.

Move your leg at the knee. Move your arm at the shoulder. How do they differ in movement?

A bluish-white, rubbery tissue called cartilage is part of most human body joints. Cartilage lines the inner surface of most joints and serves as a cushion between the bones. A fluid is also present in most bone joints. It lubricates joints to reduce friction between the two bones. You can pinch the end of your nose and feel the tough cartilage inside. Cartilage is also present in your outer ear, your voice box, and your ribs.

FIGURE 14–2. Some joints do not move (a). Others move freely (b and c).

How are the bones of the skeleton connected?

Where is cartilage found in the body and what is its function?

Making Sure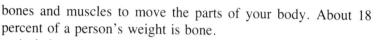

1. Name the bones that perform these functions.
   a. protect your brain
   b. protect your heart and lungs
   c. help you walk
   d. form your backbone
   e. hold your pencil when you write
2. What allows bones to move freely?
3. Compare hinge joints with ball and socket joints.

Activity 14–1   The Human Skeleton

Problem: What types of joints allow body movement?

Materials

diagram and/or model of the human skeleton
paper
pencil

Procedure

1. Observe the parts of the human skeleton using the model and/or diagram. Record your data and observations in a chart like the one shown.
2. Locate the humerus, radius, and ulna. At what point are they connected? Examine the joint that connects them. What kind of joint is it? What kind of movement does it allow?
3. Hold one arm straight out to your side. Keeping your arm straight, swing it around in a circle. Examine the joint that connects the upper arm to the shoulder. What kind of joint is it? Describe the movement at the joint.
4. Locate the femur, tibia, and fibula. At what point are they connected? Examine the joint that connects them. What kind of joint is it?
5. Lift one leg off the floor. Swing the lower part of the leg back and forth at the knee. Try to move the lower part of the leg from side to side. Describe the movement of the knee joint. To what other joint of your body is it similar?
6. Locate the cranium and vertebrae. What part of the skull moves? Examine the joints that connect the bones of the skull. What kind of joints are they? Describe the movement of the spine.
7. Locate the maxilla and mandible. How are they connected? What kind of joint allows them to move?
8. Locate the sternum and the ribs. How are they connected? How do the ribs move?
9. Locate the pelvis. How is it connected to the leg? How is it connected to the spine?
10. Move the end of your nose from side to side with your hand. Bend your ear forward. Describe the movement of your nose and ear.

Data and Observations

Bones	Location	Type of joint and movement
Humerus		
Radius		
Ulna		
Femur		
Tibia		
Fibula		
Cranium		
Maxilla		
Mandible		
Sternum		
Ribs		
Pelvis		

Questions and Conclusions

1. Compare the bone structure of the arm and leg. Write a brief description of each and explain how they are similar and different.
2. What type of joint connects the upper arm to the shoulder?
3. What type of joint is the knee?
4. What kind of tissue makes up the outer ear? What is another body part where the same kind of tissue is found?
5. Name some examples of a ball-and-socket joint, a hinge joint, and a fixed joint.
6. How are the joints between the skull bones different from other joints in the body?
7. Where is cartilage found in the body?
8. What types of joints allow body movement?

14:3 Bones

Bone is living tissue made of cells. Have you ever observed a dog chewing and gnawing a bone to obtain the marrow? **Marrow** is a soft tissue in the center of many bones. It contains nerves and blood vessels. There are two kinds of marrow. Red marrow is found in flat bones, such as the ribs. It is also found in the ends of long bones, such as those in the arms. Red marrow produces blood cells.

The other kind of marrow is yellow marrow. It is mostly fat tissue and is found in the center of long bones. Yellow marrow may produce red blood cells when there is a great loss of blood. Yellow marrow also produces red blood cells when a person has certain blood diseases.

Bones have a thick membrane that covers them. The membrane, periosteum (per ee AHS tee um), is a living tissue and contains blood vessels. Other blood vessels connect the interior of the bone with the membranes around it. These blood vessels are in tubes that run through the bones. These tubes are called Haversian (huh VUR zhun) canals. Blood vessels in the Haversian canals transport oxygen and digested food to the bone cells. They also remove waste materials. Blood helps keep bone cells alive.

Bone tissue contains living cells, minerals, organic matter, and water. Mineral elements give bone its hardness. The main minerals in bone are calcium and phosphorus. Bone material varies in hardness from very hard to spongy. The matter in solid bones is tightly packed for strength. Spongy bone has empty spaces that make the bone lightweight, yet strong enough to withstand stress. The degree of hardness depends on the amount of mineral present.

Describe the structure of bone.

What are the main minerals in bone?

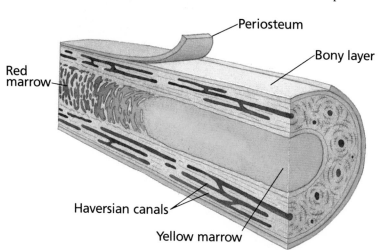

Red marrow

Periosteum

Bony layer

Haversian canals

Yellow marrow

FIGURE 14–3. Bone structure

How does the skeleton change during human development?

In the early stages of a human embryo, the skeleton is soft and flexible. It is composed largely of cartilage. As the embryo develops inside its mother, the cartilage is gradually replaced by bone cells. The bone cells release calcium and phosphorus into spaces in between the cells. These minerals are deposited as the bones of the skeleton grow and develop during pregnancy. The calcium and phosphorus make the bones hard and strong. The formation of bone tissue is called ossification (ahs uh fuh KAY shun). Bones continue to ossify as a person matures. By the time a person is 20, nearly all of his or her bones are completely ossified. In old age, a person may lose bone tissue, which causes bones to break more easily. This explains why elderly people often break bones when they fall.

Making Sure

4. How is bone different from cartilage?
5. Is a bone in your body living or nonliving? State two facts that support your answer.
6. Give a reason why a pregnant woman's diet should contain calcium and phosphorus.

a
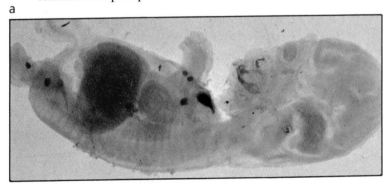

b
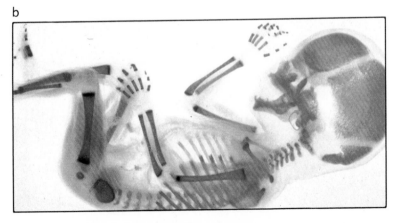

FIGURE 14–4. An embryo skeleton begins as cartilage (a). Cartilage gradually turns to bone (b). Cartilage appears white and bone appears red in these photographs.

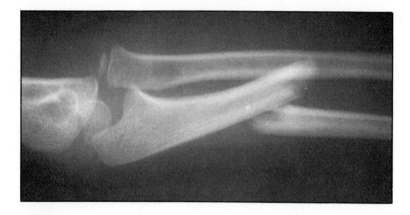

FIGURE 14–5. A break in a bone is called a fracture. Some bones are set in casts so that they will grow back together correctly.

 Activity 14–2   **Observing Bone**

Problem: What are the parts of a long bone?

Materials   beef bone cut in half along length and width, hand lens, scalpel, microscope slide, microscope, coverslip, dropper, water

Procedure   (1) Obtain a beef bone that has been cut in half along the length and width. (2) Observe the bone and identify the periosteum, bony layer, Haversian canals, red marrow, and yellow marrow. (Refer to Figure 14–3.) (3) Look at each of the parts with a hand lens. Draw a diagram of the bone and label the parts you identified. (4) Using a scalpel, remove a small piece of red marrow. Make a temporary wet mount of it. **CAUTION:** *Always use extreme care when using sharp instruments.* (5) Examine under low power.

Questions   (1) What did you observe in the bone marrow? (2) How is the marrow different from the other bone parts? (3) What is the function of each structure you observed? (4) How do blood cells get out of the marrow? (5) What are the parts of a long bone?

14:4 Muscles

You use muscles when you talk, nod your head "yes," or shake your head "no." Muscles are also used when you write and walk. **Muscles** are tissues that move parts of your body. Your head, jaw, arms, and legs are moved when muscles pull against the bones inside these body parts. Other muscles aid in digestion, flow of blood, and removal of body wastes.

There are more than 600 muscles in your body. Muscles make up about 40 percent of a man's weight and 30 percent of a woman's weight. Muscles that are exercised regularly are strong, firm, and

How are muscles used?

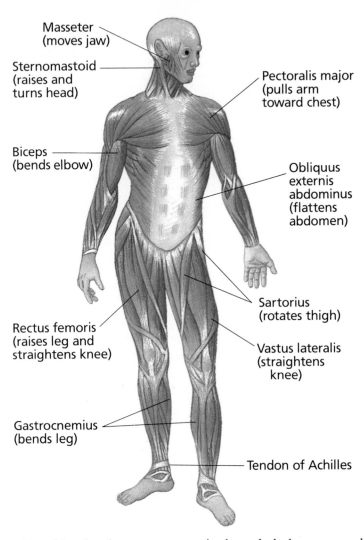

Masseter
(moves jaw)

Sternomastoid
(raises and
turns head)

Pectoralis major
(pulls arm
toward chest)

Biceps
(bends elbow)

Obliquus
externis
abdominus
(flattens
abdomen)

Rectus femoris
(raises leg and
straightens knee)

Sartorius
(rotates thigh)

Vastus lateralis
(straightens
knee)

Gastrocnemius
(bends leg)

Tendon of Achilles

FIGURE 14–6. Some muscles of the human body

Name examples of voluntary and involuntary muscles.

healthy. Muscles that are not exercised regularly become weak, soft, and flabby.

Muscles may be classified into two groups—voluntary and involuntary. **Voluntary muscles** are those muscles that you can control. Arm and leg muscles are voluntary. You control them when you move your arms and legs. Movement happens because the bones of the arm and leg are attached to muscles. Tough bands of tissue called tendons attach muscles to bones.

Involuntary muscles are muscles you cannot control. Your heart muscle is an example of an involuntary muscle. Muscles in your digestive tract are also involuntary. Thus, you cannot control their movements. Some muscles, such as those that control breathing and move your eyelids, are both voluntary and involuntary.

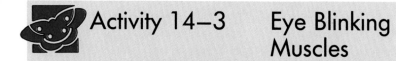

Activity 14–3   Eye Blinking Muscles

Problem: Are eye blinking muscles voluntary or involuntary?

Materials watch or clock with second hand

Procedure (1) Record a hypothesis for the problem. (2) Blink your eyelids three times. (3) Now try not to blink. Time yourself to see how long it is before you blink. (4) Repeat this procedure two more times.

Questions (1) What is the average time you can keep from blinking? (2) How does your average compare with other students' averages? (3) Was your hypothesis correct or incorrect? (4) Are your eye blinking muscles voluntary or involuntary?

14:5 Kinds of Muscles

The human body contains three kinds of muscle—smooth, striated (STRI ayt ud), and heart. Heart muscle is also called cardiac (KARD ee ak) muscle.

Smooth muscle is present in the walls of many internal body organs. The walls of the digestive tract and the walls of the blood vessels contain smooth muscle. Smooth muscle is involuntary. The muscles in your digestive organs and in your blood vessels move without your thinking about them.

Striated muscle has bands called striations (stri AY shunz). Striated muscles in your body are voluntary muscles. You can move them at will. When you walk, talk, jump, and run, you use striated muscles. Since they are attached to the skeleton, striated muscles are also called skeletal muscles. Skeletal muscles

List the three kinds of muscles and the characteristics of each.

FIGURE 14–7. Smooth muscles (a) move many internal parts of the body. Striated muscles (b) are attached to bones. Heart muscle (c) is found only in the heart.

a
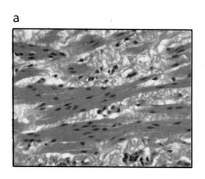

b
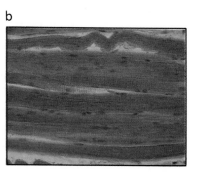

c
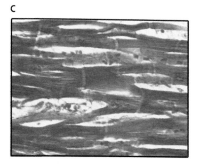

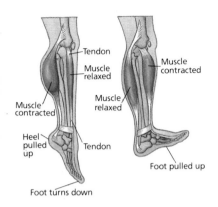

FIGURE 14–8. Muscles in the leg are paired. When one muscle contracts or shortens, the other muscle relaxes causing the joint to move.

FIGURE 14–9.

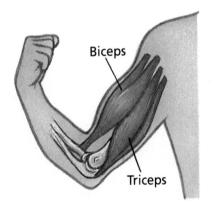

allow people to perform feats of strength like lifting huge weights. They also allow people to make precise actions such as the fingerwork of a violinist. Striated muscles are connected to bones by tough bands of tissues called **tendons.**

Muscles work by contracting or becoming shorter. They can also relax and return to their original length. Also, muscles are paired. One muscle in the pair contracts and pulls one way while the other muscle relaxes. The joints in your arms and legs are moved when striated muscles alternate contracting and relaxing.

Heart muscle is present in your heart. Heart muscle contracts to pump blood. Heart muscle contains striations, but unlike striated muscle, heart muscle is involuntary. The pumping of the heart is automatic. This means that you do not have to think to make your heart beat. The heartbeat is controlled by a small bundle of tissue inside the top part of the heart.

Making Sure

7. Why are striated muscles also called skeletal muscles?
8. How are muscles connected to bones?
9. How is heart muscle different from striated muscle?
10. In what ways are all muscle tissues similar?

Activity 14–4   Arm Muscles

Problem: How do pairs of muscles work together to move the arm?

Materials   rug or mat

Procedure   (1) Place your left hand over the biceps muscle of your right arm. Move your right arm up toward the shoulder and away from the shoulder slowly. (2) Place your left hand over the triceps muscle. Again, move your arm up and down. (3) Use a meter stick as a barbell to do several curls. (4) Lie on a rug or mat and do three push-ups.

Questions   (1) What happens to the biceps muscle as the arm is moved up? (2) What happens to the muscle as the arm is lowered? (3) What happens to the triceps muscle as the arm is moved up? (4) What happens to the muscle as the arm is moved down? (5) Which muscle works harder doing curls? (6) Which muscle works harder doing push-ups? (7) A flexor is a muscle that bends a joint. An extensor is a muscle that straightens a joint. Is the biceps a flexor or an extensor? (8) Which kind of muscle is the triceps? (9) How do pairs of muscles work together to move the arm?

FIGURE 14–10. The nervous systems of basketball players control their responses to a stimulus, such as a tossed ball.

14:6 The Nervous System

Muscles you use to move the parts of your body are controlled by your nervous system. A nervous system consists of nerve cells that run throughout the body. Nerves carry messages back and forth between the brain and the rest of the body. When you opened this book, your nervous system sent messages to contract the voluntary, striated muscles in your arms and hands. Involuntary muscles are also controlled by the nervous system. Messages sent through nerves cause the contractions of smooth muscles in the digestive system and blood vessels.

Playing basketball is an example of the nervous system regulating behavior. At the start of the game, two players jump swiftly toward the ball tossed by the referee. The referee's toss is a stimulus to which the players respond by jumping. Receiving and responding to stimuli in basketball and other activities involve the nervous system. A basketball player receives stimuli mainly through the eyes and ears. Movements of the other players and the referees' whistles and calls are examples of these stimuli. In response, the player must make split-second decisions. The player must decide instantly whether to run, stop, throw, or shoot for a basket. All of this must be coordinated by the nervous system. At no time is coordination more important than in shooting. The distance and direction of the target must be sighted by the eyes and this information sent to the brain. Based on the sighting, the brain immediately sends messages to the player's muscles. As the muscles react, the ball is fired upward to the basket.

Two major centers in the nervous system are the brain and spinal cord. Together these two organs make up the **central**

Explain how the nervous system controls voluntary acts.

nervous system. Vision, hearing, taste, thinking, and voluntary acts are controlled by the brain. The central nervous system is enclosed and protected by bone and bathed in a special, protective fluid. All the nerves outside the brain and spinal cord make up the **peripheral** (puh RIHF uh rul) **nervous system.** These nerves carry messages between the central nervous system and the rest of the body.

A person's endocrine system also controls behavior. The endocrine (EN duh krihn) system consists of glands in different parts of the body that produce chemicals carried in the blood. The stress and stimulation of playing basketball causes a chemical to be released by an endocrine gland. This chemical acts to increase the sugar supply the blood carries to the body's cells. The increased sugar supply results in a higher energy level that assists in performing the game's strenuous activities.

Making Sure

11. Explain how stimuli, responses, and the nervous system are involved in playing Ping-Pong.
12. What is the difference between the central and peripheral nervous systems?

14:7 The Brain

A human brain is equal to about 1/40 of total body mass. There are about ten billion nerve cells in a human brain. Your **brain** is the major control center of your body. It contains three major parts—cerebrum (suh REE brum), cerebellum (ser uh BEL um), and medulla (mih DEW luh).

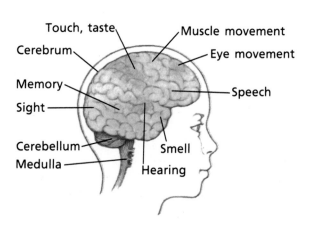

FIGURE 14–11. Certain areas of the cerebrum are associated with certain senses and activities.

a

b

The cerebrum is the largest part of the human brain. It is located in the upper part of the head. Human intelligence is due largely to a highly developed cerebrum. The cerebrum is the origin of thinking and awareness. For example, knowing what you are doing and why is controlled by your cerebrum. The cerebrum controls memory, learning, and some voluntary movements. In a basketball game, for instance, a player's decision to shoot for a basket is made in the cerebrum. Seeing, hearing, touching, tasting, and smelling are also controlled by the cerebrum. Brain operations on humans have revealed the location of control centers within the cerebrum. If any one of these centers is destroyed, the activity or sense it controls is lost.

The cerebellum is smaller and lies behind and below the cerebrum. The cerebellum's major function is to maintain the body's sense of balance. It also coordinates muscular activity such as walking, running, and swimming. Suppose you pick up a ball and throw it. The motion of your fingers, hand, and arm are controlled by the cerebellum. Muscle coordination by the cerebellum enables a basketball player to make the complex body motions required for a hook shot.

The medulla is the smallest part of the brain. It is located at the base of the skull, just below the cerebellum. The medulla is continuous with the spinal cord. It controls breathing, heartbeat, muscular action of the digestive tract, and the secretions of some glands. These activities take place in your body unnoticed, unless you decide to think about them. When you play basketball, your breathing and heartbeat proceed automatically. Their rates are regulated by the medulla. All nerve fibers connecting the brain and spinal cord pass through the medulla. The medulla also controls certain reflexes such as coughing, sneezing, swallowing, and vomiting.

FIGURE 14-12. During a basketball game, a player's decision to shoot for a basket is made in the cerebrum (a). Maintaining balance and muscular coordination (b) are controlled by the cerebellum.

List the three main parts of the brain and the function of each.

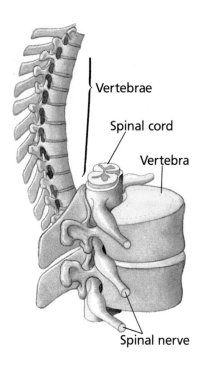

FIGURE 14–13. Vertebrae protect the spinal cord and spinal nerves.

Define neuron.

14:8 The Spinal Cord

Reach around to the center of your back and feel the bones in your spine. Your spine is made up of a series of bones called vertebrae. A channel, called the vertebral canal, is formed by these vertebrae. Through the vertebral canal runs a thick cord of nerves called the **spinal cord.** The spinal cord extends from the medulla almost to the end of your spine. A liquid called spinal fluid bathes the spinal cord.

The spinal cord relays messages between the brain and the rest of the body. Thirty-one pairs of nerves branch from the spinal cord. One nerve in each pair carries impulses to the spinal cord from body organs or parts. Then the messages move to the brain. Messages also move from the brain to the spinal cord. Then the other nerve in each pair carries impulses away from the spinal cord to body organs or parts. If a person's spinal cord were cut in two, all parts of the body below the cut would become paralyzed. Why? The nerves would no longer be able to receive nerve impulses from the brain, nor send them to the brain.

Making Sure

13. How is the body affected by damage to each of these body parts?
    a. cerebrum
    b. cerebellum
    c. medulla
    d. spinal cord
14. Diagram the human brain and label the three major parts.

14:9 Neurons

There are more than 160 000 kilometers (about four trips around Earth) of nerves in your nervous system. Each nerve is composed of cells called neurons (NOO rahnz). A **neuron** is a nerve cell that carries impulses. Each impulse is a "message" or signal that travels the length of the neuron. The speed of an impulse is from 0.5 meter per second to 100 meters per second. Many neurons are very long, such as the neurons in nerves that go from the toes to the spinal cord. Other long neurons are in nerves that extend from the fingertips to the spinal cord. In some individuals, neurons may be about one meter in length.

A typical neuron consists of a cell body to which are attached bushy branches called dendrites. Inside the cell body is most of the cytoplasm, a nucleus, and other cell parts. Dendrites are structures that receive stimuli. A long fiber attached to a thickened area of the cell body is the axon. This structure ends in nerve branches. The axon carries a nerve impulse from the cell body to another neuron or cell. Some neurons have a coating of fatty material that forms a sheath that speeds the movement of nerve impulses.

The space between the axon of one neuron and the dendrites of another is the synapse (SIHN aps). Movement of a nerve impulse across a synapse is aided by a chemical produced and released at the end of the axon. The chemical moves from the tip of the axon to the dendrites and cell body of the second neuron. Passage of messages through a nerve is a one-way street. Impulses always travel across a synapse from the axon of one neuron to the dendrites of another neuron.

There are three kinds of neurons in the human body—sensory, motor, and interneurons. Each kind of neuron has a different function. **Sensory neurons** carry impulses from receptors (rih SEP turz) to the central nervous system. Receptors are those parts of the nervous system that detect stimuli. Receptors are in sense organs such as taste buds, eyes, ears, nose, and skin. When the nerves in a receptor receive a stimulus, impulses are produced. In Figure 14–15, the nerves in the skin receive the stimulus from the tack. Impulses are carried to the brain by the nerves. This is how you feel pain. Pain also may be produced by impulses from diseased organs or from injuries.

Interneurons connect sensory neurons and motor neurons. They are in the spinal cord and brain. Interneurons transfer incoming impulses from sensory neurons to outgoing impulses in motor neurons.

Motor neurons carry impulses away from the central nervous system to effectors. Effectors are parts that respond when stimulated by nerve impulses. Muscles and glands are examples of effectors. Muscles contract and certain glands release chemicals when stimulated by nerve impulses. In Figure 14–15, motor neurons cause the finger muscles to straighten the finger.

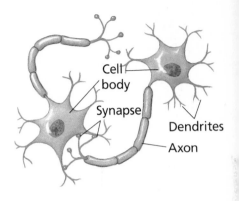

FIGURE 14–14. Nerve impulses travel from the axon of one neuron to the dendrites of another neuron across a synapse.

Name the three kinds of neurons. Compare the functions of the three.

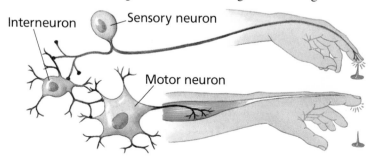

FIGURE 14–15. In a neuron, nerve impulses travel from the dendrites through the cell body to the axon.

Activity 14–5

Reaction Time

Problem: How can reaction time be measured?

Materials

penny
metric ruler

Procedure

Part A

1. Hold your right arm out with the palm down. Put a penny on the center of the back of your hand.
2. Slowly tilt your hand to the side so that the penny slides off. Try to catch the penny with your right hand.
3. Repeat step 2 nine more times. Record how many times you catch the penny.
4. Repeat steps 2 and 3 with your left hand.

Part B

1. Work with a partner. Hold your hand out with the palm up.
2. Have your partner hold a penny about 0.5 m above the palm of your hand.
3. When your partner drops the penny, try to move your hand out of the way before the penny can hit it.
4. Ask your partner to hold the penny at different distances from your hand. Repeat step 3 for each distance.
5. Record the distance and how many times the penny hits your hand.
6. Repeat Part B with your other hand.

Part C

1. Work with a partner. Hold your hand out with your thumb and index finger separated.
2. Have your partner hold a metric ruler at one end so that the other end of the ruler is between your thumb and index finger.
3. Keep your eyes on the bottom of the metric ruler. Have your partner release the top at any time. Try to catch the metric ruler.
4. Repeat step 3 nine more times.
5. Record the distance the ruler has fallen each time you catch it.
6. Repeat Part C with your other hand.

Data and Observations

Part A

	Right hand		Left hand	
Trial	Caught	Not caught	Caught	Not caught
1				
2				

Right Hand

Part B

Trial	Distance above hand	Hit	Not hit
1			
2			

Part C

	Distance fallen	
Trial	Right hand	Left hand
1		
2		

Questions and Conclusions

1. What is meant by reaction time?
2. What is a stimulus?
3. What was the stimulus in each part of the activity?
4. What was the response in each part of the activity?
5. List the steps your nervous system had to go through to catch the penny in Part A, to avoid the penny in Part B, and to catch the ruler in Part C.
6. What is the variable in each part of the activity?
7. How can reaction time be measured?

a

b

14:10 How the Nervous System Works

FIGURE 14—16. Delivering a newspaper (a) is a voluntary act. Breathing rapidly to replace lost oxygen (b) is an involuntary act.

Voluntary acts are behaviors you control by using your brain. Involuntary acts are behaviors that occur without thinking. Suppose your finger is accidentally stuck by a sharp pin. Receptors in your finger are stimulated. They send impulses along sensory neurons up your arm to your spinal cord. Interneurons in the spinal cord transfer the impulse from sensory neurons to motor neurons. The motor neurons send nerve impulses to your arm muscles. This causes the muscles to pull your hand away. It happens so fast that you pull your finger away before you feel the pain.

Pulling away from the pin is an involuntary act. Involuntary means you do not decide to pull it away. It happens without thinking about it. Recall that such an automatic response to a stimulus is a reflex act.

Although the brain does not directly control a reflex act, an impulse is sent to the brain. This impulse makes you aware that you pricked your finger with a pin. Also, it makes you aware that you quickly pulled your finger away. Your brain may then direct you to look at your finger to see if it is bleeding. Further, your brain may direct you to take action to prevent this unpleasant event from happening again.

The autonomic nervous system is involuntary and automatic. However, functions of the autonomic nervous system do involve the brain and spinal cord. The autonomic nervous system has several jobs. It regulates the heartbeat and the release of substances

Explain how your nervous system controls involuntary acts.

List the functions of the autonomic nervous system.

from certain glands. It controls the supply of blood to the arteries. Movement of smooth muscles in the stomach and intestines is also controlled by this nervous system. It helps the body respond to stimuli faster than the chemical response made by glands.

Making Sure

15. What is the path of a nerve impulse in
    a. a voluntary act?
    b. a reflex act?
16. Which type of neuron has probably been damaged in a person who cannot
    a. feel pain in the left hand?
    b. move the left hand?
17. Draw and label the parts of a neuron.

Activity 14–6   Demonstrating a Reflex Act

Problem: What is a reflex?

Materials   plastic wrap, cotton ball

Procedure   (1) Sit down and cross your legs so that one leg swings freely. (2) Using the side of his or her hand, have a partner strike the soft area below the kneecap of your free leg. (3) Hold a sheet of plastic wrap in front of your face. (4) Watch as your partner tosses a cotton ball at the sheet of plastic. Try to keep from blinking. (5) Reverse roles with your partner.

Questions   (1) What happens to your leg? (2) What is the stimulus? (3) What is the response? (4) Are you able to keep from blinking when the cotton ball is thrown? (5) What is the advantage of a blinking reflex? (6) Diagram the pathway of a nerve impulse in the leg swing part of the activity. (7) What is a reflex?

FIGURE 14–17.

14:11 The Endocrine System

The response of animals to stimuli may be nervous or chemical. Some responses are both nervous and chemical. The chemical response to stimuli is controlled by the endocrine system.

Together, the endocrine system and the nervous system control all body functions. The **endocrine system** is composed of ductless glands that produce hormones. **Hormones** are chemicals that regulate certain body activities. The hormones produced go directly into the blood where they are circulated through the body.

The organs that make up the endocrine system are located in different parts of the body. They are not connected together. A small endocrine gland lying just below the brain is the pituitary (pih TOO ih ter ee). The **pituitary gland** is sometimes called the "master gland." It produces hormones that control the secretion of hormones from many other endocrine glands. For example, hormones produced by the ovaries and testes are regulated by the pituitary gland. The ovaries and testes help regulate reproductive functions in males and females.

Another endocrine gland, the thyroid (THI royd), is located in the neck. One hormone it produces is thyroxin. Thyroxin regulates the metabolism of the body. Metabolism is the rate at which cells convert food to energy. In some people, the thyroid gland becomes enlarged due to a lack of iodine. The enlarged thyroid gland causes swelling of the neck called goiter. Use of iodized salt in

Define endocrine system, pituitary gland, and hormone.

FIGURE 14—18. Glands of the endocrine system

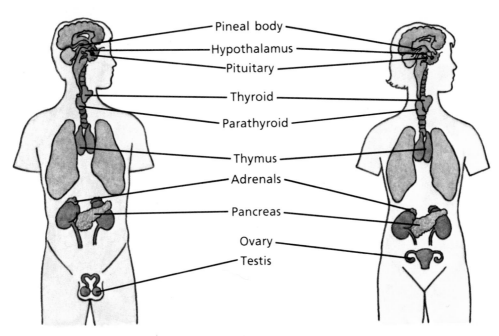

Pineal body
Hypothalamus
Pituitary
Thyroid
Parathyroid
Thymus
Adrenals
Pancreas
Ovary
Testis

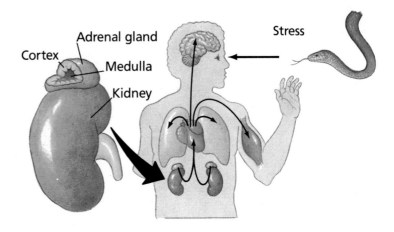

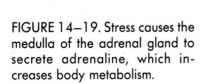

FIGURE 14–19. Stress causes the medulla of the adrenal gland to secrete adrenaline, which increases body metabolism.

diets supplies sufficient iodine and prevents goiter.

Parathyroids are pealike endocrine glands on the thyroid's surface. Parathormone produced by these glands regulates calcium and phosphorus levels in the blood and tissues.

Insulin is a hormone produced by the pancreas gland. Insulin regulates the amount of sugar in the blood and the storage of glycogen (GLI kuh jun) in the liver. A lack of insulin causes a disease called diabetes (DI uh bee teez). A person with uncontrolled diabetes has a high level of sugar in the blood and urine. Body metabolism is upset, and the person becomes very tired and weak. Diabetes is treated with injections of insulin or drugs that stimulate the pancreas to produce insulin.

Two endocrine glands that lie on top of the kidneys are the adrenals (uh DREE nulz). Each adrenal gland has an inner core, the medulla, and an outer cortex. Adrenaline and noradrenaline are hormones produced in the medulla that regulate body metabolism. Hormones produced by the cortex control the salt level in blood and regulate the metabolism of fats and proteins. Small amounts of sex hormones are also produced in the adrenal cortex.

The sex glands, testes and ovaries, produce sex hormones. Male sex hormones, produced in the testes, control the secondary sex characteristics. Examples of these characteristics are the development of a deeper voice at puberty (PYEW bur tee) and the growth of facial hair. Female sex hormones, produced in the ovaries, regulate the menstrual cycle. They also stimulate development of female secondary sex characteristics such as the development of breasts and broader hips in puberty.

Making Sure

18. Name the endocrine glands and list a function of each.
19. Name three hormones and state the function of each.

Technology

Looking at the Living Brain

The study of the human brain has been one of the most challenging scientific issues of our time. Until recently, scientists studied the living human brain from analyses of the liquid that surrounds the brain and spinal cord. The functions of the brain tissues could only be guessed at. With modern technology, however, scientists are able to see a living human brain at work.

With the development of the positron–emission–tomography (PET) scanner, the living brain can be observed. The scanner provides a detailed portrait of a brain at work. Neurotransmitters are the brain's chemical messengers that carry signals between its neurons. Damage to the pathways the neurotransmitters travel can cause health and behavior changes. These nerve pathways throughout the brain can be examined. Brain disorders can be mapped and analyzed. The action of drugs in the brain can be studied directly. PET scans will also provide information on how certain diseases affect a normal brain.

In order to make a PET scan, a patient is given a controlled amount of a radioactive chemical called a tracer. The tracer travels to the brain and attaches to individual brain cells. The tracer then gives off positrons. A positron is a particle that has the same mass as an electron, but with a positive charge. These positrons collide with electrons, which have negative charges, in the brain. This causes radiation to be given off, which is picked up by a ring of detectors around the patient's head. The detectors transmit this information to a computer. The computer then produces a color-coded picture. Different colors indicate different densities. For example, a brain tumor would be a different color than normal brain tissue. The entire process of scanning, recording, computer analyzing and displaying takes only five to ten minutes.

PET can provide valuable information about the effects of disease on the brain and analyze the resulting disorders. PET can also identify some brain diseases, such as Huntington's disease, before the symptoms even begin. This is valuable information since treatment is often more successful when started in the early stages of the disease.

Scientists have long been unable to understand certain problems of the brain. How do tumors invade and transform normal tissue? Are pain centers in the brain involved in drug addiction? How do brain diseases like epilepsy originate? PET technology may help in providing answers to these questions.

FIGURE 14–20. A PET scan of a healthy person's brain compared with that of a person with Parkinson's disease shows a lack of an amino acid in brain areas affecting muscle control.

The Discovery of Insulin

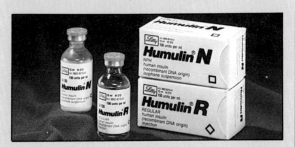

Over 10 million people in the United States have diabetes mellitus. These people are unable to absorb certain sugars into their body cells. They do not produce enough of the hormone called insulin that increases the entry of glucose into cells. Without treatment, a person with diabetes could die. Treatment for diabetes consists of insulin injections.

The story of the discovery of insulin begins in 1889 when two German doctors, Joseph von Mering and Oskar Minkowski, studied the functions of different digestive organs. They removed each organ, one at a time, from experimental animals. The animals were then observed to see how they behaved in the absence of each of these organs. In this way, the two scientists could determine the function of each organ.

One of the organs von Mering and Minkowski examined was the pancreas. After removing the pancreas from several dogs, they expected to find changes in digestion. Instead, they found an increase in the dogs' thirst and urination. Fortunately for the German doctors, the animals' caretakers made an important observation. They noticed that ants were attracted to the urine of the experimental dogs, but not to the control dogs. The urine of a dog lacking a pancreas was found to contain sugar. This symptom, along with the unusual thirst, was identical in humans who suffered from diabetes mellitus. Minkowski and von Mering concluded that the pancreas is the site of an "antidiabetic" substance. Due to an unexpected result and a chance observation, these early researchers provided the first real clues in the discovery of insulin.

The next breakthrough came in 1901. An American doctor, Eugene L. Opie, found that specific cells in the pancreas, known as the islets of Langerhans, secrete a substance that controls blood sugar. To test this hypothesis, a Canadian doctor, Frederick Banting, injected islet pancreatic tissue into dogs whose pancreases had been removed. Diabetes symptoms disappeared. Finally, in 1921, Banting and a medical student, Charles Best, isolated the "antidiabetic" substance from the pancreas. They called it insulin. The insulin from different mammals was found to be similar so animal insulin was then used to treat human diabetes.

In 1955, after ten years of research, Frederick Sanger determined the structure of insulin. This achievement made it possible to manufacture the hormone. When synthetic insulin was finally made in the laboratory, it was shown to be effective against diabetes. This was the final proof that insulin regulated blood sugar.

Unfortunately, synthetic insulin could not be produced on a commercial scale. As a result, diabetics still had to rely on insulin taken from the pancreases of animals. But in the late 1970s, genetic engineers were able to program bacteria to make human insulin, or humulin. Many diabetics use genetically engineered humulin.

The discovery of insulin is like a detective story that has taken nearly a century to solve. Due to the work of many scientists, thousands of lives have been saved, and the quality of these lives improved.

Summary

1. The human body is composed of systems, organs, tissues, and cells.   14:1
2. The skeleton provides a framework for the body, protects various organs, and is used to move body parts.   14:2
3. Bones contain large amounts of calcium and phosphorus.   14:3
4. Muscles produce movement when they contract and relax.   14:4
5. Smooth muscles and heart muscles are involuntary. Striated muscles are voluntary.   14:4, 14:5
6. Bones are held together at joints by ligaments. Muscles are attached to bones by tendons.   14:2, 14:5
7. Human behavior and body functions are controlled by the nervous system and the endocrine system.   14:6
8. Conscious behavior is controlled by the cerebrum. Body balance and muscular coordination are controlled by the cerebellum. The medulla regulates breathing and heartbeat.   14:7
9. Impulses travel through neurons from receptors to effectors.   14:9
10. Hormones, produced in endocrine glands, are chemicals that regulate body activities.   14:11

Vocabulary

Write a sentence using the following words or terms correctly.

brain	ligament	sensory neuron
central nervous system	marrow	skeleton
	motor neuron	smooth muscle
endocrine system	muscle	spinal cord
heart muscle	neuron	striated muscle
hormones	peripheral	tendon
interneuron	nervous system	voluntary
involuntary muscle	pituitary gland	muscle

Questions

Do not write in this book.

A. True or False

Determine whether each of the following sentences is true or false. Rewrite the false statements to make them correct.

1. A tissue is a group of similar cells performing a specific function.
2. Striated muscle is a kind of involuntary muscle.

3. Cartilage is present in most human body joints.
4. Bones contain calcium and phosphorus.
5. Cartilage develops as bones increase in mineral content.
6. Thinking is regulated by the cerebellum.
7. The spinal cord is inside the backbone.
8. Paralysis results if the spinal cord is cut in two.
9. Glycogen is stored in the kidneys.
10. Sensory and motor neurons connect to the central nervous system.

B. Multiple Choice
Choose the word or phrase that correctly completes the following sentences.
1. An endocrine gland secretes (*enzymes, hormones, saliva*).
2. Your backbone protects your (*heart, brain, spinal cord*).
3. Muscles are attached to bones by (*ligaments, tendons, cartilage*).
4. Muscles that you can control are called (*voluntary, involuntary, tissues*).
5. Two bones move against each other at a (*tendon, joint, Haversian canal*).
6. The (*medulla, cerebellum, cerebrum*) regulates muscle coordination.
7. The brain and spinal cord are part of the (*central, peripheral, autonomic*) nervous system.
8. (*Sensory neurons, Interneurons, Motor neurons*) are in the brain and spinal cord.
9. (*Adrenaline, Glycogen, Insulin*) is produced in the pancreas.
10. Seeing is controlled by the (*medulla, cerebellum, cerebrum*).

C. Completion
Complete each of the following sentences with the correct word or phrase.
1. Your knee contains a(n) _____ joint.
2. A bone rotates in a(n) _____ joint.
3. Most of the skeleton in an embryo is made of _____.
4. The walls of the digestive tract contain _____ muscle.
5. The heart is a(n) _____ muscle.
6. _____ muscles are voluntary muscles you use to move your body.
7. _____ are those behaviors controlled by using the brain.
8. A(n) _____ connects the spinal cord with an effector.
9. Messages are carried from one neuron to another by a(n) _____ that forms at the ends of neurons.
10. The messages that travel along neurons are called _____.

D. How and Why
1. What problems would a person have if his or her skeleton was made of cartilage instead of bone?
2. How do you use your bones and muscles when you play sports such as volleyball?
3. How are tendons different from ligaments?
4. How does a cast aid repair of a broken leg bone?
5. How are voluntary muscles different from involuntary muscles? List examples of the use of each.
6. Name the three parts of the brain. List the functions of each part.
7. How does the nervous system regulate behavior?
8. Trace the path of an impulse in a reflex act.
9. How do your sense organs enable you to learn about your environment?

Ideas to Explore
1. **Challenge:** Obtain a book on the anatomy of a cat. Report on how the structure of a cat is different from the structure of a human being.
2. **Project:** Obtain prepared slides of human tissues from a medical laboratory. Study these slides with a microscope to identify tissues and cells. Make drawings of your observations.
3. **Project:** Make a large drawing of the human skeleton. Label the bones with their names.
4. **Challenge:** Hormones such as insulin are used to treat certain diseases. Prepare a report on the medical use of hormones.
5. **Challenge:** Research some of the operations that professional atheletes undergo. Prepare a report on one such operation, such as an operation for ligament damage in football players.
6. **Challenge:** Scientists are now investigating differences controlled by the right and left brain hemispheres. Using library sources, prepare a list of "right brain" and "left brain" characteristics.

Readings

Baskin, Yvonne. "The Way We Act." *Science 85*. November, 1985, pp. 94–100.

Cobb, Vicki. *How to Really Fool Yourself: Illusions for All Your Senses.* New York: J. B. Lippincott, 1981.

Facklam, Margery and Howard Facklam. *The Brain: Magnificent Mind Machine.* San Diego: Harcourt Brace Jovanovich, 1982.

Ward, Brian R. *Body Maintenance.* New York: Franklin Watts, 1983.

The network of pipes in the photo is part of an oil refinery. They provide a pathway for water, oil, and steam used in various parts of the refinery. Some of these pipes remove wastes from the oil. The human body is also made of transport systems. The circulatory system moves blood around the body. The respiratory system circulates air. How does the excretory system help the body? How are these systems similar to the pipe network of the oil refinery?

CHAPTER 15
BODY TRANSPORT SYSTEMS

15:1 The Heart

Major parts of the human circulatory system are blood tissue, blood vessels, and a heart. Oxygen and nutrients are carried to the tissues by blood. Blood also carries wastes away from the tissues. Blood is pumped through the blood vessels by the heart. A human heart is a muscular organ about the size of a large fist. The heart is located in the center of the chest behind the breastbone and between the lungs.

A human heart contains four chambers, two upper and two lower. The upper chambers are the right **atrium** (AY tree um) and left atrium. The lower chambers are the right **ventricle** (VEN trih kul) and left ventricle. Right and left refer to the body's right and left sides. A wall separates the chambers on the right side from the chambers on the left side of the heart. A valve separates each atrium from the ventricle below it.

The bottom tip of the heart points toward the left side of the body. Here the beat of the heart is strongest, so you are most likely to feel the heart's beat on the left side of your chest.

For you to stay alive, your heart must pump constantly. Pumping is produced by alternate contraction and relaxation of the atria and ventricles. The human heart beats at a rate of between 60 and 80 times per minute. When you are running, your heart beats even faster. Your heart muscle keeps pumping all through your life—more than two billion times during a normal lifetime! Your pulse is caused by your heart pumping blood. Your pulse keeps perfect time with your heartbeat.

GOALS:
1. You will learn the parts of the circulatory, respiratory, and excretory systems.
2. You will learn the functions of these systems.
3. You will learn how these systems work together.

Name the four chambers of the heart.

How does the heart pump blood?

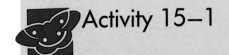

Activity 15–1   Determining Pulse Rates

Problem: How does exercise affect the pulse rate?

Materials   clock or watch with second hand

Procedure   (1) Predict what will happen to your pulse rate after exercise. (2) Place the fingers of one hand on the front of your neck. Move your fingers around until you feel your pulse. (3) Determine your pulse rate. (Count the beats for one minute.) (4) Sit quietly for three minutes. (5) Count your pulse for one minute. Record this number as pulse rate at rest. (6) Stand in one place for three minutes. (7) Count your pulse rate for one minute. Record this number as pulse rate standing. (8) Run in place for three minutes. (9) Count your pulse rate for one minute. Record this number as pulse rate after exercise. (10) Compare your pulse rates with the pulse rates of other students in your class.

Questions   (1) How does your pulse rate at rest compare with your pulse rate after exercise? (2) What causes the pulse? (3) What is the relationship between heartbeat and pulse? (4) How do your pulse rates compare with the pulse rates of other students in your class? (5) How does exercise affect the pulse rate?

15:2 Blood Vessels

Arteries, veins, and capillaries are blood vessels. **Arteries** carry blood away from the heart. **Veins** carry blood to the heart. **Capillaries** connect arteries to veins.

An artery has a thick wall and a smaller inside diameter than a vein. The walls of arteries are muscular and elastic. They expand and contract easily. The walls of veins are thin and contain less

FIGURE 15–1. Arteries and veins have three layers—an outer layer of connective tissue, a middle layer of smooth muscle, and an inner layer of epithelial cells. Capillary walls are one cell thick.

Artery

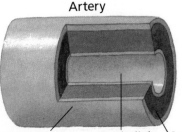

Connective tissue   Epithelial tissue   Smooth muscle

Vein   Valve

Connective tissue

Capillary

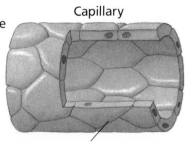

Epithelial tissue

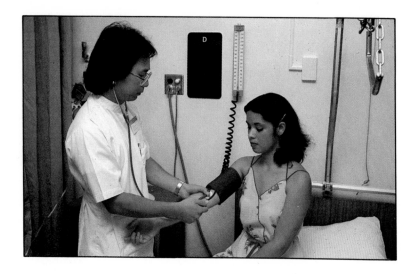

FIGURE 15–2. Blood pressure is usually taken during a health checkup. Continued high or low pressure may indicate poor health.

muscle tissue than arteries. The walls of capillaries are only one cell thick. Capillaries cannot be seen without a microscope.

The arteries help the heart pump blood throughout the body. Each ventricle of the heart is connected to a large artery that branches into smaller arteries. Blood is forced into these arteries every time the ventricles contract. Each beat of the heart makes an artery expand. When the heart relaxes, the artery contracts. The contraction of the artery exerts a force that pushes blood through it. You can feel your arteries expand and contract by placing your fingers on the inner side of your wrist. Your pulse has the same rhythm as your heartbeat.

How is blood moved throughout the body?

Veins have cuplike valves that prevent the backflow of blood. These valves keep blood flowing toward the heart. Most veins carry dark red blood that is low in oxygen. The veins in your skin appear blue because of the color in your skin and blood vessels. Where on the surface of your body can you see veins?

What prevents blood from flowing backward in veins?

Blood in the veins has much lower pressure than blood in the arteries. Therefore, blood moves more rapidly through the arteries. Blood pressure is a measure of the pressure of blood in arteries. Every time the heart beats, the pressure increases. When the heart relaxes between beats, the pressure decreases. Perhaps you have had your blood pressure taken during a health checkup. Blood pressure is expressed in millimeters of height of a column of mercury. When the human heart contracts, normal blood pressure in the arteries ranges from 110 to 150 millimeters of mercury. Normal pressure is 60 to 80 millimeters when the heart relaxes. Blood pressure varies from one person to another and even within the same person. It goes down when you are asleep and goes up

FIGURE 15–3. Valves in veins are like gates that allow blood to flow in one direction only.

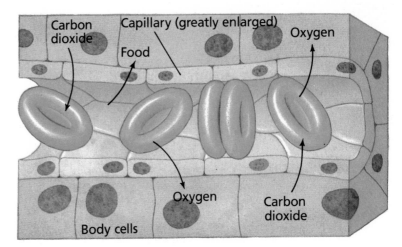

FIGURE 15–4. Nutrients and oxygen diffuse from blood in capillaries out into the tissues. Wastes such as carbon dioxide go from the tissues into the capillaries.

What are the functions of the capillaries?

when you are excited. Continued high or low blood pressure may indicate poor health or disease. Changes in the amount of blood, clogging of blood vessels, and rate of heartbeat may affect blood pressure.

The most numerous vessels, capillaries, are spread throughout body tissues. Because capillaries are the smallest vessels, materials go back and forth between the capillaries and the tissues through which they pass. For example, food and oxygen in blood are carried through arteries to capillaries. The food and oxygen diffuse from the blood in capillaries out to the tissues. Waste materials such as carbon dioxide move in the opposite direction, from tissues into capillaries. Blood carries the wastes away from the tissues through the capillaries to the veins.

Capillaries also help control the amount of heat lost from the body. During exercise, heat is picked up by the blood and carried to the capillaries. Capillaries in the skin allow warm blood to flow to the body surface. The body is cooled as heat from the blood escapes to the air around it. When the air temperature is low, blood flow through the capillaries in the skin is reduced. This decreases heat loss from the body.

Making Sure

1. What is the function of the blood?
2. State one reason why the flow of blood to the capillaries in muscle increases when a person exercises.
3. What prevents backflow of blood in veins?
4. What is blood pressure?
5. Your hand will turn red if you hold it under hot water. Give a reason to explain the change in color.

Activity 15–2

Comparing Pressures

Problem: How does pressure in the arteries compare with pressure in the veins?

Materials

plastic squeeze bottle
2-hole rubber stopper to fit squeeze bottle
red food coloring
glass tubing, 20 cm and 2.5 cm long
plastic tubing, 20 cm long
metric ruler
pan
water
glycerin
towel
dropper

FIGURE 15–5.

Procedure

1. Make a data table similar to the one shown to record your observations.
2. Attach the plastic tubing to the short glass tubing.
3. Insert both lengths of glass tubing into the rubber stopper, Figure 15–5. **CAUTION:** *Wet one end of the tubing with glycerin. Hold the other end with a towel as you insert it into the stopper.*
4. Fill the plastic squeeze bottle with water.
5. Add a few drops of red food coloring.
6. Place the rubber stopper into the bottle opening.
7. Place the ends of the tubes over the edge of the pan, Figure 15–5.
8. Place the metric ruler on the pan as shown.
9. Predict from which tube the water will travel farther when the bottle is squeezed.
10. Squeeze the bottle. Measure how far the water travels from each tube.
11. Record your results in a chart.
12. Refill the bottle and repeat step 10 four times. Record each result.
13. Calculate the average distance the water travels from each tube.

Data and Observations

Trial	Tube	Distance (cm)
1	Plastic	
	Glass	
2	Plastic	
	Glass	

Questions and Conclusions

1. In which tube was the water pressure greater?
2. In which tube was the water pressure lower?
3. Which tube corresponds to arteries?
4. Which tube corresponds to veins?
5. What part of your body can be compared to the squeeze bottle?
6. What part of your body can be compared to the water?
7. How does pressure in the arteries compare with pressure in the veins?

15:3 Circulation of Blood

Blood rich in oxygen is forced into the large arteries attached to the heart each time the heart pumps. This blood flows on through smaller arteries and capillaries to all parts of the body. Then the blood enters the veins and circulates back to the heart.

As blood low in oxygen returns to the heart, it enters the right atrium. (See Figure 15–6.) Contraction of the right atrium forces the blood into the right ventricle. A valve between the right atrium and the right ventricle is very important. It prevents the blood from backing up into the atrium. The valve opens only in the direction of the ventricle. If blood pushes against the valve in the direction of the atrium, the valve is forced closed. No blood passes through.

Contraction of the right ventricle forces blood into the pulmonary artery. (See Figure 15–6.) Blood travels through the pulmonary artery to the lungs and into the lung capillaries. There it picks up oxygen and loses carbon dioxide by diffusion. The oxygen-rich blood then travels through the pulmonary veins to the left atrium of the heart. **Pulmonary circulation** is the flow of blood through the heart, to the lungs, and back to the heart.

Blood is pumped from the left atrium to the left ventricle. (See Figure 15–6.) Another valve between the two chambers prevents the blood from going back into the atrium. Oxygen-rich blood is pumped out of the left ventricle into the aorta (ay ORT uh). The aorta is the largest artery in the body. It branches into smaller arteries, which connect to capillaries. When the left ventricle contracts, it exerts more force than any other heart chamber. The

What is pulmonary circulation?

FIGURE 15–6. Blood flows from veins into the right atrium. Contraction of the right atrium forces blood into the right ventricle (a). Contraction of the right ventricle forces blood into the pulmonary artery. Blood flows to the lungs and back. It reenters the heart in the left atrium (b).

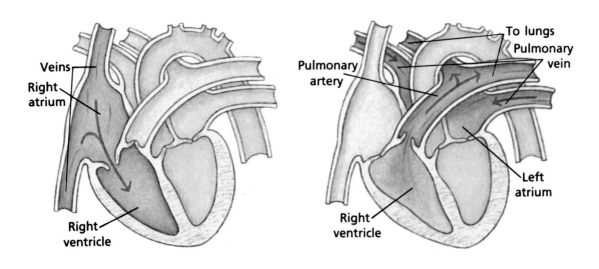

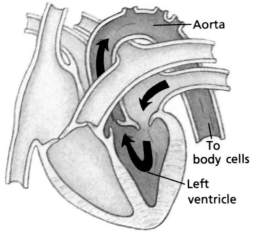

Aorta

To body cells

Left ventricle

FIGURE 15–7. Blood is pumped from the left atrium into the left ventricle and then into the aorta.

oxygen-rich blood in the aorta is pumped throughout the body. It loses oxygen to body cells and gains carbon dioxide by diffusion. The blood returns to the right atrium in two large veins called vena cavae (VEE nuh KAY vee).

A stethoscope is used to hear the heartbeat. The heartbeat has two sounds—"lub" and "dupp." The "lub" sound comes from the ventricles contracting and the valves closing. When the ventricles relax, a "dupp" sound is heard. The "dupp" sound is produced by the closing of the valves at the entrance to the aorta. Contractions of the heart force blood through the arteries and veins. When the heart chambers relax, they fill with blood.

What causes the lub-dupp sound of the heartbeat?

Making Sure

6. What prevents blood from backing up into the atrium?
7. Trace the flow of blood through the body.
8. Why does blood circulate through the lungs?

15:4 Coronary and Systemic Circulation

Every cell in the heart needs food and oxygen. The food and oxygen are brought to the cells by the circulation of blood. Movement of blood through the tissues of the heart is the **coronary circulation.** If the tissues of the heart do not receive food and oxygen, they may be damaged. This condition might be related to a heart attack. One type of heart attack is caused by a blood clot in a coronary artery. A blood clot is a mass of blood that has hardened and formed a solid lump. The clot blocks the artery and prevents the flow of blood. Many people survive heart attacks.

What is the function of the coronary circulation?

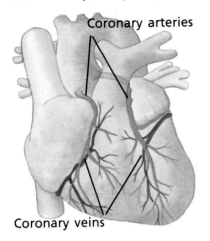

Coronary arteries

Coronary veins

FIGURE 15–8. Coronary circulation carries nutrients and oxygen to the cells of the heart.

FIGURE 15–9. Circulation of blood to the kidneys (a) and digestive organs (b) is part of the systemic circulation.

Their damaged heart is slowly repaired by the growth of scar tissue. New capillaries form around the damaged tissue.

There is a third main pathway through which blood flows each time the heart pumps. **Systemic** (sihs TEM ihk) **circulation** supplies all the body tissues, except the lungs and heart, with oxygen and nutrients. Blood in this pathway leaves the left ventricle. It is forced into the aorta and branches of the aorta. This blood continues to flow on into capillaries in all parts of the body. As it flows, materials diffuse between the capillaries and the tissues. Finally, the blood returns in veins to the right atrium.

One part of systemic circulation is renal (REEN ul) circulation. Renal circulation includes blood vessels that pass through the kidneys where wastes are filtered from the blood. Another part of systemic circulation is portal circulation. The portal circulation carries blood away from the small intestine, an organ that digests food. It includes a network of small veins that join to form a single, large portal vein. The portal vein passes into the liver. Sugar may be removed from the blood and stored in the liver as glycogen. This stored sugar can be released back into the blood very quickly when the body has a sudden need for energy.

Making Sure

9. What is the function of the systemic circulation?
10. What causes a heart attack?
11. Name the three main pathways through which blood flows.

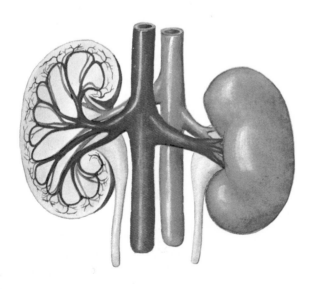

a

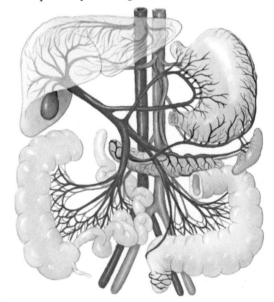

b

15:5 Blood and Lymph

The average person has about 5.5 liters of blood. Blood is a complex tissue containing plasma, red and white blood cells, and platelets. The solid parts of blood are the cells and platelets. About 55 percent of blood is liquid **plasma.** Plasma is about 90 percent water. Nutrients and oxygen are dissolved in plasma. About one percent of blood plasma is dissolved salts. These salts contain mineral elements. Some of the minerals present are calcium, sodium, magnesium, and potassium. Plasma also contains substances that fight microbes that cause disease.

Body cells get needed materials from the blood. Blood carries
1. oxygen from the lungs to the tissues,
2. substances from the digestive system to the tissues,
3. carbon dioxide from the tissues to the lungs,
4. wastes and excess water from the tissues to the kidneys,
5. disease-fighting substances to the tissues,
6. hormones to various parts of the body.

Some of the liquid portion of the blood leaves the capillaries. The liquid passes through the capillary walls into the surrounding tissues. This liquid plasma outside the capillary is called tissue fluid. Tissue fluid is the colorless liquid in a blister. Tissue fluid moves through spaces between the tissues and cells. It collects in tubes and becomes **lymph** (LIHMF). Then lymph returns to the blood through a large lymph tube.

Lymph is a vital part of the circulatory system. It helps in the absorption of nutrients, such as fat, by the body. Lymph also helps to rid the body of wastes. Dead cells and bacteria are removed from the lymph before it returns to the blood.

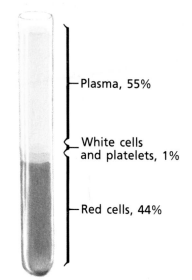

FIGURE 15–10. The composition of blood

Define lymph.

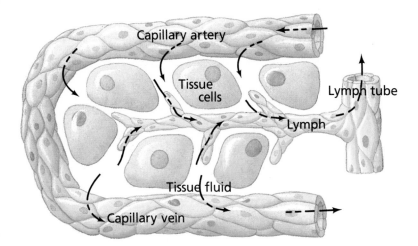

FIGURE 15–11. Tissue fluid collects in tubes and becomes lymph, which returns to the blood through a large lymph tube.

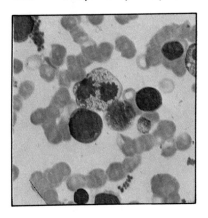

FIGURE 15–12.

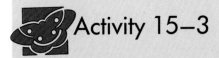

Activity 15–3   Observing Blood Cells

Problem: What are the solid parts of human blood?

Materials   prepared slide of human blood, microscope

Procedure   (1) Examine a prepared slide of human blood under low power and then switch to high power. (2) Refer to Figure 15–12. Locate the red blood cells. They are saucer-shaped. Draw a red blood cell and label the cell membrane and cytoplasm. (3) Slowly move the slide until you see some white blood cells. They are usually larger than the red blood cells and they have different shapes. They may be stained blue. Note the tiny blue or red dots in the cytoplasm. Draw one or two white blood cells and label the parts. (4) While still using high power, move the slide until you see platelets. They look like very small dots. Usually they will appear blue. Draw one or two platelets.

Questions   (1) Do red blood cells appear red? (2) How do the white and red blood cells compare in size? (3) Do any of the blood cells have a nucleus? (4) Which blood cells were the least numerous? (5) What are the solid parts of human blood?

15:6 Red Blood Cells

What is the function of red blood cells?

Red blood cells are saucer-shaped cells in plasma that carry oxygen. They are the most plentiful blood cells. There are about 5 million red blood cells in one cubic millimeter of blood. Being small, about 2000 placed in a row would stretch across a dime. Their small size enables them to squeeze through the capillaries.

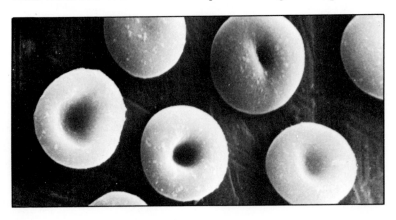

FIGURE 15–13. Red blood cells magnified approximately 7000 times

Fully developed human red blood cells do not contain nuclei.

Red blood cells contain hemoglobin (HEE muh glo bun). **Hemoglobin** carries oxygen to tissues. Oxygen becomes attached to hemoglobin as blood circulates in the lungs. A single blood cell can pick up as many as 1 million oxygen molecules. As blood flows through body tissues, oxygen separates from hemoglobin. This change takes place in the capillaries. The oxygen released from the hemoglobin diffuses into the tissues.

Hemoglobin can form bonds with other gases besides oxygen. One of these gases is carbon monoxide. Carbon monoxide is a colorless, odorless gas that is seldom present in clear air. However, it is present in the exhaust gases from cars, buses, and trucks, and in cigarette smoke. Also, it is sometimes produced by stoves that are not working right.

Carbon monoxide in large concentrations can be harmful. It enters the blood of a person who breathes it. The bond carbon monoxide forms with hemoglobin is much stronger than the bond formed between hemoglobin and oxygen. Therefore, the carbon monoxide prevents oxygen from combining with hemoglobin. The amount of oxygen carried to the tissues decreases. Soon the person faints. Unless quickly moved into fresh air or given oxygen, the person will die.

Blood removes carbon dioxide waste from the tissues. Some carbon dioxide combines with hemoglobin and is carried by the red blood cells. Hemoglobin carries the carbon dioxide from the tissues to the lungs. Carbon dioxide is also carried by the blood plasma. In the lungs, carbon dioxide and water are released. You add carbon dioxide and water vapor to the air when you exhale.

FIGURE 15–14. Red blood cells in the capillaries carry oxygen to tissues. Red blood cells also carry carbon dioxide from the tissues to the lungs.

Making Sure

12. How does the life of a body cell depend on the circulation of blood?
13. How is blood involved in the excretion of wastes?
14. How is lymph different from blood?

15:7 White Blood Cells

White blood cells are produced in bone marrow, lymph nodes, and in the spleen. Lymph nodes are clumps of tissue such as tonsils and adenoids. As lymph passes through a lymph node, dead microbes are removed from it. An infection may cause lymph nodes to increase in size and cause swelling. You may have noticed swelling in a part of your body if you have ever had an

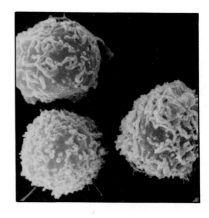

FIGURE 15–15. White blood cells magnified

infection. Swelling is caused by fluid that builds up when you have an infection.

White blood cells live from a few days to many weeks. Each white blood cell has a nucleus. The number of white blood cells increases rapidly when infection occurs. The number may go from 7000 to about 25 000 white blood cells per cubic millimeter. An increase in white cells is one way the blood reacts to infection.

Leukemia (lew KEE mee uh) is a blood cancer. In leukemia the number of white cells increase to high level and do not return to normal. A person with leukemia might have as many as 50 000 white cells in each drop of blood.

White cells can leave the capillaries. They enter the tissues by squeezing between the cells of the capillary wall. If you get a splinter in your finger, many thousands of white cells will surround the splinter. Have you ever observed pus in an infected wound? Pus is composed largely of dead white blood cells. The white cells were used by the body to destroy harmful microbes.

What is the function of white blood cells?

There are several types of white blood cells. One type produces antibodies. Antibodies attack foreign substances that enter the body.

15:8 Platelets

What is the function of platelets?

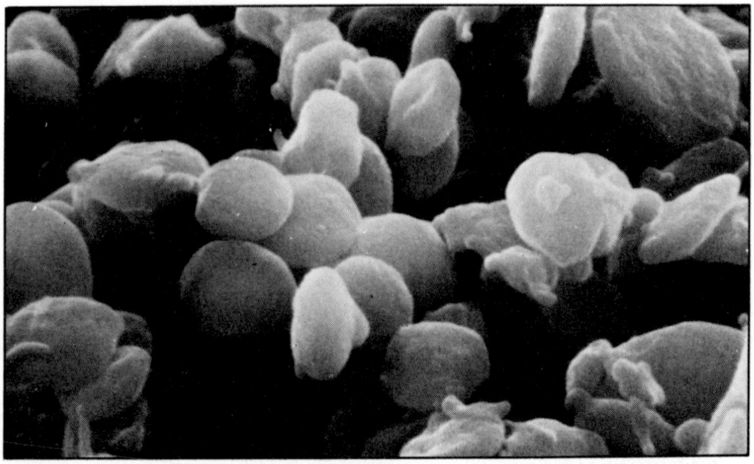

Loss of blood occurs if the skin is cut or broken open in any way. Bleeding stops when a clot forms in the wound. **Platelets** are odd-shaped, colorless bodies that help clot blood. They are much smaller than red blood cells. A blood protein called fibrinogen (fi BRIHN uh jun), the mineral calcium, and vitamin K are also used to form a clot.

FIGURE 15–16. Platelets are shown magnified.

FIGURE 15–17. Red blood cells caught in fibrin threads form the basis of a blood clot (magnified).

How does a blood clot form? Clots form when blood is exposed to air. Otherwise, a person with a very small wound would lose a lot of blood and die. As blood escapes from a blood vessel, the platelets come apart. They release a substance that causes changes in fibrinogen. As a result, a substance called fibrin forms. Fibrin resembles tiny threads. These threads form a mesh or net which traps blood cells among its fibers. The fibrin and cells form a clot which prevents further bleeding. As the clot dries, it forms a scab. Both vitamin K and the mineral calcium must be present for blood to clot. If the supply of vitamin K or calcium is low, it takes longer than normal for a clot to form.

What factors are necessary for the formation of a blood clot?

Blood clots can form inside the body as well as on the skin. For example, a black-and-blue mark that forms a bruise is caused by a blood clot. Sometimes a blood clot forms inside a blood vessel. The clot can cut off the supply of blood and cause illness or death. A stroke may be caused by a blood clot that forms in an artery within the brain. The clot cuts off or reduces the flow of blood to some brain cells. If certain brain cells are damaged or destroyed, a part of the body may become paralyzed. Sometimes a loss of memory, speech, sight, or hearing may result from damage to brain cells. A lack of oxygen can destroy brain tissue.

15:9 Blood Types

All blood is not exactly the same. Your blood is different in some ways from other people's blood. There are four main types of blood. The four main **blood types** are called A, B, AB, and O. Each blood type is somewhat different in composition from each other blood type. What is your blood type?

What are the four main blood types?

When certain blood types are mixed, a clumping or clustering of the red blood cells occurs. Suppose the wrong type of blood is injected into a person's veins. Clumps formed in the blood

Table 15–1

Blood Transfusion Possibilities		
Type	Can receive	Can donate to
A	O, A	A, AB
B	O, B	B, AB
AB	all	AB
O	O	all

might prevent or slow the normal circulation and cause death. Persons with type AB blood are called universal receivers because they may safely receive type AB blood or any of the other three types.

A person who has type O blood is known as a universal donor. This means blood from a type O person can be injected into people with other blood types. However, it is best if a person receives his or her own blood type. Type O can be given in an emergency when a person's own blood type is not available for a transfusion.

The **Rh factor** refers to the presence of certain proteins in the blood. The proteins were first discovered in the blood of Rhesus (REE sus) monkeys. Rh negative (Rh −) blood lacks the proteins present in Rh positive (Rh +) blood.

The Rh factor may have a bad effect on an unborn baby. About one out of every 300 to 400 babies born in the United States has a mother with Rh − blood and a father with Rh + blood. The baby may inherit Rh + blood from its father. If an Rh − mother carries an Rh + baby, the life of the baby may be in danger. The problem occurs if Rh antibodies from the mother's blood enter the blood of the baby. The mother's antibodies have the ability to destroy the baby's red blood cells. If too many red blood cells are destroyed, the baby could die.

An Rh baby's life may be saved by a blood transfusion. Soon after birth, most of the baby's blood can be withdrawn and replaced with the proper Rh blood. This procedure is called an exchange transfusion. Blood transfusions can also be given to an unborn baby. Also, an Rh − mother can receive an injection after the birth of each baby. The injection prevents the buildup of antibodies that may endanger her future children.

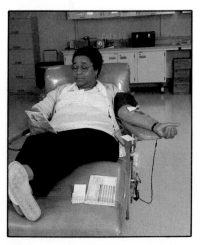

FIGURE 15–18. People donate blood for use in transfusions.

Making Sure

15. Explain why lymph is a vital part of the circulatory system.
16. Describe what happens when a blood clot forms.
17. How can a blood transfusion be harmful? Helpful?

15:10 Respiration

Human body cells need oxygen. Oxygen carried to the cells by the circulatory system comes from the air a person breathes. Breathing and supplying the blood with oxygen are two functions of the respiratory system. Removing carbon dioxide from the blood is another function. The main parts of the respiratory system are the nose, mouth, trachea, lungs, and diaphragm.

As air passes through the nose, it is warmed. Dust particles are filtered by fine hairs. Also, tissues lining the nose add moisture to the air. Air passes from the back of the nose and mouth toward the trachea. The trachea is a tube that transports air into the chest cavity.

Located above the trachea is a structure called the larynx (LAR ihnks). The larynx is a boxlike structure made of cartilage. It contains flexible vocal cords. Air passes between the vocal cords and causes them to vibrate. The vibrating vocal cords, combined with movements of your mouth and tongue, produce the sounds of speech. The larynx is also called the voice box since it contains the vocal cords.

The trachea and larynx are protected by the epiglottis, a flap of cartilage. Most of the time the trachea is open. Air passes freely into and out of the lungs. However, when you swallow, the epiglottis closes. This prevents food from entering the trachea.

In the chest cavity, the trachea divides into two bronchi (BRAHN ki). The bronchi divide and form the bronchial (BRAHN kee ul) tubes. In the lungs, the bronchial tubes divide into many smaller tubes. These tubes connect to tiny sacs called alveoli (al VE uh li).

Describe the path air follows after it enters the respiratory system.

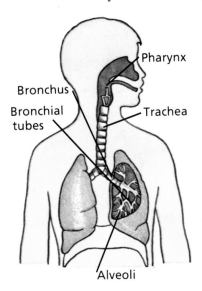

FIGURE 15–19. The organs of the respiratory system

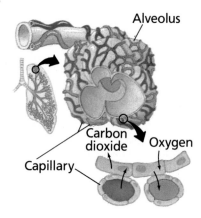

FIGURE 15–20. Oxygen moves into the blood in capillaries surrounding the alveoli. Carbon dioxide moves from the capillaries to the alveoli.

Describe the movement of the rib cage and diaphragm during inhalation and exhalation.

Alveoli are spongy, air-filled sacs lined with delicate membranes. The lungs in an adult contain about 600 000 000 alveoli.

The alveoli are surrounded by capillaries. When you inhale, the alveoli fill with oxygen. Oxygen diffuses into the capillaries and binds to red blood cells. The blood carries the oxygen to body cells. At the same time, carbon dioxide produced by body cells diffuses into the blood and is carried to the alveoli. The carbon dioxide then diffuses from the blood to the alveoli. The carbon dioxide is pushed out of the lungs when you exhale.

When you breathe, you may feel a slight movement in your chest. Your diaphragm (DI uh fram) and chest muscles pump air into and out of your body. The diaphragm is a sheet of muscles across the bottom of the chest cavity. The diaphragm contracts and relaxes as you breathe. When relaxed, the diaphragm is shaped like a dome. The upper side of the dome extends up into the chest cavity. The diaphragm flattens slightly as it contracts. As the diaphragm flattens, there is an increase in the volume of the chest cavity.

Increased volume of the chest cavity causes a decrease in air pressure in the lungs. Air pressure is now greater in the air outside the body than inside the lungs. Air moves from areas of high pressure to areas of low pressure. The greater air pressure outside the body forces air into the lungs through the nose and mouth.

When you exhale, your diaphragm relaxes and your ribs move inward. The volume of your chest cavity decreases. Air pressure in your lungs increases. Air pressure inside your lungs is greater than pressure outside your body. Thus, air is forced out of your lungs. You exhale carbon dioxide, some oxygen, and water vapor.

Making Sure

18. Draw a diagram of the respiratory system and label its parts.
19. Explain how the sounds of speech are produced.

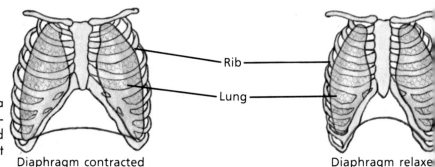

Rib
Lung

FIGURE 15–21. Breathing is a process in which the ribs and diaphragm alternately increase and decrease the size of the chest cavity.

Diaphragm contracted   Diaphragm relaxe

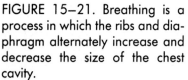

Activity 15—4   Respiration

Problem: How does exercise affect the amount of carbon dioxide exhaled by the lungs?

Materials   clock or watch with second hand, straw, bromthymol blue solution, 2 beakers

Procedure   (1) Make a hypothesis for the problem. (2) Put 100 mL bromthymol blue solution into the beaker. Bromthymol blue will turn light yellow or straw color when carbon dioxide is added to it. (3) Exhale through the straw into the bromthymol blue solution. **CAUTION:** *Do not inhale through the straw.* Continue exhaling through the straw for 15 seconds or until the bromthymol blue solution changes color. (4) Record the time it takes for the color change to occur. (5) Pour 100 mL bromthymol blue solution into another beaker. (6) Exercise by running in place for three minutes. (7) Exhale into the bromthymol blue solution. Exhale at the same rate and force as before. (8) Record the time it takes for the bromthymol blue to change color. (9) Compare your results with results of other students in your class.

Questions   (1) What caused the bromthymol blue to change color? (2) Compare the time it took the bromthymol blue solution to change color before exercise and after exercise. Explain the difference in times. (3) What was the control in this experiment? (4) How does exercise affect the amount of carbon dioxide exhaled by the lungs?

FIGURE 15—22.

15:11 Excretion

Take a deep breath and then exhale. When you breathe out, you excrete carbon dioxide from your body. Carbon dioxide is a waste product. **Excretion** means getting rid of waste products. Another waste product excreted from the lungs is water vapor. In addition to lungs, kidneys and skin are organs of excretion.

Define excretion.

If wastes are not removed, body tissues may fill with poisonous waste products. These wastes would destroy cells and tissues. If water collects in the tissues, it will cause swelling. Fever, poisoning, coma, and death may result from wastes building up in tissues.

Kidneys are organs located on either side of the spine in the small of the back. A human kidney is a reddish-brown colored organ shaped like a bean. It is about 10 centimeters in length. During its circulation through the body, blood passes through the

How are wastes removed from the body?

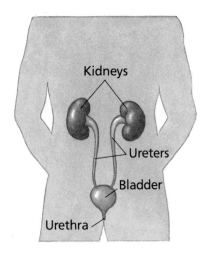

FIGURE 15–23. Organs of the excretory system

What are the functions of the skin?

FIGURE 15–24. The structure of skin

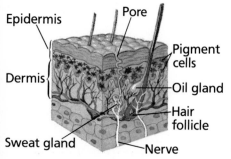

kidneys. The kidneys remove excess water, minerals, and urea, a protein waste, from the blood.

In the kidney, wastes filtered from the blood form a liquid called urine. Urine is carried through two long tubes, called ureters, from the kidney to the urinary bladder. The bladder stores urine.

Urine is mostly water. It contains urea, mineral salts, and other body wastes. Urine is excreted from the bladder and out of the body through a tube called the urethra (yoo REE thruh). Muscular contractions of the bladder force the urine out.

People whose kidneys do not function properly can have their blood cleaned by a kidney dialysis (di AHL ih sus) machine. Blood circulates from the body into the machine. The machine removes wastes and returns the blood to the body.

15:12 Skin

Skin and hair, fingernails, and toenails make up the integumentary (ihn teg yuh MENT uh ree) system. Skin keeps germs and other harmful materials out of the body and keeps body fluids in. Sweat produced by the skin's sweat glands helps maintain body temperature. When a person's body temperature increases, the person sweats more. The evaporation of sweat has a cooling effect on the body. Sweat is mostly water, but it also contains small amounts of waste products. Skin constantly renews itself as old cells on its surface die and wear off. The dead cells are replaced by the growth of new cells from underneath. Skin has the ability to repair itself when cut.

Skin is composed of two layers. The outer layer is the epidermis. The inner layer is the dermis. The outer cells of the epidermis are dead. Specialized cells deeper in the epidermis produce a dark pigment called melanin. The color of skin and hair depends on the size and amount of melanin particles in the specialized cells. Nerves in the dermis provide a sense of touch. Also present in the dermis are the roots of hair, oil glands, and sweat glands, Figure 15–24.

Hairs are composed of dead epidermal cells. A hair is rooted in the skin by a knob called a bulb. The socket containing each hair is the hair follicle. Attached to each hair follicle is a muscle. "Gooseflesh" occurs when these muscles contract.

Oil glands are in the skin all over the body except for the palms of the hands and the soles of the feet. They are usually associated with hair follicles and are abundant in the scalp. Oil secreted by the oil glands keeps the skin and hair soft and moist.

Problem: Which areas of the skin are more sensitive to touch?

Materials

index card
8 toothpicks
glue
metric ruler

Procedure

1. Make a hypothesis for the problem.
2. Glue the toothpicks onto the card as shown in Figure 15–25. Accurately measure distances between the toothpicks so they are 1 mm, 3 mm, 5 mm, and 10 mm apart.
3. After your partner's eyes are closed, use the part of the card with toothpicks 1 mm apart and carefully touch the skin surface. Touch the fingertip, palm of the hand, back of the hand, forearm, and back of the neck. **CAUTION:** *Do not apply heavy pressure when touching your partner's skin.*
4. If your partner can feel two points, record a 2 in the chart. If your partner cannot feel two points, record a 1.
5. Again, after your partner's eyes are closed, use the part of the card with toothpicks 3 mm apart to carefully touch the skin surface. Touch each area listed in the data table.

FIGURE 15–25.

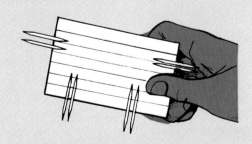

6. Record whether your partner can feel one or two points.
7. Repeat steps 5 and 6 with the 5 mm and 10 mm sections of the card.
8. Record your results in the Data and Observations chart.
9. Repeat the activity with you and your partner switching roles.

Data and Observations

Distance	1 mm	3 mm	5 mm	10 mm
Fingertip				
Palm				
Back of hand				
Forearm				
Back of neck				

Questions and Conclusions

1. Which parts of the body that you tested have the most touch receptors?
2. Which parts of the body that you tested have the least touch receptors?
3. Rank the body parts you tested in order from the one most sensitive to touch to the one least sensitive to touch.
4. What are located in the dermis that provide a sense of touch?
5. Which areas of the skin are more sensitive to touch?

Frontiers

The Framingham Heart Disease Study

Very few people died of heart disease before 1900. Heart disease has since become the number one killer in the United States. Since 1900, technology has created an easier lifestyle that favors heart disease. Heart diseases include strokes and heart attacks. An individual suffers a stroke when blood vessels become clogged preventing blood from passing to the brain. A heart attack results when blood does not reach parts of the heart.

The rate of heart disease increased so noticeably between the years 1940 and 1967 that the World Health Organization called it the most serious epidemic facing the world. To combat the epidemic, physicians began an intensive 30-year investigation into the nature and causes of heart disease. This investigation was started in 1948 in Framingham, Massachusetts, and became known as the Framingham Study. Researchers wanted to discover a way to predict who would develop heart disease.

Physicians selected 5127 people between the ages of 30 and 62 who showed no signs of heart disease. The study group comprised 2282 men and 2845 women. Every two years, each person in the group was given a physical examination. The examination included blood chemistry tests, heartbeat tests, chest X rays, and blood pressure measurements.

Over the next thirty years, the scientists developed a "heart disease profile." The subjects who had heart attacks or strokes
1. had higher blood pressure.
2. weighed more.
3. had greater amounts of the fat compound cholesterol in their blood.
4. smoked more.
5. suffered more stress.
6. were less physically active.

The physicians could then predict with a few simple tests which people were likely to suffer from a heart attack or stroke. They could also recommend avoidance of the risk factors in the "heart disease profile" to reduce the chances of a heart attack or stroke.

Other important discoveries were:
1. Risk of death from stroke increased as soon as blood pressure rose above 120/80.
2. A person 20 percent over ideal weight is three times more likely to die from a heart attack.
3. Ninety percent of the people in the Framingham Study group who developed clogged arteries had smoked.
4. Sixty-six percent of the people in the study group who suffered heart attacks died within one hour of onset.
5. Thirty-nine percent of the subjects who experienced strokes had early warning signals. Six months before their strokes, these people had brief periods of dizzy spells or blurred vision.
6. Thirty percent of the subjects who had occasional irregular heartbeats had strokes. These people had no other signs of heart disease.

The Framingham Study was a breakthrough in helping people prevent heart disease. However, over 40 million people in the United States have defects in their hearts or blood vessels. About one million die each year. Heart disease costs the United States $40 billion a year in medical services and lost earnings. Medical advancements are continuing to reduce the threat of this serious disease.

CHAPTER 15
Review

Summary

1. The heart is a muscular organ that pumps blood through the body. 15:1

2. Arteries carry blood away from the heart. Veins carry blood back to the heart. Exchange of materials between blood and tissues occurs in the capillaries. 15:2

3. Blood transports nutrients and oxygen to the cells. It transports carbon dioxide and other wastes away from the cells. 15:4

4. Pulmonary, systemic, and coronary circulation are part of the human circulatory system. 15:3, 15:4

5. Lymph is a connecting link between the capillaries and tissues. Lymph transports dissolved substances to and from the blood. 15:5

6. Red blood cells contain hemoglobin that carries oxygen to tissues. 15:6

7. White blood cells and antibodies fight infection. 15:7

8. Each of the four blood types is different in composition from each other blood type. When certain types are mixed, clumping and slowed circulation can result. 15:9

9. An exchange of carbon dioxide and oxygen occurs between blood and air inside the lungs. Another exchange takes place between blood and tissues. 15:10

10. Waste products are excreted by the lungs, kidneys, and skin. 15:11, 15:12

Vocabulary

Write a sentence using the following words or terms correctly.

artery	hemoglobin	Rh factor
atrium	lymph	systemic circulation
blood type	plasma	vein
capillary	platelet	ventricle
coronary circulation	pulmonary circulation	white blood cell
excretion	red blood cell	

Questions

Do not write in this book.

A. True or False
Determine whether each of the following sentences is true or false. Rewrite the false statements to make them correct.

1. Blood is pumped from atria to ventricles.
2. Both atria contain blood rich in oxygen.

3. The aorta carries blood away from the left ventricle.
4. Arteries carry blood away from the heart.
5. Capillaries connect arteries and veins.
6. When you exercise, the flow of blood to your muscles decreases.
7. Coronary circulation carries blood to the kidneys.
8. Vitamin K and calcium are needed for blood clotting.
9. Air pressure inside your lungs never changes.
10. Lungs, kidneys, and skin are organs of excretion.

B. Multiple Choice

Choose the word or phrase that correctly completes the following sentences.
1. (Arteries, Veins, Capillaries, Lymph vessels) are the smallest blood vessels.
2. The vein that comes out of the *(lungs, kidneys, small intestine)* contains blood low in mineral and organic wastes.
3. The average human pulse is about *(40–60, 60–80, 80–100)* pulses per minute.
4. Blood pressure is highest in the *(capillaries, arteries, veins)*.
5. Valves are present in the *(capillaries, arteries, veins)*.
6. *(White blood cells, Red blood cells, Platelets)* fight disease.
7. The *(portal, coronary, pulmonary)* vein carries blood away from the lungs.
8. As blood passes through the kidneys, wastes are *(added, removed, unchanged)*.
9. The *(diaphragm, epiglottis, lymph node)* helps pump air into and out of your lungs.
10. Urine is carried from the kidneys to the *(lungs, heart, skin, bladder)*.

C. Completion

Complete each of the following sentences with the correct word or phrase.
1. _____ is carried by the _____ molecules in red blood cells.
2. The four main blood types are A, B, AB, and _____.
3. _____ is a liquid part of blood that bathes the tissues.
4. Rh _____ blood contains the Rh factor.
5. Hemoglobin is present in _____ cells.
6. A stroke is caused by a blood _____ that forms in the brain.
7. Urine is mostly _____.
8. When swallowing, the _____ closes to prevent food from entering the air passages.
9. The tube carrying air toward the lungs is the _____.
10. Perspiration is excreted through sweat glands in the _____.

CHAPTER 15
Review

D. How and Why
1. How does the heart pump blood?
2. Why is hemoglobin vital to human life?
3. Trace the path of a drop of blood through the pulmonary circulation.
4. Explain how blood types are related to blood transfusions.
5. Why are white cells important to good health?
6. How does lymph carry food and oxygen to cells?
7. Explain how a blood clot forms.
8. How do your chest muscles and diaphragm cause you to breathe?
9. How are wastes produced in the body?
10. Why will a person die if the kidneys stop working?

Ideas to Explore

1. **Project:** Visit a hospital laboratory to learn how blood is typed.
2. **Challenge:** Send for literature from the American Heart Association to learn about diseases of the circulatory system.
3. **Challenge:** Write to the American Cancer Society for information about the harmful effects of smoking on the heart and circulation. List several reasons why most people are choosing not to smoke.
4. **Project:** Make a colorful bulletin board poster showing the heart and circulatory system. You may wish to supplement the poster with a model of the human heart made from colored clay.
5. **Challenge:** Prepare a short report on one of the following: kidney dialysis, diabetes detection, synthetic blood.
6. **Challenge:** Many physicians believe exercise can prevent disease of the heart and the circulatory system. Prepare a report on exercise and heart disease.

Readings

Barnard, Christiaan (Ed.) *Junior Body Machine: How the Human Body Works.* New York: Crown, 1983.

Davis, Goode P., Jr. and Edwards Park. *The Heart: The Living Pump.* Washington, DC: US News Books, 1981.

James, Daniel E. *What About Blood Pressure?* Burlington, NC: Carolina Biological Supply, 1981.

The American Heart Association. *Heartbook.* New York: E.P. Dutton, 1980.

Food is fuel for the human body. Energy to do work is produced by breaking down food within the body. A balanced diet is important for a person's general physical and mental health. Water, minerals, carbohydrates, fats, proteins, and vitamins are essential nutrients. Lack of some of these nutrients can produce diseases, poor growth and development, and other disorders. What essential nutrients are provided by vegetables? What are some of the problems caused by eating some nutrients in excess?

CHAPTER 16
DIGESTION AND NUTRITION

16:1 Food and Health

Eating right is important to staying healthy. It is important because your cells need materials for growth and repair. Also, your cells need materials that will provide energy for life processes. These materials are supplied to your body cells in the food that you eat. The study of food and its use by the body is called **nutrition** (new TRIHSH un).

The materials needed by your body for good health are called **nutrients** (NEW tree unts). There are about 50 nutrients that your body needs. Water, minerals, carbohydrates (kar boh HI drayts), fats, proteins, and vitamins are nutrients. The nutrients in servings of many packaged foods are listed on the labels.

What you choose to eat affects your health. Good health requires that you eat a combination of foods to get all the nutrients you need. This kind of eating is called a balanced diet. A balanced diet provides nutrients in the correct amounts. It contains foods from each of the four basic food groups. The four basic groups are the milk group, the meat group, the fruit-vegetable group, and the grain group. See Table 16–1. Combination foods include servings or partial servings from the four basic food groups. Other foods may complement but do not replace foods in the basic food groups. Reading nutrition labels on packaged foods can help you choose the right foods for a balanced diet.

GOALS:
1. You will learn the importance of nutrition to good health.
2. You will learn how the body uses food for growth and maintenance.
3. You will learn the parts of the digestive system.

What are the basic food groups?

335

Table 16–1

How to Eat for Good Health			
Milk group	**Meat group**	**Fruit - vegetable group**	**Grain group**

Supplies these key nutrients:
    calcium
    riboflavin
    (vitamin B$_2$)
    protein
for strong bones and teeth, healthy skin, and good vision
	Supplies these key nutrients:
	    protein
	    niacin
	    iron
	    thiamin
	    (vitamin B$_1$)
	for muscle, bone and blood cells and healthy skin and nerves
		Supplies these key nutrients:
		    vitamin A
		    vitamin C
		for night vision and to help resist infections and heal wounds
			Supplies these key nutrients:
			    carbohydrate
			    thiamin
			    (vitamin B$_1$)
			    iron
			    niacin
			for energy and a healthy nervous system

16:2 Water

If you have any pets, you know it is important to give them water each day. You need water, too. If you do not get enough water, your body suffers. A serious illness or death may result.

About 60 to 70 percent of your body is water. Water is used by the body to break down food. Also, foods must be dissolved in water to be absorbed into the blood. In sweat glands and the kidneys, waste products dissolved in water are removed from the blood. Both sweat and urine consist mostly of water. The body releases about 2.5 liters of water each day.

You obtain water by drinking it and by drinking milk and juices. Most vegetables and fruits have a high water content. Some water is produced when food is broken down within cells.

How does the body use water?

Making Sure

1. Make a list of your favorite foods. Classify those foods into the four basic food groups. Some foods, such as pizza, may fall into the combination group. (See Table 16–1.) How many of your favorite foods fall into each group?

16:3 Carbohydrates

Spaghetti, potatoes, bread, and cereals are examples of food rich in carbohydrates. A **carbohydrate** is a compound composed of carbon, hydrogen, and oxygen. The ratio of hydrogen to oxygen in a carbohydrate is 2:1. Sugar and **starch** are two carbohydrates.

Carbohydrates are important sources of energy. During digestion, most carbohydrates are changed to a simple sugar called glucose. Glucose is carried to the body's cells by the circulatory system. In the cells, glucose is broken down with the help of oxygen in a chemical change that releases energy. The energy is used for the growth and repair of cell parts and for other cell activities.

Glycogen (GLI kuh jun) is another carbohydrate present in the human body. It is formed from glucose and stored in the liver and muscle cells. Glycogen contains stored energy. Glycogen is converted back to glucose as it is needed by the body's cells.

Some foods that are rich in carbohydrates are low in other nutrients. Candy, potato chips, doughnuts, soda pop, and french fries are examples. Snacks such as these are tasty and fun to eat. Eating snacks from time to time is not usually harmful. However, a diet that contains a lot of snacks may be unhealthy. A person who eats too many snacks may have plenty of energy but does not get all the nutrients he or she needs. Health problems may often result.

Too many processed foods in your diet can also be unhealthy. Examples of processed foods are cookies, white bread, and many

What are the functions of carbohydrates in the body?

How is glycogen formed in the body? How is it used?

FIGURE 16–1. Snacks such as these may not supply all the nutrients your body needs.

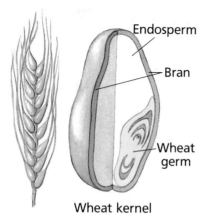

Endosperm

Bran

Wheat germ

Wheat kernel

FIGURE 16–2. In the process of refining wheat into white flour, fiber, vitamins, and minerals are lost.

FIGURE 16–3.

Iodine Solution

canned items. Many processed foods have added substances, such as flavorings or preservatives. Processing foods can reduce nutrients and roughage. Roughage is fiber that is not digested. It is needed to keep the digestive tract working properly. Raw fruits and vegetables, whole grains, and beans are high in roughage.

Wheat is refined into white flour to make white bread. In the refining process, fiber, vitamins, and minerals are lost. White bread may be enriched to replace the vitamins and minerals. Whole wheat bread has more roughage because it is made from flour that is less refined.

Processed foods often contain chemical additives. Chemicals are added to improve the taste, change the color, or replace or add the vitamins of a food. Chemical additives may also prevent spoilage of foods. The long-term health effects of eating these chemicals is uncertain.

You can enjoy eating snack foods or processed foods occasionally if your diet contains enough foods from the four basic food groups. If you eat junk foods or processed foods, you should balance your diet by eating whole wheat bread or brown rice. Try carrot and celery sticks instead of potato chips for a snack. Substitute an apple or an orange for a candy bar.

 Activity 16–1   Identifying Starch

Problem: Which foods contain starch?

Materials iodine solution, dropper, bread, turnip, cooked egg white, potato, rice, cereals, lima beans, scalpel, other foods as needed, apron

Procedure (1) A potato contains starch and has a predictable color reaction with iodine. (2) Put on the apron. Then put three drops of iodine solution on a potato. **CAUTION:** *Iodine stains skin and clothing and is poisonous.* When iodine is added to starch, the solution turns from brownish-red to blue-black. (3) Observe and record the reaction of the potato with iodine. (4) Predict whether the other foods to be tested contain starch. Record your predictions. (5) Test each food by adding one drop of iodine solution to each food. Record any color changes. (6) Compare your results with your predictions.

Questions (1) What food was the control? (2) Which foods turned blue-black with iodine? (3) Which foods contain starch?

16:4 Fats

Like carbohydrates, fats are an important source of energy. Healthy skin and hair depend on having the right amount of fats in the diet. Fats are also an important part of the cell membrane.

Fats, like carbohydrates, are compounds that contain carbon, hydrogen, and oxygen. However, there are many more carbon and hydrogen atoms than oxygen atoms in fat compounds. Fats provide more than twice as much energy as carbohydrates. Fats contain compounds called fatty acids that are needed for good health. Cheese, milk, butter, and nuts are sources of fats. Fat is stored when people eat more food than they need. Stored fat is normally found under the skin and around organs. This stored fat is used by the body when people eat less food than they need. The fat is a reserve supply of energy. Also, fat helps protect organs from injuries.

Although your body needs fats to stay healthy, too much fat in your diet can be harmful. The fat that is stored when people overeat can cause them to become overweight, which puts extra stress on body systems. Fat may build up inside blood vessels, especially as people get older. The fat clogs the blood vessels and reduces the flow of blood. Many medical doctors suggest a diet low in certain kinds of fats for adults. Such a diet may help prevent heart attacks and diseases of the heart.

Foods from animal sources contain fats that are thought to do damage to the heart and blood vessels. They may do more damage

FIGURE 16–4. Cheese, milk, and butter are sources of fats.

What is the importance of fats?

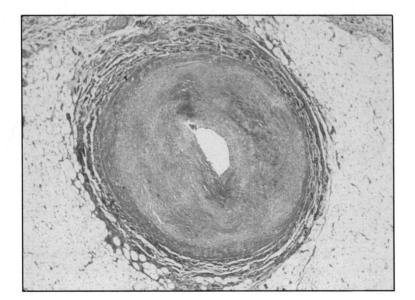

FIGURE 16–5. Fat can build up inside an artery and reduce the flow of blood.

FIGURE 16–6. To control their fat intake, many people include skim milk, margarine, and low-fat cottage cheese in their diets.

than foods from plant sources. For example, butter is made from cream. It may be more damaging than margarine, which is made from vegetable oil. In general, red meats contain more fats than fish or poultry. Whole milk is about four percent fat. Skim milk is less than one percent fat. To control their intake of fats, some people drink skim milk instead of whole milk. They may also eat more chicken than hamburger and use margarine instead of butter.

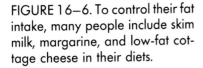 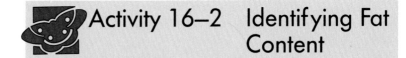Activity 16–2   Identifying Fat Content

Problem: What foods contain fats?

Materials   brown paper, butter or margarine, mayonnaise, peanut butter, cooked egg white, potato

Procedure   (1) Hold a piece of brown paper toward the light. (2) Record your observations. (3) Rub a small amount of butter or margarine on the paper. Allow it to dry. (4) Hold the paper toward the light. (5) Record your observations. (6) Predict whether mayonnaise, peanut butter, cooked egg white, and potato contain fat. (7) On separate pieces of paper, repeat the procedure using peanut butter, cooked egg white, and potato. Allow a few minutes for drying. (8) Record your observations.

Questions   (1) What foods contain fats and oils? (2) Why must you wait for the spots to dry? (3) Have you seen such spots on notebook paper? (4) What caused them? (5) Why do you think potato chips are high in fat content? (6) What foods contain fats?

16:5 Proteins

Protein is a nutrient made of amino acids. All **amino acids** are organic compounds that contain carbon, hydrogen, oxygen, and nitrogen. Two amino acids contain sulfur. Amino acids are building blocks of larger protein molecules. More than 20 different amino acids are required to keep your body healthy. The 20 amino acids can form an almost endless number of proteins.

Amino acids are used for the growth and repair of body tissue and to make hormones, enzymes, and antibodies. They are also a source of energy. Some amino acids can be made in your body from other nutrients. Eight amino acids are not made in your body. To get these essential amino acids, you must eat proteins that contain them.

The proteins in foods that come from animals are complete. Complete means the proteins supply all the amino acids your body needs. Lean meat, eggs, milk, fish, and cheese are good sources of complete proteins. The proteins in foods that come from most plants are incomplete. However, beans are a good source of protein. For example soybeans contain all eight essential amino acids. Some beans are low in some amino acids needed for good health. Many whole grains supply the amino acids missing in beans. For this reason, beans and grains are called complementary proteins. Together they supply all eight essential amino acids. For good nutrition, diets low in animal proteins must be balanced with a variety of plant proteins that complement each other. Meals that combine beans and whole grains provide good sources of complete proteins.

Define protein and amino acid.

How is protein used by the body?

FIGURE 16–7. Meatless meals can be nutritious and provide complete protein.

Making Sure

2. How can a diet high in fat be harmful?
3. Plan a meal without animal proteins that provides complete proteins.

16:6 Minerals

Some chemical elements needed by the body are **minerals.** Vegetables, fruits, fish, meat, eggs, milk, and cereals are good sources of minerals. Milk and other dairy products are sources of two minerals, calcium and phosphorus. Calcium and phosphorus are needed for strong bones and teeth.

Minerals are needed for the formation of hormones, enzymes, and other body substances. If minerals are lacking, body functions may be upset. Iron is needed for the formation of the protein hemoglobin in the blood. A lack of hemoglobin is called anemia (uh NEE mee uh). It can be caused by a diet low in iron or by disease. If there is a lack of iodine in the diet, the thyroid gland may become enlarged. This is called a goiter. Chlorine is needed by glands in the stomach to make hydrochloric acid. Human hair is mostly protein and contains four to six percent sulfur. Minerals are used by the body in the form of ions. An ion is a form of an element that can be involved in chemical changes more easily than the element itself. An ion of iodine is called iodide. The body uses iodine, sodium, and chlorine in their ionic forms. For example, the iodide in potassium iodide is needed for good health. The sodium and chloride in table salt are also required in small amounts by the body.

What are the functions of minerals in the body?

FIGURE 16–8. Fruits and vegetables are good sources of minerals, roughage, and water.

Table 16–2

Some Minerals Needed by the Human Body

Mineral	Some sources	Some functions
calcium	milk and milk products, leafy green vegetables	strengthens bones and teeth; important for nerves, muscles, and blood; activates enzymes
chlorine	table salt, cheese, cured meats, other foods with added salt	helps form stomach acid used in digestion; helps blood carry carbon dioxide to lungs
copper	liver, crabmeat, nuts, whole grain products, beans and peas	helps form hemoglobin; involved in metabolism of carbohydrates
iodine	iodized table salt	used to make thyroid hormones
iron*	liver, lean meats, raisins, beans and peas, whole grain products	carries oxygen as part of hemoglobin in blood
magnesium	foods in the milk group, cheese, nuts, leafy green vegetables, beans and peas	helps regulate body temperature; helps regulate muscles, nerves, and blood
manganese*	nuts, whole grain products, leafy green vegetables, fruits	helps form and use many enzymes; helps body make use of fats and carbohydrates
phosphorus	foods in meat group, milk, cheese, whole grain products	needed for strong bones and teeth; used in muscle functions and cell wall formation
potassium	bananas, avocados, meats, nuts, potatoes	helps maintain fluid levels in cells; needed for nerve impulses
sodium	table salt, cheese, cured meats, other foods with added salt	helps regulate fluid levels in body; needed for nerve impulses
sulfur	meats, milk, eggs, beans and peas	used in synthesis of some amino acids
zinc*	seafoods, meats, cereals, nuts, vegetables	used to make certain enzymes; needed for growth of tissues; helps in healing wounds

*trace amounts

16:7 Vitamins

In the days of sailing ships, sailors on long ocean voyages often got a disease called scurvy. A person with scurvy has sore, bleeding gums and suffers from a lack of energy. The British Navy discovered that eating limes or other citrus fruit, such as oranges, grapefruit, and lemons, prevents scurvy. Today it is known that scurvy is caused by a lack of vitamin C.

What are vitamins?

A **vitamin** is an organic nutrient that is needed in small amounts for good health. Lack of a vitamin in the diet may cause a deficiency disease such as scurvy. Another deficiency disease called rickets results from a lack of vitamin D. If young people have rickets, their bones and muscles will not develop properly. Vitamins are used by the body to help enzymes to regulate changes inside cells.

All the vitamins needed by people are present in foods. Vitamins are also added to many foods to increase their nutrient value. For example, vitamin D is added to milk and B vitamins are added to flour. The best way to obtain the vitamins you need is to eat a balanced diet. Most people who eat a balanced diet do not need to take vitamins. Vitamins should be taken only upon the advice of a physician for treating a special health problem.

Making Sure

4. Name five minerals. Tell how each is used in the body.
5. How can most people get all the vitamins they need?

FIGURE 16–9. Vitamins are often added to foods such as milk, cereal, and bread.

Table 16–3

Food Sources and Functions of Vitamins

Name	Sources	Function
vitamin A	milk, butter, margarine, eggs, liver, leafy green and yellow vegetables	normal growth in children, good vision, healthy skin and hair
vitamin B_1 (thiamine)	cereals, fish, lean meat, liver, milk, poultry, green vegetables	proper function of heart and nervous system, prevents beriberi
vitamin B_2	eggs, bread, cereals, leafy green vegetables, lean meat, liver, dried yeast, milk	healthy skin, prevents sensitivity of eyes to light, building and maintaining tissues
vitamin B_6 (pyridoxine, pyridoxamine)	wheat germ, vegetables, dried yeast, meat, whole grain cereals	healthy teeth, blood vessels, red blood cells, and nervous system
vitamin B_{12} (cobalamin)	liver, kidney, milk, fish, lean meat, eggs	healthy nervous system, proper growth in children, prevents pernicious anemia
niacin (niacinamide)	lean meat, liver, dried yeast, cereals and bread, eggs, green vegetables	prevents pellagra and appetite loss, aids nervous system and food conversion to energy
vitamin C (ascorbic acid)	citrus fruits, berries, tomatoes, cabbage, green vegetables	prevents scurvy, builds strong body cells and blood vessels
vitamin D (includes D_2, D_3, and D_4)	vitamin D fortified milk, cod liver oil, salmon, tuna, egg yolk	prevents rickets, aids use of calcium and phosphorus
vitamin E (tocopherols)	vegetable oils, whole grain cereals	prevents damage to red blood cells
vitamin K	leafy vegetables, pork liver	aids blood clotting

Activity 16-3   Identifying Vitamin C Content

Problem: Which juices contain vitamin C?

Materials

indophenol solution
graduated cylinder
glass marking pencil
10 test tubes
test tube rack
10 dropping bottles containing water, orange juice, pineapple juice, apple juice, lemon juice, tomato juice, cranberry juice, carrot juice, lime juice, mixed vegetable juice

Procedure

1. Label the test tubes 1 through 10.
2. Make a data table like the one shown to record your observations.
3. Predict which juices contain vitamin C. Record your predictions.

Data and Observations

Test tube	Juice	Prediction (yes or no)	Observation (number of drops)
1	water		
2	orange		
3	pineap-ple		
4	apple		
5	lemon		
6	tomato		
7	cran-berry		
8	carrot		
9	lime		
10	vegeta-ble		

4. Measure 5 mL of indophenol into each of the 10 test tubes. Indophenol is a blue liquid that turns colorless when vitamin C is present. The more vitamin C there is in a juice, the less juice it will take to turn indophenol colorless.
5. Add 20 drops of water to test tube 1. Record your observations.
6. Begin adding orange juice, one drop at a time, to test tube 2.
7. Record the number of drops needed to turn indophenol colorless.
8. Repeat this procedure by adding a different juice to each test tube. Record the number of drops needed to turn indophenol colorless. Follow the order listed in the data table.

FIGURE 16-10.

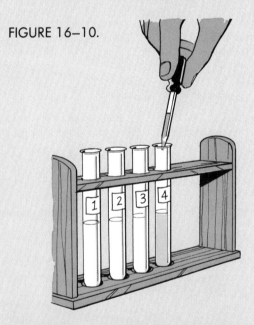

Questions and Conclusions

1. What was the purpose of test tube 1?
2. Which juices do not contain vitamin C?
3. Does the amount of vitamin C vary in fruit juices?
4. Which juices contain vitamin C?

16:8 The Digestive System

Digestion involves chemical and physical processes in which nutrients are changed from insoluble to soluble forms. Soluble means the nutrient dissolves in water. Only soluble nutrients can be absorbed by blood and diffuse into body cells. Starch, protein, and fat are insoluble. To be used by the body, these nutrients must be digested.

Digestion occurs in the body system made up of the digestive tract and the organs that aid digestion. The **digestive tract** is a long tube through which food passes. It includes the mouth, esophagus, stomach, small intestine, large intestine, rectum and anus. The liver and pancreas (PAN kree us) are organs that aid digestion. These two organs are not part of the digestive tract.

Rhythmic movements of the muscular walls of the digestive tract push food through it. The wall of the digestive tract directly in front of a mass of food relaxes. This causes the tract to widen. The wall around and behind the food contracts and pushes the food forward. Push after push, the food is moved through the digestive tract from one end to the other. Roughage helps stimulate the muscles of the digestive tract.

Digestion occurs through the action of enzymes and water. An enzyme is a protein molecule produced by a living organism that changes the rate of a chemical change. In the chemical change, the enzyme is not used up or changed in any way. Specific enzymes digest specific kinds of nutrients. When a nutrient is digested by enzymes, it is combined with water. Water molecules break the bonds between the atoms of large nutrient molecules. Smaller molecules that result from this change are different from the original nutrient. The smaller molecules are in a form that can be used by cells.

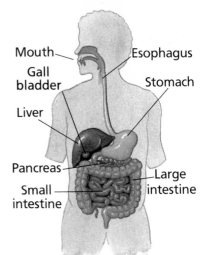

FIGURE 16—11. The digestive system processes food so that the body can use it.

FIGURE 16—12. In digestion, large molecules are combined with water. Enzymes speed up the chemical reactions that break the large molecules into smaller molecules. The enzymes are not used up or changed in the process.

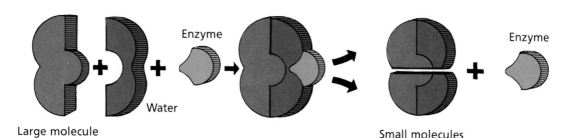

Large molecule Water Enzyme Small molecules Enzyme

FIGURE 16–13. In the small intestine, thousands of villi increase the surface area. The villi have blood and lymph vessels to absorb digested food.

16:9 Digestion

Physical digestion begins inside the mouth where chewing grinds the food into tiny pieces. Breaking up the food into tiny pieces increases the surface area of the food. The increased surface area speeds up the action of the digestive enzymes to make chemical digestion more rapid.

Describe the changes that occur as food passes through the digestive tract.

With the aid of the tongue, teeth mix the food with saliva inside the mouth. Saliva is a liquid released into the mouth from salivary glands. Saliva adds water and mucus to the food. Mucus smoothes the passage of food through the digestive tract. Saliva also contains an enzyme that helps in the chemical breakdown of starch.

When food is swallowed, it enters the esophagus (ih SAHF uh gus). The **esophagus** is a tube about 30 centimeters long. It connects the mouth to the stomach. In physical digestion, muscles in the **stomach** walls contract forcefully and mix food.

Gastric glands in the wall of the stomach secrete a digestive liquid called gastric juice. Gastric juice contains dilute hydrochloric acid and enzymes that begin the chemical digestion of protein. Heartburn occurs if acid gets up into the esophagus. Sometimes acid actually digests the stomach wall, causing an ulcer. Secretions of mucus from glands in the stomach wall help protect it.

From the stomach, this mixture enters the small intestine in a series of squirts. The **small intestine** is a coiled tube about seven meters long and 2.5 centimeters in diameter. Most of the food a person eats is chemically digested inside the small intestine. Three important digestive juices—intestinal juice, pancreatic (pan kree AT ihk) juice, and bile—are in the small intestine.

Intestinal juice contains enzymes that digest carbohydrates, fats, and proteins. It is secreted by glands in the wall of the small intestine. Large amounts of mucus are also secreted by glands in the small intestine. The mucus helps protect the intestinal wall.

Pancreatic juice is formed in the pancreas and carried to the small intestine through a tube. Pancreatic juice contains enzymes that digest starch, fat, and protein. Glucose, fatty acids, glycerol, and amino acids are produced in the digestion here. Pancreatic juice also contains a substance that neutralizes the acid in the food mixture that comes from the stomach.

Bile is produced in the liver and stored in the gallbladder. The gallbladder is a greenish-colored bag attached to the liver. Bile is carried to the small intestine by the bile duct. **Bile** does not contain enzymes, but it does perform a vital function. It breaks apart fats into tiny particles. This increases the surface area of the fats and speeds their digestion.

Digested food diffuses into the blood through the wall of the small intestine. The lining of the small intestine is covered with thousands of small, fingerlike projections called villi (VIHL i). Villi increase the surface area of the small intestine. There are so many villi that they give a velvety surface to the intestinal lining. Each villus contains blood and lymph vessels that absorb the digested food from the intestine. Amino acids, sugar, some vitamins, and minerals go into the blood. Fatty acids, glycerol, and some vitamins go into the lymph. Together, the blood and lymph carry food nutrients to all parts of the body.

A watery mass of undigested food leaves the small intestine and enters the large intestine. The main function of the **large intestine** is to remove excess water from undigested food. It also secretes mucus that smoothes the passage of undigested wastes out of the body through the rectum and anus.

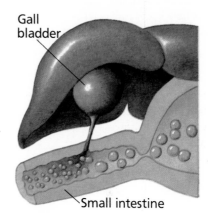
Gall bladder

Small intestine

FIGURE 16–14. Bile is produced in the liver and stored in the gall-bladder. It is carried to the small intestine by the bile duct and breaks down fat.

Making Sure

6. Draw and label a diagram of the digestive tract.
7. Trace the movement of your favorite food through the digestive tract.
8. How do muscles move food through the digestive tract?

FIGURE 16–15. Rhythmic movements of the esophagus push food down into the stomach. Contractions of the stomach force food into the small intestine. Digested food enters the bloodstream; undigested food enters the large intestine.

First Day
7:00 AM
Breakfast

Food chewed
Saliva starts
digestion process

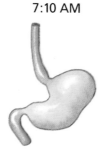

7:10 AM

Gastric juice
continues digestion

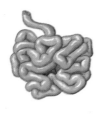

12 noon to 3:00 PM

Digestion continues
Absorption occurs

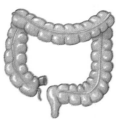

Second Day

First waste ready to
leave large intestine

Activity 16–4   Digestion of Fat and Protein

Problem: What happens to protein and fat in the digestive system?

Materials

5% pepsin solution	flat toothpick
5% bile solution	graduated cylinder
7 test tubes	glass marking pencil
baking soda	2 large beakers
0.2% hydrochloric acid	droppers
vegetable oil	scalpel
hard-boiled egg white	3 stoppers
water	

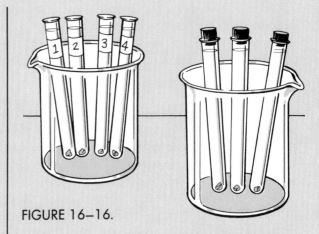

FIGURE 16–16.

Procedure

Part A

1. Cut four small equal-sized cubes from the hard-boiled egg white. **CAUTION:** *Use scalpels carefully.*
2. Label four test tubes 1, 2, 3, 4.
3. Add one cube of egg to each test tube.
4. Add 10 mL of water to tube 1.
5. Add 10 mL of 5% pepsin solution to tube 2.
6. Add 10 mL of 0.2% hydrochloric acid to tube 3. **CAUTION:** *Hydrochloric acid causes burns. Avoid skin contact.* Wash spills with plenty of water.
7. Add 10 mL of 5% pepsin solution and two drops of 0.2% hydrochloric acid to tube 4.
8. Place all four tubes in a beaker.
9. Let the test tubes stand in the beaker at room temperature for 48 hours.
10. Examine the tubes after 48 hours at room temperature. Record your observations.

Part B

1. Label three test tubes A, B, and C.
2. Add 10 mL of water to each tube.
3. Add three drops of vegetable oil to each tube.
4. Add a small amount of baking soda (the amount that stays on the wide end of a flat toothpick) to tube B.
5. Add five drops of 5% bile solution to tube C.
6. Place a stopper in each test tube.
7. Shake each tube five times to mix the contents.
8. Allow the tubes to stand for 10 minutes. Observe and record any changes.

Data and Observations

Tube	Contents	Observations
1	egg + water	
2	egg + pepsin	
3	egg + hydrochloric acid	
4	egg + pepsin and hydrochloric acid	
A	water + oil	
B	water + oil + baking soda	
C	water + oil + bile	

Questions and Conclusions

1. What kind of nutrient is the egg white used in Part A?
2. What substances are needed to digest the egg white?
3. What nutrient is in the vegetable oil of Part B?
4. How does bile affect the vegetable oils?
5. What happens to protein and fat in the digestive system?

16:10 Energy from Food

The energy value of food is measured in Calories (KAL uh reez). One **Calorie** is the amount of heat needed to raise the temperature of 1 kilogram of water one degree Celsius.

Carbohydrates, fats, and proteins are good sources of energy. Fats have a higher energy content than proteins and carbohydrates. Fats yield 2.25 times more energy than proteins or carbohydrates.

How many Calories do you need each day? The number of Calories needed depends on the amount of energy a person uses. It depends on the person's age, body size, sex, and daily activities. The greater the amount of energy used up in activities, the greater the number of Calories needed. People engaged daily in athletic activities or hard physical work require a large number of Calories in the food they eat. They require much more energy than those who are less active. For example, a 54 kg person who is walking uses up 180 Calories in one hour. The same person uses up 700 Calories in an hour of running. Also, a larger person uses more Calories than a smaller person uses doing the same activity.

FIGURE 16–17. The number of Calories needed each day depends on the amount of energy a person uses in activities.

Table 16–4

Minimum Calorie Requirements		
Sex	Age	Calories per day
Male	9-12	2400
	12-15	3000
Female	9-12	2200
	12-15	2500

What happens when a healthy person takes in more Calories than are used up each day? Excess food energy is stored in the body as fat. A person will gain weight if too much food is eaten and daily activity remains the same. An overweight person must eat less food or become more active in order to lose weight. If a person consumes fewer Calories than are used up, stored fat in the body will be broken down and weight will be lost. Maintaining proper weight depends on keeping the Calorie intake equal to the number of Calories used by the body.

Making Sure

9. Why does strenuous exercise increase the number of Calories a person needs?
10. Why might a diet that includes many snack foods cause a person to be overweight?

FOCUS ON
People and Careers

Weight Control Specialists

Dr. G. Michael Steelman is a bariatrician (bair ee uh TRISH un), a physician who helps people with eating disorders. Many of his patients are overweight. Others, however, are treated by Dr. Steelman because they are afraid of gaining weight. After making a diagnosis, Dr. Steelman helps a patient form a sensible diet plan to change his or her eating habits. A regular exercise program is often part of Dr. Steelman's treatment.

Dr. Steelman begins his day by making hospital rounds, usually to see patients with anorexia nervosa (an uh REK see uh · nur VOH suh) and bulimia (byew LIHM ee uh) patients. Anorexia nervosa is an eating disorder characterized by loss of appetite. A person with bulimia eats large amounts of food and then induces vomiting. After Dr. Steelman finishes at the hospital, he goes to his office. There he reviews medical histories and physical examinations of new patients, performs necessary laboratory tests, and gives the patients a diet and exercise program. Dr. Steelman checks the progress of returning patients, gives them support and counseling, and adjusts the treatment if necessary.

Dr. Steelman believes that anyone who wants to become a bariatrician should be able to tolerate frustration, have boundless energy, and be sensitive to the feelings of others.

Dr. Steelman's assistant, Jeannine L. Mancinelli, helps plan diet and exercise programs for the patients. To prepare for her career, Ms. Mancinelli took two years of nurse's training along with her regular college work. In addition to her science courses, she found psychology and sociology very helpful because they prepared her to understand human behavior.

Ms. Mancinelli spends much time researching eating problems and new methods of treating them. Some of her other responsibilities include organizing group discussions on eating problems and weight control, gathering information on the success of treatment methods, writing a newsletter about weight control and eating disorders, and making appointments for patients with anorexia nervosa and bulimia. What Ms. Mancinelli likes most about her career is the opportunity to work directly with patients and apply her research toward improving treatments.

Her career offers so much variety that Ms. Mancinelli rarely has a "typical" day, and the job requires a wide range of skills. She recommends that anyone pursuing this career be self-motivated, flexible, and a sympathetic listener. Ms. Mancinelli also recommends that people interested in this type of work earn a college degree, participate in activities that develop communication skills, and learn to set realistic goals.

CHAPTER 16
Review

Summary

1. Four groups of foods needed for good nutrition are the milk group, meat group, fruit-vegetable group, and grain group.   16:1
2. Among the nutrients needed for good health are water, minerals, carbohydrates, fats, proteins, and vitamins.   16:1
3. Growth, digestion, and production of body fluids require water.   16:2
4. Sugar, starch, and glycogen are carbohydrates. They are composed of carbon, hydrogen, and oxygen.   16:3
5. Fats provide energy and essential fatty acids to the body.   16:4
6. Protein is used to build body tissues and produce certain substances inside cells.   16:5
7. Minerals are needed for body functions such as bone formation.   16:6
8. Vitamins are needed by the body in very small amounts. A deficiency disease can result if they are lacking.   16:7
9. Digestion is a process that chemically and physically changes food as it passes through the organs of the digestive tract.   16:8
10. Enzymes break down food as it moves through the digestive tract.   16:9
11. The energy value of foods is measured in Calories.   16:10
12. Fats contain more energy than proteins and carbohydrates.   16:10

Vocabulary

Write a sentence using the following words or terms correctly.

amino acid	esophagus	nutrition
bile	glycogen	protein
Calorie	fat	small intestine
carbohydrate	large intestine	starch
digestion	mineral	stomach
digestive tract	nutrient	vitamin

Questions

Do not write in this book.

A. True or False

Determine whether each of the following sentences is true or false. Rewrite the false statements to make them correct.

1. The mouth is part of the digestive tract.
2. Most food is digested in the esophagus.
3. Enzymes are produced in the small intestine.

CHAPTER 16
Review

4. For a balanced diet, a person should eat foods from each of the four basic food groups.
5. Water is a compound.
6. Water yields energy when used in the body.
7. Digestion produces large molecules from small molecules.
8. Carbohydrates are a good source of energy.
9. Iron is required for the formation of hemoglobin.
10. Diseases may result from the lack of vitamins or minerals.

B. Multiple Choice
Choose the word or phrase that correctly completes the following sentences.
1. Sugar and starch are *(wastes, carbohydrates, elements, proteins)*.
2. The *(liver, pancreas, small intestine)* is part of the digestive tract.
3. Carbohydrates are most plentiful in *(cereals, meats, eggs)*.
4. The enzyme in saliva digests *(fats, proteins, starch)*.
5. The removal of excess water from food occurs largely in the *(stomach, small intestine, large intestine)*.
6. Fats contain *(more, less)* energy than carbohydrates.
7. When the surface area of solid food increases, its rate of digestion *(increases, decreases, remains the same)*.
8. Digestion begins in the *(mouth, esophagus, stomach, small intestine)*.
9. Water makes up about *(20, 45, 65, 95)* percent of your body.
10. Dried beans are part of the *(meat, fruit-vegetable, grain, combination)* group.

C. Completion
Complete each of the following sentences with the correct word or phrase.
1. Digestion is a(n) _____ change.
2. _____ diseases are caused by a lack of vitamins.
3. Proteins are broken down into _____ when digested.
4. Digestion changes food from an insoluble to a(n) _____ form.
5. _____ increase the surface area of the small intestine.
6. Snack foods may be high in carbohydrates or fats but are low in _____.
7. Taking in more Calories than are used each day may cause a person to gain _____.
8. An active person requires _____ Calories than an inactive person.
9. A Calorie is the amount of heat needed to raise the temperature of _____ 1°C.
10. _____ and _____ are two nutrients containing only the elements carbon, hydrogen, and oxygen.

D. How and Why

1. Why must food be digested for use by the body?
2. Name six food nutrients. List one body use for each nutrient.
3. How can you make sure that you are eating a balanced diet?
4. What is a vitamin deficiency disease? Describe one example.
5. How does digested food get to the body cells?
6. What minerals are essential to body health? How are the minerals used?
7. Explain how the caloric content of a person's diet determines whether the person is overweight, normal, or underweight.

Ideas to Explore

1. **Project:** Visit a pet shop or feed store to learn the different kinds of foods available for pets and laboratory animals. Obtain information on the nutrients these foods contain. Prepare a report for your class.
2. **Challenge:** Through library reading, investigate research leading to the discovery of vitamins. Prepare a timeline showing important vitamins, their discoverers, and the dates of discovery.
3. **Challenge:** Report on the use of preservatives and other chemicals in food.
4. **Project:** Interview a dietitian at a hospital to learn how diets are prepared for patients.
5. **Project:** Determine the protein, fat, carbohydrate, and sodium content of a typical meal from a fast-food restaurant.

Readings

Beeshad, Carol and Deborah Bernick. *Bodyworks: The Kid's Guide to Food and Physical Fitness.* New York: Random House, 1980.

Campbell, T. Colin. *What About the Food You Eat?* Burlington, NC: Carolina Biological Supply Company, 1981.

Fleege, Francis J. *How to Eat: Chewing, Toothcare, and Diet.* New York: Elsevier/ Nelson Books, 1980.

Insulin is a hormone produced in all vertebrates by groups of endocrine cells. Insulin regulates the level of glucose in the blood, affects RNA and protein synthesis, as well as metabolism, and the storage of fats. Low levels of insulin can cause diabetes in humans. If changes in diet and exercise do not regulate the levels, insulin must be injected or taken orally to control diabetes. Insulin can be produced and bottled under sterile conditions as shown here. How are diseases controlled? Are all diseases cured by treatment?

CHAPTER 17
MAINTAINING HEALTH

17:1 Health Problems

When harmful microbes grow unchecked inside your body, you have a health problem. Microbes such as viruses, bacteria, protozoans, or fungi can cause diseases. Polio and chicken pox are just two of the many diseases caused by viruses. When you do not eat the right foods, your body is not healthy. If your diet lacks one or more nutrients your body can become diseased. Some people have other health problems such as allergies, anemia, diabetes (di uh BEET eez), or hemophilia (hee muh FEE lee uh). Some diseases are inherited. The cause of the disease may be present in a person's body at birth. Other diseases may develop as a person grows older. Accidents cause many health problems. Injuries may result from sports or automobile accidents but most injuries are the result of accidents in the home.

Communicable (kuh MYEW nih kuh bul) **diseases** are those that can be passed from one person to another. They are caused by microbes. Two communicable diseases caused by viruses are the common cold and flu. A sexually transmitted disease, or STD, is a communicable disease passed from person to person during sexual contact. STDs are also known as venereal diseases. In many cases, a person may be able to pass on a communicable disease even if he or she does not have the illness. The person is called a carrier. The microbes do not infect the **carrier** but the carrier may pass them to another person. Malfunctions of the body such as allergies and diabetes are not caused by microbes. Therefore, they are not communicable.

GOALS:
1. You will learn the causes of health problems and diseases.
2. You will learn how diseases can be prevented.
3. You will learn ways to stay healthy.

What are the possible causes of health problems?

Table 17–1

Some Communicable Diseases		
Cause	**Disease**	**Symptoms**
virus	common cold	inflammation of mucous membranes
virus	influenza	fever, cough, headache, sore throat
virus	mononucleosis	chills, fever, sore throat, swollen lymph glands
virus	cold sores or fever blisters	sores in or around mouth, burning sensation
virus or bacteria	pneumonia	chills, fever, chest pain, fatigue
bacteria	strep throat	sore throat, fever, headache
protist	dysentery	diarrhea, fever, abdominal pain
protist	malaria	chills, fever
fungus	athlete's foot	itching, inflammation
fungus	yeast infection	itching, inflammation

What diseases have you had from which you recovered? Many diseases are only temporary. The person may recover and become well again. However, diseases such as malaria and cancer may last a long time. Some diseases cause permanent damage or death.

FIGURE 17–1. Robert Koch developed a set of steps for determining whether a certain microbe caused a disease.

17:2 Koch's Postulates

The theory that microbes cause diseases was made by Robert Koch (KAHK), a German physician. In 1882, Koch showed that bacteria cause a disease called anthrax (AN thraks) in farm animals. He also discovered that bacteria cause tuberculosis (too bur kyuh LOH sus) in people.

Koch developed a set of steps for proving whether or not a disease is caused by a microbe. This set of steps is known as **Koch's postulates** (PAHS chuh lutz). Postulate is another word for principle. Here is how Koch's postulates are used to prove that a microbe causes a disease in people.

(1) A microbe believed to cause a disease must be present in the organism when the disease occurs. This organism is the host.

Example: A bacterium is found in the spinal fluid of a person who has meningitis (mehn ihn JI tus).

(2) The microbe believed to cause the disease must be isolated

Bacteria are removed from infected rat.

Infectious bacteria are grown in a pure culture.

A healthy rat is innoculated to determine if the bacteria cause infection.

from the host and grown in pure cultures. A pure culture contains only one species.

Example: The bacteria are removed from the spinal fluid. They are grown as a pure culture.

(3) When injected into healthy individuals, microbes from the pure culture must produce the disease.

Example: Injection of a healthy monkey with bacteria from the pure culture causes it to become ill with meningitis.

(4) The microbe must be isolated from the new host, grown in pure culture, and compared to the microbe from the original host.

Example: Bacteria are removed from the spinal fluid of the monkey. They are the same as the bacteria taken from the person.

Koch's postulates illustrate the idea of cause and effect, the basis of modern medical science. Simply stated, cause and effect in medicine means that there is a specific cause for each disease. The cause is often a microbe. Koch's postulates have been useful for determining the microbes that cause many diseases.

Koch's postulates are a good example of the scientific method. First, a hypothesis is made that a microbe causes a disease. Then experiments are done to test the hypothesis. If the experiments support the hypothesis, a theory about the cause of a disease is formed.

Sometimes all of Koch's postulates cannot be satisfied. For example, viruses were not known in Koch's time. Since they grow only inside living cells, they cannot be isolated and grown in a pure culture. Other microbes grow only in certain kinds of organisms. If a disease is specific to humans, it does not occur in other organisms exposed to the microbe. Other humans would not usually be used to test the third postulate because they would get the disease. In some cases, however, such as experiments with the common cold, people may volunteer to help scientists understand these infections. These volunteers are given cold viruses

FIGURE 17–2. Koch's postulates are tested.

How are Koch's postulates used to show that a microbe causes a disease?

in nose drops. They are then given various "cold cure" medicines to test their effectiveness.

Even if all of the postulates cannot be satisfied, other scientific methods may provide data to support a hypothesis. Cause and effect still may be shown.

Making Sure

1. You can "catch" the flu but not diabetes. Which is a communicable disease and which is a noncommunicable disease? Explain the difference.
2. How are Koch's postulates an example of the scientific method?

17:3 Natural Defenses

How do natural defenses help prevent disease?

You have several natural defenses against disease. Natural defenses are tissues, organs, and systems that fight and resist germs. For example, unbroken skin prevents the entrance of microbes into the body. Mucus in the nose and throat also helps keep germs out of the body. Cilia line the nasal passages and trachea. Cilia filter microbes and help keep them out of the lungs. Unbroken skin, mucus, and cilia are primary defenses because they prevent germs from entering the body. What primary defenses protect the eyes?

What are your primary and secondary defenses against disease?

Some germs get past your primary defenses. Secondary defenses fight disease microbes that have entered your body. Stomach acid destroys microbes brought into the body by food. White blood cells and lymph cells are important to the body's secondary defense system. More of these cells are produced when an infection occurs. They help kill germs. The white blood cells digest the invading germs. The lymph cells produce antibodies that kill the germs. An **antibody** is an organic compound in the blood

What is an antibody?

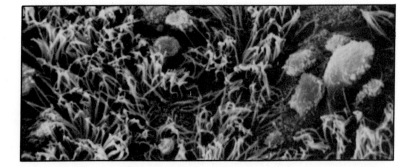

FIGURE 17–3. Cilia lining the trachea filter microbes and help keep them out of the lungs.

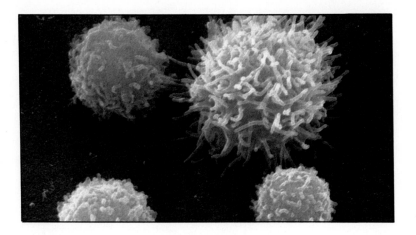

FIGURE 17–4. White blood cells help to protect the body from invading microbes.

that attacks a germ or the poisons it produces. Antibodies are formed in response to microbes that have passed through other defenses and invaded body tissues. They are specific to different germs. This means for certain germs there are certain antibodies that fight them. Antibodies are an important part of the body's immune system.

Another secondary defense against disease is interferon. In the presence of a virus, cells may produce interferon, which interferes with the ability of the virus to reproduce. Therefore, it helps to control diseases caused by viruses. Also, interferon produced by infected cells can be taken in by healthy cells nearby. The healthy cells are then also protected. Interferon was discovered in 1957 by Dr. Alick Isaacs, a British scientist. Scientists have now found a way to artificially produce interferon that may be used in the treatment of diseases.

How does interferon help control diseases?

AIDS, or acquired immune deficiency syndrome, is caused by a virus that attacks the body's defense systems. It reduces the ablity of the body to fight other infections. Because AIDS reduces the body's resistance to other diseases, people with the virus easily get diseases such as pneumonia and cancer. The AIDS virus belongs to a family of viruses well known as the cause of cancer in animals. AIDS can be transmitted through sexual contact with a person who has the disease. It can also be acquired through a transfusion of blood that contains the AIDS virus. For this reason, all blood used in transfusions should be tested to be certain it is free of AIDS. A pregnant woman who has AIDS can pass the disease to her unborn child.

By what is AIDS caused?

Natural defenses against diseases are strongest when an organism is healthy. Lack of proper rest, exercise, and good food can cause an organism to have less resistance to disease.

Activity 17–1   Microbes and Infection

Problem: How do microbes spread infection?

Materials

6 fresh apples
decaying apple
alcohol
labels
6 plastic bags
soap
water
paper towels
paring knife

Procedure

1. Label six plastic bags 1 through 6.
2. Put one fresh apple in bag 1.
3. Rub a decaying apple over the outside of the other five fresh apples.
4. Discard the decaying apple.
5. Wash your hands with soap and water.
6. Drop one of the apples on the floor and bruise it. Put the apple in plastic bag 2.
7. Gently puncture another of the fresh apples with a knife several times. **CAUTION:** *Point the knife away from you and not toward anyone else.* Place this apple in plastic bag 3.
8. Wash another one of the apples with soap and water. Dry the apple well and place it in plastic bag 4.
9. Cover another apple with alcohol. Rinse the apple with water and dry it thoroughly. Place the apple in plastic bag 5.
10. Do not do anything more to the last fresh apple. Place it in the plastic bag 6.
11. Store all of the apples in a dark place for one week. Write hypotheses about what will happen to all six apples.
12. At the end of the week, compare all the apples. Record your observations.

Data and Observations

Apple	Observations
1	
2	
3	
4	
5	
6	

Questions and Conclusions

1. What was the purpose of apple 1?
2. Were there any changes on the bruised surfaces of apple 2? Explain.
3. What happened to the cut places on apple 3?
4. Did washing apple 4 with soap and water have any effect on the apple?
5. What happened to the apple covered with alcohol?
6. Did you observe any changes in apple 6?
7. What caused the changes you observed?
8. Why is it important to wash your hands before eating?
9. Why is it important to clean a wound?
10. Why is alcohol used to clean a site on the body before an injection?
11. How do microbes spread infection?

FIGURE 17–5.

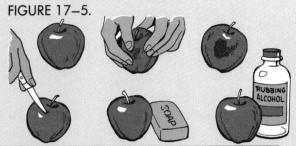

362

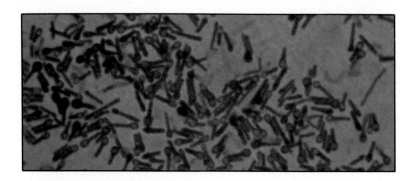

FIGURE 17—6. Bacteria cause tetanus, which affects muscle contractions.

17:4 Immunity

Immunity means that a person's body has the ability to defend itself against a disease without becoming ill from the disease. In some cases this immunity may be natural. Immunity can also be acquired by vaccination. There are two ways the body can become immune to a disease—passive or active.

Passive immunity is acquired when antibodies to a disease are directly introduced into the body. This occurs naturally in a baby. The baby receives antibodies from its mother before it is born and from the mother's first milk. This natural immunity protects the baby for a few months until the baby can develop its own antibodies.

The passive means of immunity also occur artificially by vaccination with antibodies. These antibodies are formed in the blood of other humans or animals. They are added to a person's blood. For example, antibodies from the blood of horses are used to prevent tetanus. Tetanus (also called lockjaw) is caused by a poison formed by tetanus bacteria. The disease affects the muscles and causes violent muscle contractions. Spores of the tetanus bacteria are everywhere but especially in the topsoil. Normally these spores are of no risk to humans but they may enter the body through a puncture or deep cut. Tetanus "boosters" are recommended if you get a deep cut and you have not had a tetanus shot within the past three years.

Active immunity is acquired when the body itself produces the antibodies. Active immunity can also be natural or artificial. Immunity occurs naturally when a person comes into contact with a disease. When the person comes in contact with the disease for a second time, the body will immediately produce the antibodies and the person will not get ill. For example, typhoid bacteria cause the formation of typhoid antibodies. Typhoid antibodies fight typhoid bacteria. These antibodies remain in the blood after

Define immunity.

How does a person get passive immunity?

How does a person get active immunity?

the infected person becomes well. They prevent future infections.

Active immunity may also be acquired artificially by vaccination with weakened or modified viruses. As a result of the vaccination, a person's body develops disease-fighting antibodies. Smallpox and polio are diseases that have been effectively prevented by vaccinations.

Passive immunity is immediate but does not last long. The body does not produce antibodies and when antibodies are introduced, they are slowly rejected. Active immunity takes a few days to develop but usually lasts for many years. The body's defense systems may take a few days to react to the presence of a vaccine or a disease. Once the body has produced antibodies, it will have the protection each time it becomes exposed to the same disease.

17:5 Vaccinations

In the vaccination against such diseases as smallpox, diphtheria, or polio, the **vaccine** (vak SEEN) is a solution of dead or weakened germs. When a vaccine is injected or swallowed, it stimulates the formation of antibodies that fight a disease.

How do vaccinations prevent disease?

Use of a vaccine was developed by an English physician, Edward Jenner (1749–1823). In his research, Jenner observed that milkmaids (girls who tended cows) seldom had smallpox. Smallpox was a serious disease that usually resulted in death. In Jenner's time, it caused epidemics in Europe. An **epidemic** is large numbers of people getting a disease in a short period of time. Jenner also observed that milkmaids often had a similar but much milder disease called cowpox. Cowpox is a disease that affects cows. He assumed the milkmaids got cowpox from cows

FIGURE 17–7. Edward Jenner carried out a bold experiment to test his hypothesis that having cowpox made a person immune to smallpox.

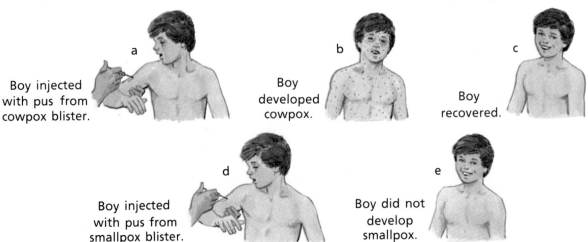

a   Boy injected with pus from cowpox blister.

b   Boy developed cowpox.

c   Boy recovered.

d   Boy injected with pus from smallpox blister.

e   Boy did not develop smallpox.

infected with the disease. Jenner concluded that recovery from cowpox gave the milkmaids an immunity to smallpox.

In 1796, Jenner carried out a bold experiment to test his hypothesis. With a needle, he scratched the skin of a young boy with the pus from a cowpox blister. This was the first vaccination known to be given. The boy got a mild case of cowpox from which he soon recovered. Next came the major test. Was the boy immune to smallpox? Jenner vaccinated the boy with pus from a smallpox blister. As Jenner suspected, the boy did not get the smallpox. The cowpox had produced antibodies in the boy's blood that made him immune to smallpox.

Vaccination to prevent smallpox soon became standard practice. As a result, smallpox epidemics have become a thing of the past. Today worldwide vaccination has eliminated all cases of this disease.

Polio is a disease in which a virus destroys nerve cells. Paralysis or even death can result. Polio occurs 90 percent less frequently today than it did in the first half of the 1900s. The development of polio vaccines resulted in this decrease. The first polio vaccine contained dead polio viruses. It was produced by Dr. Jonas Salk in 1954. A few years later, a second vaccine was made by Dr. Albert Sabin. This vaccine contained weakened, but live polio viruses.

Vaccines for many other diseases have also been developed. It is a good health practice for people to obtain the vaccinations they need and to renew them as required. You probably received the standard vaccinations when you were a baby. Table 17–2 shows the vaccinations recommended by the U.S. Public Health Service for children who did not begin their immunization series before age 15 months. Vaccinations are important for pets and farm animals, too.

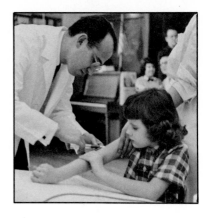

FIGURE 17–8. Dr. Jonas Salk developed the first polio vaccine in 1953.

Table 17–2

Immunization Schedule for Children Age 7 and Older*		
Spacing	**Vaccines**	**Explanation**
1st visit	Td (adult) TOPV M/M/R	Td-tetanus and diphtheria adult vaccine TOPV—trivalent oral polio vaccine M/M/R—one dose of measles/mumps/rubella combined vaccine
2 months after first	Td (Adult) TOPV	
6–12 months after 2nd	Td (Adult) TOPV	

*who did not begin their immunization series before age 15 months

Making Sure

3. What scientific methods did Jenner use in developing a small-pox vaccine? What kind of immunity did the milkmaids have to smallpox?
4. Why might a person be given a tetanus shot after stepping on a nail?

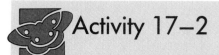

Activity 17–2   Disease Immunity

Problem: How can you become immune to disease?

Materials   reference books, pencil and paper

Procedure   (1) Use reference books to find out what causes these diseases: polio, smallpox, tetanus, diphtheria, rubella, measles, scarlet fever, typhoid fever, whooping cough, rabies. (2) Find out the symptoms of each disease. (3) Determine how you acquire immunity to each disease.

Questions   (1) Which diseases can be prevented by vaccination? (2) Which diseases can cause epidemics? (3) How is each disease caused? (4) How can you become immune to diseases?

17:6 Preventive Measures

FIGURE 17–9. Antiseptics prevent the growth of microbes on living tissue.

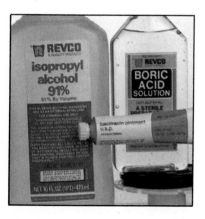

In the nineteenth century, 75 percent of the patients who had operations died soon after surgery. The deaths of many of these patients were caused by infections introduced into the body during surgery. Joseph Lister (1827–1912), an English surgeon, wondered how these infections could be prevented.

How did Lister solve the problem? He sprayed microbe-killing carbolic acid on the area of a patient's body where surgery was to be performed. As a result, deaths from surgery infections were greatly reduced. Chemicals that kill or prevent the growth of microbes on living tissue are called **antiseptics.** Alcohol is used as an antiseptic to clean skin before an injection. Iodine and hydrogen peroxide are also antiseptics. **Disinfectants** are used to destroy microbes on nonliving objects. Some antiseptics are dilute disinfectants. Chlorines and carbolic acid are disinfectants.

A major part of disease prevention is the destruction or control of disease carriers. A carrier is a transmitter of disease microbes.

Many insects, such as flies and mosquitoes, are disease carriers. Other animals, people, air, water, and food are also carriers.

Common houseflies can transfer large quantities of bacteria that cause disease. Flies breed in moist, organic material like garbage and manure. They have sticky pads on each foot. When they walk over dirty objects, flies pick up germs on their legs and feet. The flies carry these disease-causing microbes to food, dishes, and other things used by people. Cockroaches spread germs much the same as flies do.

Mosquitoes can become infected with disease organisms when they bite infected animals and people. Later, the organisms are passed on to other animals or people who are bitten by the infected mosquito. Certain kinds of mosquitoes carry certain kinds of disease organisms. The sporozoan that causes malaria in people is carried by the *Anopheles* mosquito.

Quarantine (KWOR un teen) is a way to control disease carriers. To **quarantine** means to isolate an infected organism for a time to prevent the spread of disease microbes. Animals as well as people may be quarantined. Great Britain has kept itself free of rabies by a quarantine on imported dogs. The dogs are isolated until it is certain that they are free of rabies. Then they are admitted into the country.

Water can carry microbes. Infected water can cause a major epidemic within a city. For example, typhoid (TI foyd) fever is caused by a bacterium that lives in water. Chlorine is added to drinking water and swimming pools to prevent disease. Chlorine kills microbes in the water.

Food is another major carrier of disease microbes. Local, state, and federal regulations govern food inspection. Standards of cleanliness in food stores and restaurants are maintained through inspection. Regulations control handling, processing, and packaging of foods for safety. For example, milk is pasteurized to kill harmful microbes. You may have seen stamps on milk, meat, eggs, and other products showing that they meet food inspection standards.

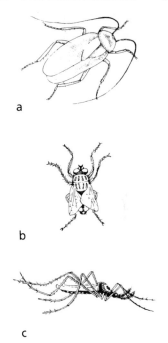

a

b

c

FIGURE 17–10. A cockroach (a), a fly (b), and a mosquito (c) are common carriers of disease-causing microbes.

How can diseases be prevented?

Making Sure

5. Why might you use an antiseptic cream on a cut or scrape?
6. Why is milk pasteurized?
7. Why should you stay home from school when you are sick with the flu?
8. Why should you not drink water from a stream when you are on a camping trip?

Activity 17–3

Preventing Microbe Growth

Problem: What will prevent the growth of microbes?

Materials

4 petri dishes of sterile nutrient agar
filter paper
disinfectant solution
mouthwash
alcohol
hydrogen peroxide
glass-marking pencil
scissors
metric ruler
forceps
pencil

Procedure

1. Label the petri dishes 1 through 4.
2. Remove the covers from the dishes one at a time.
3. Rub a finger over the nutrient agar in each dish.
4. Cut four 2 cm squares of filter paper. Label the squares in a corner D, A, H, M with the pencil.
5. Soak D in disinfectant. Soak A in alcohol.
6. Soak H in hydrogen peroxide.
7. Soak M in mouthwash.
8. With forceps, place all the squares in the nutrient agar in petri dish 1. Cover the dish.
9. Place petri dishes 1 and 2 in a warm, dark place for two days.
10. Remove the cover from petri dish 3. Leave 4 covered.
11. Place both petri dishes 3 and 4 in direct sunlight for about 20 minutes.
12. Replace the cover on petri dish 3.
13. Store both dishes 3 and 4 in a warm, dark place for two days.
14. Record a hypothesis for what will occur in all four dishes.
15. After two days, examine all the petri dishes.
16. In dish 1, compare the growth under each square and the growth where there are no squares.
17. Compare petri dishes 1 and 2.
18. Compare petri dishes 3 and 4.
19. Record your observations.

Data and Observations

Square	Observations
D	
A	
H	
M	

Petri dish	Observations
1	
2	
3	
4	

Questions and Conclusions

1. Under which square did you find the most growth?
2. Under which square did you find the least growth?
3. What is the purpose of dish 2?
4. Which dish had the most growth?
5. What effects do antiseptics and disinfectants have on the growth of microbes?
6. What effect does direct sunlight have on the growth of microbes?
7. Did you accept or reject the hypothesis you made? Explain.
8. What will prevent the growth of microbes?

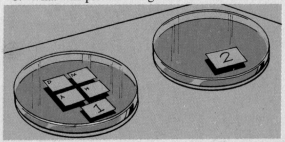

FIGURE 17–11.

FIGURE 17–12. Modern medicine involves many types of surgery, including kidney transplants.

17:7 Modern Medicine

Modern medicine employs many different methods to treat health problems. One method is the use of certain drugs to cure infections. Perhaps you have taken medicines to cure strep throat or other bacterial infections. Allergies may be treated with a group of drugs called antihistamines. Drugs are used to kill cancer cells in patients who have this disease. The treatment is called **chemotherapy** because it involves the use of strong and potent chemicals. In chemotherapy, the drug is carried by the blood through the body to the diseased organ.

One of the first chemicals used to treat a disease was Salvarsan. Paul Erlich (1854–1915), a German chemist, found that Salvarsan, an arsenic compound, was effective in treating syphilis (SIHF uh lus). Syphilis is a sexually transmitted disease caused by a certain type of bacterium that infects the blood and sex organs. In 1935, the usefulness of sulfa drugs for the treatment of infections in flesh wounds was discovered. Sulfa drugs are an important family of microbe-killing chemicals.

Surgery is treatment by operations. Surgery is sometimes used for the removal of a cancer from a person's body. Skin can be grafted, or transferred, from one part of the body to another in the treatment of burns and wounds. Heart surgery is done to repair heart valves that are not working properly. Some athletic injuries such as a torn knee cartilage are repaired with surgery. Through surgery, some diseased organs may be replaced. The organ is removed and replaced with a healthy organ transplanted from another person. The organs used in transplant surgery are often from people who have donated their bodies to science on their deaths. Even though not all organs are used for transplants, much

Name five methods used to treat health problems. Give one example of each.

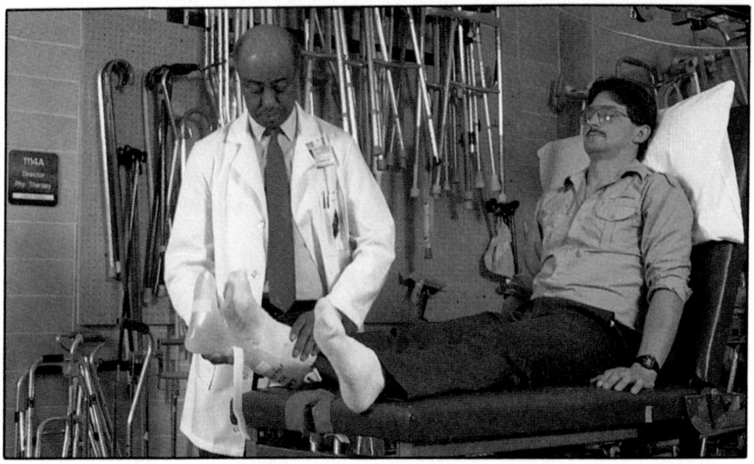

FIGURE 17–13. Physical therapy can help a person recover the use of an injured body part.

FIGURE 17–14. Penicillin is the product of a mold, *Penicillium notatum.*

can be learned by medical students from this generous gift. Organs transplanted by surgeons include the kidney, heart, and liver.

Some health problems are treated by changing a person's diet. For instance, a person may have an unhealthy reaction after eating certain foods. Skin tests can be done to determine which foods cause the reaction. One form of diabetes is treated by carefully controlling a person's food intake.

Physical therapy may be used to treat health problems involving the muscles. People who have been in accidents may have suffered damage to legs, arms, hands or feet. The use of these limbs may often be recovered by physical therapy. It is also used to treat pains in the back and joints. Physical therapy involves exercises carried out with the aid and supervision of a trained physical therapist. As a result of therapy, the muscles may become stronger. Control of limbs by the nervous system may be regained.

In modern medicine, health professionals are more aware of the relationship between the health of people's minds and the health of their bodies. Good mental health is likely to increase the body's ability to fight disease. Similarly, counseling intended to improve a person's mental outlook can help a patient recover from an illness. Reducing stress through relaxation, humor, happy experiences, and the companionship of other people or pets promotes good mental health.

17:8 Antibiotics

An **antibiotic** (an ti bi AHT ihk) is a substance produced by a living organism that slows down or stops the growth of microbes. Antibiotics are obtained from bacteria, molds, and other microbes. Table 17–3 lists some examples of antibiotics.

Penicillin (pen uh SIHL un) is the most widely used of all antibiotics. It was discovered in 1928 by Alexander Fleming, a British scientist. Fleming observed a blue-green mold, *Penicillium notatum*, growing in a bacteria culture. Fleming noted that bacteria did not grow near the mold. This had been observed before by other scientists. However, Fleming reasoned that the mold must contain a substance that prevented the growth of bacteria. Fleming separated the substance from the mold and named it penicillin.

Little use was made of the discovery of penicillin until 1938. At that time, scientists developed the process to produce penicillin in large quantities. Penicillin became available for widespread medical use. During World War II penicillin was used in treating wounds and infections. Without it, the death rate might have been three times higher.

How are antibiotics used?

Many antibiotics have been separated from microscopic soil-growing bacteria. Streptomycin (strep tuh MISE un) is an antibiotic that comes from a soil bacterium. It is used in treating tuberculosis, whooping cough, and some forms of pneumonia.

Table 17—3

Sources of Some Antibiotics	
Antibiotic	**Source**
Ampicillin	Fungus
Bacitracin	Bacteria
Chloramphenicol	Bacteria
Erythromycin	Bacteria
Gentamicin	Fungus
Kanamycin	Bacteria
Neomycin	Bacteria
Penicillin	Fungus
Polymixins	Bacteria
Streptomycin	Bacteria
Tetracycline	Bacteria

Making Sure

9. Name three ways health problems are treated.
10. What is physical therapy?
11. How are antibiotics different from antiseptics?
12. From where does streptomycin come?
13. How was penicillin discovered?

17:9 Medical Research

Medical scientists search for new ways to cure diseases. New drugs from chemicals or from extractions of microbes, plants, and animals can be prepared in laboratories. For example, thousands of new chemicals are tested each year on laboratory animals with cancer. If a drug proves effective against cancer in an animal, it may be tested on humans. In these tests a group of people who have cancer are given the drug. This is the experimental group. The test also includes a control group of people who have cancer and do not receive the drug. The resulting health of the experimental group that received the drug is then compared with the health of the control group. Any harmful reactions are recorded. If the experimental drug is effective in treating a disease, it may be approved by the U.S. Food and Drug Administration (FDA). Approval means the drug may be used in general practice by physicians. Government approval of the value and safety of a new drug helps prevent people from being harmed by drugs that are not thoroughly tested.

Another area of medical research is the development of vaccines. Scientists are trying to develop vaccines for the common cold, flu, AIDS, and herpes. A vaccination for these diseases would allow people to gain an immunity. The main problem in developing a vaccine for the common cold and flu is that many different viruses cause these illnesses. The AIDS virus presents another kind of problem. The proteins of this virus change frequently. The antibodies first produced by the body in response to the infection are effective only until the virus changes. Therefore, it is difficult to develop a vaccine that will cause the production of antibodies to fight all forms of the virus.

How can scientists test the effectiveness of a new drug?

What is the main problem in developing a vaccine for the common cold and flu?

FIGURE 17–15. Medical researchers test the skins of rats for reactions to new products.

FIGURE 17–16. A cancer virus causes cells to divide too rapidly, resulting in a tumor.

Medical scientists are also searching for more effective antibiotics. Excessive use of an antibiotic within a society over time causes new resistant strains of disease bacteria to develop. New antibiotics may be more effective in combating disease organisms that are resistant to antibiotics currently in use.

How is research about cells important in the treatment of health problems?

Research on cell functions will lead the way to new methods of disease prevention and control. Germs cause disease because they enter the body's cells and upset the normal cell functions. For example, a cancer virus causes cells to begin dividing too rapidly, resulting in a tumor. Someday it may be possible to change the nucleic acids of white cells so that they will produce the antibody to a particular germ.

17:10 Health Maintenance

A person's lifestyle is a major factor in staying healthy. Exercise, proper sleep, good nutrition, cleanliness, friendships, play, and work are all part of a healthy lifestyle. Staying healthy also includes the use of safety devices such as seat belts, ear protectors, and safety glasses. Not smoking and avoiding drug and alcohol abuse are also important to health maintenance.

Maintaining good health is a personal responsibility. Your body lets you know when something is wrong. Itching, swollen glands, coughing, stiff joints, upset stomach, constipation, and pain are among the many warning signals. When a warning sign appears you should do something about it. For example, if you often feel tired, try getting more sleep. If you still feel overly tired, you may need to see a physician to learn what is wrong.

Regular physical checkups are part of health maintenance. In a checkup, information is requested about past and current health problems. When physicians examine a patient, they check blood

FIGURE 17–17. Regular physical checkups are part of health maintenance.

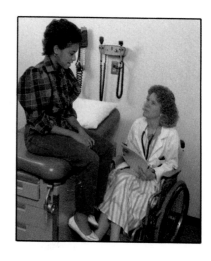

FIGURE 17–18. A pharmacist can explain how to take prescribed drugs properly.

pressure, temperature, weight, breathing, and heartbeat. If any of these are abnormal, it may indicate a health problem. The physician may have other tests made such as a laboratory analysis of the patient's blood or urine. It is important for a patient to ask the physician about the results of the tests.

The patient should talk with the physician about any health problem that is diagnosed so that the cause and treatment is understood. A patient should also become fully informed about how to take any prescribed medicine properly. This information can be obtained from the physician and the pharmacist who fills the prescription. Medical information is helpful to staying in good health.

Making Sure

14. Describe current health research about three diseases.
15. Why are regular health checkups important?

Activity 17–4   Maintaining Health

Problem: What is your personal responsibility for maintaining good health?

Materials pencil and paper, reference books

Procedure (1) Good health habits can add years to your life. Read the health habits listed below. (2) Make a list of the ones that you follow.

Eat balanced meals each day.
Avoid eating foods containing too much fat and sugar.
Eat high fiber foods.
Eat breakfast each day.
Brush and floss your teeth daily.
Have a dental checkup twice a year.
Exercise three or more times a week.
Sleep seven to eight hours each night.
Take a bath or shower regularly.
Brush or comb your hair daily.
Maintain good posture.
Have regular medical checkups.
Wear seat belts.

Questions (1) Which health habits do you need to start improving? (2) What is good health? (3) How can you plan for good health? (4) How do you think good health habits now will build your future health? (5) What is your personal responsibility for maintaining good health?

═══ Technology ═══

The Laser: Beams That Heal

Theodore H. Maiman made the first laser in 1960. The word laser comes from *Light Amplification by Stimulated Emission of Radiation*. Lasers contain a gas, crystal, or liquid that releases energy. This energy is emitted from the laser as a powerful beam of light. The substance used in the laser depends on what is needed for a particular job. An important use for lasers is in medical therapy.

At a Detroit hospital, surgeons perform over 5000 operations a year using the laser. Called "bloodless scalpels," lasers can make precise incisions, reunite torn nerves or blood vessels, and vaporize tumors. Carbon dioxide lasers can restore damaged oviducts. These are the ducts leading from the ovary to the uterus. Clogged blood vessels can be cleared with a laser catheter. Detached retinas can be repaired with an argon laser. The argon laser has also been used to release fluid buildup in the eyes of glaucoma patients. Because of the laser's precision, neighboring tissue remains undamaged.

Lasers are being used to treat some types of cancer. Photodynamic therapy kills cancer cells with a liquid-dye laser. The patient is given a special laser-sensitive dye that stays only in cancer cells. The laser is then aimed at the tumor, and the cancer cells are destroyed.

Lasers can be used to diagnose medical conditions, for example, poor blood circulation. A helium-neon laser is focused on blood vessels that reflect the beams in a certain pattern. The pattern is analyzed, and a computer prints out the rate of blood flow.

FIGURE 17–19. Scientists use a low intensity helium-neon laser to compare a healthy eye (a) to an eye with blurred vision (b). In the unhealthy retina, tiny patches of blood have burst from blood vessels.

a
b

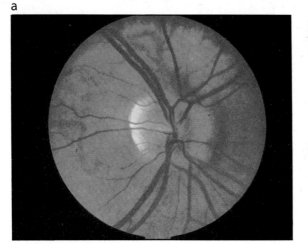
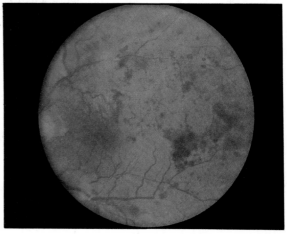

Vaccines—Past to Present

Until forty years ago, as many as a quarter of a million people died annually of smallpox. This disease has existed since at least the tenth century B.C. But in 1978, the World Health Organization announced that smallpox had been eliminated from the world's human population. This was made possible by the use of a vaccine discovered nearly 200 years ago. This achievement was a tribute to the vaccine's discoverer, Edward Jenner. When he carried out his experiments with cowpox on a boy in 1796, Jenner did not realize that he was actually scratching a virus into the boy's skin. It wasn't until 100 years later that viruses were even discovered. It is now known that smallpox is caused by the variola virus. Cowpox is caused by a related virus named vaccinia.

The cowpox vaccinia virus protects people from smallpox in two ways. First, it produces only mild symptoms in humans. Second, the antibodies made against the cowpox virus also work against the closely related, but more serious smallpox virus.

It was not until the 1930s that vaccines for other viruses were developed. Two important discoveries in the 1930s helped scientists develop viral vaccines. One was the introduction of tissue culture as a way to grow viruses in the laboratory. The other was the development of the electron microscope. Once a virus could be grown in the laboratory, scientists were able to study its structure and function. They could then manufacture the vaccines.

The first viral vaccine to be developed was for yellow fever. Max Theiler, a biologist, produced this vaccine in the late 1930s. In 1945, an influenza vaccine was made. Dr. Jonas Salk developed the polio vaccine in 1954. Vaccines for measles and rubella were produced in the 1960s.

Although these vaccines have saved countless lives, some risks have been involved with vaccinations. During the early 1950s millions of people were vaccinated with the Salk polio vaccine. It was then discovered that the monkey cells used for growing the vaccine carried cancer viruses! Fortunately the vaccine is not believed to have caused any cancer in humans. Because a vaccine is made of the disease-causing virus, there is also a slight risk of getting the disease when vaccinated. The risk is low compared with the protection vaccines provide to millions each year.

Modern research has made it possible to develop safe vaccines. Scientists have found that only a certain part of a virus causes antibodies to be made. This part of the virus is usually a surface protein, and researchers can isolate it to make a subunit vaccine. Since subunit vaccines do not contain the hereditary material of the virus, they are much safer. Subunit vaccines have been made for hepatitis, herpes, and malaria. Development is now underway for subunit vaccines against bacterial diseases such as meningitis.

Advances in genetic engineering have led to other breakthroughs in vaccines. Ironically, the latest discovery in vaccinations was made possible by the oldest vaccine known. Using the cowpox virus, researchers can splice in the genetic material from other disease-causing viruses. With one injection, immunity to as many as a dozen diseases is possible. So far, the genetically engineered vaccinia vaccine has been tested on animals, but the results are promising. Genetic engineering is also an important technique in solving the problem of AIDS. If the virus could be altered so that it is unable to reproduce in the cells of the host, then this could also be used as a safe vaccine.

Summary

1. Communicable diseases are caused by microbes.   17:1
2. Noncommunicable diseases are not passed between persons.   17:1
3. Koch's postulates are a set of steps used to prove whether or not a disease is caused by a specific microbe.   17:2
4. Skin, blood, mucus, white cells, blood, lymph cells, interferon, and antibodies are part of the body's natural defenses against disease.   17:3
5. Immunity to a disease may be passive or active. These can be naturally or artificially acquired.   17:4
6. Vaccinations result in the formation of antibodies to fight diseases.   17:5
7. Some diseases can be prevented through the use of antiseptics, disinfectants, cleanliness, quarantines, chlorination of water supplies, and food inspection.   17:6
8. Drugs, surgery, nutrition, physical therapy, and counseling are important aspects of modern medicine.   17:7, 17:8
9. Scientists do research to find new ways to prevent and cure diseases.   17:9
10. Good health habits lessen the chance of a person's becoming ill.   17:10

Vocabulary

Write a sentence using the following words or terms correctly.

active immunity	chemotherapy	Koch's postulates
antibiotic	communicable disease	passive immunity
antibody	disinfectant	quarantine
antiseptic	epidemic	vaccine
carrier	immunity	

Questions

Do not write in this book.

A. True or False

Determine whether each of the following sentences is true or false. Rewrite the false statements to make them correct.

1. A germ is a microbe that causes a communicable disease.
2. Athlete's foot is caused by bacteria.
3. Viruses do not cause diseases in people.
4. The common cold is caused by fungi.
5. Polio is caused by a virus.
6. There is a vaccine for every known disease.

7. Active immunity is an inborn resistance to disease.
8. Physical therapy involves supervision by medical professionals.
9. An insect can be a disease carrier.
10. Malfunctions in cells do not cause health problems.

B. Multiple Choice
Choose the word or phrase that correctly completes the following sentences.
1. A pure culture of microbes contains *(one, two, three, many)* species of microbes.
2. Koch's postulates illustrate the principle of *(immunity, chemotherapy, cause and effect)*.
3. Penicillin prevents the growth of *(viruses, bacteria, protozoans)*.
4. If a person has a disease and recovers, the person may develop a(n) *(naturally active, artificially active, artificially passive)* immunity.
5. Edward Jenner discovered that *(milk, cowpox, bacteria)* can produce immunity to smallpox.
6. Many harmful microbes are destroyed in the stomach by *(hormones, pancreatic juice, acid)*.
7. *(Platelets, Red blood cells, Hormones, Lymph cells)* are a major natural defense of the body against disease.
8. Injection of tetanus antibodies produces a(n) *(naturally active, naturally passive, artificially passive)* immunity.
9. Smallpox vaccination produces a(n) *(naturally active, artificially active, artificially passive)* immunity to the disease.
10. AIDS is caused by a *(bacteria, virus, yeast, mold)*.

C. Completion
Complete each of the following sentences with the correct word or phrase.
1. A(n) _____ is a substance produced by microbes that is used to fight germs.
2. _____ in blood are part of an organism's natural defenses against germs.
3. Cancer is an abnormal growth of _____.
4. Use of chemicals to treat diseases is called _____.
5. Sulfa drugs are used to treat _____ infections.
6. A(n) _____ is when a large number of people get the same disease.
7. A(n) _____ is a substance containing dead or weakened microbes that is used to produce immunity to a disease.
8. _____ is a substance added to water to kill germs.
9. _____ to a disease may be passive or active.
10. A quarantine is used to prevent the spread of disease by _____.

D. How and Why

1. Why are children less likely to die of a microbe-caused disease today than they were 25 years ago?
2. List five communicable diseases and the kind of microbe that causes each disease. Tell how each disease can be prevented or treated.
3. What are the natural disease defenses of the human body?
4. Why are Koch's postulates still used by medical scientists?
5. How do vaccines help prevent disease?
6. How are communicable diseases spread among people?
7. Why are medical checkups important to maintaining good health?
8. What good health habits should a person develop?

Ideas to Explore

1. **Challenge:** Obtain information about cancer from the local chapter of the American Cancer Society. Prepare a report for your class.
2. **Challenge:** Obtain information about careers in the health-care field. Prepare a brochure about a career that interests you.
3. **Challenge:** Prepare a report on antibiotics. Find out how they were discovered and how they are used to fight disease.
4. **Project:** Survey the cleaning supplies in your household. Make a list of the ones that kill disease-causing organisms. List the disease-causing organisms that each one kills.
5. **Project:** Set up a health bulletin board. Obtain posters from local health organizations for display.

Readings

Burns, Sheila L. *Allergies and You*. New York: Messner, 1980.

Burns, Sheila L. *Cancer: Understanding and Fighting It*. New York: Messner, 1982.

Ellis, Ronald W. "Disease Busters." *Science 85*. November, 1985, pp. 50–52.

Jacobs, Francine. *Breakthrough: The True Story of Penicillin*. New York: Dodd, Mead, 1985.

Klein, Aaron E. *The Parasites We Humans Harbor*. New York: Elsevier/Nelson, 1981.

Nourse, Alan E. *Viruses*. Rev. ed. New York: Franklin Watts, 1983.

Patent, Dorothy Hinshaw. *Germs*. New York: Holiday House, 1983.

Aspirin, antibiotics, caffeine, alcohol, narcotics, and painkillers are all drugs. Drugs change life processes within the body. Some drugs are used to treat diseases and illnesses. Other drugs may reduce pain and discomfort. How are drugs classified? Physical and psychological dependence can develop from drug use. What problems are caused by dependency on drugs?

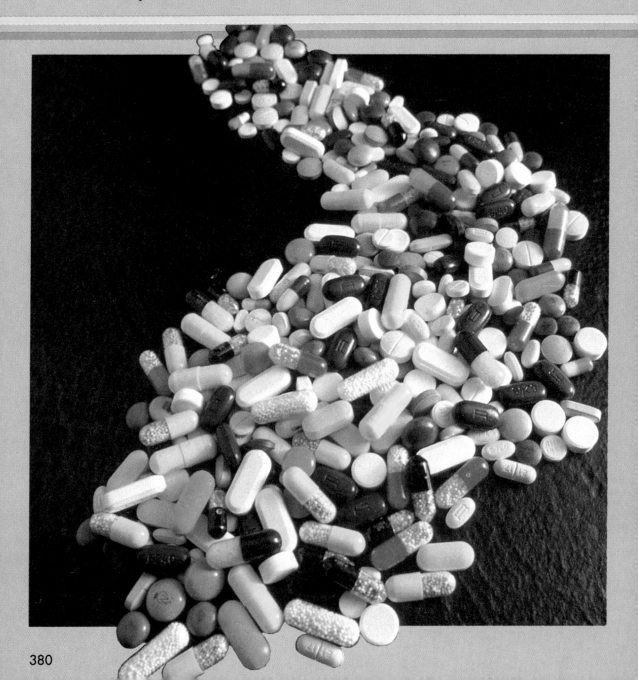

CHAPTER 18
DRUGS AND HEALTH

18:1 Drugs

When we think of drugs, we usually think of medicines used to treat disease. However, to scientists a **drug** is a substance that can change life processes within the body.

Medicines are drugs that are used to treat diseases. Some medicines actually cure diseases. Perhaps you have had an infection that was cured by an antibiotic. A few types of cancer can also be cured with drug treatments. However, most drugs do not cure diseases. Drugs may reduce pain or other symptoms of a disease. If a bone is broken, a painkiller may provide comfort, but it will not help the bone heal. Other drugs are used to replace chemicals normally found in the body. For example, diabetes is a disease in which the pancreas does not make enough insulin. Insulin taken as a drug replaces the missing insulin.

A prescription drug is a drug ordered by a doctor for a specific patient. Because these drugs can be harmful if not taken according to a doctor's instructions, it is illegal to buy or sell them without a prescription. Drugs that can be bought without a prescription are called **over-the-counter drugs** or OTCs. OTCs are usually less dangerous than prescription drugs. Still, if OTCs are misused or taken in large amounts, they are hazardous. Their labels should be read carefully for information about the proper use and safe dosage. There are many kinds of OTCs. Two of the most common are aspirins and antihistamines. Aspirins are taken for headaches, body aches, and fever. Antihistamines are taken to ease the symptoms of hay fever.

GOALS:
1. You will learn the effects of drugs on the body.
2. You will learn helpful and harmful uses of drugs.
3. You will learn the effects of drug abuse on society.

What is a prescription drug?

What are two common OTCs and for what are they used?

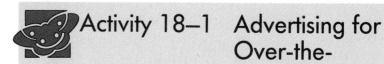

Activity 18–1   Advertising for Over-the-Counter Drugs

Problem: In advertising, what information is given about over-the-counter drugs?

Materials   magazines, television, paper, pencil

Procedure   (1) Watch six advertisements for over-the-counter drugs on television (2) Read six advertisements for over-the-counter drugs in a magazine. (3) For each advertisement, record the following: a. For what is the drug used? b. Who is its intended user? c. What instructions are given for taking the drug? d. Are any warnings or side effects presented in the advertisement? e. What techniques does the manufacturer use to get people to buy the drug?

Questions   (1) What instructions are given for taking over-the-counter drugs in advertisements? (2) Are warnings or side effects presented in advertisements? (3) Do most advertisements specify for whom the drug is intended? (4) In advertising, what information is given about over-the-counter drugs?

18:2 Effects of Drugs

Define side effect and give an example of one.

Drugs usually have more than one effect. When a drug causes an unintended result, the result is called a **side effect**. For example, many drugs that relieve the symptoms of allergies cause sleepiness as a side effect.

Sometimes it may be necessary to take more than one drug at a time. Taking more than one drug at a time can be dangerous because of drug interaction. **Drug interaction** is one drug changing, increasing, or decreasing the effect of another drug. For example, drug interaction occurs if a drug to produce sleep is

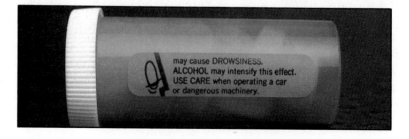

FIGURE 18–1. Dangerous drug interactions can be avoided by carefully reading warning labels on drug bottles.

taken with another drug to calm the nerves. The effect of one drug is greatly increased by the effect of the other drug. Drug interaction results in more risks than either of the drugs would have if taken by themselves.

Some drugs are addictive. **Addictive** means that the drug causes the user to develop a physical dependence upon it. **Physical dependence** means the addict must continue to take the drug or else withdrawal will occur. The sickness that results when a physically dependent person stops taking an addictive drug is called **withdrawal.** Some common symptoms of withdrawal include nervousness, depression, stomach cramps, and diarrhea.

Some drugs are habit-forming because they can cause a psychological dependence. **Psychological dependence** means the person taking the drug has developed a craving for the drug and has a strong emotional need to take that drug. This need to take the drug develops even though the person has no physical need for the drug. The person is psychologically dependent on the drug—not physically dependent. A drug causing psychological dependence is called habit forming. Some drugs can cause both physical and psychological dependence.

What is the difference between addictive and habit-forming drugs?

18:3 Tobacco

Tobacco and tobacco smoke contain a drug called **nicotine.** Nicotine is a stimulant. A **stimulant** speeds up the rate of body activities. Alertness is increased and fatigue is reduced by a stimulant. Although nicotine is a drug, it is not used as a medicine. It is taken into the mouth, throat, and lungs when a person smokes tobacco. In addition to nicotine, tobacco smoke contains tobacco

What is nicotine?

FIGURE 18–2. Tobacco leaves are the source for the stimulant nicotine.

Mice breathe cigarette smoke.

Mice breathe normal air.

Bronchial and lung tissues from both groups are studied.

FIGURE 18–3. Experiments with smoking machines helped prove that smoking causes cancer.

How did the lung tissue of the two groups of mice differ?

FIGURE 18–4. Smoking is so harmful to health that warning labels are required on all packages.

tars. Tars are black, gummy substances that remain in the lungs after smoking. Cigarettes, cigars, and pipes are used to smoke tobacco. Tobacco is also chewed or placed between the cheek and gum in small amounts.

Scientists have discovered that smoking and other uses of tobacco are harmful. In one experiment, two groups of mice were compared. One group was connected to a smoking machine. The second group breathed only clean air. After several months, the mice were studied to determine if the smoke had any effect on the mice's lungs. Tissues from the lungs of the two groups of mice were examined under a microscope. The tissues of the mice that breathed smoke showed changes similar to the early stages of cancer. These changes were not found in the mice that had not breathed smoke.

It has now been shown that smoking tobacco causes lung cancer in humans. Tobacco tars cause lung cancer as well as other types of cancer. The risk of getting lung cancer is ten times greater for cigarette smokers than for nonsmokers. Evidence shows that tobacco is responsible for one-third of all deaths due to cancer. Heart disease and emphysema (em fu SEE muh) can also be caused by smoking. Emphysema is a disease of the lungs that prevents normal breathing. Smoke inhaled by pregnant women may cause injury to their unborn babies, premature births, and low birth weights.

Smokeless tobacco and chewing tobacco cause some of the same problems as smoking tobacco. Continued use of tobacco in the mouth can cause cancer in the mouth and throat. Gums and bones that support the teeth may be damaged, causing teeth to fall out.

Tobacco smoke contains carbon monoxide. Carbon monoxide is a harmful gas that is also found in car exhaust and other types of smoke. Carbon monoxide prevents the blood from carrying normal amounts of oxygen to body cells. Breathing carbon monoxide causes the circulatory system to work harder. This can lead to heart disease, the number one cause of death in the United States. One-third of these deaths are linked to smoking.

Scientists have evidence that nonsmokers may be harmed by breathing air containing tobacco smoke. Also, nonsmokers may find breathing air polluted by tobacco smoke unpleasant. For this reason, airplanes and restaurants have areas for nonsmokers. Some cities also require nonsmoking areas for workers. These measures protect nonsmokers from cigarette smoke produced by others. States have laws against selling tobacco products to children. Federal law requires every package of cigarettes to carry a warning of the health hazards of smoking.

By not starting to smoke a person avoids the health problems it creates and leads a healthier life. When a smoker gives up smoking, the person's health improves. Damaged lung tissue begins to heal itself. Other body organs that suffered the harmful effects of smoking begin to work better.

FIGURE 18–5. Many public places designate areas where smoking is not permitted.

How do smokers benefit when they give up smoking?

Activity 18–2   Reasons for Smoking

Problem: Why do some adults smoke?

Materials   notebook, pencil

Procedure   (1) Make a hypothesis about why adults smoke. (2) Conduct a survey. Ask five adults who smoke why they smoke and why they began to smoke. Ask five adults who do not smoke why they do not. (3) Compile a class list of the reasons why people smoke and why they started smoking. (4) Compile a class list of the reasons why people do not smoke.

Questions   (1) Is there any evidence from your survey that cigarette smoking is an addiction? (2) What two chemicals are taken into the body as a result of smoking? (3) What are the dangers of these chemicals? (4) What diseases can be caused by smoking? (5) How is smoking a safety hazard? (6) Why do some adults smoke?

FIGURE 18–6.

FIGURE 18–7. Coffee beans are used to make coffee that contains the habit-forming stimulant caffeine.

18:4 Caffeine

Many foods and drinks contain naturally-occurring drugs that are not taken for medical reasons. Caffeine found in coffee, tea, chocolate, cocoa, and many soft drinks is an example of such a drug. **Caffeine** is a habit-forming, mild stimulant. Drinks that have caffeine in them help people stay awake when they are tired or sleepy. However, caffeine also has side effects. It may affect the central nervous system and can be harmful to people who have heart disease or ulcers, open sores in the wall of the stomach or intestine.

Caffeine is also habit-forming. People who drink a lot of caffeine may have difficulty sleeping because of the stimulant effect of the drug. Tiredness from lack of sleep then leads to more caffeine use the next day.

Caffeine can be poisonous if taken in large amounts, but it is safe under normal use. The fatal caffeine dose in humans is about 10 g. This is the amount in 70 to 100 cups of coffee.

Table 18–1

Caffeine Count			
Source	mg Caffeine	Source	mg Caffeine
tea (148 mL)	30-47	milk chocolate (56 g)	45
coffee (148 mL)	40-150	carbonated diet soft drink (392 mL)	32-54
cocoa (148 mL)	13	carbonated regular soft drink (392 mL)	34-65

18:5 Alcohol

Ethyl alcohol is probably the oldest known drug. It is the kind of alcohol found in beer, wine, whiskey, and other alcoholic beverages. Alcohol is made from various grains, fruits, and vegetables that undergo fermentation. In fermentation, the sugar in these foods is changed to ethyl alcohol and carbon dioxide through the action of enzymes in the yeast cells. **Alcohol** is a depressant and can be habit-forming. A **depressant** is a drug that slows down the body processes. In other words, a depressant is a drug that decreases alertness.

Define depressant.

Methyl alcohol, commonly called wood alcohol, differs from ethyl alcohol. Methyl alcohol can be made by heating wood chips to a very high temperature in a sealed container with no air. Methyl alcohol is used for heating and for making other chemical compounds. It is highly poisonous and can cause blindness and even death if consumed. Rubbing or isopropyl alcohol is also poisonous.

Alcohol affects the body rapidly because it is not digested. It is absorbed directly by the blood and carried to all the body parts. In body tissues, alcohol is broken down to form carbon dioxide and water. An alcohol level of 0.05 percent in the blood causes a change in behavior in most people. A level of 0.1 percent is considered legal intoxication in many states. Intoxication by alcohol results in loss of coordination, slurred speech, and loss of judgment. Because alcohol causes slowed reactions and loss of control, it is dangerous and unlawful for people who are intoxicated to drive a car. About one-half of all car accident deaths involve intoxicated drivers. Intoxicated drivers kill over 25 000 people each year on United States highways. Intoxicated drivers usually misjudge speeds and their position on the road. They drive around curves too fast, fail to signal turns, and often become sleepy.

Alcoholism is a disorder in which a person cannot control his or her drinking. An alcoholic is a person who suffers from alcoholism. Some people are more likely than others to become physically and psychologically dependent upon alcohol. Alcoholics cannot keep their alcohol use at low levels. They also suffer severe withdrawal when drinking is stopped. The withdrawal symptoms include convulsions and delusions. In very serious cases, alcoholics may die from withdrawal.

Alcoholics often suffer from other diseases related to their use of alcohol. One of the functions of the liver is to neutralize alcohol and other poisons in the blood. Long-term use of alcohol can cause the tissues of the liver to shrink and harden. This disease of the liver is called cirrhosis (suh ROH sus). If cirrhosis causes

FIGURE 18–8. Alcohol use places a great strain on the families of alcoholics.

What is an alcoholic?

FIGURE 18–9. A normal liver (a) neutralizes poisons in the blood. A liver with cirrhosis (b) allows these poisons to remain in the body.

a

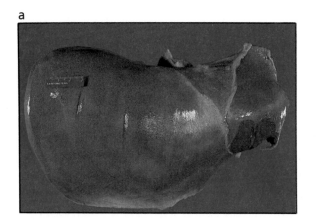

b

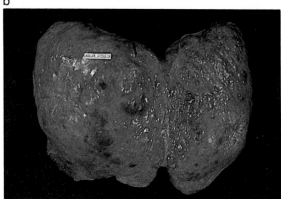

the liver to stop working, death results. Alcoholics often do not eat a balanced diet. Not eating a balanced diet can result in vitamin deficiencies and poor health. If a pregnant woman uses alcohol, it can cause birth defects in the fetus. If the mother has a severe case of alcoholism, it can cause permanent brain damage to the fetus.

Alcohol causes more problems in our society than any other type of drug. Alcohol-related diseases account for millions of dollars spent on health care and lost time in the workplace. Research shows that drinkers have twice as many off-the-job accidents as nondrinkers. Alcohol use also places great strain on families of alcoholics.

Making Sure

1. What are the effects of caffeine on the body?
2. List five problems sometimes caused by drinking too much alcohol.

18:6 Marijuana

Marijuana is a plant that can be a stimulant or a depressant. The dried leaves, stems, and flowering tops of marijuana plants are usually smoked, although they may be eaten as well. Marijuana is not addictive but can produce psychological dependency. The type and amount of marijuana used and the personality of the user may determine its effects.

Marijuana contains many drugs. The most active of these is THC, which causes many changes in the body. Marijuana affects the circulatory system by increasing the heartbeat rate by as much as 50 percent. Smoking marijuana also damages lung tissue and may lead to a higher risk for respiratory infections. Harm to the reproductive system may include producing abnormal sperm, injuring a developing fetus, or disturbing hormone levels.

Marijuana affects behavior by acting on the nervous system. Effects include difficulty in thinking and speaking clearly, slowed physical reactions, and loss of coordination. For these reasons, it is dangerous to drive a car when intoxicated with marijuana.

When a person smokes marijuana, the THC quickly leaves the bloodstream and passes into tissues with a high fat content. These tissues include the brain, liver, heart, kidney, and glands. THC is stored in the cells and builds up. Daily users may have ten times more THC in their bodies than once-a-month users.

FIGURE 18–10. Concentration and coordination are necessary for perfect balance. Marijuana use causes a loss of complete control.

FIGURE 18–11. The leaves, stems, and flowering tops of marijuana are dried and then smoked or eaten.

Regular users of marijuana may be less motivated to do well in school or at their jobs. Research is being done to understand the effects of marijuana and to determine the results of long-term use. Most states have laws prohibiting the use and possession of marijuana.

Although marijuana use is dangerous, under strict supervision the THC component has been used as a medicine. In some instances, cancer patients undergoing drug therapy may use THC to decrease their nausea and vomiting. THC also can help to control glaucoma, a disease that causes blindness.

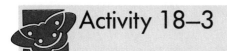

Activity 18–3   Tobacco and Alcohol Advertising

Problem: What are the laws controlling the advertising of tobacco and alcohol?

Materials paper, pencil

Procedure (1) Contact the advertising department of your local newspaper, radio station, and television station. Find out what laws about alcohol and tobacco advertising apply to their advertising. (2) Ask if these laws have changed within the past five years. (3) Ask if the laws are federal or local laws. (4) Make a chart that has one column "Alcohol" and another column "Tobacco" across the top. Along the side, list "radio advertising laws," "newspaper advertising laws," and "television advertising laws."

Questions (1) Why do tobacco and alcohol advertising laws exist? (2) Are these laws federal or local laws? (3) What are the laws controlling the advertising of tobacco and alcohol?

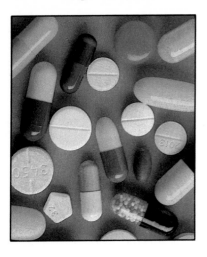

FIGURE 18–12. Amphetamines speed up all the body's processes.

18:7 Amphetamines

Amphetamines (am FET uh meenz) are stimulants that are strongly habit-forming but not addictive. Amphetamines increase the heartbeat rate, breathing rate, and blood pressure. Restlessness, nervousness, and loss of appetite are other effects of these drugs.

In the past, amphetamines were sometimes prescribed for people who wanted to lose weight. Using these drugs for weight loss often led to drug abuse. Now, physicians rarely prescribe amphetamines. However, they are used to treat some children who have Attention Deficit Disorders (ADD), also referred to as hyperactivity. Other than treating ADD, there are few medical uses for amphetamines.

Today amphetamines are used illegally by people who want the stimulant effects of these drugs. Their street name is "uppers." Amphetamine abuse may lead to poor judgment and violent or aggressive behavior. Regular use may cause heart problems and mental disorders.

18:8 Cocaine

Cocaine comes from the leaves of the coca plant found in the mountains of South America. **Cocaine** is a strong stimulant that is very habit-forming.

Cocaine is used medically as a painkiller, but like amphetamines, it is also used illegally as a stimulant. Cocaine can make the user feel powerful or "in control" for a short time. Its users consider using it a sign of high social status and often do not realize its harmful effects. Regular cocaine use can cause heart problems, violent behavior, and mental disorders. The practice of sniffing the drug causes the nasal membranes to become irritated. Also, regular users may experience restlessness, anxiety, and irritability.

What health problems are caused by regular use of cocaine?

Illegal cocaine is very expensive, and the high cost causes problems for its users and society. Because the amount of cocaine used in a single day can cost hundreds or even thousands of dollars, family and work life are affected. Some users may turn to illegal activity to earn enough money to pay for cocaine. As a result, police agencies must devote much time and money to fighting cocaine-related crime.

FIGURE 18–13. Cocaine is an expensive stimulant. A day's use can cost hundreds, or even thousands, of dollars.

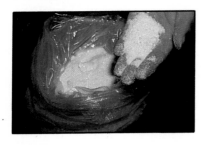

Making Sure

3. How does marijuana affect the respiratory, circulatory, and reproductive systems?

18:9 Other Depressants

Barbiturates (bar BIHCH uh ruts) are depressants. Barbiturates are prescribed by physicians in low doses to relieve anxiety and in higher doses to help people sleep. Barbiturates come from a synthetic substance called barbituric acid. High doses of barbiturates cause intoxication similar to alcohol, resulting in loss of coordination and poor judgment. The user may become confused and, as a result, take too much of the drug by accident. An overdose of barbiturates, especially if taken with alcohol, may cause death.

The barbiturates cause physical and psychological dependence. If taken for long periods of time, they will have to continue being taken to prevent withdrawal. Withdrawal from barbiturates can be very dangerous, causing convulsions, body twitchings, severe nervousness, and death. A person withdrawing from barbiturates should be under a physician's supervision. Because prolonged use can cause dependence, physicians usually now prescribe other, safer drugs.

Tranquilizers are depressants used to reduce stress and relax muscles. They are often given to patients the night before surgery. Drug addiction occurs if a patient continues taking the tranquilizer after the problem for which it was prescribed no longer exists. Because they are often taken over a period of time in ever-increasing doses, tranquilizers are one of the most widely abused drugs. It is illegal to use tranquilizers without a prescription.

Fumes from substances including some types of paint and glue are sometimes misused as depressants. The user inhales the fumes until dizziness or light-headedness occurs. Inhaling fumes is extremely hazardous. Use of these substances, even for short periods of time, can cause brain damage, liver damage, and kidney disease. Some people have died because inhaling fumes prevented them from breathing enough fresh air to supply the blood with oxygen.

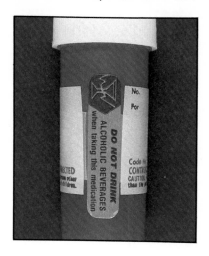

FIGURE 18–14. Barbiturates should never be taken with alcohol because a dangerous drug interaction can occur.

Name a medical use of tranquilizers.

Making Sure

4. What are the effects of amphetamines on the body?
5. Why are amphetamines and cocaine dangerous to the body?
6. How is the use of cocaine harmful to society?
7. What are the medical uses for depressants?
8. What are tranquilizers?
9. Why is it dangerous to use depressants and alcohol together?
10. What are the hazards of inhaling fumes from paint or glue?

Activity 18–4   The Effect of Drugs on Heart Rate

Problem: How do drugs affect the heart rate of an animal?

Materials

Daphnia culture
microscope
dilute solutions of adrenaline
ethyl alcohol
tea
coffee

cola
a tranquilizer
an amphetamine
culture slide
dropper
aged tap water

Procedure

1. Use a dropper to place a *Daphnia* on a culture slide.
2. Place the slide under the microscope. Use low power and count the number of times the daphnia's heart beats in one minute. (Do not mistake the beating of the gills for the heartbeats.) Record your observations.
3. Record a prediction of which substances on the chart are stimulants and which are depressants.
4. Add one or two drops of one of the drug solutions.
5. Count the heart rate again. Record your observations.
6. Use a dropper to remove the solution. Flush carefully with aged tap water.
7. Repeat steps 1 through 6 with each drug solution.
8. Note whether each drug is a stimulant or a depressant.

Data and Observations

Drug solution	Heart rate per minute	Stimulant or depressant
No drug		
Adrenaline		
Ethyl alcohol		
Tea		
Coffee		
Cola		
Tranquilizer		
Ampheta-mine		

Questions and Conclusions

1. What is the control in this experiment? What are the variables?
2. How did the drugs affect the Daphnia?
3. Which drug caused the greatest change in heartbeats per minute?
4. Which drugs are stimulants?
5. Which drugs are depressants?
6. Compare your predicted results with the actual results.
7. How do you think the drugs studied in this activity affect people who use them?
8. How do drugs affect the heart rate of an animal?

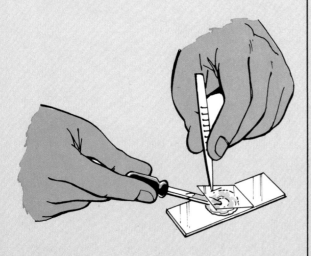

FIGURE 18–15.

392

18:10 Hallucinogens

Hallucinogens (huh LEWS un uh junz) are drugs that cause hallucinations. A hallucination occurs when a person sees and hears images and sounds that do not exist. Some hallucinations are mild, such as color changes or unusual sounds. Others may be very frightening. For example, a hallucinating person may see and react to terrible scenes that do not exist. Persons with hallucinations might think someone was chasing them and jump out a window to escape. Hallucinogens affect brain activities, causing a loss of control over emotions or actions. Hallucinogens cause changes in awareness of time and space that may be mild or overwhelming, depending on the dose and quality of the drug. The effects of these drugs are variable. The same person may have different reactions on different occasions. Sometimes the effects may return months after the drug has been taken. There is no way to predict what effect hallucinogens will have or what kind of hallucination will occur.

There are many types of hallucinogens. LSD is a powerful hallucinogen accidently discovered by a Swiss chemist in 1942. LSD is made from ergot, a fungus that grows on rye and wheat. Very small amounts of LSD can have effects lasting up to 12 hours. Continued use can result in serious personality breakdown. Psilocybin (si luh SI bun) is made from mushrooms. Other hallucinogens come from plants. Mescaline (MES kuh leen) is made from the peyote cactus. Some forms of marijuana may also be hallucinogens.

FIGURE 18–16. Hallucinogens distort the way we see the world around us.

FIGURE 18–17. Many hallucinogens are made from natural substances. The source of LSD is ergot, a fungus (a). Psilocybin is made from *Psilocybe* mushrooms (b). The peyote cactus (c) is the source of mescaline.

a

b

c

FIGURE 18–18. PCP is often used to anesthetize large animals. PCP is extremely dangerous for human use.

Explain why PCP is dangerous.

PCP, the most dangerous hallucinogen, can be smoked, sniffed, or eaten. PCP can be a depressant or a stimulant. PCP scrambles the brain's messages, causing users to change how they see and react to their environment. PCP users often become violent and injure themselves or others. The drug dulls some of the senses so the person may not feel the injury. Some PCP users experience loss of memory that can last for days or weeks. Because PCP users often think that they can fly, the drug is also known as "angel dust." Bizarre behavior caused by the drug often leads to serious or fatal accidents.

Explain why illegal drugs are especially dangerous.

Hallucinogens and all illegal drugs are especially dangerous because their manufacture is not controlled. Illegal drugs are not labelled and packaged safely. Some may contain poisons or other contaminants. Many illnesses have been reported by people who thought they were purchasing hallucinogenic mushrooms but got poisonous mushrooms instead.

The only legal use of hallucinogens is in research laboratories that have been granted special permission to use the substances. Hallucinogens mimic symptoms of severe mental disorders. Researchers hope to find clues to the causes of the disorders by observing laboratory animals that have been injected with hallucinogens.

Making Sure

11. Why are hallucinogens dangerous to the user's health?
12. List two examples of hallucinatory drugs and describe their effects on the body.
13. From where do LSD, psilocybin, and mescaline come?

18:11 Narcotics

Narcotics are addictive depressants that relieve pain and often cause sleep. Narcotics such as morphine and codeine are known as opiates because they are made from the opium poppy plant. Another narcotic, heroin, is made from morphine. There are other narcotics that do not come from plants but are made in laboratories. Because narcotics are depressants, they slow down circulation and respiration and lower blood pressure. They can produce drowsiness, loss of consciousness, and sleep.

Opium substances have been used as a medication for at least 7000 years. Until this century, they were the most useful painkillers available to physicians. They were used to treat many diseases. Although there were some helpful effects of these drugs, patients were often harmed by becoming dependent upon them.

Narcotics such as morphine, heroin, and codeine cause strong psychological and physical dependence. A regular user who stops taking a narcotic will experience severe withdrawal. A heroin addict deprived of the drug for 12 hours will become sick. Nervousness, runny nose, goose bumps, hot and cold flashes, diarrhea, and stomach cramps are common symptoms. The intensity of these symptoms depends on the degree of addiction of the addict. Another problem with narcotics is that tolerance to their effects develops when they are taken regularly. **Tolerance** is a condition in which the body develops a resistance to the action of a drug. Tolerance causes a need for larger doses of the drug to produce the desired effect. As a result, the person takes larger doses and develops even more tolerance. A person with a high level of tolerance can take 200 times more than the usual fatal dose of a drug. The uncertainty of what is a safe dose poses a great risk to life for those using unprescribed drugs.

Name three examples of narcotics and give the source of each.

Define tolerance.

a

b

FIGURE 18–19. The flower of the opium poppy (a) is the source of opiates, such as morphine and codeine. They are prepared from the dried sap of the flower pod (b).

FIGURE 18–20. Professional counselors are an important part of drug addiction treatment.

What are two problems created by narcotic addiction?

Some people become dependent upon illegal narcotics. Because their addiction is so strong, narcotic addicts will pay large amounts of money for the drugs they need. Because the addiction keeps them from holding a job, most addicts must steal to get enough money to buy narcotics. Narcotic addiction creates crime problems as well as health problems for the addicts. Narcotic addiction has become a worldwide problem. International regulations control the import and sale of opium and its related narcotics. The penalties for illegally importing drugs are very severe.

Narcotic addiction is difficult to cure. Many methods have been tried. One approach uses the narcotic methadone. Methadone reduces the cravings for heroin, but it is not a cure for addiction. Once an addict has stopped taking a drug, the main problem of addiction treatment begins. The addict must not resume the habit. Successful treatment usually requires professional counseling and a change in lifestyle for the addict.

18:12 Why People Use Drugs

There may be many reasons people use drugs for nonmedical purposes. Four of the main reasons are listed below.

1. A drug prescribed for a medical reason may create drug dependency.
2. Using drugs is a social habit. Drinking alcohol may be seen as a sign of growing up; marijuana or cigarettes may be smoked to "fit in" with friends.

3. Boredom, curiosity, or the wish to experience new sensations may lead to drug use.
4. An attitude that a drug can quickly cure every bad or uncomfortable feeling is a cause of drug use.

In many of these cases, the drug may be taken in response to a problem. The problem may be a lack of friends or feelings of inferiority. Taking the drug as a solution to the problem then becomes a larger problem—a trap from which the person may not be able to escape without professional help.

How can a person avoid using drugs for nonmedical reasons? One way is to find other methods for solving personal problems. Talking about a personal problem with a parent, teacher, or friend can be helpful. Resisting the pressure of peers to use drugs may be easier if friends who do not use drugs are supportive. Participating in sports and drug-free social activities are good alternatives to using drugs. Counselors can provide information about local organizations that assist people with drug problems.

What can be the result of taking drugs in response to a problem?

Making Sure

14. Define narcotics.
15. Why must narcotic pain relievers be used rarely?
16. What are the common symptoms of heroin withdrawal?
17. What is the main problem of drug addiction treatment?
18. What are the social costs of narcotic addiction?
19. List four nonmedical reasons people use drugs.

FIGURE 18-21. Talking with a parent or counselor (a) can help a young person solve problems without using drugs. Enjoying outdoor activities with friends (b) is a way to have fun without taking drugs.

a

b

FOCUS ON
People and Careers

Pharmaceutical Workers

Suzette Smith is a pharmacist at a large city hospital. Her job involves reading and interpreting the physician's orders for medicines. She prepares drugs and other medicinal compounds according to specific regulations. She then dispenses the medicines to the correct floor or area of the hospital. Working in a hospital pharmacy is much different from working in a retail pharmacy. In a retail pharmacy, a pharmacist works directly with the patients, assuring that, among other things, patients understand the prescribed instructions. A hospital pharmacist works only with the hospital staff.

Licensing requirements for pharmacists differ slightly for each state, but five years of college are needed to earn a degree in pharmacy. Most pharmacy schools require chemistry, economics, accounting, life science, math, and physics for admission. Taking these courses usually requires two years at a university. Students can then apply for entrance to a pharmacy school. There they spend three years taking pharmacy courses. After graduation, students take an examination by the State Board of Pharmacy to be licensed.

Ms. Smith recommends that pharmacy students work in a pharmacy while attending school. Some states require as much as 2000 hours of

work experience before students can apply for a pharmacy license.

Computers are now used to prepare many medicines. In fact, modern technology is rapidly changing the field of pharmacy. Ms. Smith feels that a pharmaceutical career offers a wide range of career opportunities for the future.

Samanthia Banks is a sampler for a vitamin company. Her job is to see that the correct materials are used in the company's products, and that the company's goals for quality are maintained. In addition to examining the vitamins made in her work area, Ms. Banks is responsible for seeing that bottles, seals, caps, and labels meet the company's health and safety standards. Because these particular vitamins are for people, it is extremely important that the product be of high quality and be packaged under sanitary conditions. If any portion of the product does not meet the company's standards, Ms. Banks must reject it for sale to the public.

To be a sampler, Ms. Banks received on-the-job training. Even though this particular job does not require a college education, she does have a college degree. Many manufacturers believe that a broad educational background, including college and on-the-job technical training, gives their employees a good chance for career growth.

CHAPTER 18
Review

Summary

1. Medicines are drugs that are used to treat diseases. Two kinds of drugs are prescription drugs and over-the-counter drugs.   18:1
2. Side effects, drug interaction, and addiction may result from taking drugs.   18:2
3. Tars and carbon monoxide present in tobacco smoke are harmful to the lungs and heart.   18:3
4. Alcohol is a habit-forming depressant that can cause cirrhosis and other diseases and disorders.   18:5
5. Marijuana is a drug that can be a stimulant or a depressant and can produce psychological dependency.   18:6
6. Cocaine is a strong stimulant used as a painkiller. It can produce psychological dependency.   18:6
7. Barbiturates are depressants that cause physical and psychological dependence.   18:9
8. Hallucinogens are drugs that cause hallucinations.   18:10
9. Narcotics are addictive depressants. Narcotic addiction is very difficult to cure.   18:11
10. Taking drugs as a solution to a personal problem may lead to drug dependency.   18:12

Vocabulary

Write a sentence using the following words or terms correctly.

addictive	drug interaction	physical dependence
alcohol	hallucinogen	psychological dependence
caffeine	marijuana	side effect
cocaine	narcotic	stimulant
depressant	nicotine	tolerance
drug	over-the-counter drug	withdrawal

Questions

Do not write in this book.

A. True or False
Determine whether each of the following sentences is true or false. Rewrite the false statements to make them correct.

1. A drug is a substance that can change life processes within the body.
2. The drug found in beer, wine, and whiskey is caffeine.

CHAPTER 18
Review

3. Narcotics are stimulants.
4. A drug prescribed for a medical reason may create drug dependency.
5. Two of the most common over-the-counter drugs are antihistamines and insulin.
6. A depressant increases alertness.
7. Carbon monoxide in tobacco smoke can cause lung cancer and emphysema.
8. A drug changing, increasing, or decreasing the effect of another drug is drug dependence.
9. Nicotine is a drug found in tobacco and tobacco smoke.
10. Inhaling fumes can cause brain damage, liver damage, and kidney disease.

B. Multiple Choice
Choose the word or phrase that correctly completes the following sentences.
1. The most dangerous of the hallucinogens is *(PCP, barbiturates)*.
2. Drugs that cure infections caused by microbes are *(antibiotics, painkillers)*.
3. The risk of getting lung cancer is *(five, ten)* times greater for cigarette smokers than for nonsmokers.
4. A drug ordered by a physician for a specific patient is a(n) *(prescription, over-the-counter)* drug.
5. *(Alcohol, caffeine)* is absorbed directly by the blood and carried to all parts of the body.
6. Morphine, codeine, and heroin are *(stimulants, narcotics)*.
7. The substance in tobacco that causes physical dependence is *(tar, nicotine)*.
8. LSD, mescaline, and psilocybin are all *(hallucinogens, barbiturates, narcotics)*.
9. A plant that can be a stimulant or a depressant is *(cocoa, marijuana)*.
10. An illegal, expensive stimulant that causes serious problems for police is *(codeine, cocaine)*.

C. Completion
Complete each of the following sentences with the correct word or phrase.
1. _____ is a stimulant present in tea, coffee, chocolate, cocoa, and many soft drinks.
2. _____ is a common name for PCP, a powerful hallucinogen.
3. An unintended result of taking a drug is called a(n) _____.
4. A(n) _____ is a person who is physically dependent on a drug.
5. _____ prevents red blood cells from carrying normal amounts of oxygen in the blood.
6. Long-term use of alcohol can cause a liver disease called _____.

7. A(n) _____ speeds up the rate of the body's activities.

8. A medical use of amphetamines is to treat _____.

9. _____ are depressants used to help people sleep and relieve anxiety.

10. _____ is a condition in which the body develops a resistance to the action of a drug.

D. How and Why

1. What are two harmful chemicals in tobacco smoke? How are they harmful?

2. Why does alcohol have a rapid effect on the body?

3. How is a stimulant different from a depressant? Give some examples of each.

4. What problems are caused by regular use of cocaine?

5. Why do alcoholics often not eat a balanced diet?

Ideas to Explore

1. **Challenge:** Obtain information about a career as a pharmacist.

2. **Challenge:** Find out what drugs come from plants and how the drugs are made from the plants. Make a poster displaying the information.

3. **Project:** Take the pulse of a person who smokes. Take the pulse of that person while the person is smoking a cigarette and determine if the pulse rate changes. Compare the pulse rate with a nonsmoker of the same age and physical size.

4. **Project:** Interview an emergency room physician or nurse about drug abuse cases they have treated.

5. **Challenge:** Research the connection between the Salem Witch trials and the ergot fungus.

6. **Challenge:** Compile a list of drug references in TV shows, commercials, ads, and movies.

Readings

Arkava, Morton L. and John Russell. *Coping with Smoking*. New York: Rosen Publishing, 1983.

Comfort, Alex and Jane Comfort. *What About Alcohol?* Burlington, NC: Carolina Biological Supply, 1983.

Edwards, Gabrielle. *Coping With Drug Abuse*. New York: Rosen Publishing, 1983.

Weiss, Ann. *Over-the-Counter Drugs*. New York: Franklin Watts Inc., 1984.

Nutrition
Background Data

In Chapter 16, you learned about the nutritional requirements of humans. Humans need several types of substances to remain healthy. Water is an important part of a person's diet. It is needed for digestion, removal of waste, and general body processes. Minerals are important because they are needed for the formation of hormones and enzymes. Vitamins are needed to assimilate food and prevent disease. Starchy foods, such as breads, spaghetti, potatoes, and rice, are good sources of carbohydrates, which provide the body with energy. Fats and oils can be used by the body as a source of energy, and are important in maintaining healthy hair and skin. Dairy products provide fats as well as minerals and proteins. Proteins contain amino acids that are needed for the growth and repair of body tissues. A complete selection of amino acids can be obtained by eating meat, eggs, milk, fish, cheese, whole grains, and certain vegetables.

This program deals with only one aspect of nutrition, Calorie intake. Remember when counting Calories to also consider other aspects of good nutrition.

Input/Output

Enter the program into your computer exactly as it is printed. After you enter the entire program, type RUN. If there is a problem, type LIST and check that you have entered the program exactly as it is printed. Remember, symbols and punctuation are important and must be typed as printed here. When all corrections have been made, be sure to save the program.

Once the program is running, the computer will ask for your name and sex. It will then tell you the approximate number of Calories you need each day. You will then be presented with a menu from which you may select the items you wish to eat for breakfast. When you have made your selections, type FINISHED, and the computer will show you a lunch menu, and then a dinner menu. The computer will then list all the foods that you have selected for the day as well as your total Calorie intake. If you wish to repeat the program, retype RUN.

Programming Notes

The computer reads each line of the program and executes the command listed there. Line 20 clears the screen. Some computers use the command CLS, others use HOME. Use the command your computer recognizes to clear the screen.

The amount of data that can be used for each variable is set in line 10. Lines 40 and 50 contain the introduction. Line 60 states the number of Calories required per day at 2400, asks the user to enter name and sex, and increases the Calorie allotment to 2900 if the user is male. Data are read in line 90. Lines 120 and 130 print a list of foods. Lines 170 and 180 record the foods eaten and list them on the screen. The total Calorie intake is printed in line 190. Lines 200 through 300 contain data pertaining to the food.

Challenge: On Your Own

Changes in the menu can be made by modifying the data lines. Be sure to follow the format DATA FOOD, SIZE OF SERVING, CALORIES. The total number of selections is limited to 120, but this number can be increased by modifying line 10. If you enjoy programming, you may wish to modify the program to compute the amount of protein, vitamins, minerals, or fats as well as Calories.

Program

```
10   DIM F$(120): DIM A$(120): DIM
     C(120): DIM M$(120): DIM M(1
     20): DIM G(120)
20   HOME : IF Q = 1 THEN 120: REM
     MAY BE DIFFERENT ON YOUR CO
     MPUTER
30   IF Q = 2 THEN 180
40   PRINT "THIS PROGRAM WILL COU
     NT CALORIES": PRINT "AND COM
     PARE THESE TO AN AVERAGE": PRINT
     "CALORIE USE BY BOTH MALES A
     ND FEMALES"
50   PRINT "BETWEEN THE AGES OF 1
     2-15.": PRINT : PRINT "MALES
     NEED APPROXIMATELY 2900 CAL
     ORIES,": PRINT "FEMALES NEED
     ABOUT 2400 CALORIES PER DAY
     "
60   N = 2400: PRINT : PRINT "WHAT
     IS YOUR NAME ";: INPUT N$: PRINT
     "MALE <M> OR FEMALE <F>";: INPUT
     S$: IF S$ = "M" THEN N = N +
     500
70   PRINT : PRINT "ENTER WHEN RE
     ADY FOR BREAKFAST MENU": INPUT
     Q$
80   Y = I + 1
90   I = I + 1: READ F$(I),A$(I),C
     (I): IF F$(I) = "END" OR F$(
     I) = "FINISHED" THEN 110
100  GOTO 90
110  Z = Y + ( INT ((I - Y) / 2))
     :Q = 1: GOTO 20
120  PRINT A$(I);" <PICK FOOD B
     Y NUMBER>":B = 0:D = 0: FOR
     X = Y TO Z
130  PRINT X;" ";F$(X); TAB( 22)
     ;X + 1 + (Z - Y);" ";F$(X +
     1 + (Z - Y)): NEXT X: INPUT
     B: IF F$(B) = "END" THEN 80
140  IF F$(B) = "FINISHED" THEN
     Q = 2: GOTO 20
150  IF B > 2 * Z OR B < Y THEN
     110
160  PRINT "MENU AMOUNT IS ";A$(
     B);" UNITS": PRINT "HOW MUCH
     FOR YOU ";: INPUT D:T = T +
     (D * C(B))
170  U = U + 1:M$(U) = F$(B):M(U)
     = C(B):G(U) = D: GOTO 110
180  FOR X = 1 TO U - 1: PRINT M
     $(X);"=";M(X);"*";G(X);"=";M
     (X) * G(X): NEXT X
190  PRINT "TOTAL CALORIES FOR "
     ;N$;" IS ";T: PRINT "COMPARE
     AVERAGE CALORIE NEED OF ";N
200  DATA  MILK, 1 GLASS,150,SKI
     M MILK,1 GLASS,85,EGG (ANY),
     ONE,90,SLICE BREAD BUTTER,ON
     E,100,BANANA,ONE,100,GRAPEFR
     UIT,ONE HALF,45,BACON,2 STRI
     PS,85
210  DATA  FRUIT JUICE,1 SMALL
     GLASS,80,CEREAL & MILK,1 BOW
     L,240,BUTTERED BAGEL,ONE,195
     ,COFFEE CAKE,1 PIECE,230,FAN
     CY DOUGHNUT,ONE,175
220  DATA  END,BREAKFAST FOODS,9
     99
230  DATA  COTTAGE CHEESE,MEDIU
     M SERVING,220,SLICE OF CHEES
     E,ONE,80,MILK,1 GLASS,150,SK
     IM MILK,1 GLASS,85,ICE CREAM
     ,ONE KIND,270,SLICE BREAD,ON
     E,70,BEEF PATTY,ONE,185
240  DATA  BOLOGNA,ONE SLICE,85,
     HOT DOG & ROLL,ONE,290,TUNA
     SALAD,ONE SERVING,200,HAM SL
     ICES,SANDWICH FILLING,245,GR
     EEN VEGETABLES,ONE SERVING,50
250  DATA  CHICKEN BREAST,ONE,24
     0,SOUP,1 BOWL,150,PIE,ONE PI
     ECE,300,COLA,1 CAN,140,APPLE
     ,ONE MEDIUM,80
260  DATA  END,LUNCH FOODS,999
270  DATA  STEAK,ONE SMALL,330,P
     ORK CHOP,ONE SMALL,330,CHICK
     EN,HALF BROILER,240,HOT DOG
     & ROLL,ONE,290,FISH BROILED,
     ONE SMALL,135,FISH SANDWICH,
     ONE ON A ROLL,150
280  DATA  BEEF STEW,1 BOWL,220,
     CHICKEN A LA KING,1 BOWL,470
     ,RICE,1 MEDIUM SERVING,180,P
     OTATO BAKED,ONE MEDIUM,145,G
     REEN VEGETABLES,1 MEDIUM SER
     VING,50,NOODLES,1 MEDIUM SER
     VING,200
290  DATA  SPAGHETTI,1 SMALL SE
     RVING,330,COOKIES,FOUR,205,P
     IE,ONE PIECE,300,MILK,1 GLAS
     S,150,SKIM MILK,1 GLASS,85,I
     CE CREAM,1 MEDIUM SERVING,27
     0
300  DATA  FINISHED,DINNER FOODS
     ,999
```

HEREDITY AND
EVOLUTION

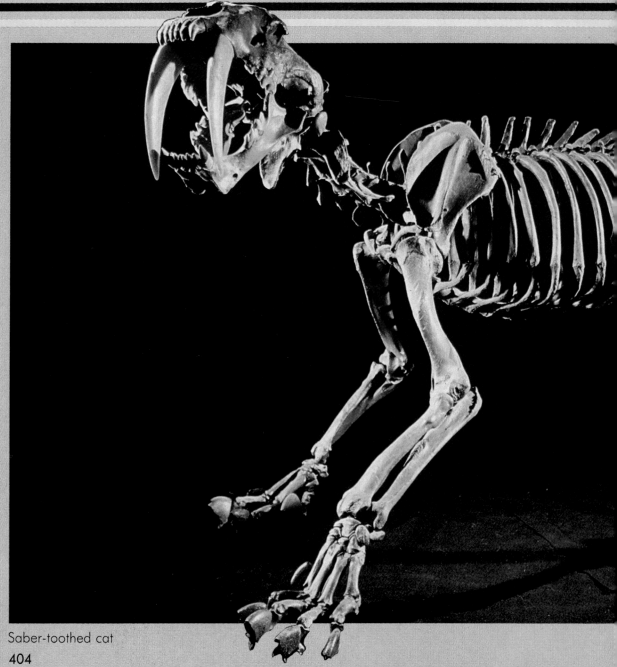

Saber-toothed cat

UNIT 6

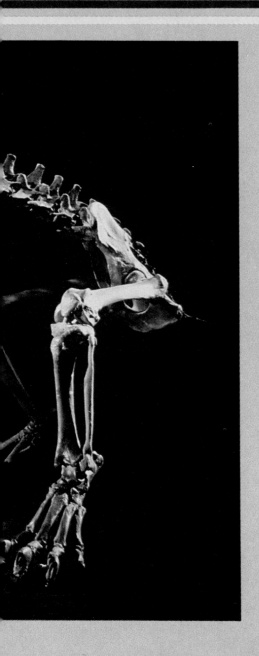

Discoveries of fossil organisms that no longer exist provide us with evidence for evolution. Throughout time, there have been continued evolutionary changes in plants and animals. Small cats that had large upper canines for stabbing prey evolved 40 million years ago. By 10 million years ago, the saber-toothed cat had evolved large, heavy bones. Bones found in archaeological sites are removed carefully and preserved for later study. How can organisms change? How did humans evolve?

Archaeological site

405

Human beings reproduce by sexual reproduction. The development of male and female reproductive organs is controlled by hormones. Primary and secondary sexual characteristics are also controlled by these hormones. These hormones are produced by the pituitary gland located at the base of the brain. How do male hormones affect sperm production? What role do female hormones play in the menstrual cycle? How does fertilization occur?

CHAPTER 19
HUMAN
REPRODUCTION

19:1 Reproductive Organs

Human beings reproduce by sexual reproduction. One offspring is usually born at a time. However, twins are sometimes produced. Multiple births of more than two children can also occur.

Hormones control the development of male and female reproductive organs. Regular changes in the hormones prepare the female's body for fertilization and pregnancy. The time when a human being is first able to reproduce is called puberty. At puberty, hormones are produced that control the development of the reproductive organs, which then become functional. The pituitary gland at the base of the brain releases hormones that stimulate the production of male and female sex hormones by the reproductive organs.

Human reproduction is based on the production of male and female sex cells. Male sex cells, called sperm, are produced in the testes (TES teez) of males. The **testes** are two oval-shaped male sex glands. They each contain over 200 meters of threadlike tubes. The testes are enclosed in an external sac located behind the penis (PEE nus). The sac is called the scrotum (SKROH tum).

The testes produce a male sex hormone that controls the production of sperm. Sperm produced in the tubes of the testes pass into another coiled tube where they mature. As sperm are released

GOALS:
1. You will learn the organs of the male and female reproductive systems and the function of each organ.
2. You will learn the main processes in human reproduction.
3. You will learn the stages in the human life cycle.

What are the male reproductive organs?

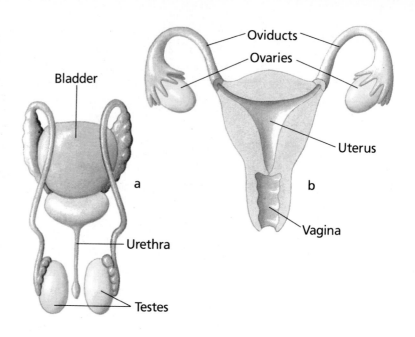

FIGURE 19–1. Organs of the male (a) and female (b) reproductive systems.

What are the female reproductive organs?

from the body, they pass through a series of glands. These glands secrete fluids that mix with the sperm and help the sperm to "swim." The mixture of sperm and fluids is called semen (SEE mun). Semen is carried in a tube to the penis where it passes out of the body through the urethra. The urethra is also the passage for urine.

Sperm are formed continuously in the testes. The life of a sperm within the testes may be up to three months. Some may be released and some are absorbed into the body. There are hundreds of millions of sperm in each release of semen from the body. The life of the sperm outside the male body is short because of low temperatures.

Female sex cells, called eggs, are produced by two ovaries. The **ovaries** are reproductive organs located in the abdominal cavity of the female. One at a time, each ovary releases an egg into a tube called an oviduct. The two oviducts are sometimes called fallopian tubes. The oviducts connect to the uterus. The **uterus** is a hollow, sac-shaped organ that narrows to a small opening that leads to the vagina. The vagina is a canal that opens to the outside of the body. It is a separate passage from that through which urine is passed.

19:2 Menstrual Cycle

A mature human female goes through a reproductive cycle that averages 28 days but this can vary from 20 to 40 days. This cycle is called the **menstrual** (MEN strul) **cycle.** The menstrual cycle is controlled by the release of hormones from the pituitary and from the ovaries.

During a menstrual cycle, an egg develops fully inside the ovary. At this time, the walls of the uterus thicken and the blood supply to the uterus increases. Then **ovulation** (ahv yuh LAY shun), release of the egg from the ovary, occurs. Ovulation usually occurs 14 days before the onset of menstruation.

An egg is alive for about 24 to 48 hours after it is released from the ovary. During this time it travels along the oviduct. It is at this time in the menstrual cycle that a female can become pregnant. If live sperm are present in the oviduct at the time of ovulation or within 48 hours of ovulation, the egg is usually fertilized. It takes only one sperm to fertilize an egg. The resulting zygote continues along the oviduct to the uterus. The zygote moves into and attaches to the wall of the uterus, which is prepared for its arrival. The menstrual cycle ceases for the duration of the pregnancy that follows.

If the egg is not fertilized by a sperm, the menstrual cycle continues. Almost 14 days after ovulation, there is a breakdown of the soft tissues lining the uterus. Then menstruation (men STRAY shun) occurs. **Menstruation** is a discharge of blood and tissues from the uterus. The material leaves the body through the vagina. Menstruation usually lasts four or five days. After menstruation ends, another egg begins to develop in an ovary, and the menstrual cycle is repeated. All the changes involved in the menstrual cycle are controlled by the sex hormones.

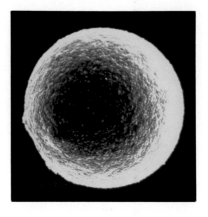

FIGURE 19–2. An egg is many times larger than a sperm. Only one sperm penetrates one egg.

How does fertilization occur in humans?

FIGURE 19–3. The menstrual cycle averages 28 days in human females and involves the preparation of the uterus for ovulation and pregnancy. If fertilization does not occur, menstruation follows and the cycle continues.

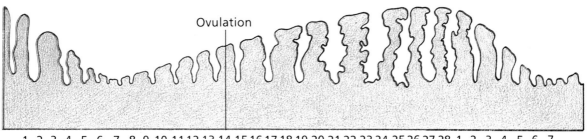

Ovulation

1 2 3 4 5 6 7 8 9 10 11 12 13 14 15 16 17 18 19 20 21 22 23 24 25 26 27 28 1 2 3 4 5 6 7

Menstruation

Build-up of lining of uterus

Menstruation

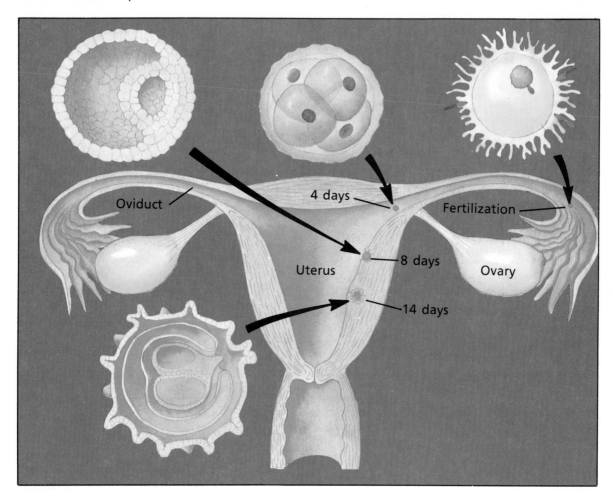

FIGURE 19–4. Stages in the development of a human from fertilization to birth.

Human females begin to menstruate at about age thirteen or fourteen. However, menstruation may begin from as early as age nine to as late as age twenty-one. A female menstruates until she reaches menopause, usually between ages 45 and 55. **Menopause** is the time in a female's life when ovulation ceases. The female loses the ability to reproduce.

19:3 Fertilization

Internal fertilization occurs in humans as in all other mammals. Sperm deposited in the vagina swim into the uterus and on to the oviducts. An egg may be in an oviduct if ovulation has occurred recently. Even though millions of sperm are deposited, only a few hundred sperm ever reach the oviducts, and only one sperm fertilizes an egg. Fertilization of the human egg usually occurs

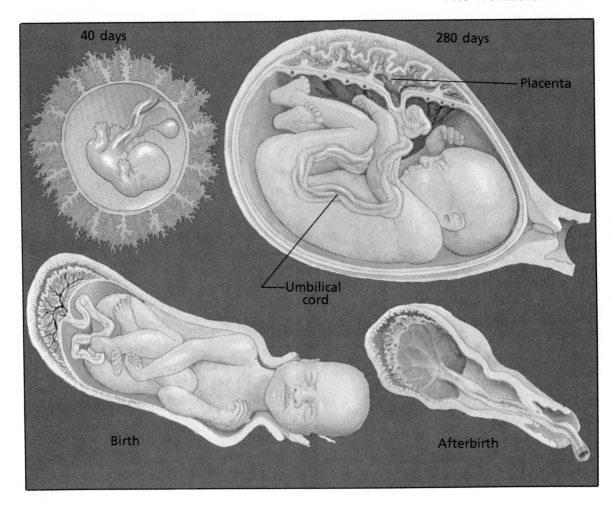

in an oviduct. The fertilized egg moves through the oviduct to the uterus.

Remember that an egg lives for only 24 to 48 hours after ovulation. If sperm are deposited in the vagina during this time, fertilization is likely to occur and the female will become pregnant. Sperm may survive in the female's reproductive system for up to five days. Therefore, fertilization still may occur if sperm are deposited in the vagina up to five days before ovulation. The moment of fertilization is called **conception** (kun SEP shun).

When a sperm fertilizes an egg, a zygote is produced. The zygote becomes attached to the wall of the uterus which becomes thickened and protective. The zygote divides by mitosis to form an embryo that is surrounded by small, finger-like structures called villi. Nutrients from the uterus wall are carried to the embryo through these villi. The embryo develops three layers of cells.

Describe the growth of a human embryo from conception.

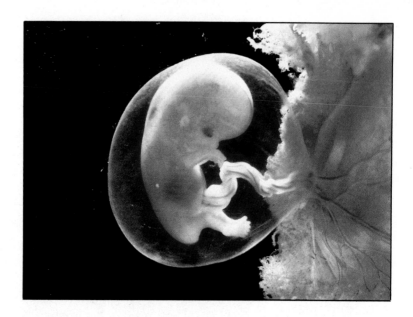

FIGURE 19–5. A placenta supplies food and oxygen to the human embryo from the mother's blood.

Define placenta.

From these cells different tissues are formed, such as bone, nerve, digestive system, and blood tissues.

As the embryo grows, a tissue develops from the villi within the wall of the uterus. This forms the placenta. The placenta has a rich blood supply and is connected to the embryo by a ropelike tube called the umbilical cord. The placenta brings two separate blood supplies close together. One blood supply circulates through the mother. The other circulates through the embryo. Food and oxygen diffuse from the mother's blood into the placenta. They are carried to the embryo through blood vessels in the umbilical cord. Blood vessels in the umbilical cord transport carbon dioxide and other wastes from the embryo to the placenta. The wastes diffuse out of the placenta and into the mother's blood of the uterus. In this way, materials are exchanged between mother and child without the mixing of blood.

The embryo begins to exhibit the characteristics of a human baby by the ninth week. It is now called a fetus. The fetus is fully developed by this time. It has a head, brain, fingers, and toes. Facial features have begun to appear. From then on it grows and matures. The excretory system and skin develop. At four months the fetus begins to move its arms and legs. At six months it can respond to sounds. Full development of the new baby takes about 266 days from conception, which is about nine calendar months. As the fetus grows, it causes the uterus to expand in size. Table 19–1 summarizes the development of a human embryo from the zygote to the fetal stage.

In humans, usually only one embryo develops during pregnancy to form a new baby. However, twins and other multiple births do occur. Human twins may occur in two ways. One way is for a zygote to divide during early development. Each part of the zygote grows to form a fetus. Twins from the same zygote are always the same sex and have similar physical features. They are called identical twins.

Twins may also be produced if two eggs are released and fertilized at the same time. The two fertilized eggs grow and develop into two fetuses. Twins from two zygotes are called fraternal twins. Fraternal twins do not have to be the same sex, and they do not have to look alike. Fraternal twins are generally no more alike than any other two children born of the same parents.

Making Sure

1. Describe the changes that occur in the menstrual cycle.
2. Compare the production of sperm in males and eggs in females.
3. When can a human female become pregnant?
4. How does an embryo first get nutrients?

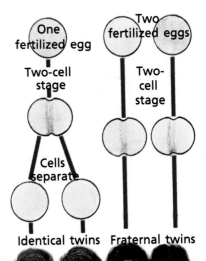

FIGURE 19–6. Identical twins come from a single fertilized egg. Fraternal twins come from two fertilized eggs.

Table 19-1

Development of a Human Embryo	
Week	**Development**
1	Zygote becomes embedded in uterus wall.
2	Cells of zygote divide.
3	Spine and nervous system begin to form.
4	Brain and spinal cord formed. Heart and blood vessels in embryo and umbilical cord develop.
5	Arms and legs formed. Heartbeat and circulation begin.
6	All the major organs are now formed. Face develops with ears, eyes, nose, and mouth.
7	Fingers and toes begin to form. Spinal movements occur.
8	Major organs continue to develop.
9	Reproductive organs now formed. Embryo now identified as a fetus. Majority of organs begin to function.
10	Muscles develop.
11	Placenta now rapidly develops.
In the remaining weeks of pregnancy, the fetus grows to a size and maturity necessary for independent survival.	

Activity 19–1   Growth of the Human Fetus

Problem: When do the major increases in length and mass occur in the fetus?

Materials

graph paper
pencil

Procedure

1. Construct a graph similar to Figure 19–7a. Put time in weeks on the horizontal axis and length in millimeters on the vertical axis.
2. On the graph, plot the data shown in the first two columns of the table. Several of the first points have been plotted for you.
3. Construct a second graph similar to Figure 19–7b. Put time in weeks on the horizontal axis and mass in grams on the vertical axis.
4. On the graph, plot the data shown in the first and third columns of the table. Several of the first points have been plotted for you.

Data and Observations

Change in Size of Average Developing Fetus		
Time (weeks)	Length (mm)	Mass (g)
4	7	0.5
8	14	1
12	75	15
16	160	100
20	240	300
24	300	650
28	350	1100
32	410	1700
36	460	2400
40	500	3300

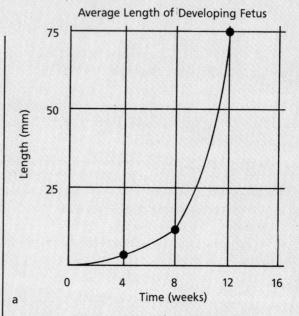

a

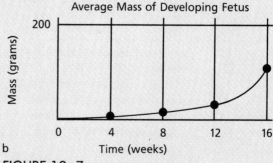

b

FIGURE 19–7.

Questions and Conclusions

1. How long is the average fetus at 38 weeks?
2. What is the average mass of the fetus at 38 weeks?
3. The halfway point in development is about 20 weeks. Is the average fetus about half of its full length at 20 weeks?
4. At what week does the fetus reach half its total mass?
5. When do the major increases in length and mass occur in the fetus?

FIGURE 19–8. Many parents choose to have their babies in a birth center where a homelike atmosphere is created.

19:4 Childbirth

A baby is normally born about 40 weeks from the first day of the mother's last menstrual period. Childbirth begins with labor. Labor is involuntary contractions of the pregnant woman's uterus. During the first part of labor, the protective sac around the fetus breaks open. The fluid inside is released. The fetus is gradually pushed down to a position ready for birth. The contractions of labor move the fetus down and out of the uterus through the vagina. Normally, a baby is delivered headfirst.

After birth, the umbilical cord connecting the placenta to the newborn is tied or clamped to prevent bleeding, and then cut. The stump of the cord attached to the baby eventually shrivels and falls off. It leaves a depressed scar called the navel. Soon after birth of the baby, contractions of the uterus continue forcing the placenta out of the mother. While a baby is inside the uterus, it is surrounded by fluid within the sac. The baby's lungs are not inflated with air. Immediately after birth the lungs expand and the baby takes its first breath of air.

Sometimes a baby cannot be born through the vagina. The baby may then need to be delivered by Caesarean section. In this operation, an incision is made in the mother's abdominal wall and uterus. Then the baby can be lifted out.

During childbirth, a physician may give the mother anesthetics, which are drugs that relieve labor pains. A local anesthetic affects only the mother who remains conscious throughout. A general anesthetic enters the circulation of both mother and baby. With this kind of anesthetic, the mother is unconscious during the birth, and the baby may be born sleepy and have slow respiration. Some research indicates that fear of the birthing process can create tension that increases a mother's pain. In natural childbirth, the mother learns to deliver her baby without interfering with the

How is a baby born?

What is natural childbirth?

natural birth process. The mother learns ways to relax during labor and let the uterus do its natural work of contracting.

Childbirth education classes are provided by many hospitals and health groups. Details of pregnancy and labor are explained so that the mother and father know what to expect. Breathing exercises and relaxation techniques learned in the classes may reduce the time spent in labor. The goal of most childbirth education classes is to promote safe births and help mothers and fathers experience the joy of birth.

It is important for a woman to visit her physician regularly as soon as she realizes she is pregnant. If the woman has any health problems, they can be dealt with to protect the health of the fetus. Good nutrition is important during pregnancy because the mother supplies the nutrients for the developing offspring. Poor nutrition may slow the growth of the fetus, causing an underweight baby to be born. The mother's diet must contain enough calcium and phosphorus for the development of a healthy fetal skeleton. If a diet lacks enough protein, the brain and nervous system of the fetus may not grow properly. This can cause mental retardation in the newborn.

Drugs taken by a pregnant female can have a harmful effect on the fetus. For example, heroin can cause death of the fetus or result in a premature birth and addiction of the fetus. Drinking alcohol during pregnancy can cause the newborn to be mentally or physically retarded. Mothers who smoke usually deliver babies with lower than average birth weights. Proper prenatal care requires that a pregnant female not smoke or drink alcohol during pregnancy. Drugs should be taken during pregnancy only when they are prescribed by a physician for medical reasons.

What might be the result of poor nutrition during pregnancy?

How does smoking by a pregnant woman affect the fetus?

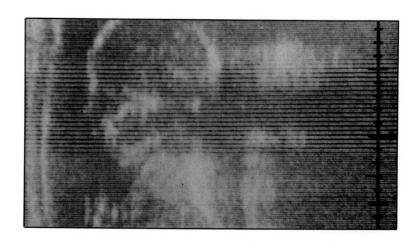

FIGURE 19–9. Ultrasound produces a picture of a 24-week-old fetus that helps to determine its position and structure.

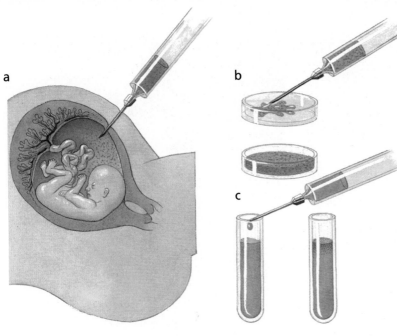

FIGURE 19–10. In amniocentesis, a sample of the fluid around the fetus in the uterus is removed (a). Cells floating in the fluid are cultured (b). They are studied for signs of inherited disease. The cell-free portion of the fluid is analyzed for other defects (c).

Ultrasound (UL truh sound) can be used to check on a fetus. The ultrasound machine has a quartz crystal that is placed on the pregnant female's abdomen. The crystal beams high frequency sound waves to the fetus. A picture of the fetus based on the sound wave pattern is produced by the machine. Ultrasound indicates whether the fetus is alive and gives the exact position of the fetus in the uterus. It also can serve to identify disorders such as fluid on the brain and tumors in the uterus.

Certain inherited defects in a fetus may be detected by amniocentesis (am nee oh sen TEE sus). In this procedure, a sample of the fluid around the fetus that is inside the uterus is removed. The fluid can be analyzed for the presence of certain chemicals that indicate inherited disease. The fluid contains cells from the fetus, and these cells can be studied to detect genetic defects and other diseases. The age and sex of the fetus can also be detected using the process of amniocentesis.

Making Sure

5. What is labor in childbirth?
6. Name two different methods of childbirth.
7. How does a mother's nutrition and use of drugs affect the health of a fetus?
8. Why are calcium and phosphorus important for the development of a healthy baby?
9. Explain the use of ultrasound and amniocentesis during pregnancy.

a

b

FIGURE 19–11. The stages of a human life cycle are infancy (a), childhood (b), adolescence (c), and adulthood (d).

What are the stages in the human life cycle?

19:5 Human Life Cycle

During a lifetime, a person progresses through stages. A new-born baby grows through infancy, childhood, adolescence, and adulthood followed by old age and eventually death. Unlike many other animals, a newborn human baby cannot survive without help. It must be fed and cared for. Compared to other animals, the rate of development of an infant is slow. For example, many animals can stand and run within minutes of being born. A child does not begin to walk until about 12 months of age.

The greatest increase in growth in a person's lifetime occurs during infancy. For example, a baby's brain more than doubles in mass the first year after birth. Teeth begin to show between 5.5 and 10 months. About 27 months after birth, the full set of first teeth have appeared. Speech begins to develop at about one year of age. Development of muscle coordination proceeds throughout infancy. At about five months, a baby will deliberately grab objects such as a rattle. At eight months, a baby can sit unsupported. At 10 months, the infant is strong enough to pull itself into a standing position.

Infancy is followed by childhood. A child's first teeth begin to be replaced by permanent teeth when the child is about six years old. The child's mental abilities continue to develop. For example, the child learns to read and compute with numbers. Muscle control, strength, and athletic ability increase.

c

d

At an age between 9 and 17 years, the child enters puberty.
Puberty is the start of sexual maturity and the ability to reproduce.
Puberty occurs during **adolescence** (ad uh LES uns), the stage
that follows childhood. Puberty is brought about by an increased
output of hormones from the pituitary gland. These hormones
stimulate the reproductive organs to produce sex hormones. The
sex hormones affect the development of secondary sex characteristics. In males, these include increases in height, weight,
musculature, and body hair growth. Also, the larynx and vocal
chords enlarge causing a deepening of the male voice. In females,
the menstrual cycles begin and the breasts develop. In females
there is also an increase in body hair growth and fat deposits on
legs and hips. In both males and females, the sweat and oil glands
in the skin become more active. This often results in facial skin
eruptions called acne.

A person becomes an adult when the body is full-grown. There
are few changes at this stage. The adult stage is marked by maturity
(muh TOOHR ih tee). **Maturity** is full development of body and
mind. The adult years may be marked by reproduction and the
gradual degeneration of tissues and organs. In women, the ability
to reproduce is lost at menopause. The ovaries become smaller
and no longer produce eggs. In men, production of sperm may
continue throughout their lives.

What is puberty?

FIGURE 19–12. Environment is as important as heredity in the development of many human traits.

19:6 Effects of Environment

Different people have different traits. Why do some people have freckles? Why do some people have curly hair? How is it that some people are tall and others are short? Many human traits are controlled by factors inherited from parents. For example, skin color, height, and body build are inherited.

Traits can also be affected by the environment. For example, people with freckles may have more freckles in the summer. The skin of some people becomes darker in summer. Sunlight causes the skin to produce a pigment that makes it darker.

Describe three effects of environment on human traits.

Environmental factors that affect inherited traits include diet, pollution, radiation, microbes, chemicals, education, and other people. The food a person eats is part of a person's environment. Research shows that over the last few generations Americans have become taller. The principal cause of the increase in height is believed to be a better, more balanced diet.

Often, bright parents tend to have bright children. This could be the result of inheritance. However, environment could also be a factor. Bright parents may have a better education and may be enthusiastic about learning. They may take a strong interest in school, books, travel, family discussions, projects, and current events. Thus, the children are in an environment where learning is encouraged and desired. Both inherited traits and environment probably have an effect on intelligence.

Making Sure

10. What changes occur at puberty?
11. Compare the changes that occur in infancy with those that occur in adolescence.
12. How can environment affect the intelligence of children?

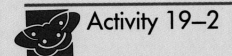

Activity 19–2

Average Normal Growth in Humans

Problem: Is average normal growth the same in males and females?

Materials

graph paper
red pencil
blue pencil

Procedure

1. Construct a graph similar to Figure 19–13a. Plot mass in kilograms on the vertical axis and age in years on the horizontal axis.
2. On the graph, plot the data given for the average female growth in mass from ages 7 to 18 in red. Connect the points with a red line.
3. On the same graph, plot the data given for the average male growth in mass from ages 7 to 18 in blue. Connect the points with a blue line.
4. On a separate graph similar to Figure 19–13b, plot height in centimeters on the vertical axis and age in years on the horizontal axis.
5. On this second graph, plot the data given for the average female growth in height from ages 7 to 18 in red. Connect the points with a red line.

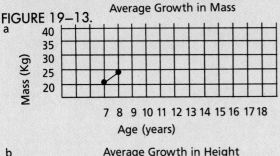

FIGURE 19–13.
Average Growth in Mass

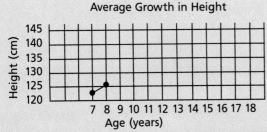

Average Growth in Height

6. On this same graph, plot the data given for the average male growth in height from ages 7 to 18 in blue. Connect the points with a blue line.

Data and Observations

Averages for Normal Growth in Humans				
Age	Male		Female	
	height	mass	height	mass
	(cm)	(kg)	(cm)	(kg)
7	122	21	121	21
8	124	25	123	25
9	130	28	129	28
10	135	31	135	31
11	140	37	141	35
12	145	38	147	40
13	152	43	155	47
14	161	50	159	50
15	167	57	162	54
16	172	62	163	57
17	174	65	163	58
18	178	68	163	58

Questions and Conclusions

1. Up to what age is average normal growth in mass similar in males and females?
2. Up to what age is average normal growth in height similar in males and females?
3. Based on your graph, during what ages do females increase the most in height?
4. Based on your graph, during what ages do males increase the most in height?
5. Based on your graph of average growth in mass, when does the mass of females change the most?
6. How can you explain the differences in growth between males and females?
7. Is average normal growth the same in males and females? Explain your answer.

FOCUS ON
People and Careers

Genetic Specialists

Genetic diseases such as color blindness, cystic fibrosis, sickle-cell anemia, and hemophilia are inherited from parents and grandparents. A geneticist studies inheritance and variation of traits in individuals. Dr. Adolfo D. Garnica is a clinical geneticist who diagnoses and treats genetic disorders in children. As a professor at a university medical school, he teaches students about the importance of genetics. As a physician, he provides help for children with genetic diseases and for their parents.

After completing his medical degree, Dr. Garnica furthered his education for three years as a pediatric resident. Pediatrics is a branch of medicine that deals with children. He then earned certification in pediatrics and clinical genetics.

Dr. Garnica sees patients and their families at his office, makes hospital rounds, and does laboratory research. He also has administrative tasks at the school, and teaches medical students, residents, and technicians. Dr. Garnica recommends the field of genetics to medical students who have not yet chosen a field of specialization. "It is a chance to do a much-needed service," he says.

Dr. Garnica's attitude about clinical genetics is shared by Mary Ann Coffman, a genetic counselor. Her job includes teaching families about potential genetic problems, or counseling parents who have a child with a genetic disease. She also helps coordinate the work of physicians with other medical or social services that the family may need.

Ms. Coffman's office is in a university medical school. To prepare patients to see a physician, she asks questions and writes a family medical history. This information is then given to the physician who consults with the family. After the consultation, Ms. Coffman answers any other questions the family may have.

Ms. Coffman also does library research on rare genetic diseases and helps write case studies. Case studies are in-depth reports of individuals with certain genetic problems. Case studies help reveal how and why genetic problems occur. Another of her tasks is to update computer files on people who have received genetic services.

In addition to family counseling, Ms. Coffman aids nurses in the screening of new patients. She also gives public lectures about clinical genetics and takes part in other informative projects. One project is a service that detects carriers of hemophilia.

Ms. Coffman has a bachelor's degree in bacteriology and public health and a master's degree in biochemistry and genetic counseling. Other counselors may have backgrounds in nursing or social work, but all must have a national board certification.

CHAPTER 19
Review

Summary

1. Hormones control the growth and development of the reproductive organs in males and females.   19:1
2. A mature human female goes through menstrual cycles that average 28 days.   19:2
3. The menstrual cycle is controlled by the sex hormones from the pituitary and from the ovaries.   19:2
4. Human embryos develop inside a female in the uterus.   19:3
5. A placenta allows material exchange between mother and embryo without the mixing of blood.   19:3
6. Fertilization of a female egg usually occurs in an oviduct and development of the fetus takes place in the uterus.   19:3
7. During childbirth, contractions of the uterus and abdomen cause the baby to be born.   19:4
8. During a lifetime, a person passes through stages of infancy, childhood, adolescence, adulthood, and old age.   19:5
9. At puberty, sex hormones begin to produce the secondary sex characteristics developed during adolescence.   19:5
10. Environment and inheritance affect the traits of organisms.   19:6

Vocabulary

Write a sentence using the following words or terms correctly.

adolescence	menstrual cycle	puberty
conception	menstruation	testes
maturity	ovary	uterus
menopause	ovulation	

Questions

Do not write in this book.

A. True or False
Determine whether each of the following sentences is true or false. Rewrite the false statements to make them correct.

1. Adolescence is a stage that comes after childhood.
2. The menstrual cycle in the human female is about 28 days.
3. Ovulation in the human female occurs during menstruation.
4. Twins can only be produced when a zygote divides into two parts.
5. Eggs are produced in the oviducts.

6. A fetus develops in a uterus.
7. Female sex hormones control the menstrual cycle.
8. Internal fertilization occurs in humans.
9. Ultrasound is the removal of a sample of fluid around a fetus.
10. The zygote is supplied by a placenta.

B. Multiple Choice

Choose the word or phrase that correctly completes the following sentences.
1. *(Ovulation, Menstruation, Fertilization)* is the release of an egg from an ovary.
2. Fertilization occurs when *(one, some, many)* sperm enter(s) an egg.
3. Sperm are produced in the *(oviducts, uterus, testes, vagina)* of a male human.
4. Semen contains *(eggs, sperm, both eggs and sperm)*.
5. An egg can live up to *(48, 72, 80)* hours after ovulation.
6. The *(navel, fallopian tube, oviduct, umbilical cord)* connects the embryo to the placenta.
7. In humans, *(one, two, several)* embryo(s) normally develop(s) during pregnancy.
8. An embryo develops *(two, three, four)* layers of cells that later form bone, nerve, skin, and blood tissues.
9. Secondary sex characteristics are controlled by *(menstruation, hormones, environmental factors)*.
10. An infant gets its full set of first teeth at about *(birth, two months, 27 months)*.

C. Completion

Complete each of the following sentences with the correct word or phrase.
1. Growth rate of the human body is greatest during the life stage called _____.
2. The height and weight of a person is determined by inheritance and _____.
3. _____ refers to the onset of sexual maturity and the ability to reproduce.
4. _____ twins are always the same sex.
5. The location of a fetus in the uterus may be determined with _____.
6. The sex of a fetus can be determined through _____.
7. After birth, the _____ is cut.
8. The greatest increase in growth in a person's lifetime occurs during _____.
9. A human female usually ovulates _____ days before her menstruation.
10. A mixture of sperm and fluids is called _____.

D. How and Why

1. How might environment cause many people to be taller today than people 100 years ago?
2. List the human life stages and describe the main characteristics of each.
3. How do inherited traits and environment play a part in the development of a champion tennis player?
4. What should a pregnant woman do to increase the chance of giving birth to a healthy baby?
5. What is childbirth education and where can it be obtained?
6. How does the pituitary affect puberty?

Ideas to Explore

1. **Project:** Arrange to interview your school nurse on the subject of prenatal care. Survey your class to find out the questions they have about the topic. Use the questions in your interview and report back to the class.
2. **Challenge:** Do research on growth and development of a human embryo and fetus. Prepare a poster with drawings that show the different stages of development.
3. **Challenge:** Research *in vitro* fertilization. Report on the procedure, why the technique is used, and how successful it is.
4. **Challenge:** Report on the effects of alcohol, caffeine, and smoking during pregnancy.

Readings

Arnold, Caroline. *Sex Hormones*. New York: William Morrow, 1981.

Hall, Stephen S. "The Fate of the Egg." *Science 85*. November 1985, pp. 40–49.

Hotchner, Tracy. *Pregnancy and Childbirth*. New York: Avon, 1984.

Koebner, Linda. "Surrogate Human." *Science 82*. July/August, 1982, pp. 32–39.

Miller, Jonathan and David Pelham. *The Facts of Life*. New York: Viking, 1984.

Simon, Nissa. *Don't Worry, You're Normal*. New York: T. Y. Crowell, 1982.

The offspring of organisms are reproductions or copies of their parents. Differences between newborns and their parents are mainly due to different stages of development. Adult male Jackson's chameleons of Africa have three bony horns on their heads. In the young male, these horns have not yet developed. How do you know that the adult and the newborn in the photo are the same species? Chameleons can change color with changes in emotions. How do they inherit this particular characteristic?

426

CHAPTER 20
HEREDITY

20:1 Heredity

Why do some people look like their parents or grandparents? How is it possible for a brown dog to have two black dogs for parents? Why is each species of plant and animal different from every other species? These questions can be answered by a study of heredity (huh RED ut tee).

Heredity is the passing of traits from parents to offspring. A trait is a property or characteristic of an organism. Blue eyes and black hair are examples of traits. The basic laws of heredity were first discovered by an Austrian monk, Gregor Mendel (1822–1884). For eight years Mendel used scientific methods in his experiments with pea plants. Peas were a good choice because they usually self-pollinate. Pollen from the stamens of a pea flower lands on the stigma of the same flower. Also, peas have several observable traits that can differ. Mendel studied pairs of traits such as tallness or shortness, yellow seed or green seed, and smooth seed coat or wrinkled seed coat in pea plants.

Mendel was more successful in his studies of heredity than all the plant breeders before him for several reasons. First, he studied only a few traits at a time. He also worked with thousands of plants and kept complete records of their ancestry. The laws he discovered from experimenting with pea plants apply to all plants and animals.

GOALS:
1. You will learn basic principles of heredity.
2. You will learn how people inherit traits.
3. You will learn how genes control life activities.

What is heredity?

427

20:2 Mendel's Discoveries

In his study of heredity, Mendel crossed tall pea plants with short pea plants. Crossed means that pollen from one plant was transferred to the flower of another. This resulted in cross fertilization and seeds were produced. Mendel found that all of the resulting offspring were tall. No short pea plants were produced. The tall plants from the first cross produced offspring. Most of the offspring were tall plants, but some were short. Mendel experimented with other traits such as wrinkled or smooth seeds in pea plants and got similar results.

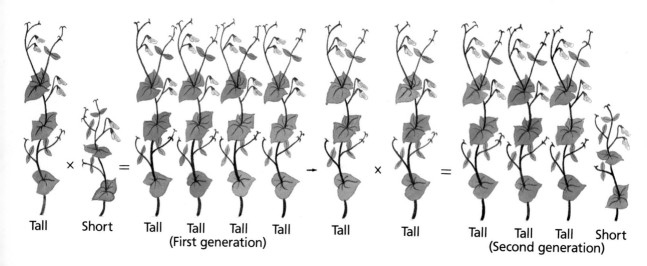

Tall   Short   Tall   Tall   Tall   Tall   Tall   Tall   Tall   Tall   Tall   Short
                        (First generation)   (Second generation)

FIGURE 20–1. A cross between a tall plant and a short plant produced all tall plants (a). A cross between two of these tall offspring (b) produced both short and tall pea plants (c).

How is a dominant trait different from a recessive trait?

Mendel's experiments showed that a trait can skip a generation. Shortness skipped the second generation of plants and appeared again in the third generation. Mendel assumed that an inherited trait may be present but not visible in a pea plant. The shortness trait must have been present in the second generation even though it was not visible.

Mendel concluded that the trait coming from one parent may hide the trait coming from the other. One trait was dominant over another. A **dominant** (DAHM uh nunt) **trait** is one that prevents another trait from appearing. A **recessive** (rih SES ihv) **trait** is one that does not appear when a dominant trait is present. Dominant traits prevent recessive traits from appearing. Recessive traits appear only when no dominant traits are present. For example, tallness is a dominant trait in pea plants. Shortness is a recessive trait. If the trait for tallness is present, the shortness trait will not appear.

Making Sure

1. Describe one example of heredity.
2. Mendel crossed yellow seed pea plants with green seed pea plants. He concluded that yellow seeds are dominant and green seeds are recessive. What kind of offspring must have been produced by the cross?

 ## Activity 20–1 Dominant and Recessive Traits

Problem: What is a dominant trait in plants?

Materials   10 specially selected corn seeds, soil, small milk carton, hand lens, water, jar

Procedure   (1) Examine the seeds with a hand lens to determine if there are differences in the 10 seeds. (2) Put the seeds in a jar with water and soak them overnight. (3) The next day, fill a milk carton two-thirds with soil. Moisten the soil with a little water. (4) Space the seeds evenly in a carton and cover them with 1 cm of soil. Place the carton containing the seeds in a warm, lighted area. (5) Check the seeds each day. Add more water if the soil feels dry. (6) Record the length of time it takes the seeds to sprout. Observe the young plants each day for two weeks and record your observations. (7) Compare your plants with those of your classmates. Record your observations in a combined class data table comparing the traits.

Questions   (1) What observed trait of the plants is dominant? (2) How does this trait relate to survival of the plants? (3) What is a recessive trait? (4) What observed trait of the plants is recessive? (5) When is a recessive trait harmful? (6) When is a recessive trait helpful? (7) What is a dominant trait in plants?

FIGURE 20–2.

20:3 Genes

A **gene** (JEEN) is the unit of inheritance that is passed from parents to offspring. For each trait, there are at least two genes that control its inheritance. Genes occur in pairs on chromosomes inside the nucleus of a cell. There are dominant genes for dominant traits and recessive genes for recessive traits. A dominant gene may mask a recessive gene when the genes are paired.

A new organism obtains its inheritance through its genes. One half the organism's genes come from the sex cell of one parent. The other half of its genes come from the sex cell of the other parent. In each gene pair, one gene is from the father and one gene is from the mother.

A **Punnett** (PUN ut) **square** is used to show the possible ways genes are combined when passed from parents to offspring. A dominant gene is shown with a capital letter. The recessive gene is shown with the lowercase of the same letter. Letters representing the parent's genes are placed on the outside edges of a Punnett square. Letters in the boxes of a Punnett square show the possible gene combinations for an offspring.

As an example, consider Mendel's cross between tall pea plants and short pea plants. Let T represent the gene for the tallness trait, which is dominant. Let t represent the gene for the shortness trait, which is recessive.

Pure traits are the result of all dominant or all recessive genes. Therefore, pure tall plants have genes TT. Pure short plants have genes tt. The Punnett square in Figure 20–4 shows the possible gene combinations in the offspring. A trait that is the result of a

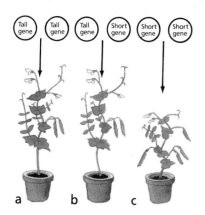

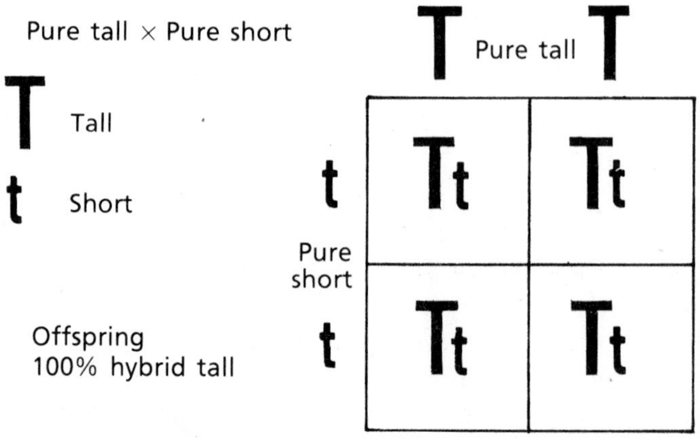

FIGURE 20–3. A pair of dominant genes produces a dominant trait (a). A dominant gene masks a recessive gene when the genes are paired (b). A pair of recessive genes produces a recessive trait (c).

FIGURE 20–4. The Punnett square shows the results of a cross between pure tall and pure short hybrid plants.

Pure tall × Pure short

T Tall
t Short

Offspring
100% hybrid tall

	T Pure tall	T
t	Tt	Tt
t (Pure short)	Tt	Tt

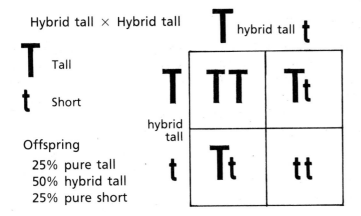

Hybrid tall × Hybrid tall

T   Tall

t   Short

Offspring
25% pure tall
50% hybrid tall
25% pure short

hybrid tall

	T	**t**
T	**TT**	**Tt**
t	**Tt**	**tt**

hybrid tall

FIGURE 20–5. The Punnett square shows the result of a cross between two hybrid plants.

combination of dominant and recessive genes is called a **hybrid** (HI brud) trait. Usually only the dominant trait is visible in a hybrid. The recessive trait is usually hidden. A recessive trait hidden in parents may be passed on to their offspring. All of the offspring in the cross above will be hybrid (Tt) because they receive one gene from each parent.

In Mendel's second experiment, he crossed the hybrid pea plants produced in the first cross. The offspring could receive a gene for tallness or a gene for shortness from either parent. The Punnett square in Figure 20–5 shows the outcome of that cross. In the second generation about three-fourths of the offspring were tall (TT or Tt). About one-fourth were short (tt).

Each box of a Punnett square shows a possible gene combination that an offspring might receive. In any one cross between the two parents, there is a one in four chance of the offspring receiving any of the four combinations of traits. One in four is twenty-five percent. The number of boxes with one or more capital letters shows the proportion of dominant traits expected to appear in the offspring. The number of boxes with only lowercase letters shows the proportion of recessive traits expected to appear in the offspring. One box out of four is 25 percent. Two out of four is 50 percent. Three out of four is 75 percent. Four out of four is 100 percent.

Percentages shown by a Punnett square hold true only when there are large numbers of offspring. To have three-fourths of all plants to be tall, thousands of offspring would be needed. With very small numbers of offspring, any proportion could occur because of the one in four chance of inheriting any of the four combinations. For example, parents may have five girls and no boys even though for each birth there is a 50 percent chance for a boy or girl.

What was the outcome of Mendel's cross between hybrid pea plants?

Making Sure

3. Use a Punnett square to show the gene combinations for the following crosses. Black is dominant in guinea pigs. White is recessive.
    a. Pure trait black guinea pigs and pure trait white guinea pigs
    b. pure trait black guinea pigs and hybrid trait black guinea pigs
    c. hybrid trait black guinea pigs and pure trait white guinea pigs
4. In a cross of hybrid tall pea plants (Tt x Tt), why might the percentages shown by the Punnett square not hold true?
5. Where are genes located in a cell?

FIGURE 20–6.

Activity 20–2   Expected and Observed Results

Problem: How does chance affect the combination of genes?

Materials   2 paper bags, 100 red beans, 100 white beans

Procedure   (1) Place 50 red beans and 50 white beans in one paper bag. (2) Place the other 50 red beans and 50 white beans in the other paper bag. The bags represent hybrid plants with red and white bean traits. (3) Predict how many red and how many white beans you will select in 100 draws. (4) Hold the tops of the bags closed and shake each bag several times. (5) Without looking inside the bags, remove one bean from each bag. (6) Record the colors of both beans and put them back in the bags. (7) Repeat steps 3, 4, and 5 ninety-nine more times. (8) Count the number of red-red bean combinations you had. (9) Count the number of red-white combinations (10) Count the number of white-white combinations.

Questions   Consider the beans to be genes and the bags to be hybrid plants as you answer the following questions. Red is dominant and white is recessive. (1) How many new plants would have pure dominant genes? (2) How many would have pure recessive genes? (3) How many would be hybrids? (4) How many combinations are possible using two kinds of beans? (5) Why is it necessary to select so many pairs? (6) What are the chances of selecting the same color in a gene pair each time? (7) What are the chances of selecting a different color each time? (8) How does chance affect the combination of genes?

20:4 Mendel's Laws

Scientists have found that Mendel's discovery explains the inheritance of many traits in organisms. The basic laws he discovered led to the science called genetics (juh NET ihks). **Genetics** is the study of heredity. Three basic laws of heredity are listed below.

(1) *Genes occur in pairs.* One gene is from the male parent and the other is from the female parent. The genes control inheritance of traits.

(2) *Genes can be dominant or recessive.* One gene of a pair may hide the trait of the other gene. The trait that appears is dominant. The hidden trait is recessive.

(3) *Genes of pairs separate from each other when gametes are formed.* Only one gene of each pair goes into a sex cell.

Mendel was able to make simple explanations of heredity mainly because he used pea plants. Inherited traits such as red or white flower color of peas were clear-cut. It was later found that heredity does not always follow Mendel's simple laws. Heredity can be non-Mendelian. For example, many traits vary gradually, such as from large to small or from heavy to light. Another example of non-Mendelian heredity is the inheritance of skin color ranging between black and white. Mendel's methods do not apply to these mixed traits.

FIGURE 20–7. Andalusian chickens are examples of incomplete dominance.

Define genetics.

20:5 Incomplete Dominance

In some cases of inheritance, one gene is not dominant over another. **Incomplete dominance** occurs when a pair of genes show up independently. For example, when red shorthorn cattle are crossed with white shorthorns, the offspring are roan. They are neither all red nor all white. Roan is a combination of red and white hairs.

When does incomplete dominance occur?

Andalusian chickens may be black, white, or "blue" feathered. When black Andalusians are mated with white Andalusians, the offspring are "blue." "Blue" color is a combination, or mixing, of black and white feathers. Thus, these chickens are hybrids. "Blue" Andalusians are an example of incomplete dominance.

Making Sure

6. What are the basic laws of heredity?
7. How is incomplete dominance different from dominance?
8. Describe an example of incomplete dominance.
9. What is non-Mendelian heredity?

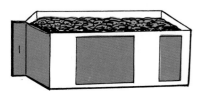

FIGURE 20–8.

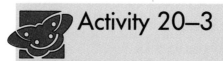

Activity 20–3   Incomplete dominance

Problem: Does incomplete dominance occur in the color of soybean leaves?

Materials eight specially selected soybean seeds, beaker of water, large milk carton, scissors, potting soil, metric ruler

Procedure (1) Soak eight soybean seeds in a beaker of water for an hour. (2) Cut the side out of a large milk carton. (3) Fill the carton two-thirds with potting soil. (4) Plant the eight soaked seeds 1 cm deep and 5 cm apart in the soil. (5) Sprinkle the surface of the soil with water. (6) Set the carton aside. (7) Sprinkle the soil daily to keep it moist. Do not add too much water. (8) When the seeds sprout, place the carton in a sunny place. (9) Observe the colors of the leaves. Combine the results of the class in a data table. Determine how many plants show different colors.

Questions (1) What color leaves do the soybean plants have? (2) What is the genetic ratio? (3) Does incomplete dominance occur in the color of soybean leaves?

FIGURE 20–9. Eye color is controlled by multiple genes.

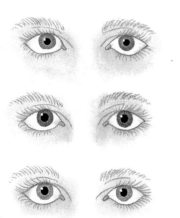

20:6 Multiple Gene Inheritance

The inheritance of some traits is controlled by a single pair of genes—one gene from the mother and one gene from the father. However, few human traits are controlled by a single pair of genes. Most human traits, including the color of eyes, hair, and skin are controlled by multiple genes. Multiple gene inheritance means that more than one pair of genes control the trait.

Several pairs of genes appear to control eye color. Eye colors range from blue to hazel, green, gray, light brown, dark brown, and black. Color depends on the amount of brown pigment, melanin, in the iris. Melanin is the same pigment that gives color to skin and hair. If there is no melanin in the iris, the eye appears pink. If there is a small amount of melanin in the iris, the eye is blue. It appears blue because blue light is reflected back to the observer. Melanin particles may be present in the iris in large amounts. The brown color of the melanin combines with the blue background to give the iris its color. The more particles of melanin, the darker the eye color. The amount and pattern of melanin in the iris are inherited. Eye color is controlled by different combinations of several pairs of genes.

Activity 20–4   Multiple Genes

Problem: Is hand size controlled by multiple genes?

Materials

metric ruler
10 different colored pencils
paper

Procedure

1. Place your left hand palm down on a sheet of paper.
2. Trace around your hand carefully with a colored pencil. Make a mark on the paper to show the bottom of your hand.
3. Put your initials in the lower right hand corner of the paper using the same colored pencil.
4. Draw a straight line across the widest part of the drawing of your hand.
5. Measure the line and record the measurement.
6. Draw a straight line from the tip of your middle finger in the drawing to the point marking the bottom of your hand.
7. Measure the line and record the measurement.
8. Ask a classmate to place his or her left hand palm down on top of the drawing of your left hand.
9. Using a different colored pencil, trace around your classmate's hand. Make a mark to show the bottom of the hand.
10. Put the classmate's initials in the lower right hand corner of the paper using the same colored pencil that you used to trace his or her hand.

FIGURE 20–10.

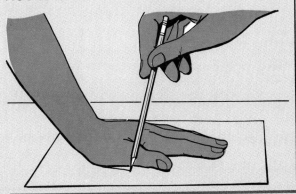

11. Draw a straight line across the widest part of the hand.
12. Measure the line and record the measurement.
13. Draw a straight line from the tip of the middle finger to the line marking the bottom of the hand.
14. Measure the line and record the measurement.
15. Repeat steps 8 through 14 with eight more classmates so that there are ten hand tracings.

Data and Observations

Person	Hand width	Hand length

Questions and Conclusions

1. Which person had the smallest
   a. hand width?
   b. hand length?
   c. hand size?
2. Which person had the largest
   a. hand width?
   b. hand length?
   c. hand size?
3. What is the average
   a. hand width?
   b. hand length?
   c. hand size
4. What is the median
   a. hand width?
   b. hand length?
   c. hand size?
   (Median is the value below and above which there are an equal number of values. In this case, the median will be the average of the two middle values.)
5. Does the data indicate that hand size is controlled by multiple genes? Explain your answer.

20:7 Cell Division

Since Mendel's time, scientists have sought answers to the following questions.

(1) How are genes passed from parents to offspring?

(2) Why do offspring receive half their genes from each parent?

(3) Where are genes located?

(4) What is a gene and how does it produce a trait?

The body cells of plants and animals divide by a process called mitosis. Mitosis occurs during the production of new cells to replace old or dead cells. In a cell that is not dividing the nucleus can be seen as a denser area. This resting stage is called interphase. Within the nucleus are chromosomes. Chromosomes are thread-like strands that become visible during the first stage of mitosis. Before mitosis, each chromosome is duplicated. During mitosis, the cell material passes through four stages. Prophase is the first stage of mitosis. Each duplicated chromosome is composed of two identical halves. The double chromosome is held together at a point called the centromere. The second stage of mitosis is metaphase. Each double chromosome moves to the center of the cell. The third stage is anaphase. This is when the centromere splits and the two halves of the duplicated chromosomes move to opposite ends of the cell. In the final stage, telophase, the cell divides into two. Each new cell has an exact copy of the original

What is mitosis?

FIGURE 20–11. Mitosis is a cell division resulting in two new cells with exact copies of the chromosomes in the original cell.

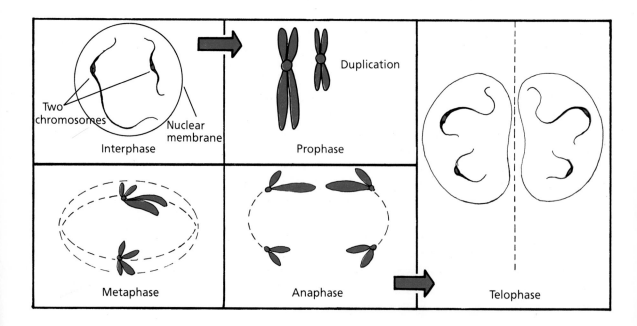

Two chromosomes

Nuclear membrane

Interphase

Duplication

Prophase

Metaphase

Anaphase

Telophase

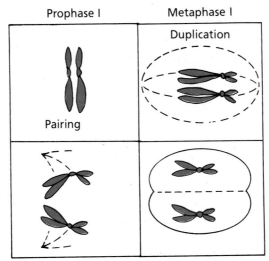

First division

The reduction division

Interphase

One pair of chromosomes

Prophase I

Pairing

Metaphase I

Duplication

Anaphase I

Telophase I

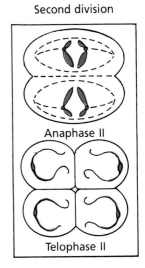

Second division

Anaphase II

Telophase II

chromosomes. The chromosomes disappear again as the new nuclei are formed.

During the formation of sex cells (sperm or eggs) a special kind of cell division occurs. This cell division is called **meiosis** (mi OH sus). In meiosis the chromosome number is reduced by one half. Each sex cell has one half the number of chromosomes as in a body cell. For example, a body cell of a frog has 26 chromosomes. Half this number, or 13 chromosomes, are in each frog sperm and each frog egg. A human body cell normally has 46 chromosomes. Thus, there are 23 chromosomes in each human egg and each human sperm. Before meiosis occurs, each nucleus contains chromosomes from the mother and the father in equal numbers. The chromosomes from the mother match the chromosomes from the father. Each chromosome has a partner. Genes from the mother are on one chromosome of the pair. Similar genes from the father are on the matching chromosome.

In meiosis there are two cell divisions instead of the one for mitosis. In the first division the chromosome number is halved. This is called the reduction division. During prophase I of meiosis the matching chromosomes come together in pairs. Each chromosome of the pair is then duplicated exactly as in mitosis. Each pair now has two doubled chromosomes. At metaphase I the chromosome pairs move to the center of the cell. Anaphase I of meiosis is the stage when the number of chromosomes is halved. Each double chromosome of the pair is drawn to opposite ends of the cell. Two cells are formed in telophase I. Each cell now has half the number of doubled chromosomes.

FIGURE 20–12. Meiosis is a cell division that results in sex cells that contain half the number of chromosomes for the species.

What is meiosis?

What happens to the chromosome number in the first division of meiosis?

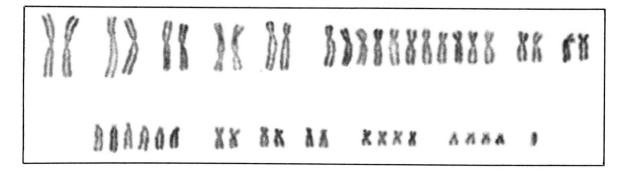

FIGURE 20–13. The human chromosomes are identified in 23 pairs.

In the second division each of the two cells divides again. This division is similar to that seen in mitosis. In anaphase II, the centromeres split and the halves of the double chromosomes move to opposite ends of the cell. The four egg or sperm cells are produced in telophase II. Each cell has half of the original chromosome number of the species. When a sperm fertilizes an egg, the two cells fuse. In humans, the resulting zygote has 23 chromosomes from the egg and 23 from the sperm. The zygote has the full number of chromosomes. Fertilization restores the pairing of chromosomes.

Genes are located on the chromosomes. A pair of chromosomes contains pairs of genes. One gene of each pair is on one chromosome and the other gene is on the matching chromosome.

A string of pearls may be used as a simple model of a chromosome. Each pearl represents a gene. The row of pearls is like a chromosome with its genes.

In a sexually reproducing species, a new organism obtains half its genes from the chromosomes in the egg. The other half comes from the chromosomes in the sperm. Thus, a new organism obtains half its heredity from each parent.

Genes from both parents are combined in the fertilized egg. Genes present in the fertilized egg are duplicated as each body cell is formed. Genes are passed to each cell through the orderly division of the chromosomes during mitosis.

Making Sure

10. Draw a diagram showing the stages of mitosis.
11. Draw a diagram showing the stages of meiosis.
12. How is meiosis different from mitosis?
13. Why is the first stage of meiosis also called the reduction division?
14. How many chromosomes are present in human body cells?
15. How many chromosomes are present in human sex cells?

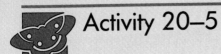

Activity 20–5 Comparing Mitosis and Meiosis

Problem: What is the difference between mitosis and meiosis?

Materials
prepared slide of onion root tip mitosis
prepared slide of lily ovulary meiosis
microscope

Procedure

Part A
1. Examine the onion root tip slide on low power.
2. Switch to high power and examine the onion root tip.
3. Find a cell that is not dividing. Identify the cell wall, cytoplasm, and nucleus.
4. Make a labeled drawing of the cell.
5. Refer to Figure 20–14. Identify a cell in the prophase stage of mitosis. Describe prophase.
6. Identify a cell in the metaphase. Describe metaphase.
7. Identify a cell in the anaphase. Describe anaphase.
8. Identify a cell in the telophase. Describe telophase.

FIGURE 20–14.

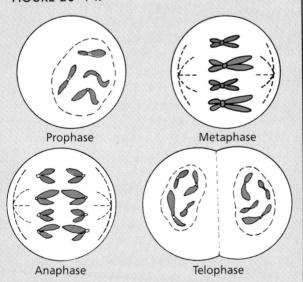

Prophase   Metaphase

Anaphase   Telophase

Part B
1. Examine the lily ovulary slide on low power.
2. Switch to high power and examine the slide.
3. Refer to Figure 20–15. Find a cell in each stage of meiosis. Write a description of each stage.

Data and Observations

FIGURE 20–15.

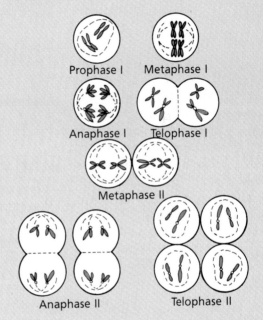

Prophase I   Metaphase I

Anaphase I   Telophase I

Metaphase II

Anaphase II   Telophase II

Questions and Conclusions
1. What are the two types of cell division? Describe each one.
2. What kinds of cells are produced by mitosis?
3. What kinds of cells are produced by meiosis?
4. Why does mitosis occur?
5. Why does meiosis occur?
6. How is mitosis related to heredity?
7. How is meiosis related to heredity?
8. What is the difference between mitosis and meiosis?

a

b

FIGURE 20–16. The traits of a female cardinal (b) are different from those of a male cardinal (a).

How are the chromosome pairs in males and females of a species different?

20:8 Sex Determination

Some traits make males and females different from each other. These traits are called sex characteristics. For example, a bull has a thicker neck than a cow. Men have lower-pitched voices than women. A male peacock has brightly-colored feathers while the female peahen has drab-colored feathers. Sex characteristics, like all other traits, are controlled by genes.

Scientists have studied the chromosomes in many animal species. They have discovered that there is a difference in one chromosome pair between males and females of all species. This special pair of chromosomes that determines the sex of the organism is called **sex chromosomes**.

Sex chromosomes are not always an identical pair. They have been given special names. In many species the larger chromosome in the pair is called the X chromosome. The smaller chromosome is called the Y chromosome. A human female has a matched pair of X chromosomes (XX). A human male has one of each sex chromosome (XY). In some other animal species the Y chromosome is absent. Genes located on the X and Y chromosomes produce the traits that make males and females different.

Sex of humans is inherited through the X and Y chromosomes. The sperm usually determines whether an offspring will be male or female. The cells of a female contain XX chromosomes. Therefore, each egg produced in the female by meiosis will contain one X chromosome. Because a male cell contains X and Y chromosomes, two kinds of sperm are produced. Half the sperms have an X chromosome and half have a Y chromosome. An egg fertilized by an X-carrying sperm results in a zygote with XX, which becomes a female. An egg fertilized by a Y-carrying sperm results in a zygote with XY, which becomes male.

How is the sex of humans determined?

20:9 Sex-Linked Traits

Most physical traits appear about equally in men and women. Blue eyes, black hair, and type O blood occur in men and women in the same numbers. However, there are some traits more common in men than in women. Color blindness and hemophilia are examples of these traits. These traits are said to be sex-linked traits. This means they are inherited along with the sex of an individual. Inheritance of **sex-linked traits** is controlled by genes located on the sex chromosomes.

Just as chromosomes occur in pairs, genes for a trait usually occur in pairs. One gene is present in each of the two chromosomes of a chromosome pair. However, sex chromosomes are believed to be different. The recessive genes for some traits are on the X chromosome. But there may not be a corresponding dominant gene on the Y chromosome. Therefore, males (XY) have only one gene for some traits instead of a pair since the Y chromosome has no gene for those traits.

What are two examples of sex-linked traits?

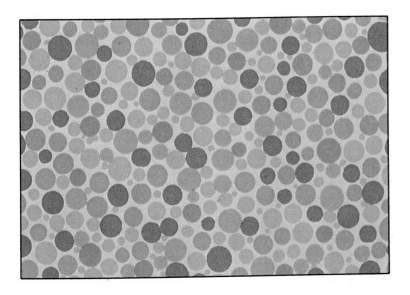

FIGURE 20–17. People with the most common type of color blindness cannot distinguish the colors red and green. What numbers do you see?

How are sex-linked traits inherited?

For a female (XX) to have a recessive sex-linked trait, she needs two recessive genes. One gene is needed on each X chromosome. If one X chromosome has the dominant gene, then the trait will be hidden. For a male (XY) to have the recessive sex-linked trait, he needs only one recessive gene. Why? The recessive gene on the X chromosome is not masked or covered up by a dominant gene on the Y chromosome.

Color blindness for red and green is a recessive sex-linked trait. Suppose a color-blind woman marries a man with normal color vision. All the woman's sons will be color-blind. But, none of her daughters will be color-blind. However, all the daughters will be carriers of color blindness. A carrier is a person who does not show the trait, but carries a recessive gene for it. The gene could be passed on to offspring. This cross and others show that men always inherit sex-linked traits from their mothers.

Color-blind women are rare. A woman cannot be color-blind unless her father is also color-blind. Also, her mother must be either color-blind or a carrier. Fathers do not pass color blindness to their sons. They can pass color blindness only to their daughters. This occurs because fathers always pass a Y chromosome to their sons. The Y chromosome does not carry the recessive gene.

Hemophilia is a relatively rare sex-linked trait. Hemophilia is a disease in which blood does not clot. The body does not produce a chemical needed to form a blood clot. People with hemophilia lose large amounts of blood even during minor cuts or bruises. A lack of ability to produce the chemical for clotting is usually inherited from mothers who are carriers. Although there is no cure for hemophilia, people with the disease can live normal lives with treatment and cautions.

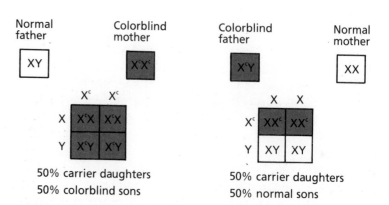

FIGURE 20–18. Possible crosses involving color blindness.

Inheritance of hemophilia is similar to the inheritance of color blindness. Hemophilia is inherited through a recessive gene carried on the X chromosome. A man inherits hemophilia from his mother. A woman cannot have hemophilia unless her father has hemophilia and her mother either has the disease or is a carrier. A man can never be a carrier of hemophilia. If a man inherits a trait for hemophilia from either parent, he will have the disease.

A few minor human traits show linkage with the Y chromosome. These traits are not carried by females. The rare human trait for webbing between the second and third toes is a Y-linked trait. The Y chromosome affects the inheritance of other traits in birds and insects.

How is hemophilia inherited?

Making Sure

16. What are the chances of a baby's being female?
17. What are the chances of a baby's being male?
18. Explain why a color-blind male inherits the condition from his mother.

20:10 DNA

Every inherited trait is controlled by DNA. DNA is deoxyribonucleic (dee AHK sih ri boh noo klay ihk) acid. **DNA** is the genetic material in the nuclei of cells. The chromosomes that appear in the nucleus of a cell during mitosis are made of DNA. DNA molecules can be very large. Scientists think that each chromosome is made of just one molecule of DNA with proteins attached to it. DNA contains a code with information that regulates the activities of a cell. The DNA code controls the chemical changes that make up a cell's life activities. Genes responsible for different inherited traits are short sections of DNA molecules.

DNA regulates a cell by controlling the production of cell enzymes and other proteins. Enzymes regulate the chemical changes involved in cell activities such as respiration. DNA also has the ability to replicate or make more DNA just like itself.

DNA is a long, threadlike molecule with the shape of a double helix. The shape of a helix is like a corkscrew. The two helixes in the molecule wind around each other and are connected by bonds that form a spiral ladder. You can think of the DNA structure as a ladder twisted into a helical shape with the rungs kept parallel. Building blocks that make up the molecule are arranged in a pattern that creates the DNA code. It is estimated that the DNA in a typical cell totals one to two meters in length.

What is DNA?

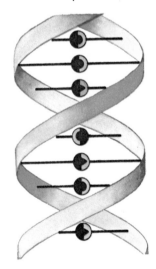

FIGURE 20–19. The structure of DNA is like a spiral ladder.

What is RNA?

Another nucleic acid present in cells is **RNA**. RNA is ribonucleic (ri boh noo KLAY ihk) acid and is similar to DNA in structure, but it is single-stranded. RNA works together with DNA to regulate a cell. Like DNA, RNA controls cells through the making of proteins. Inside the nucleus, a copy of the DNA code is made like a blueprint in the form of RNA molecules. The RNA molecules leave the nucleus and enter the cytoplasm. They are messengers that carry information from the DNA to the ribosomes. Ribosomes work like assembly lines that make enzymes and other cell proteins. These substances are made according to the cell's DNA code. All species contain a genetic code based on the structure of DNA. Inherited differences in species and individuals are due to variations in the DNA code.

20:11 Pedigrees

What is a pedigree?

Pedigrees are used in studying heredity. A **pedigree** is a record of an organism's ancestors. An organism tends to produce offspring like itself or its ancestors. Therefore, a pedigree gives clues to the kinds of traits that may be passed on to offspring.

Breeders use pedigrees in choosing plants or animals for mating. For example, in breeding milk cows, the breeder would check the animals' pedigrees for ancestors that were high milk producers. A plant breeder may wish to breed a flower with extra petals. A plant's pedigree could be examined for this trait.

Pedigrees are also used by scientists to learn how different traits are inherited from generation to generation. For example,

FIGURE 20–20. Jersey cows are a breed of milk producers.

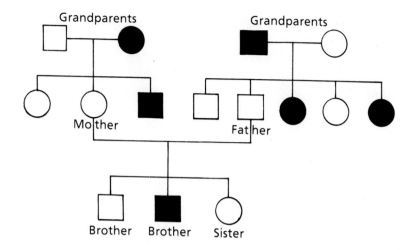

Grandparents   Grandparents

Mother   Father

Brother   Brother   Sister

FIGURE 20–21. Pedigree charts may be used to trace and study family histories.

a pedigree might show that a certain trait in humans skips a generation. The trait may be present in the grandparents and grandchildren but not in the parents.

In recent years, much has been learned about human heredity despite certain difficulties. The scientific study of human heredity is difficult for several reasons. One problem is the long span of years, about 20, between generations of people. It takes a long time for traits to be passed through several generations. Also, there is usually a small number of children per family. Thus, the chances of seeing the passing of traits from parents to offspring are not as great as in many other living things.

Why is human heredity difficult to study?

A human pedigree is sometimes charted with circles and squares connected by lines. The circles represent females. Squares represent males. A horizontal line between a circle and square shows a marriage or mating. A vertical line that extends down connects to the child born from the mating. If there are several children, the line extending down ends at another horizontal line. Squares and circles that stand for the children are connected to this line. Solid circles and squares represent persons that have the trait being studied. Open circles and squares represent persons without the trait. Family pedigrees are developed from facts taken from birth certificates and other legal papers. Family records, old pictures, hospital records, and biographies also give information.

Explain the meaning of each symbol in a pedigree.

Making Sure

19. What is the relationship between DNA, genes, and chromosomes?
20. How do DNA and RNA compare in structure and function?
21. How are pedigrees used in plant and animal breeding?

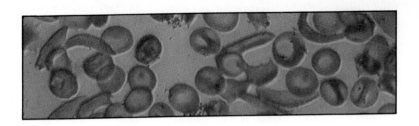

FIGURE 20—22. Sickle cells magnified 500 times.

20:12 Genetic Diseases

What are genetic diseases?

Some diseases are inherited. They are called genetic diseases. Many genetic diseases are controlled by a single gene. These diseases are inherited in the same way as Mendel's crosses of tall and short peas. The single genes are recessive and they work by preventing the production of certain vital enzymes or proteins.

Down syndrome is a condition caused by the presence of an extra chromosome in body cells. The cells have 47 chromosomes instead of the normal 46. The extra chromosome can come from the mother or the father. During meiosis an extra chromosome may result when one of the duplicated chromosomes does not separate at anaphase II. The extra chromosome upsets the usual orderly development of the body and brain. The chances of a woman having a child with Down syndrome increase with her age.

Describe two examples of genetic diseases.

Sickle-cell anemia is another inherited condition. The trait occurs in 10 percent of the black population in the United States. The condition is known for its curved, or sickle-shaped red blood cells. These sickle-shaped cells form clumps that clog small blood vessels. Victims often die at an early age. Sickle-cell anemia is caused by a recessive gene that prevents the normal development of blood. A person who has the condition has two recessive genes for the trait in each body cell. Carriers of the disease have only one gene for the trait. Sometimes a carrier shows mild symptoms of the disease.

Cystic fibrosis (SIHS tihk · fi BROH sus) is passed on in Caucasian families. Cystic fibrosis is caused by a recessive gene, so both parents must be carriers of the disease. About one in 20 people carries the recessive gene. When two carriers have children there is a one in four chance of the baby's having cystic fibrosis. Cystic fibrosis is a general disorder of certain glands that produce mucus, saliva, and sweat. This condition interferes with the lungs and digestive system and can cause early death. Scientists are working to solve the mystery of this disease. More and more patients with cystic fibrosis are living longer today.

Technology

Recombinant DNA

Recombinant DNA is combined DNA from two different organisms. The technique for this recombination is now well established, but it was first developed from a knowledge of bacteria. By 1970, it was known that bacteria used special enzymes to destroy viruses. These enzymes chopped up the viral DNA when it was inserted into the bacteria. The enzymes were very specific as to where they cut the DNA and would continue to be so even if removed to other organisms. The fragments of DNA were left with "sticky" ends that allowed two pieces of DNA from different organisms to be "glued" or spliced together. In 1973, researchers from Stanford University successfully spliced the genes from a toad and a bacterium with the use of bacterial enzymes. This was the beginning of genetic engineering.

The technique of recombination begins with the isolation of DNA from a plant or animal cell. A piece of the DNA is selected for its importance in the production of a useful protein such as insulin or interferon. A fragment of the DNA containing the gene of interest is then cut out with the special enzyme. This DNA fragment is usually spliced into the DNA of a bacterium. The bacterial DNA is also cut with the special enzyme and the "sticky" ends of the DNA from both organisms join together. This genetically engineered DNA is then placed back into the bacterium, where the newly spliced gene makes unlimited amounts of the desired protein. Several important proteins that have been produced by recombinant DNA techniques include: human growth hormone; tumor necrosis factor—a cancer fighting protein; tissue plasminogen activator—a protein that dissolves blood clots; interferon—a protein effective in fighting viral infections; and Factor VIII—a blood-clotting protein.

Perhaps the most important use of recombinant DNA will be in treating genetic diseases. There are 3000 known genetic diseases. None can be cured at the present time, but the technical ability to cure a genetic disease has now been demonstrated. The first successful gene therapy in a mammal was reported in 1984. A growth hormone gene was injected into the fertilized egg of a mouse. Normally, the mouse would have developed into a dwarf because of a genetic disease. Instead, it grew to nearly twice normal size.

The first clinical trials for treatment of human genetic diseases began in 1986. Genetic engineering will be the lifeline for many people suffering from previously incurable diseases.

FIGURE 20–23. Scientists inserted human growth hormone genes into a mouse embryo and produced the giant mouse pictured on the right.

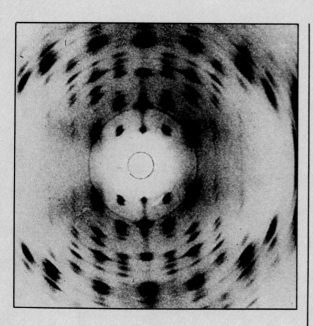

The History of DNA

DNA was first discovered in 1869 by a Swiss chemist named Friedrich Miescher. Miescher was investigating the chemistry of white blood cells taken from pus on the bandages of hospital patients. By adding a weak acid to the pus, the nuclei were released from the cells. These nuclei were treated with an enzyme and an unknown substance was isolated. This new substance was tested and found to be acidic and rich in phosphorus. Miescher named this material nuclein and hypothesized that it was the stuff of heredity.

In 1877, Walther Flemming developed new staining techniques for cells. The stains revealed rodlike structures in the cell nucleus.

These structures are now known as chromosomes. Chromatin and nuclein were later realized to be the same.

A stain, specific for DNA, was developed in 1914 by a German chemist, Robert Feulgen. The amount of DNA in a nucleus could be estimated by examining the color of the stain. Experiments showed that every cell nucleus of an organism contains the same amount of DNA. The nuclei of sex cells (sperm and egg), however, were stained and shown to have half the normal amount.

The confirmation of the purpose of DNA for heredity first came in 1927. Fred Griffith found that genetic material could be passed from one strain of bacterium to another. In 1944, O.T. Avery, C.M. MacLeod, and M. McCarthy isolated Griffith's genetic material and identified it as DNA.

Once DNA was shown to be the genetic material, attention turned to finding out how it worked. In 1950, Erwin Chargaff discovered that DNA was made up of molecules called bases. These bases were present in pairs of either adenine with thymine or cytosine with guanine abbreviated as A-T and C-G.

In 1952, Rosalind Franklin and Maurice Wilkins made some X-ray pictures of DNA, such as the one shown, to interpret its size and shape. Franklin was able to conclude that the structure of DNA was a tightly shaped helix. With this information, James Watson and Francis Crick were able to make models of DNA. Chargaff's data, showing the presence of equal amounts of DNA bases, were crucial to Watson and Crick's final solution in 1953. They connected all the A bases with the Ts and all the C bases with the Gs. The DNA model then matched the dimensions of the X-ray images. By combining data from the work of previous scientists, Watson and Crick were able to develop a model that revolutionized the life sciences.

CHAPTER 20
Review

Summary

1. Heredity is the passing of genes from parents to offspring.   20:1
2. Some inherited traits are dominant and some are recessive. Other traits result from a mixing of traits.   20:2, 20:5
3. Inherited traits are controlled by pairs of genes located on pairs of chromosomes. One-half of an offspring's genes come from one parent and one-half from the other parent.   20:3
4. Mendel discovered the laws of heredity.   20:4
5. Most traits are controlled by multiple genes.   20:6
6. Mitosis and meiosis are the two types of cell division.   20:7
7. The sex of an animal is determined by the kinds of sex chromosomes it has.   20:8
8. Color blindness and hemophilia are sex-linked traits. They appear more often in males than in females.   20:9
9. DNA contains a life code that controls the activities of a cell and the traits of an organism.   20:10
10. Pedigrees are used to predict inheritance.   20:11
11. Many genetic diseases are controlled by a single gene.   20:12

Vocabulary

Write a sentence using the following words or terms correctly.

DNA	hybrid	pure trait
dominant trait	incomplete dominance	recessive trait
gene	meiosis	RNA
genetics	pedigree	sex chromosome
heredity	Punnett square	sex-linked trait

Questions

Do not write in this book.

A. True or False
Determine whether each of the following sentences is true or false. Rewrite the false statements to make them correct.

1. Heredity is the passing of traits from parents to offspring.
2. Tallness is a recessive trait in pea plants.
3. Many traits are controlled by a gene.
4. A carrier is a person that carries a recessive gene for a trait.

5. Most of an animal's genes come from its mother.
6. An enzyme is a protein.
7. A recessive trait is always visible.
8. Hemophilia occurs more frequently in males than females.
9. Skin color is controlled by a single pair of genes.
10. Genetic diseases are caused by single recessive genes.

B. Multiple Choice
Choose the word or phrase that correctly completes the following sentences.
1. Tt represents a *(pure, hybrid)* trait.
2. XX represents the chromosomes for a *(male, female, male or female)* human.
3. In a cow, the sex of the offspring is determined by the *(egg, sperm)*.
4. A human body cell contains *(23, 46, 92, 64)* chromosomes.
5. Proteins are produced on a cell's *(ribosomes, nucleus, cell membrane)*.
6. Reduction division occurs during *(mitosis, every cell division, production of sex cells)*.
7. *(Nn, NN, nn)* is a gene combination for a carrier.
8. For a dominant trait to appear in a child, the trait must be present in *(both parents, one parent)*.
9. *(Color blindness, Hemophilia, Eye color)* is an example of multiple gene inheritance.
10. The nucleic acid of chromosomes is *(DNA, RNA)*.

C. Completion
Complete each of the following sentences with the correct word or phrase.
1. If a woman is a carrier of color blindness there is a(n) _____ percent chance her son will be color-blind.
2. A man with hemophilia inherited the trait from his _____.
3. Sex-linked traits appear more often in _____ than in _____.
4. If there are 26 chromosomes in the body cell of an animal, its sex cell will contain _____ chromosomes.
5. Genes from both parents are combined during the _____ of an egg.
6. A capital letter in a Punnett square represents a(n) _____ gene.
7. _____ is one exception to the law of dominance.
8. A(n) _____ is part of a DNA molecule that controls the inheritance of a trait.
9. XY is the chromosome combination for the _____ sex.
10. _____ is the blueprint for the making of RNA.

D. How and Why

1. How did Mendel discover the basic laws of heredity?
2. How is incomplete dominance different from the inheritance of a dominant trait?
3. Round seeds are dominant and wrinkled seeds are recessive in pea plants. Find the ratio of offspring in a cross between pea plants with hybrid round seeds and those with pure wrinkled seeds.
4. Suppose ten seeds are produced in the cross in question 3. Why might the actual number of plants with round or wrinkled seeds be different from the predicted ratio?
5. How is meiosis different from mitosis?
6. How is it possible for a trait to skip a generation?
7. Why do women rarely exhibit sex-linked traits such as hemophilia?
8. What is a human pedigree and how is it made?
9. What are genetic diseases? Name two such diseases.

Ideas to Explore

1. **Challenge:** Research the life of Gregor Mendel. Prepare a short biography.
2. **Challenge:** Locate the book *Double Helix* by James Watson in a library. Use information in this book to prepare a report on the discovery of the structure of DNA.
3. **Project:** Visit a local pet shop to obtain information on animal pedigrees and their use in breeding.
4. **Challenge:** Based on library research, prepare a report on a genetic disease such as sickle-cell anemia.

Readings

Asimov, Isaac. *How Did We Find Out About Genes?* New York: Walker, 1983.

Keller, E. F. *A Feeling for the Organism: The Life and Work of Barbara McClintock*. New York: W. H. Freeman, 1983.

Monagan, David. "Horse of a Different Culture." *Science 82*. May, 1982, pp. 46–53.

Silverstein, Alvin and Virginia Silverstein. *The Genetics Explosion*. New York: Four Winds, 1980.

Slatin, Montgomery. "The Descent of Genes." *Science 85*. November, 1985, pp. 80–84.

Stwertka, Eve. *Genetic Engineering*. New York: Watts, 1982.

The largest animal ever to have flown became extinct 65 million years ago. The fossil wing bones of a pterosaur named Quetzalcoatlus northropi *were discovered in Texas. But the mystery of how this reptile with a 12-meter wingspan flew remained hidden. This model of the pterosaur with only a 6-meter wingspan can fly. It was designed by paleontologists and engineers. How do we know that pterosaurs lived millions of years ago? How many different kinds of animals do you know that have evolved wings but are not extinct?*

CHAPTER 21
EVOLUTION

21:1 Change Through Time

Methods used to determine the age of rocks indicate Earth is about 5 billion years old. Evidence shows that life may have been on Earth for at least three billion years. The earliest organisms resembled bacteria and blue-green algae. Some scientists think Earth's earliest organisms did not make their own food. Other scientists reason that the first organisms did make their own food because the oldest fossils are of photosynthetic organisms. Most species that have lived in the past are no longer alive today. New species have appeared throughout the time life has existed on Earth. New species provide a variety of life forms and a greater chance for survival in an ever-changing environment.

Organisms evolve, or change, over a period of time. New species that appear have evolved from older species and all species descend from a common ancestor. **Evolution** is a change over time in the hereditary features of a species. Evidence for evolution includes data obtained through a study of fossils. Evidence also comes from the study of heredity and the structures of organisms.

GOALS:
1. You will learn how organisms have evolved.
2. You will learn theories to explain evolution.
3. You will learn scientific evidence that explains evolution.

What is evolution?

a

b

c

FIGURE 21–1. Fossils may be the imprint of a fern (a), part of an animal trapped in tar (b), or the foot bones of a camel (c).

How are fossils formed?

21:2 Fossils

How do we know about animals and plants that lived long ago? Facts about these living things come from a study of fossils (FAHS ulz). A **fossil** is any evidence of prehistoric life. Here are some examples of fossils.

(1) Imprint of a leaf or stem in a rock
(2) An animal trapped and frozen in ice
(3) Bones preserved in tar pits
(4) An insect trapped in hardened plant sap
(5) Wood replaced by minerals

Most fossils were formed at the bottoms of shallow seas that once covered a large part of Earth. Many plants and animals died in the shallow waters. When they died, they settled to the bottom and were gradually covered by mud or sand. The mud or sand slowly turned to rock. The change took hundreds of thousands of years. In some cases, a plant or animal may have left only an imprint in the rock. In other cases, the plant or animal may have been completely covered. When the organism decayed, its outline was left in the material that turned to rock. Often the hard parts of an organism such as a bone or tooth were preserved.

Sometimes a whole organism is turned into a fossil. Bit by bit, minerals in the water filter into and replace the material of the organism. The dead organism becomes petrified (PEH truh fide), meaning the original material is replaced by minerals. Most dead plants and animals do not become fossils because they usually decay before the mud or sand around them turns to rock.

Mud, sand, and other fine particles at the bottom of shallow seas are called sediments. Sediment is material that has settled

FIGURE 21–2. Sedimentary rock is an excellent source of fossils.

out of a liquid such as seawater. These sediments may form rocks called sedimentary (sed uh MENT uh ree) rocks. Shale, sandstone, and limestone are sedimentary rocks. Sedimentary rocks are formed in layers stacked on top of each other.

Fossils almost always occur in sedimentary rocks. The fossil organisms died shortly before the rock began forming from the sediment. Fossils found in the lower layers of rock are usually of organisms older than fossils of organisms found in the upper layers of rock. If you keep your newspapers stacked and add each day's paper to the top of the pile, then the papers on the bottom of the stack are the oldest. The papers on the top are the most recent. Similarly, fossils in lower layers of rock are older than fossils in upper layers of rock. The approximate time of the appearance on Earth of many organisms can be determined by the position of their fossils in the layers of rock.

The age of a rock or fossil can be determined by radioactive dating. **Radioactive elements** are elements whose atoms give off nuclear radiation. A radioactive element loses its radioactivity at a known rate. In the process it changes into a different element. By finding out how much of a certain radioactive element in a rock has changed into the different corresponding element, scientists can determine the age of the rock. The ages of fossils can be determined according to the ages of the rocks where they were found.

FIGURE 21–3. Scientists carefully dig through the soil looking for fossils.

Making Sure

1. Fossil shark teeth have been discovered in the rocks of mountains located hundreds of miles from the sea. How can this be explained?
2. What is radioactive dating?
3. How are fossils related to evolution?

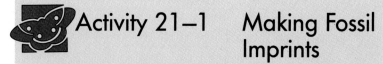

Activity 21–1   Making Fossil Imprints

Problem: How is a fossil imprint made?

Materials   plastic container, petroleum jelly, modeling clay, plaster of Paris, water, small natural object—seashell, leaf, bone, nut

Procedure   (1) Coat the outside of your object with petroleum jelly. (2) Press the object into the clay until the clay surrounds most of it. (3) Remove the object carefully to leave a good imprint in the clay. (4) Coat the imprint with petroleum jelly. (5) Use the plastic container to mix the plaster of Paris. Add water a small amount at a time until you have a thick paste. (6) Pour the plaster of Paris into the imprint in the clay. Let it dry for 30 minutes. (7) Carefully remove the clay from the plaster.

Questions   (1) List the ways in which the plaster of Paris fossil is like the original object. (2) How could an imprint like the one you made be formed naturally? (3) Why do you think scientists who study ancient life make molds and casts? (4) How is a fossil imprint made?

21:3 Reading the Fossil Record

Fossils are a record of the life that lived very long ago. The record shows that most species alive today are very different from the fossil species. For example, fossils of Archaeopteryx (ar kee AHP tuh rihks), a birdlike dinosaur about the size of a crow, have been found. Its skeleton was like a reptile's; its feathers made it birdlike. Archaeopteryx had teeth like a reptile, but it also had a tail with feathers. The remains of woolly mammoths that lived 25 thousand years ago have been discovered preserved in ice. Fossils of dragonflies resembling birds with wingspans of 75 cm have been found. Marine reptiles similar in appearance to today's seals and porpoises lived 150 million years ago. Fossils of the

FIGURE 21–4. The first horse, *Hyracotherium*, was the size of a fox and had several toes on each foot. It is the ancestor of the modern horse, *Equus*, which has a hoof with only one toe.

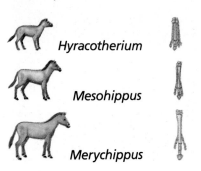

Hyracotherium

Mesohippus

Merychippus

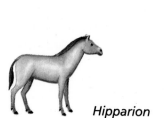

Hipparion

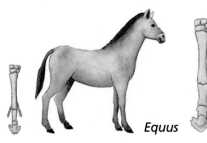

Equus

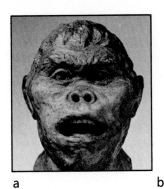
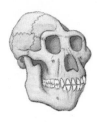

a   b   c   d

first horses show the animals were about the size of foxes. They had several toes on each foot. Over time these animals evolved into the modern horse that is larger in head, neck, and body, with a hoof having only one toe.

Some of the organisms alive today are more complex than any organisms that lived in the distant past. For example, seed plants are the most common plants on Earth today. In the past, ferns, which are less complex than seed plants, were the most plentiful. There were no seed plants. Conifers existed before flowering plants, which arose about 150 million years ago. At one time in Earth's history, reptiles were the most plentiful of all animals. There were no birds and mammals. Today, many different species of birds and mammals are alive on Earth. Birds and mammals are more complex than reptiles. In general, the changes in organisms over time have been from simple to more complex organisms. However, many simple organisms also exist today.

Scientists have divided Earth's history into segments of time called eras and periods. Each era and period has certain fossils and other features that make it different from the others. Compare the main features that mark each era shown in Table 21–1.

Fossils indicate that monkeys, apes, and humans probably evolved separately from a common ancestor. Over millions of years, the human species evolved from an apelike form. During this time the jaw became shorter and the teeth smaller. The braincase of the skull became larger, and a prominent vertical forehead appeared. Eyebrow ridges and the nose became more prominent, and the arms became shorter. The oldest humanlike fossils of *Australopithecus afarensis* are about 3.5 million years old. Found in Africa, these creatures stood erect and walked on two legs. They had large jaws and no forehead. The brain capacity of their skulls was greater than that of chimpanzees, but less than half that of humans. It is believed they used simple bone tools. Fossils of a more recent humanlike species, *Homo erectus*, that lived

FIGURE 21–5. By making casts from fossil skulls, scientists can make models of early humans' heads. *Australopithecus afarensis* (a,b) had large jaws, no forehead, and a brain capacity less than half that of modern humans. *Homo erectus* (c,d) had a receding forehead, large jaws, and heavy eyebrow ridges.

FIGURE 21–6. This hand ax is a stone tool probably used by hunters more than 400 000 years ago.

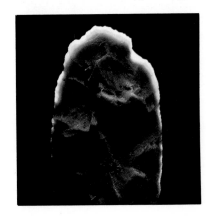

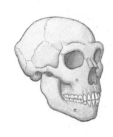

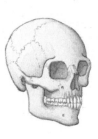

a   b   c   d

FIGURE 21–7. Neanderthals (a,b) and Cro-Magnons (c,d) are classified as *Homo sapiens*, the same as modern humans.

How have humans evolved?

FIGURE 21–8. Neanderthals used several kinds of tools.

about 1 million years ago have been discovered in Asia and Africa. The brain capacity of this species is larger than the older humanlike species, but smaller than that of humans. The face of this species had a projecting massive jaw, large teeth, almost no chin, and a receding forehead. It also had heavy eyebrow ridges and a broad, low-bridge nose. This species used fire as well as tools. Fossil evidence shows that *Homo erectus* or "upright man" was the first of the humanlike ancestors to have left Africa. Fossils have been found in India, China, and Southeast Asia as well as Africa.

Homo sapiens or "modern man" appears in the fossil record about 300 000 years ago. At first these people were still big-browed and flat-skulled but had smaller teeth than *Homo erectus*. The brain capacity increased steadily until 125 000 years ago when a variety of *Homo sapiens,* called Neanderthal, arose. Neanderthals had a heavier skeleton than that of modern humans, indicating a people capable of great strength. They lived in more northern areas of the world and were able to survive the extreme cold winters.

A Neanderthal was about 1.5 to 1.7 meters tall and had a receding forehead, prominent eyebrow ridges, and a receding chin. A Neanderthal's brain was larger than that of a modern human. Neanderthals made many different kinds of tools.

The Neanderthals disappeared from the fossil record 30 000 years ago. Fossils of modern *Homo sapiens* dated more recently than 30 000 years are found all over the world.

In 1868 in France, fossils of a more recent type of *Homo sapiens* were found and named Cro-Magnon (kroh MAG nun). Their high forehead, chin, and greatly reduced eyebrow ridges give the appearance of people today. Cro-Magnon people lived from 35 000 to 10 000 years ago and were excellent toolmakers, highly skilled hunters, and artists. The tools they made were very carefully designed.

FIGURE 21–9. Cro-magnon peoples made sculptures, decorated tools, and carved wall art such as this bison licking an insect bite.

Activity 21–2 Comparing the Geologic Time Periods

Problem: How can you compare the geologic time periods?

Materials graph paper, pencil, ruler or straightedge

Procedure (1) Make a bar graph showing the length of time for each geologic period from Cambrian to Quaternary. Place the units for lengths of time along the horizontal (x) axis of the graph. (2) List the periods vertically along the vertical (y) axis of the graph. (3) Draw a bar for the number of years for each period on the graph. Compare the lengths of the periods.

Questions (1) Which period is the longest? (2) Which period is the shortest? (3) Why is a very large scale needed to graph geologic time? (4) What geologic period to you live in? (5) How can you compare the geologic time periods?

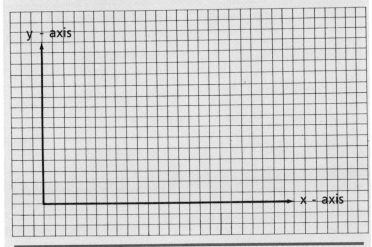

FIGURE 21–10.

Table 21-1

Geologic History and Characteristics

Eras	Periods	Start of Periods (years ago)	Climate	Geological features
Cenozoic *(kainos*-recent; *zoe*-life)	Quaternary	2 000 000	warmer in modern times	periodic glaciers
	Tertiary	65 000 000	warm; gradually cooling	formation of Alps and Himalayas; volcanoes active; continents raised; North America and Europe connected
Mesozoic *(mesos*-middle; *zoe*-life)	Cretaceous	130 000 000	mild to cool	formation of Rocky Mountains and Andes; inland seas; swamps
	Jurassic	180 000 000	warm	continental seas in parts of United States and Europe
	Triassic	230 000 000	warm	deserts, swamps, lakes; Americas separate from Europe and Africa
Paleozoic *(palaios*-ancient; *zoe*-life)	Permian	260 000 000	cold, dry and moist	formation of Appalachians and Urals
	Pennsylvanian	310 000 000	moist, warm	shallow inland seas; lowlands
	Mississippian	350 000 000	warm, humid	inland seas; lowlands
	Devonian	400 000 000	arid	inland seas; lowlands
	Silurian	430 000 000	mild	formation of European mountains; inland seas
	Ordovician	475 000 000	warm, mild	flooding of land; increased size of oceans
	Cambrian	600 000 000	mild	lowlands; inland seas
Precambrian		5 000 000 000	warm, moist to cool dry	volcanoes; glaciers; sedimentary, igneous, and metamorphic rocks

Plants	Animals
modern species	modern species, dominance of humans
spread of modern flowering plants; rise of grasses, herbs	abundance of arthropods, mollusks; modern invertebrates; modern mammals, birds, and reptiles
rise of flowering plants; decline of cone-bearing plants	extinction of dinosaurs; flying and marine reptiles, spread of birds, insects; rise of primitive mammals
dominance of conifers	dominance of dinosaurs, marine and flying reptiles, abundance of insects; first birds
spread of conifers; extinction of seed ferns	first dinosaurs, crocodiles, turtles, and flying and marine reptiles
first conifers	great extinction of many marine invertebrates including trilobites
coal formation in swamp forests; dominance of spore-bearing trees	first reptiles; giant insects; amphibians
depositing of coal; dominance of seed ferns	rise of amphibians, shark; bony fish; crinoids
horsetails; ferns; seed ferns; first forests	fish amphibians; rise of fishes; mollusks; decline of trilobites
first land plants; dominance of algae	primitive fish; corals; mollusks; first arthropods; first land invertebrates
dominance of marine algae	abundance of trilobites; spread of early vertebrates
algae	rise of major marine invertebrates; dominance of trilobites
algae	sponges; soft-bodied animals; microscopic life; first multicelled and shelled animals

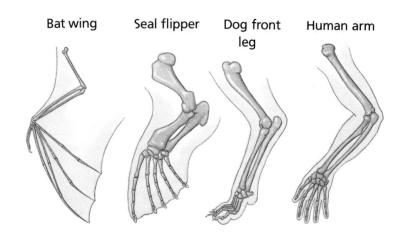

Bat wing   Seal flipper   Dog front leg   Human arm

FIGURE 21–11. These limb structures are homologous. They may have different functions but similar structure and origin.

21:4 Other Evidence of Evolution

Similarities in the structures of organisms are also evidence of evolution. For example, a bat wing, dog paw, seal front flipper, and the human hand and arm serve different functions. Yet they are all similar in basic structure. Each has about the same number of blood vessels, bones, nerves, and muscles. These limbs have the same basic structure because they developed in similar places. They are said to have a common origin or beginning because they developed from similar embryonic tissues. Structures that are similar in form and origin are called **homologous**. Species with homologous structures are considered to be related and descended from a common ancestor. The more homologous structures shared by two organisms, the more closely related the organisms are in their evolutionary history.

Body parts that have a similar function, but a different structure, indicate two species are not closely related. For instance, both birds and butterflies have wings they use for flying. Although used for the same function, the wings of birds and butterflies differ in structure. These are not homologous structures.

Vestigial (veh STHJ ee ul) organs also furnish evidence for evolution. A vestigial organ is a body structure that is not needed by an organism. Vestigial organs are usually undersized or lack some essential part. Examples of vestigial organs in the human body are the appendix, wisdom teeth, and muscles that move the nose and ears. Vestigial hind leg bones are present in whales and pythons. Wingless birds such as the kiwi have vestigial wing bones. Vestigial structures are small body structures that may have been functional in the ancestors of a species. Genetic changes

FIGURE 21–12. The two small toes on a pig's foot are vestigial structures.

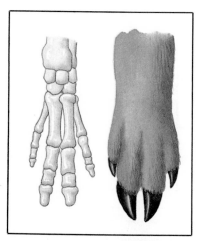

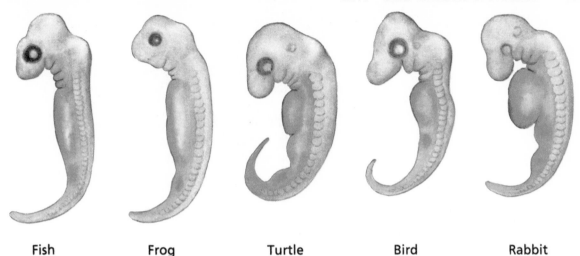

Fish   Frog   Turtle   Bird   Rabbit

occurred over time, and the size and function of the organ decreased. The changes were inherited by the descendants of the organism. Survival of these descendants was not affected because the useless organ was not needed for the life activities of the organisms. If the organ were necessary for survival, individuals with the genetic changes would have died. The changed trait could not have been passed on to offspring.

More evidence for evolution is found in the study of embryos. All vertebrate embryos in their earliest development are very much alike. It is difficult to tell them apart at certain stages in their development. This fact suggests a close relationship among vertebrate species. In their earliest development the embryos of vertebrates resemble embryos of simpler species. The early stages have characteristics in common with those of fish, amphibians, and reptiles. An early human embryo, for instance, has a tail and gill pouches. As the embryos continue to develop, the characteristics that distinguish different species from each other begin to appear.

Similarity in the structures of protein molecules also indicates a close relationship between species. For example, the complex protein hemoglobin in the blood of chimpanzees and in humans appears to be identical. In the gorilla, two of the building blocks of hemoglobin are different from those of humans. The monkey has a hemoglobin molecule that differs from humans in 12 of these building blocks. Scientists conclude that the greater the similarity in protein structure among species, the more recent their common ancestor. Evidence obtained from the study of similarities in protein supports the same evolutionary relationships determined by the study of animal structures.

FIGURE 21–13. In the early stages of development, it is difficult to distinguish among the embryos of different animals. As they develop, the embryos take on the characteristics of the different species.

The relatedness of living things is supported by the fact that all organisms have DNA. The DNA of all organisms is made of the same kinds of compounds. Thus, the genetic code itself provides evidence for relationships among organisms.

Making Sure

4. How has life on Earth changed with time?
5. What are the main features of the four eras?
6. What are three comparisons scientists use as evidence for evolution?

21:5 Explanations for Evolution

The fossil record tells us that many times in the past species have become extinct. Extinct means all of the members of a species have died. New species have appeared in the fossil record. It also shows that through millions of years, many animals and plants have become more complex. How and why have organisms evolved?

What is Lamarck's theory of acquired traits?

In 1809, Jean Baptiste De Lamarck, a French zoologist, stated a theory of evolution. Lamarck stated that evolution occurs because an organism develops characteristics it needs for survival. He believed these characteristics were acquired through the use and disuse of body parts. For example, the giraffe's long neck was acquired by the animal stretching its neck to eat the leaves of trees instead of grass. Lamarck stated that acquired characteristics are passed on to offspring and produce new species. Lamarck's theory has been criticized because it assumes an organism can sense its needs and then change to meet its needs. Studies of inheritance show that acquired traits cannot be inherited because they affect only body cells. Acquired traits do not change the genes in sex cells used to produce offspring.

In 1858, two Englishmen, Charles Darwin (1809–1882) and Alfred Wallace (1823–1913), introduced identical theories of evolution to answer questions about changes in species. Darwin was a naturalist and Wallace was a biologist. At the time, Darwin was in England and Wallace was in Malaya.

Like a number of other scientists, Darwin and Wallace understood that different species are related to each other. Also, they reasoned that new species come from older species. The older species are the ancestors of the new species. These ideas formed the basis of the theory of evolution widely accepted by modern biologists.

FIGURE 21–14. Lamarck would have explained giraffes' long necks by saying that individual giraffes stretched their necks to reach tree leaves. Longer necks were then passed to future generations.

a

b

Darwin and Wallace formed their theories separately at about the same time. However, Darwin is given the major credit for the theory of evolution. This is because he spent many years gathering evidence to support his ideas. Darwin had developed his ideas more fully than Wallace.

As a young man, Darwin was a naturalist on a ship sailing around the world. During the voyage he observed many plant and animal species, including species preserved as fossils. He was particularly interested in the unique forms of life on the Galapagos Islands at the equator. There he studied species not found anywhere else on Earth. Darwin saw that these organisms were similar to life present in other parts of the world. He collected specimens that he took back to England to study. For 20 years after his voyage, Darwin studied the material he had collected. He also studied the breeding of plants and animals on British farms. During this time, Darwin developed a theory of evolution by natural selection. According to Darwin, the organisms best fitted for their environments survive, reproduce, and eventually give rise to new species. A species can become extinct when its environment changes and it is not suited for survival in the new environment.

In the process of evolution, small changes occurring over a long period of time within a species can produce new species. However, gaps in the fossil record often suggest that new species appear suddenly and not gradually. One explanation for the gaps in the fossil record is a theory called punctuated equilibrium.

FIGURE 21–15. Darwin did much study in the Galapagos Islands. The *Brachycereus* cactus (a) and the land iguana (b) are native to the Galapagos Islands.

What is punctuated equilibrium?

According to this theory, the changes in species over time were sudden and swift, and not gradual.

21:6 Natural Selection

Charles Darwin explained his theory of evolution by natural selection in a book he wrote called *On the Origin of Species by Means of Natural Selection*, published in 1859. According to Darwin, changes in species occur through natural selection. **Natural selection** is the process in which the factors in an organism's surroundings determine whether or not the organism will survive and reproduce. If a plant or animal is suited to its surroundings, it has a better chance to grow, mate, and produce offspring than another that is not as well suited. Organisms that produce offspring pass their genes and traits on to the next generation.

Four factors that explain natural selection are:
(1) In nature there is overproduction of offspring.
(2) Variations or differences exist in the members of a species; therefore, no two organisms are exactly alike.
(3) These variations may be favorable for living in a certain environment. Individuals with the favorable variations have an advantage for survival.
(4) Because organisms with the advantage will be more likely to survive and reproduce, they will pass on their variations to the next generation. The population as a whole will become more "fit" for its environment.

Every species produces more young than are needed to replace those that die. In other words, there is an overproduction of offspring. Suppose all the eggs laid by a female frog were to hatch. Also, suppose all the tadpoles lived to reproduce. In five generations, 52 billion frogs could come from one pair of frogs. Darwin estimated that 19 million offspring could result from one pair of elephants in only 750 years.

Compare Lamarck's and Darwin's theories.

What factors explain natural selection?

a
b

FIGURE 21–16. Overproduction of offspring occurs in frogs (a) and dandelions (b).

FIGURE 21–17. An animal's ability to run fast may help it survive to reproduce.

Members of any given species are not exactly alike. For example, some are larger and others are smaller than the average size. Which members of a species are most likely to survive? Food and space in the environment are always limited. Those organisms that are better able to obtain food, water, and oxygen are most likely to survive. Individuals most able to avoid being eaten by their predators may live long enough to reproduce. In dry climates, animals or plants that require very little water are more suited for survival. A wild horse able to run fast may be more likely to survive than a horse that runs slowly. An animal with a high resistance to disease may survive a disease epidemic.

Changes in climate are understood to be important to the evolution of new species. For example, the first land vertebrates may have descended from fishes that lived in freshwater lakes. Changes in climate from moist to dry millions of years ago may have caused many lakes to dry up. Lake-living animals that could breathe out of water survived. They became ancestors of new land-living species.

Making Sure

7. What are two criticisms of Lamarck's theory of evolution?
8. Describe two examples of natural selection.
9. What features would make an animal suited for survival during a cold winter?
10. What kinds of animals and plants are suited for survival in a desert?

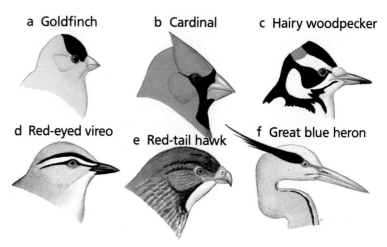

a Goldfinch   b Cardinal   c Hairy woodpecker

d Red-eyed vireo   e Red-tail hawk   f Great blue heron

FIGURE 21–18. The goldfinch (a) has a short beak for eating seeds. The cardinal (b) can crack large seeds and nuts. A hairy woodpecker (c) has a slender beak to probe insects from trees. A red-eyed vireo (d) eats insects. The predator red-tailed hawk (e) can rip and tear. How is the beak of a heron (f) adapted for catching fish?

21:7 Variation

Members of a species have similar characteristics. Yet individuals within a species possess traits that make them different. A trait that makes an individual different from others in its species is called a **variation**. Most variations are minor and not readily observed. Others are major and quite apparent. Examples of major variations are a cat with six toes, an albino deer, bacteria resistant to penicillin, or fruit without seeds. All of these variations are genetic, meaning the traits are controlled by genes. Members of a species are similar in traits because their genes are similar. Genetic variations are due to differences in genes. They are inherited and passed on to offspring.

Variations in individuals affect their ability to survive in a changing environment. Those individuals with unfavorable variations have less chance for survival. The survivors reproduce and pass on the variations to their offspring. During the course of many generations, the variations become widespread among a population. The group as a population may evolve into a new species distinct from its ancestors.

A genetic variation that increases the fitness of an organism for surviving and reproducing in its environment is an **adaptation**. The many different kinds of adaptations include traits related to size, shape, behavior, and body functions. Bird beaks are good examples of adaptations. Some birds, such as the goldfinch, have short beaks suited to eating small seeds. Others have large beaks that are strong enough to crack open large seeds and nuts. Woodpeckers have long, slender beaks they use to peck insects out of trees. The shape of a bird's beak makes it suited for eating the food present in its environment.

What is variation?

Define adaptation.

In 1850 almost all the moths of a certain species near Manchester, England were light in color. The light color blended with the natural color of trees in the area. It was difficult for the light-colored moths to be seen by birds, which would eat them. This kind of adaptation is called **protective coloration**. However, occasionally there occurred in the population some moths that were dark in color. This particular species happened to have two differently colored moths. The birds could easily see the dark moths against the light-colored trees so the dark moths were captured and eaten.

Today the situation is reversed. Most of the moths are dark while only a few are light. This change was caused by natural selection. The environment for the moths changed. In the early part of the nineteenth century, many factories were built. Black soot from their chimneys collected on the trunks and limbs of trees making them a darker color. In 1850 light-colored moths had blended with the natural color of the trees. Later when the trees became dark, light-colored moths showed up against the bark. Birds spotted the moths and ate them.

Dark moths could not be seen very well against the dark tree trunks and limbs. The dark moths had protective coloration when the color of the trees became dark. Fewer dark moths were eaten by birds, so the dark moths lived to reproduce more dark moths. Over the years, the dark moths increased in number until most moths of this species in that area were dark.

With the passage of clean air laws in England, an interesting thing has begun to happen. The population of light-colored moths has begun to grow again. Scientists have been surveying the moth populations and have learned that the dark-colored moths are decreasing in number. The cleaner air has made the environment favorable for the survival of light-colored moths again.

Give an example of protective coloration.

a   b

FIGURE 21–19. Light-colored moths are protected by protective coloration on light trees (a). Dark-colored moths are protected by protective coloration on dark trees (b).

FIGURE 21–20. A forked ear of corn is an example of a mutation.

How can a mutation cause a new trait in an organism?

How can mutation cause a change in a species?

FIGURE 21–21. Albino koalas have color mutations in which no color is produced.

21:8 Mutations and Change

How do organisms acquire adaptations that enable them to survive in a new environment? Sometimes a new trait appears in an organism that was not present in any of its ancestors. New traits can be acquired by mutation (myew TAY shun). A **mutation** is a change in the DNA of an organism. Those changes in the DNA of a gene result in a change in cell chemistry causing changes in color, size, or shape of body parts. Most of them do not cause major changes. Albino organisms have obvious color mutations. In an albino, the genes for color are changed so that the organism has white skin and hair, and pink eyes. The genes control the amount of pigment in cells. With less pigment the organism's features will appear lighter in color. Cattle born without horns, dogs born without tails, and fruit flies born without wings are other obvious examples of mutations. Mutations can be caused by X rays, nuclear or cosmic radiation, and some chemicals.

Many of these known mutations are harmful to organisms. Changes in traits can make it more difficult for an organism to survive. For example, a white albino deer is visible against the green and brown colors of the forest. Without coloration that protects it from wolves and hunters, the deer may not live long enough to reproduce.

However, a mutation can also increase the ability of an organism to survive. For example, an animal born with fewer than the normal number of toes may be able to run faster to escape organisms that hunt it. If a mutation increases an organism's chances for survival, it is likely to be passed on to offspring. Most mutations are less obvious than these examples. In addition to mutation, the exchange of chromosome pieces during meiosis is a source of genetic variation. Genetic variation also occurs when genes rearrange themselves on chromosomes.

The process of evolution is possible because of genetic variations within populations of organisms. Genetic variations resulting from mutations, chromosome exchange, or gene rearrangement may allow organisms to survive in changing environmental conditions. Through millions of years, mutations may have led to many variations in animal and plant species. These mutations may have been responsible for the extinction of some species. As the climate and physical features of Earth constantly changed, favorable mutations could have ensured the survival of many species. Plants and animals with the mutations that made them most suited to the new environments may have survived to produce offspring that were different from their ancestors.

Activity 21-3

A Genetic Factor in Plants

Problem: Do all sorghum seeds have genes for growing into green plants?

Materials

40 sorghum seeds
hand lens
1 petri dish
paper towels
dropper
scissors
forceps
pencil

Procedure

1. Examine the sorghum seeds with a hand lens. Some of the sorghum seeds will grow into green plants. Some will grow into yellow plants.
2. Cut four thicknesses of paper toweling to fit the bottom of a petri dish.
3. Place four paper towel circles in the bottom of the petri dish.
4. Carefully add water to the dish until the paper towels are wet.
5. Use forceps to place 20 sorghum seeds in the dish. Space the seeds evenly throughout the dish.
6. Label the dish with your name.
7. Place the dish where it will receive light.
8. Check the seeds each day. Add water with a dropper if the paper begins to dry.
9. When leaves begin to appear, record the color of the leaves.

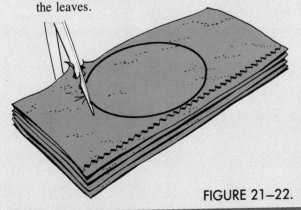

FIGURE 21-22.

10. Continue making observations and recording the results for another week.

Data and Observations

Day	Number of seeds germinated	Number with green leaves	Number with yellow leaves
1			
2			
3			
4			
5			
6			
7			
8			
9			
10			

Questions and Conclusions

1. What differences did you observe in the seeds before they were placed in the dish?
2. Compare the number of plants with green leaves to the number with yellow leaves.
3. Is the yellow color of some leaves due to the lack of light? Explain your answer.
4. Why could you not tell before the seeds germinated if they would produce green or yellow plants?
5. What substance did the green plants have that the others did not have?
6. Will the plants without chlorophyll live as long as the ones with chlorophyll? Why or why not?
7. Do all sorghum seeds have genes for growing into green plants?

FIGURE 21-23. Navel oranges, pink grapefruit, and nectarines are the results of mutations.

What is a purebred?

FIGURE 21-24. A zebpo is a cross between a zebra and a Welsh pony.

21:9 New Varieties

In addition to having a role in evolution, mutations are used by breeders to select new varieties of plants and animals. Mutants with the traits desired for a new variety are selected and bred. **Selective breeding** is the selection and mating of individuals with desired traits. For example, the California navel orange, pink grapefruit, and nectarine have desirable mutations. Each of these new varieties was produced by breeding plants that had these desired traits. Offspring from the breeding were bred again for several generations to increase the number of plants having the trait.

A **breed** is a variety of animal or plant produced through selection. An animal that is a member of a breed is called a **purebred**. Purebreds breed true. That is, the traits of the purebred offspring are like those of the parents. An example is the breed of chickens that lay a large number of eggs during a year. Chickens that are high producers are mated to roosters whose mothers were high producers. Continuous selection over many generations produces a variety of chickens that are high producers of eggs.

When selection involves the mating of two different varieties or breeds of organisms, it is called crossbreeding. It produces a **crossbreed** having the best traits of each breed or variety. Crossbreeds are often stronger and healthier than the purebreds from which they came.

The development of a variety of corn with high disease resistance and high food value is an example of crossbreeding. Corn is a major food of many people in Central and South America. However, most corn varieties are very low in a substance called lysine (LI seen) that is necessary for growth and good health. The few high-lysine varieties of corn usually had low disease resistance or produced very small ears of corn.

Through careful selection and crossbreeding, scientists hoped to develop a variety of corn with all the desired traits. After many years and hundreds of crosses, the new corn variety is high in lysine, produces large ears, and is disease resistant.

Polyploidy is also used in the development of new plant varieties. **Polyploidy** is a condition in which an organism has more than the normal amount of chromosomes. For example, most McIntosh apple trees have 34 chromosomes in their cells. The polyploid variety has 68. It produces an apple twice as large as the normal variety. Polyploid varieties of plants can be produced by treating them with the drug colchicine (KAHL chuh seen). Colchicine prevents chromosomes from splitting apart during reduction division of meiosis. As a result, sex cells are produced that have twice the normal number of chromosomes. These sex cells are polyploid.

Making Sure

11. What is genetic variation?
12. Explain why populations, not individuals, evolve.
13. Name two examples of adaptations. Tell how they help organisms survive.
14. How does selective breeding improve plants and animals?

Technology

DNA Hybridization

Closely related organisms have very similar DNA. To show possible relationships between groups of organisms, scientists can now compare the DNA of each group. The technique is called DNA–DNA hybridization. The DNA from two different organisms is isolated and mixed together. If the two organisms are closely related, the two types of DNA bind together. If the organisms are less related, the DNA material does not match so well. The degree of similarity is measured by the amount of heat needed to separate the DNA that has bound together. More heat is needed to part DNA that is more alike. When this procedure is followed for several different organisms, the levels of relationship can be plotted like a family tree. The family tree illustrates patterns of evolution within the group.

Using DNA–DNA hybridization to examine the relationships between humans and apes, scientists have found that humans are more closely related to chimpanzees than to orangutans or gorillas. This indicates that humans and chimpanzees evolved more recently than any of the other apes. Gibbons were found to be the most ancient group of apes and the most distinct from humans. The technique has also been used on extinct animals, such as the mammoth and the quagga, which is related to the zebra. It could also be used on fossil humans to help unravel the mystery of our ancestry.

DNA–DNA hybridization has already answered many questions concerning plant evolution. Scientists may, in time, be able to interpret the pathways of evolution for all organisms.

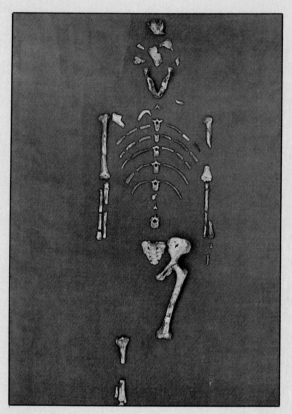

Lucy

The remarkable discovery in November of 1974, of a 3.5-million-year-old skeleton caused great excitement in the scientific world. The discovery was made by an American anthropologist, Donald Johanson, while leading a team of scientists on a fossil collecting trip in Ethiopia, Africa. While returning to camp one day, he spotted a bone sticking out of the dirt. Following a long and careful examination of the area, over 200 more bones were found. The scientists were able to piece these bones together to form an incomplete skeleton of an individual that had lived 3.5 million years ago.

From the waist up, it resembled the skeleton of an ape. It must have had a brain that was only one-third the size of that of modern humans. The jaw and teeth also resembled those of an ape. From the waist down, however, this skeleton resembled that of a human. The hip and leg bones joined together the same as in a human. The animal that once owned this skeleton would have walked upright in a way similar to modern humans. Scientists could also calculate that this individual had been a 1.1 meter, 29.5 kg female. Johanson and his group named the skeleton Lucy.

While only 40 percent of her skeleton was recovered, Lucy represents the most complete fossil of its kind. The 3.5-million-year age of the skeleton was determined by measuring the amount of radioactive material from the surrounding volcanic rock. From close examination of Lucy, scientists could deduce much about the past history of humans. Other scientists later began to question if Lucy could really have walked. They noted that Lucy's finger and toe bones are slightly curved, a feature of tree climbing animals. This was interpreted to mean that Lucy may have climbed and lived in trees. Later, new fossil finds showed that Lucy and her kind did walk upright. In 1978 Mary Leakey, a distinguished anthropologist, discovered some fossilized footprints during a fossil hunt in another part of Africa. These footprints were similar to a modern human's but were made in soft volcanic ash 3.7 million years ago. This was close to the estimated time of Lucy's existence. This set of footprints was accepted as evidence that Lucy's kind walked erect. To some scientists, Lucy represents an important link in the evolution of humans. To others, she represents a distinct, although related, group of species.

CHAPTER 21
Review

Summary

1. New species have evolved from older species and all species descend from a common ancestor. 21:1
2. Many species of the past are no longer alive today. Many species alive today did not exist long ago. 21:2
3. Fossils are evidence of the kinds of organisms that lived long ago. 21:2
4. Fossils indicate that ancient organisms were generally less complex in structure than more recent organisms. 21:3
5. Geologic history is divided into eras and periods. In different eras and periods, the kinds of life, climates, and Earth's surface were different. 21:3
6. Homologous structures, vestigial organs, and similarities in embryos and proteins provide evidence for evolution. 21:4
7. In 1858 Charles Darwin proposed a theory of evolution by natural selection. 21:5
8. Natural selection is a process in which the fittest organisms survive and reproduce. 21:6
9. An adaptation enables an organism to survive and reproduce in a certain environment. 21:7
10. Mutations are changes in the genetic code that cause changes in the traits of organisms. 21:8
11. Selective breeding is used to develop new varieties of organisms. 21:9

Vocabulary

Write a sentence using the following words or terms correctly.

adaptation
breed
crossbreed
evolution
fossil

homologous
mutation
natural selection
polyploidy
protective coloration

purebred
radioactive element
selective breeding
variation

Questions for Review

Do not write in this book.

A. True or False
Determine whether each of the following sentences is true or false. Rewrite the false statements to make them correct.

1. Fossils can be formed in sedimentary rocks.
2. Most plants and animals that lived long ago died and became fossils.

3. Evidence shows life may have lived on Earth for 3 billion years.
4. A bird wing and a butterfly wing are homologous structures.
5. The human heart is a vestigial organ.
6. Fossil records show that birds and mammals were always present on Earth.
7. Seed plants were always the most plentiful plants.
8. A mutation causes a change in a trait.
9. Methods used to date rocks indicate Earth is about five billion years old.
10. Purebred animals do not breed true.

B. Multiple Choice
Choose the word or phrase that correctly completes the following sentences.

1. Precambrian time began about *(5, 1.5, 2, 2.5)* billion years ago.
2. *(Precambrian, Paleozoic, Mesozoic, Cenozoic)* rocks are the oldest.
3. *(Minerals, Water, Rocks, Ice)* cause(s) an organism to become petrified.
4. Overproduction of offspring *(increases, decreases, does not affect)* the chances of a species surviving.
5. *(Homo erectus, Homo sapiens, Australopithecus afarensis)* is the scientific name for Neanderthals.
6. The *(Precambrian, Paleozoic, Cenozoic)* era is the most recent time.
7. Protective coloration aids survival of *(an individual, a species, both individuals and species)*.
8. Fossils of the ancestors of today's horses show that horses have *(increased, decreased, not changed)* in size.
9. A *(mutant, purebreed, crossbreed)* is a member of a breed.
10. A(n) *(mutant, breed, adaptation)* is a variety or type of animal or plant produced through selection.

C. Completion
Complete each of the following sentences with the correct word or phrase.

1. _____ of the species alive on Earth long ago are no longer alive today.
2. Dating of fossils with _____ elements is one way to tell their age.
3. Scientists have divided Earth's history into _____ major divisions.
4. The human appendix is an example of a(n) _____ organ.
5. Lamarck thought _____ characteristics are inherited.
6. _____ is the mating of two different varieties or breeds of organisms.
7. _____ selection has been described as survival of the fittest.
8. Resistance to DDT is passed from parent flies to _____ through their genes.

9. A(n) _____ can cause a change in an inherited trait that may increase an organism's chances for survival.

10. Radiation such as _____ can cause mutations.

D. How and Why

1. How does a plant or animal become a fossil? Give some examples.
2. What is natural selection?
3. How can plant and animal species change through natural selection?
4. How can mutations cause changes in species?
5. Select an animal you know and explain how it is suited to its environment.
6. How do vestigial organs provide evidence of evolution?
7. What are adaptations and how are they related to survival?

Ideas to Explore

1. **Project:** If fossils can be found in your community, make a collection and identify each one. Through library research learn about the scientific field called paleontology.
2. **Challenge:** Read a biography of Charles Darwin and make a report to your class about Darwin's life.
3. **Project:** Visit a natural history museum and locate exhibits that illustrate the theory of evolution by natural selection.
4. **Challenge:** Prepare a report on the extinction of dinosaurs.
5. **Challenge:** Do library research on the evolution of a species such as the horse. Make a poster showing changes in the species.
6. **Challenge:** Read a biography of Lamarck. Make a report to your class on Lamarck's theory of evolution.
7. **Challenge:** Make a report on the extinct flying Archaeopteryx.

Readings

Attenborough, David. *Life on Earth: A Natural History*. Boston: Little, Brown, 1980.

Bingham, Roger. "On the Life of Mr. Darwin." *Science 82*, April, 1982, pp.34–39.

Futuyma, D. J. *Science on Trial: The Case for Evolution*. New York: Pantheon Books, 1983.

Hopf, Alice L. *Nature's Pretenders*. New York: G. P. Putnam's Sons, 1979.

Leakey, Richard E. *Human Origins*. New York: Lodestar, 1982.

Ricciuti, Edward R. *Older Than the Dinosaurs*. New York: T.Y. Crowell, 1980.

Heredity
Background Data

If you look up the definition of the term genetics, you will find it means the study of heredity. Heredity is defined as the passing of traits from parents to offspring. Some examples of these traits include dimples or the lack of them, hair or eye color, and the ability or inability to roll the tongue in the shape of a U. In plants, inherited traits include stem length, leaf color, and seed type.

Traits are controlled by genes. Genes are part of a larger, very complex molecule called a chromosome. Each parent provides half the chromosomes, and therefore, half the genes that determine the characteristics of the offspring. Two genes control each trait.

Genes may be dominant, recessive, or mixed. In plants, stem length is controlled by two genes. If a plant has two long-stemmed genes or a long-stemmed and a short-stemmed gene, the plant will be long-stemmed. If a plant has two short-stemmed genes, the plant will be short-stemmed. As you can see, if only one of the two genes contains the code for long stem length, the plant will be long-stemmed. For this reason, long stem length is said to be dominant, and short stem length is said to be recessive. A hybrid contains mixed genes, that is, a gene for both the dominant and recessive trait. In these individuals, only the dominant trait is expressed. Individuals are said to be pure if they have two dominant or two recessive genes.

Input/Output

Enter the program into your computer exactly as it is printed. After you enter the entire program, type RUN. If there is a problem, type LIST and check that you have entered the program exactly as it is printed. Remember, symbols and punctuation are important and must be typed as printed here. REM statements are provided in the program to help you. They do not need to be entered in order for the program to run. When all corrections have been made, be sure to save the program by typing SAVE HEREDITY, or whatever name you wish to give the program.

Once the program is running, the computer will ask you to enter the first gene of parent one. You will enter an upper- or lowercase letter and RETURN. You will then be asked the same question for the second gene of parent one, and you will enter your response. The same questions will be asked for parent two. Using the data you enter, the computer will generate a Punnett square showing the number and type of offspring that can be expected as a result of a cross of these two parents.

Programming Notes

The computer reads each line of the program and executes the command listed there. Line 10 clears the screen. Some computers use the command CLS, others use HOME. Use the command your computer recognizes to clear the screen.

The variables used in this program are listed below.

W$,X$,Y$,Z$	genotypes for the Punnett square
A$,B$,C$,D$, E$,F$	genes for both parents
W,X,Y,Z	percentages for the genotypes in each square

Line 20 assigns the word "hybrid" to all four squares. This assignment can be changed later in the program if necessary. Lines 20 through 80 are used to enter the genetic data about both parents. Line 90 arranges the genes in a simple arrangement for the Punnett square. The genes are checked to see if they are the same in lines 100 through 130. If the genes match, PURE is printed. The conditions that give a 50:50 ratio are checked for in line 150. A 25:50:25 ratio is checked for in line 160. Line 180 clears the screen. Lines 190 through 280 print the Punnett square. Line 290 loops the program back to the beginning.

Program

```
10   HOME : IF Q = 1 THEN Q = 0: GOTO
     190
20 W$ = "HYBRID":X$ = W$:Y$ = W$
   :Z$ = W$
30   PRINT : PRINT "FOR THE FIRST
     PARENT"
40   PRINT : PRINT "THE FIRST GEN
     E (small or CAPITAL)";: INPUT
     A$
50   PRINT "THE SECOND GENE (smal
     l or CAPITAL)";: INPUT B$
60   PRINT : PRINT : PRINT "FOR T
     HE SECOND PARENT"
70   PRINT : PRINT "THE FIRST GEN
     E (small or CAPITAL)";: INPUT
     E$:C$ = E$
80   PRINT "THE SECOND GENE (smal
     l or capital)";: INPUT F$:D$
     = F$
90   IF A$ = F$ THEN C$ = F$:D$ =
     E$
100  IF A$ = C$ THEN W$ = "PURE"
110  IF B$ = C$ THEN X$ = "PURE"
120  IF A$ = D$ THEN Y$ = "PURE"
130  IF B$ = D$ THEN Z$ = "PURE"
140  IF A$ = B$ AND C$ = D$ THEN
     W = 100:X = 100:Y = 100:Z =
     100: GOTO 180
150  IF A$ = B$ OR C$ = D$ THEN
     W = 50:X = 50:Y = 50:Z = 50:
     GOTO 180
160  IF A$ = C$ AND B$ = D$ THEN
     W = 25:X = 50:Y = 50:Z = 25:
     GOTO 180
170  W = 25:X = 25:Y = 25:Z = 25
180  Q = 1: GOTO 10
190  PRINT  TAB( 13)A$; TAB( 30)
     B$
200  PRINT "--------------------
     --------------------"
210  PRINT C$; TAB( 5)"/  ";A$;C
     $; TAB( 20)"/  ";B$;C$; TAB(
     37)"/"
220  PRINT  TAB( 5)"/  ";W$; TAB(
     20)"/  ";X$; TAB( 37)"/"
230  PRINT  TAB( 5)"/  ";W;" %";
     TAB( 20)"/  ";X;" %"; TAB(
     37)"/"
240  PRINT "--------------------
     --------------------"
250  PRINT D$; TAB( 5)"/  ";A$;D
     $; TAB( 20)"/  ";B$;D$; TAB(
     37)"/"
260  PRINT  TAB( 5)"/  ";Y$; TAB(
     20)"/  ";Z$; TAB( 37)"/"
270  PRINT  TAB( 5)"/  ";Y;" %";
     TAB( 20)"/  ";Z;" %";; TAB(
     37)"/"
280  PRINT "--------------------
     --------------------"
290  PRINT : PRINT "ENTER FOR AN
     OTHER SQUARE";: INPUT Q$: GOTO
     10
```

Challenge: On Your Own

You may wish to use this program to test a series of crosses. Start with two pure parents. After the first cross, use two of the offspring to complete the second cross. You may need to record the information on a separate sheet of paper. Try to determine why seeds produced by hybrid parents often will not produce the same characteristics as those exhibited by the parents.

THE ENVIRONMENT

Moose under Alaskan pipeline

UNIT 7

*S*cience and technology are important to today's society. Advances and discoveries have made life more convenient. But what is the price of this technology? How has it affected the environment? The Trans-Alaska pipeline provides needed fuel for industry and transportation. What impact has its construction had on the tundra? Was raising the pipeline to allow animals to pass a solution? How does human influence affect Earth?

Pipeline construction

481

Natural disasters can completely destroy the life in an ecosystem. Following the volcanic eruption in 1980 of Mount St. Helens, Washington, the area was covered by a thick layer of pumice and ash. In just a few years, annual plants have recolonized the area as shown below. It will be several centuries before this area is reforested. How do plants become established on bare rock? What are the stages of succession in an ecosystem like this?

CHAPTER 22
THE BIOSPHERE

22:1 The Biosphere

Life on Earth is limited to a very narrow zone called the **biosphere** (BI uh sfihr). If Earth were reduced to the size of an apple, the biosphere would be no thicker than the apple's skin. The biosphere extends about eight kilometers above Earth's surface and below sea level. But most organisms occupy the small portion of the biosphere that extends only a few meters above and below Earth's surface. Here conditions for life are most favorable.

Organisms live within the biosphere. The part of the biosphere that surrounds an organism is called its **environment.** Organisms form complex relationships within an environment. The study of the relationships between organisms and their environments is called **ecology** (ih KAHL uh jee).

Living organisms interacting with each other and their nonliving environment make up an **ecosystem**. The word ecosystem is a shortening of the term ecological system. An ecosystem can be large, such as a whole ocean, or it can be small, such as a drop of water. A forest, a fallen log, a pond, or a puddle of water can be an ecosystem. Within each ecosystem are various kinds of living organisms. Examples of living organisms in ecosystems are people, trees, fish, algae, molds, and bacteria. Examples of the nonliving parts of ecosystems are sunlight, air, water, soil,

GOALS:
1. You will learn the major features of ecosystems, communities, and populations.
2. You will learn how communities change in size and how succession produces a climax community.
3. You will learn the characteristics of different biomes.

Define ecology and ecosystem.

heat, wind, and various chemicals. The living and nonliving parts of an ecosystem interact with each other and thereby make a system.

Each ecosystem is a region or area through which matter and energy are moved. Much of the matter is material used for food by organisms within the ecosystem. The energy involved may be in the form of sunlight or chemical energy present in food. This energy is used by the organisms in the ecosystem. All the ecosystems on Earth, large and small, combined together make up the biosphere.

Making Sure

1. In what part of the biosphere do most organisms live? Why?
2. List five examples of nonliving parts of ecosystems.

22:2 Communities

An ecosystem contains one or more communities of living organisms. All the organisms living together in a certain area make up a **community**. Each has species of animals, plants, and other organisms that live together. The life of each species depends on other species living in the community.

All the organisms of one species in a community are called a **population**. For instance, the bass population of a lake is all the bass in the lake. Mice living in a city block make up the mouse population of that block. The leopard frogs in a pond and the dandelions in a lawn are two different populations. What other plant or animal populations can you name?

What is a population?

FIGURE 22–1. Communities consist of many populations of organisms. Usually only a few species are dominant. Consider the dominant species in the communities shown (a–d).

a

b

To describe a community, you need to know what populations are present. Also, you need to know the size of each population. Any one community may contain hundreds of different populations. However, of these many populations, usually two or three are larger. The larger populations make up the dominant species.

Communities on land are often known by the dominant plant species. In some cases, these dominant plants are trees. For example, beech-maple forests have beech trees and maple trees as dominant species. Oak trees and hickory trees are the dominant species in an oak-hickory forest. These two communities differ in many ways because the dominant trees are different. What are the dominant plant species in the community where you live?

In lakes and streams, animal species may be used to identify communities. Large-mouth bass and sunfish may be dominant in a pond. Other fish species may be present, but bass and sunfish are dominant because they are present in the greatest numbers.

How is a community described?

Making Sure

3. What is the difference between a community and a population?
    a. List some examples of communities.
    b. List some examples of populations.
4. What populations or organisms are found in the community of which you are a part?
5. How are the populations in a community dependent on each other?

c

d

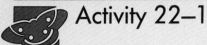

Activity 22–1
Conditions for Plant Growth

Problem: What environmental factors affect plant growth?

Materials

5 small milk cartons for each team
40 seeds for each team   labels
potting soil   scissors
sand   plastic sandwich bags
250-mL beaker   balance

Procedure

1. The class will be divided into six teams. Each team will have the same kind of seeds. Soak the 40 seeds for your team in a beaker of water overnight.
2. Cut the tops from five small milk cartons.
3. Label the cartons 1 to 5. Fill carton 1 with dry potting soil. Fill carton 2 with moistened sand. Fill cartons 3, 4, and 5 with wet potting soil.
4. Plant eight of the soaked seeds in each carton. With your fingers, gently push the seeds into the soil until they are just buried. Plant the seeds so that there is equal space around each one.
5. Place carton 3 in the refrigerator.
6. Place carton 4 in a warm, dark place.
7. Place cartons 1, 2, and 5 in a warm, lighted area.
8. Make a chart like the one shown under Data and Observations.
9. Predict which cartons will provide conditions for seeds to sprout. Record this in column A.

10. Predict the number of seeds in each carton that will grow into plants. Record this in column B.
11. Water the seeds in cartons 2, 3, 4, and 5, three times a week just enough to keep them moist.
12. For four weeks, count and record in columns C, D, E, and F, the number of plants in each carton. Make the observations at the end of each week.
13. After four weeks, cut the plants from each carton at soil level with scissors. **CAUTION:** *Be careful when using scissors.* Put the cut plants from each carton into separate sandwich bags. Measure the mass of each bag of plants on a balance and record this mass on the chart in column G.
14. Compare the masses of each carton.
15. In a class chart on the chalkboard, compare the masses of each carton for each team.
16. Compare the growths of each carton with the same numbered cartons of the other teams.

Data and Observations

Carton	Predicted Numbers		Actual Numbers of Plants				Mass
	A	B	C	D	E	F	G
1							
2							
3							
4							
5							

Questions and Conclusions

1. Which carton was the control for each variable?
2. In which carton were there two variables?
3. What were the observed differences in plant growth among each of the conditions provided?
4. Why did some seeds sprout but then fail to grow?
5. What environmental factors affect plant growth?

FIGURE 22–2.

FIGURE 22–3. The population of dandelions in a lawn may be stable or unstable.

22:3 Changes in Population

A population that is not changing in size is a stable population. An unstable population is one that is changing in size. Stocking a lake with bass illustrates changing the size of a population. The first fish added to the lake reproduce and increase the bass population. Eventually, the size of the population becomes limited by the amount of food and oxygen available. If the bass exceed the limits set by the available food and oxygen, individuals begin to die. The decrease in numbers continues until the population reaches a size for which the food and oxygen supply is adequate. A condition in the environment that stops a population from increasing in size is called a **limiting factor**. Food, oxygen, temperature, and disease are examples of limiting factors.

Runoff of fertilizer from farmland into a lake results in a massive growth of algae. When the algae die and decay, enormous levels of bacterial growth results, and the lake's oxygen is used up. A lowered oxygen supply would have a limiting effect on a population of fish. Dumping hot water used by industry into rivers increases the water temperature. The higher water temperature makes growth impossible for most kinds of organisms. Due to the lack of food supplies, fish populations decrease in size. Fish may not be able to survive because of higher temperatures and lowered oxygen levels alone.

Limiting factors that affect plants include temperature, sunlight, rainfall, and soil nutrients. For example, palm trees and orange trees will not grow in cold climates. The number of young trees that can grow on the floor of a forest is limited by the amount of available sunlight. During a drought, a farmer's crop production

What is a stable population?

How does fertilizer runoff affect a lake?

FIGURE 22–4. Changes in food supply affect the size of a population of mice in a grain field.

What are two important limiting factors for animal populations?

may be reduced because there is not enough water for all the plants. Plants that grow in a garden may die as soil nutrients are used up and not replaced with fertilizer.

Food is one important limiting factor for animal populations. Another is predators. A predator is an animal that kills and eats other animals. The animal killed by a predator is called its prey. Killing by predators helps control the size of the prey's population. Consider a population of mice that moves into a grainfield. Because of the abundance of available food, the number of mice will increase through reproduction. The population size may also be increased by other mice that migrate into the grainfield. Hawks, snakes, and other mouse predators will be attracted to the large mouse population. The predator population will then increase. Every mouse eaten by a predator limits the size of the mouse population. The food supply also becomes a limiting factor. Mice will start to die of starvation because there is not enough food. Since the mice are food for the predators, a decrease in the size of the mouse population also controls the number of predators. All species of animals that interact within a community are dependent upon one another.

Making Sure

6. Define limiting factor.
7. What are four limiting factors?
8. How does a water temperature increase affect some fish?
9. Describe an example of a change in population.

Activity 22–2

Counting Populations

Problem: How can you determine the size of a population?

Materials

glass-marking pencil
clear plastic sheet

Procedure

1. Predict the number of ladybugs in the diagram below and record the number in a chart of data and observations similar to the one shown.
2. Place a clear plastic sheet over the diagram. Make a population count by placing a checkmark next to each ladybug. Record the actual number of ladybugs at the bottom of the chart. Next to this number, record the amount of time it takes to make the count.
3. Count the ladybug population a second time by sampling. Sample by selecting and counting only a portion of the population. Count the number of ladybugs in the top left square and record the number in the chart where shown.
4. Multiply the number of ladybugs in the top left square by the total number of squares. Record these numbers in the chart.
5. Record the amount of time it takes to make the count, at the top of the chart.

Data and Observations

Predicted number _____		Time _____
Number in top left square	× Total number of squares	= Estimated total number
_____	× _____	= _____
Actual number _____		Time _____

Questions and Conclusions

1. How many ladybugs did you predict were in the diagram?
2. How many ladybugs were in the actual count?
3. How many ladybugs did you estimate with the sample count?
4. Which way was faster—making an actual count or sampling?
5. Were the results about the same?
6. What is the advantage of sampling a population for counting?
7. How can you determine the size of a population?

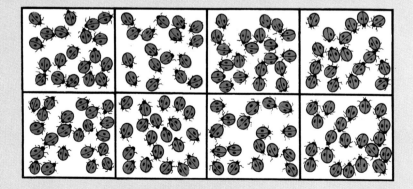

FIGURE 22–5.

FIGURE 22–6. Succession in a pond community.

What causes a pond to be filled?

22:4 Succession

When populations change in size, the community also changes. Suppose you visit a young forest now and then return in 50 years. You will probably find different dominant species. Dominant species slowly give way to other species that become dominant. This gradual change in a community is called **succession**. During succession, plant populations are slowly replaced by others.

Changes in a vacant field over time illustrate succession. If there is enough rainfall, sunlight, and warmth, annual plants begin to grow in the field. Animals such as worms, grasshoppers, and other insects appear. Plants and animals living in the field die, decay, and add to the fertility of the soil. Perennial plants, bushes, and small trees begin to grow. Populations of other animals such as rabbits, mice, foxes, skunks, and moles develop. Soon trees take root in the fertile soil and a forest begins to grow.

A **climax community** is the last stage in succession. In the example above, the mature forest is the climax community. Each region follows a certain pattern of succession depending on the climate and soil conditions. In some regions, grassland or desert may be the climax community.

A pond illustrates succession in a water community. Aquatic life such as fish, water plants, and frogs may live in the pond. Through the years, plants growing in the pond die and settle to the bottom. Water draining into the pond from the land around it carries soil that settles to the bottom. As soil and plant materials build up in the pond, it becomes shallow. After about 50 years, there is no longer enough water for the fish to survive. The pond has turned into a marsh or bog. Grasses and small trees now grow where there was once water. Animals such as frogs and turtles increase in number. The process of growth, death, and decay leads to a filling in of the open water area. In 100 years, the pond is completely filled. Eventually the grasses and shrubs will be replaced by trees and the climax community may be a deciduous forest. The animal life also changes until it is completely different from that of the earlier pond water.

Making Sure

10. Define succession.
11. Describe succession in a vacant field.
12. Define climax community.
13. Describe succession in a water community such as a pond.
14. What is a possible climax community of a pond?
15. What effect will flood, fire, or logging have on succession?

Activity 22–3   Observing Succession

Problem: What happens in succession?

Materials

dried grass
pond water
clean jar, 0.5 L
glass plate for cover
microscope
dropper
microscope slides
coverslips
metric ruler

Procedure

1. Fill the jar with pond water to within three centimeters of the top.
2. Place a handful of dried grass in the jar of water.
3. Cover the jar with the glass plate.
4. Place the jar where it will not be disturbed for three days.
5. After three days, hold the jar up to the light. Record what you observe.
6. Use a dropper to take a sample of water from around the edge of the jar.

FIGURE 22–7.

7. Place a drop of the sample on a microscope slide and add a coverslip.
8. Observe under low power and high power.
9. Record your observations. Make drawings of organisms you find. Try to find out what the organisms are.
10. Take samples from various depths in the jar and prepare wet mounts.
11. Record your observations.
12. Repeat steps 10 and 11 every two days for four weeks.

Data and Observations

Date	Appearance	Organisms present

Questions and Conclusions

1. How many kinds of organisms did you observe at the end of three days?
2. How many kinds of organisms did you observe at the end of four weeks?
3. Where did the organisms come from that were not present the first day?
4. What organisms appeared first?
5. How can you explain the changes that took place in the jar?
6. At the end of two weeks, were there still large numbers of the organisms that appeared at first?
7. What ecological idea is demonstrated by the change of populations in the jar community?
8. How would the organisms in pond water from a different pond compare with the organisms in the pond water you used?
9. What happens in succession?

a

b

FIGURE 22–8. The desert (a) and the tundra (b) are two biomes with extreme climates. The organisms that live in such conditions must be adapted to survive.

22:5 Biomes

What comes to mind when you think of a desert? You might think of a hot, dry place with sand, cactus plants, and snakes. What comes to mind when you think of a forest? Perhaps you think of a cool, green, shady place with trees, birds and small animals.

Different regions of Earth have different climates (CLI mutz) and different kinds of organisms. Climate is the average weather in a region over a long period of time. A desert climate is hot and dry. The organisms that live in a desert are adapted to living in a hot, dry climate.

What is a biome?

Scientists call a region with a distinct climate, a particular plant type, and the organisms that live in the region a **biome** (BI ohm). A desert region and the organisms that live in it may be considered a biome. A tropical rain forest or a temperate forest are other examples of biomes. Each has a distinct climate and organisms that are adapted to living in that climate.

What is an ecotone?

Biomes do not have clearly defined boundaries. Rather, one biome blends gradually into another. These areas between biomes are called **ecotones** (EE kuh tohnz). For example, a seashore may be classified as an ecotone between an ocean biome and the biome on the land.

Scientists disagree about how many kinds of biomes there are. Some scientists may classify one region as a biome. Other scientists may classify the same region as an ecotone or part of another biome. Most scientists agree on the existence of eight major biomes. These are tundra, taiga, temperate deciduous forest, grasslands, desert, tropical rain forest, ocean, and fresh water. Figure 22–9 shows the locations of the six land biomes surrounded by the ocean biome. Freshwater biomes occur throughout all the regions.

FIGURE 22–9. Six major land biomes

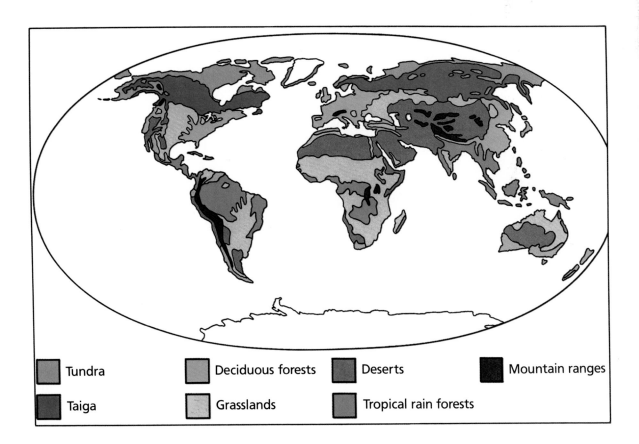

Tundra

Taiga

Deciduous forests

Grasslands

Deserts

Tropical rain forests

Mountain ranges

Making Sure

16. How is climate related to the kinds of organisms living in a biome?
17. Refer to Figure 22–9 and locate the biome where you live. Describe its climate and some organisms that live there.
18. Why do scientists disagree about the number of distinct biomes on Earth?

FIGURE 22–10. The Uakari, a monkey of the Amazon forests

Climate: 200 to 400 cm annual precipitation; 25°C constant temperature, humid
Plant life: vines, palm, orchids, ferns
Animal life: monkeys, sloths, termites, anteaters, ants, reptiles, parrots and other birds

FIGURE 22–11. *Rafflesia*, the largest flower, grows in Asian tropical rain forests.

22:6 Land Biomes
Tropical Rain Forest

Tropical rain forests are found in low-lying regions near the equator where rainfall is very high and the temperature is warm throughout the year. More species of plants and animals live in the tropical rain forest than in all of the other biomes of the world combined. The major areas of tropical rain forest exist in Central and South America, Central Africa, India, and Southeast Asia. Each one of these areas has its own particular community of plants and animals.

Because the air in a tropical rain forest is constantly humid, life of all kinds abounds. No single plant or animal is present in large enough numbers to be dominant. Tall evergreen trees, vines, and other plants that grow on the trees make up most of the plant life in the tropical rain forest. The dense tops of the trees form a canopy that shields the ground below from sunlight. This results in sparse plant life on the ground. Many plants are found on the branches of trees far above the forest floor. These are called epiphytes (EP uh fitez). Animal life is most abundant in the treetops. Mammals that live in the trees include monkeys, bats, and mice. In the canopy, animals have more protection from predators than when they are on the ground. Many insect species are found in the rain forest. Big cats, such as the leopard and jaguar, both capable of climbing trees, are usually the largest of the predators. The relationships among species are more complex than in other biomes. Some plants have evolved specialized ways of pollination that depend upon the particular behavior of a single animal species. For example, some flowers are pollinated by mice or bats.

The soil of the tropical rain forests is very poor in nutrients. When organic material falls to the forest floor it is rapidly decomposed. The constant high termperature causes dead plant and animal matter to decay before it can add humus and enrich the soil. Nutrients are quickly absorbed by roots. Heavy rainfall washes the remaining minerals out of the soil. Tropical rain forests are being clear-cut and burnt for farming. This causes rapid erosion of the soil by rain. Only short-term farming is possible because the land becomes useless within a few years. From 1966 to 1970 over 280 million hectares of forest were cut. This represented over 40 percent of the tropical forests. It is estimated that by the end of the century, most of these forests will have disappeared. Many species are being destroyed before they have even been discovered and described. The value of these to people will never be known.

FIGURE 22–12. In the hot, humid conditions of a tropical rain forest there is luxuriant growth of many different plants.

Why is rain forest soil poor for farming?

FIGURE 22–13. The clearance of a tropical rain forest for farming is permanent. In some cases species not yet known or classified are being destroyed.

FIGURE 22–14. Downy woodpecker.

Climate: 75 to 250 cm annual precipitation; −24° to 38°C temperature
Plant life: hickory, maple, beech, oak, tulip, sycamore, birch
Animal life: deer, black bears, squirrels, beetles, woodpeckers

FIGURE 22–15. Prairie dog

Climate: 25 to 100 cm annual precipitation; 0° to 25°C temperature
Plant life: grasses, bluestems
Animal life: antelope, lion, rabbits, prairie dogs, bison

Temperate Deciduous Forest

Deciduous forests once covered much of the northeastern and southeastern parts of the United States, all of Europe, and parts of Japan and Australia. Most of these forests have been cleared and the land used for farming and cities. Four seasons occur in this biome: spring, summer, autumn, and winter. In autumn, the leaves of the deciduous trees change color and fall. The trees are left bare during the winter. The falling of leaves in autumn may be related to the lack of available water during the winter.

In spring, there is a rapid growth of a variety of herbaceous, perennial plants. Most of the early spring plants have formed seeds before the leaves develop on the trees. The new tree leaves form a dense covering that prevents sunlight from reaching the forest floor. Very few herbaceous plants can survive after this time. Many bird species use the deciduous forest for nesting and feeding. Small rodents and other mammals find homes in hollow trees, or underground near tree roots, where they can survive the cold winters. Because many temperate deciduous forests have been cut for farmland or homes, some of the native animals can no longer be found there.

Grassland

Grasslands are found in the interiors of all the continents. Many different species of grasses make up the grasslands. Some grow no taller than 15 cm, while others can grow up to 250 cm. Precipitation in a grassland is irregular and is the limiting factor to plant succession. Temperatures range from very high during the hot summer to below freezing in the winter.

The great grasslands of the world, such as the savanna of Africa and the prairies of North America, are capable of supporting large herds of grazing mammals. Different animals are adapted to feed on different types of grass. In the African savanna, zebras eat tall, fibrous grasses, and antelopes, such as gnus (NEWZ) and gazelles, eat shorter grasses. Hartebeests eat the leftover dry stalks. Large herds of animals regularly move from one region to another so that their food supply is never used up. These animals are preyed upon by larger mammals such as lions and cougars. Many small animals are adapted for burrowing in the soft soils.

Grasslands have been heavily used for crop cultivation and pastureland. When grasslands are disturbed, they are often changed into either woods or deserts. Grassland soils are bound together by the roots of grasses and when these are removed, the soil is carried away by the wind.

FIGURE 22–16. A deciduous temperate forest is usually full of shade. Before the leaves open in the spring, many beautiful wildflowers cover the forest floor.

FIGURE 22–17. A grassland biome of North America has perennial wildflowers as well as grasses. These are grazed upon by herds of animals such as bison.

FIGURE 22–18. A cactus of the American deserts

Climate: less than 10 cm annual precipitation; temperature 10° to 38°C
Plant life: cacti, greasewood, sagebrush, creosote, mesquite, saguaro, euphorbias
Animal life: lizards, insects, mice, snakes, rabbits, armadillos, birds

FIGURE 22–19. A euphorbia of the old world deserts

Desert

Deserts are found in Africa, Asia, in western North and South America, and Australia. A desert is a region with less than 10 cm of rain per year. The lack of water is the limiting factor to plant and animal life in a desert. The deserts of northern Chile and the Sahara of North Africa get little or no rain. These areas are huge sandy stretches of land with very little plant life. The annual rainfall occurs within a short period of time and it is followed by rapid plant growth.

Many deserts have a wide range of daily temperatures. It is hot during the day and cool at night. Depending on the average annual temperature, deserts are classified as hot or cold. The Mojave Desert of Southern California is an example of a hot desert. Parts of Nevada, Utah, and California form the Great Basin Desert, which is a cold desert.

In deserts, individual plants grow spaced apart with bare areas separating them. Desert plants survive because they are adapted to living with a limited water supply. For example, many have a waxy outer covering to prevent excess loss of water to the air. Many have roots that spread out for great distances to take advantage of infrequent rainfall. Some have roots that reach down to water deep in the ground. Following a rainstorm, cacti of the American deserts and euphorbias (yoo FOR bee uz) of the Old World deserts store water in their stem tissues. Cacti and euphorbias have evolved other similar adaptations. Both groups have species with needlelike leaves that help to reduce water loss. This is an example of two different groups of plants becoming adapted in the same way. During the rainy season, seeds may sprout to produce beautiful, annual wildflowers. These plants sprout, grow, flower, and produce seed all within a few weeks. Seeds of annuals can survive in the soil for long periods of drought. The taller plants have fleshy tissues that conserve water or have small leathery leaves that are deciduous.

Many desert animals escape the desert's heat by being active only at night, or during cooler times of the day. Burrowing is another way that animals can avoid too much heat. Burrowing rodents such as the kangaroo rat and pocket mouse survive in the desert without the need to drink water. They obtain water from seeds and plants. Their bodies are adapted to this shortage of water by conserving and recycling the available water. The camels of the Sahara Desert can go long periods without requiring water. When water is available, they are able to store it in the fat in their humps.

FIGURE 22–20. The desert biome is dry and unattractive for most of the year. After a rainfall, the plants produce many brightly colored flowers.

FIGURE 22–21. The Sahara is Earth's largest desert. Animals such as the camel are adapted to survive with little water.

FIGURE 22–22. Plants of the tundra can withstand freezing.

Climate: 10 to 15 cm annual precipitation; −28° to 15°C temperature
Plant life: lichens, mosses, grasses
Animal life: caribou, musk oxen, polar bears, penguins, wolf, walrus, lemmings, mosquitoes

FIGURE 22–23. Fisher

Climate: 35 to 40 cm annual precipitation; −24° to 22°C temperature
Plant life: spruces, pines, firs
Animal life: moose, black bears, weasels, snowshoe hares, lynx

Tundra

The tundra biome lies south of the Arctic Ocean and within the regions of the polar ice caps. It stretches across northern North America, Europe, and Siberia. Temperatures are low throughout the year. The ground in the tundra remains frozen for most of the year so it is called **permafrost.** About 10 to 20 cm of the upper ground thaws during the short summer season. Precipitation in the tundra is low and is usually in the form of snow. There is poor drainage because the land is flat and the soil is frozen. Most of the land is wet and it is swampy in some areas during the summer.

Trees do not grow because of the cold climate, and other plant life is sparse. The growing season may be as short as 60 days. Tundra plants are adapted to frequent frosts. Many can survive being frozen, even when in flower. Large numbers of birds, particularly waterfowl, nest in the tundra in summer. The animals are usually well protected by feathers or fur. White is the protective coloration for many animals in a snowy environment. Insects abound in the tundra. Their eggs and larvae are resistant to cold. Polar bears and arctic foxes are major predators. Tundra conditions also exist above the tree line or upper limit of the tree growth in the high mountain zones of the world.

Taiga

The taiga biome lies south of the tundra. Great coniferous forests cover large portions of Canada, Alaska, and the Soviet Union. The ground is wet in many areas and there is often fog. The winters in the taiga may be as severe as in the tundra but the growing season is warmer and lasts from three to six months. Coniferous forests in the taiga are an important source of lumber.

Conifers, especially spruce, are the dominant plants in the taiga. The tree branches create dense shade on the ground. Acidic soils and the lack of sunlight on the forest floor reduces the growth of shrubs and smaller plants. Burned areas of the coniferous forest are invaded by deciduous trees such as birches but these are later replaced by conifers. Conifers are better adapted to the severe climate. Many have needlelike, waxy leaves that protect against water loss and freezing. The evergreen condition of coniferous forests is an adaptation to the colder climate. Conifers are better suited to the shorter growing season than deciduous trees because no energy is wasted in an annual loss of leaves. There are several small mammals, such as voles, that have become adapted to living in taiga. Many insects are adapted to the long winters by remaining inactive during this time.

FIGURE 22–24. Many birds nest in the tundra in summer. The Adelie penguins of the Antarctic live on and around the ice pack all year long.

FIGURE 22–25. The taiga forests are usually made up of conifers such as spruce.

FIGURE 22–26. Clown fish protected by a sea anemone

Climate: variable
Plant life: seaweeds, phytoplankton
Animal life: fish, jellyfish, whales, sharks, seals, turtles, mollusks, sponges, anemones, corals

22:7 Water Biomes
Ocean

Oceans are huge bodies of water that cover 70 percent of Earth's surface. Although ocean life is difficult to study, it is known that the total mass of organisms is greater in the oceans than on the land. The most obvious adaptation to life in oceans is a tolerance to salt water.

Most ocean organisms live near the surface. Algae that float in plankton are the main food producers. They provide food for small marine animals that are eaten in turn by larger animals. The blue whale, the largest creature on Earth, feeds on plankton.

Some marine animals live in the far depths of the ocean where light does not penetrate. Many organisms create their own light in this dark environment. These animals feed on organic matter that sinks down from above. Some deep ocean animals do not depend on other animals or plants for their food. Bacteria in their stomachs use energy from the oxidation of sulfur and convert it into food. Animals living deep below the surface are adapted to the high pressures from the water above. Many scavengers and bacteria on the sea bottom break down the dead organic matter. Water from the sea bottom wells up to the surface, and the products of bacterial decay have the effect of fertilizing the sea.

Fresh Water

Lakes, ponds, swamps, and marshes are freshwater areas in which the water is standing and not running. There is generally more life in the shallow water of lakes and ponds near the shore than in the deeper water. Streams, rivers, and creeks have running fresh water. The oxygen content of running water is greater than that of standing water. Both the oxygen content and the speed of the water influence the kinds and numbers of species present. Many organisms that live in swift mountain streams are attached to rocks on the bottom. The attachment prevents them from being carried downstream. Fish can remain in one place by swimming hard. Some salamanders lack lungs and are, therefore, heavier and remain on the stream bottom. Larvae of many animals cling to stones by spun fibers.

Many semiaquatic plants, such as cattails, are rooted in water. Some animals spend part of their life cycle in water and part on land. Many waterfowl and other birds depend on fresh water for nesting and feeding. Algae are the major plants and food producers of fresh water. Protists are also common. The main predators are reptiles such as turtles and crocodiles.

FIGURE 22–27. The kingfisher

Climate: variable
Plant life: water lilies, duckweed, cattails, pondweed, algae
Animal life: fish, crayfish, frogs, snakes, turtles, alligators, duck

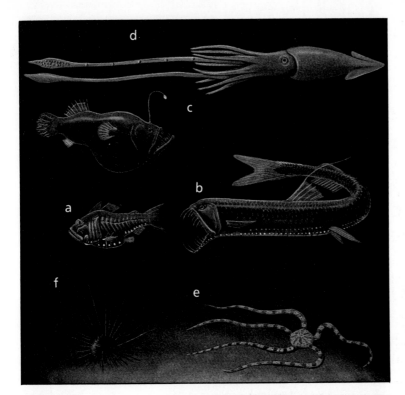

FIGURE 22–28. Many types of organisms are adapted to life in the greatest depths of the ocean biome. They include: hatchet fish (a), viper fish (b), angler fish (c), squid (d), brittle star (e), and sea urchin (f).

FIGURE 22–29. The freshwater biome provides habitats for many types of organisms such as: cattail (a), water lily (b), mallard duck (c), frog (d), dragonfly larva (e), turtle (f), crayfish (g), roundworm (h), and fish (i).

Natural Lawns

In 1973, the National Wildlife Federation began its Backyard Wildlife Habitat Program. This program encouraged homeowners to develop their backyards into wildlife refuges. Since that time, over 3000 families have planted trees, shrubs, and flowers in their yards. Some even included bird feeders, birdhouses, waterfalls, and pools. These yards attract many different kinds of wildlife by providing food, water, and shelter. These yards that were previously barren have been successfully changed into diverse mini-habitats. This program represents an important effort by homeowners to bring wildlife into their daily lives.

Most families created their wild areas by planting the kinds of trees and shrubs that most attract animals. They also allowed vegetation already on their property to grow back to its natural state. Portions of yards that were left unmowed began to sprout native wildflowers, shrubs, and even trees. By blending and growing grasses, shrubs, and trees around open areas, an "edge effect" is created. These edges attract the greatest variety and numbers of wildlife to the smallest of yards. Animals such as songbirds, rabbits, squirrels, chipmunks, raccoons, woodchucks, butterflies, and even ducks, have been attracted to these natural lawns. Owners have been happy to give up their gardens in order to have them eaten by foxes and raccoons. Because shelter and food are available, some birds have not needed to go south in winter.

There are many benefits to backyard landscaping. Lawn maintenance is reduced since there is little need to reseed, fertilize, and mow. Natural landscapes not only attract wildlife, but also conserve energy and water and do not require insecticides. Studies have also shown that property values rise with the addition of good landscaping.

Perhaps the most important benefit of natural landscaping is the education that can be gained from observing the wildlife. Wildlife in the backyard is probably the easiest way to learn the concepts of ecology. Life operates within a large interconnected system. A change in one part affects the rest of the system.

Almost any yard can be converted into a wildlife haven. The first step includes making a sketch of existing trees and shrubs. Then the sketch should be completed by adding the necessary elements that are not already there, such as cover, food, or water. Cover can be plants and shrubs, trees, or rock piles. The type of cover will vary for different animals.

The families who participated in the Backyard Wildlife Program have shown their concern for the environment. By improving their own environments, they have shown that small numbers of people can make a difference.

CHAPTER 22
Review

Summary
1. The biosphere is a life zone surrounding Earth. 22:1
2. Populations of organisms living together in an environment make up a community. 22:2
3. Changes in the population of one species affect the populations of other species in a community. 22:3
4. Through succession, the populations in a community change until it becomes a climax community. 22:4
5. The features of a biome depend upon its climate and plant and animal life. 22:5
6. The tropical forest biome has more species than in all other biomes together. 22:6
7. Temperate forest species are adapted to continual climate changes between summer and winter. 22:6
8. Grasslands support large herds of grazing animals. 22:6
9. Organisms in the desert biome are able to cope with a lack of water. 22:6
10. In the tundra and taiga biomes, plants and animals are adapted to survive the extreme cold. 22:6
11. The ocean and freshwater biomes support a wide variety of aquatic or semi-aquatic organisms. 22:7

Vocabulary
Write a sentence using the following words or terms correctly.

biome	ecology	limiting factor
biosphere	ecosystem	permafrost
community	ecotone	population
climax community	environment	succession

Questions
Do not write in this book.

A. True or False
Determine whether each of the following sentences is true or false. Rewrite the false statements to make them correct.
1. Weather and climate have no effect on the kinds of animals and plants that live in an area.
2. Lichens and insects are present in the tundra.
3. Rainfall is heavy in a tropical rain forest.
4. The tundra has warm temperatures most of the year.

5. Many burrowing animals make their homes in grasslands.

6. Many desert plants store water in their tissues.

7. A population that changes in size is called a stable population.

8. Tropical rain forests are found near the equator.

9. Four seasons occur in a temperate deciduous forest.

10. Grassland soil is usually very fertile.

B. Multiple Choice

Choose the word or phrase that correctly completes the following sentences.

1. You would expect to find (*desert, temperate deciduous forest, rain forest, grassland*) where precipitation is less than 10 cm per year.

2. A (*tundra, rain forest, desert, grassland*) has the best climate and soil for growing wheat and corn.

3. All the dandelions in a lawn make up a (*community, species, population*).

4. Vines, evergreen trees, and tree-living animals are common in (*deserts, tundra, temperate deciduous forests, rain forests*).

5. When the food supply of a species increases, the number of individuals usually (*increases, decreases, remains the same*).

6. (*Climax, Cycle, Succession*) is the slow and gradual change in a community.

7. The tundra is south of the (*Arctic Ocean, taiga, temperate deciduous forests*).

8. (*Coniferous trees, deciduous trees, shrubs, polar bears*) are dominant species in the taiga.

9. Cacti are most likely to be found growing in (*the tundra, a desert, grasslands, temperate deciduous forests*).

10. Most life in the oceans exists at (*shallow, medium, great*) depths.

C. Completion

Complete each of the following sentences with the correct word or phrase.

1. The most abundant population in a community is called the _____.

2. A(n) _____ biome has a wide range of temperatures and low rainfall.

3. The total number of living frogs in a pond is called a(n) _____.

4. An abandoned field in northeastern United States will someday become a(n) _____ if left alone.

5. In an ocean, _____ make most of the food that is produced by photosynthesis.

6. The oxygen content of _____ water is usually greater than the still water of a pond.

7. Monkeys are found in a(n) _____ biome.

8. _____ provide natural pasture for grazing animals.

9. Annual precipitation in a(n) _____ biome is 25 to 100 cm.
10. Precipitation and _____ are the two most important factors that affect life in a biome.

D. How and Why

1. Why are rainfall and temperature important to life?
2. Define the term biome. Name four biomes and list the features of each.
3. Explain why a change in the population of one species might change the population size of another species.
4. How do stable populations differ from unstable populations?
5. Explain why biomes differ in the kinds of plants and animals they contain.
6. Why is the soil in a rain forest not very fertile?
7. Why are most ocean animals not found in the deepest water?

Ideas to Explore

1. **Project:** Obtain a book containing directions to guide you in the construction of a woodland terrarium and a desert terrarium. Make a large drawing of each for exhibit on a bulletin board. Prepare a ten-minute talk on the features of the two terraria.
2. **Challenge:** Study the history of your area and determine what type of community dominated the area 100 or more years ago.
3. **Challenge:** Find an article in a magazine such as *The National Geographic* or *Natural History* about life in a biome outside the United States. Prepare a report about the article.
4. **Project:** Construct a small freshwater ecosystem in an aquarium. Observe the ecosystem and keep records of the activities of the animals. Record the growth of the plants and animals.
5. **Challenge:** Identify the kind of biome in which you live. Make an illustrated report on the kinds of plants and animals found in the biome.

Readings

George, Jean Craighead. *One Day in the Desert*. New York: T. Y. Crowell, 1983.

National Geographic Society. *Secrets of Survival*. Washington D. C.: National Geographic Society, 1983.

Newton, James R. *Forest Log*. New York: T. Y. Crowell, 1980.

The freshwater biome of the biosphere supports a large number of plant and animal species. The stippled darter is just one of about 100 species of darters. They all live in clear streams of eastern North America. They dart quickly on the bottom of streams while preying on small aquatic animals. How do the elongated body and the bright colors of the darter help it survive in a community? What other animals live in this habitat?

CHAPTER 23
ECOLOGY

23:1 Habitats

Organisms and the environment in which they live make up an ecosystem. Within an ecosystem are one or more communities of plants, animals, and other organisms. The place in an ecosystem where a population lives and grows is called its **habitat**. For example, mushrooms are part of a forest ecosystem. The dark, moist forest floor is the habitat of the mushrooms. A woodpecker flies around trees and pecks wood to obtain insects for food. Trees are the woodpecker's habitat.

Conditions such as moisture, sunlight, and temperature in a community can vary greatly within a short distance. The differences in these factors create different kinds of habitats. A habitat at the top of a forest, for example, receives much sunlight. Little sunlight reaches the forest floor. Also, the forest floor is cool and the ground moisture makes it damp. Differences in temperature and sunlight create different habitats within a lake. At the surface, there is more sunshine making the water warmer than deeper in the lake. Surface water provides a good habitat for aquatic plants. Each habitat has its own particular community of organisms.

Many species may have the same habitat. Earthworms, bacteria, molds, and insects all live together in topsoil. Topsoil is

GOALS:
1. You will learn the relationships among organisms and their environment.
2. You will learn how population growth and food affect the welfare of people.
3. You will learn how the use of energy affects the welfare of living things.

Define habitat.

List the species in a topsoil habitat.

FIGURE 23–1. The habitats of some organisms are other organisms. For example, the habitat of a gypsy moth may be a tree.

the habitat for this community of organisms. Sometimes one organism may be the habitat of another organism. For example, an insect such as a gypsy moth may live on a tree. The tree is the living organism that is the moth's habitat. A tree may also serve as a habitat for algae growing on its bark.

Explain carrying capacity.

A population reaches the carrying capacity of its habitat when it no longer increases in size. The **carrying capacity** is the maximum number of individuals of a population that a habitat can support. The number of deaths is balanced by the number of offspring produced. Changes in the food supply, water, sunlight, and temperature change the carrying capacity of an area. Important factors determining carrying capacity for animals include food and water. Sunlight, soil nutrients, and water are major factors affecting the carrying capacity for plants. Generally, the more light, soil nutrients, and water that are available, the greater the plant growth. Factors that may change include heavy spring rains that stimulate plant growth. A long drought, however, will limit plant growth. As a result, there would be less food, such as fruit and seeds, for animals.

FIGURE 23–2. What an organism eats and how it obtains food are part of its niche.

23:2 Competition

Within a community, each species has its niche. A **niche** (NEESH) is the role of an organism within a community. It is the total of an organism's activities and interactions with other parts of its environment. What an organism eats and how it obtains food are part of its niche. So are its movements or lack of movement within a community.

For example, when a termite eats the wood of a fallen tree, the tree is the termite's habitat niche. The termite's niche within the habitat is to break down the dead tree. Other organisms, such as lichens, mosses, fungi, beetles, and other insects may all have the similar role of breaking down the organic matter of the tree. They all have different niches on the tree. The organisms live side by side and each has its own role in the community. The niche also includes the effect of a species on the nonliving environment. Each species has its own niche. As a comparison, the habitat can be thought of as the address of a species, and the niche as its profession.

Competition is the contest among organisms to obtain all their requirements for life. For example, organisms may compete for food, water, sunlight, soil nutrients, and living space. Individuals in different niches do not compete against each other because they have different requirements. Within a single niche, individuals compete for the same living space. In times of limited food or space, the survivors will be those individuals that are best adapted to these conditions.

Two species cannot live together in one niche. One of them will make better use of one of its requirements. This species will survive. In a classic experiment, two species of protozoans were grown separately to form colonies. Then members of the two species were placed in the same culture with a limited amount of food. One species survived and the other did not. The species that survived was more successful in competing for the available food and space. Thus it was better adapted to fill the niche that was available within the culture.

Define competition.

How many species usually occupy a niche?

FIGURE 23–3. Competition between members of a species is necessary for survival when there are limited food supplies.

Competition among organisms is necessary for survival in situations of stress such as limited food supplies. When conditions are favorable in an area, the species do not compete with one another, resulting in a balance of nature. If one group is eliminated from an area, another group may take its place to produce a new balance.

Making Sure

1. List three examples of habitats.
2. How is a habitat different from a niche?
3. What factors do organisms compete for?

23:3 Relationships

Scientists study relationships within an ecosystem. Scientists may study the relationship between plants that make food and animals that eat plants for food. The purification of water by air and soil is another important aspect of ecosystems studied by scientists. Decay of wastes and recycling of chemicals are also important. By studying relationships among organisms and their environments, scientists learn how communities interact with each other.

Many different kinds of relationships exist among organisms within a community. A predator-prey relationship is one that is common. A **predator** is an animal that captures other animals for food. The animals eaten by a predator are called **prey**. For example, in a pond community, frogs eat insects. The frogs are

FIGURE 23–4. Frogs in a pond community are predators of insects.

FIGURE 23–5. An orchid that grows on a tree is an example of commensalism.

predators of the insects. The insects are the frogs' prey. Animals can be both predators and prey. In the frog-insect example described above, the frogs are the predators. However, frogs are eaten by raccoons in the same pond community. Then the frogs are the raccoons' prey. The raccoons are the predators.

Another relationship in communities is mutualism. **Mutualism** is two organisms living together for mutual benefit. Flagellates living in the intestines of termites are an example of mutualism. The flagellates digest the wood the termites eat. The digested wood can then be used by the termites' body cells. The termites' bodies provide the warmth, food, and moisture the flagellates need to live. Another example of mutualism is the bacteria that live in human intestines. These bacteria make vitamin B_{12} that humans need to live. The bacteria receive food from human digestion.

Commensalism is a relationship in which one organism lives on another without causing harm. One species benefits while the other receives neither benefit nor harm. One example of commensalism is an orchid plant growing on the branch of a tree trunk. The orchid uses the branch as a place of attachment. It does not harm the tree and does not take food from the tree. Certain species of fish live with sea anemones in a commensalism relationship. The anemones do not eat or harm these fish in any way. Yet the poisonous tentacles of the anemones quickly paralyze other fish that touch them. The fish benefit by being protected from their predators.

FIGURE 23–6. Termites and the flagellates that live in their intestines are an example of mutualism.

Parasitism is a relationship in which one organism lives on or in and harms another organism called a host. Worms that live inside people or other animals are examples of parasites. The worms take food from the host organism and may destroy body tissues as a result. Organisms such as ticks or lice that feed on the hair, feathers, scales, skin, or blood of another organism are parasites.

Organisms that die in a community are removed by decomposers and scavengers. **Decomposers** are organisms that bring about the decay of dead organisms and bacteria. Fungi that grow on rotting logs are examples of decomposers. **Scavengers** are animals that feed on and remove dead animals. Vultures, hyenas, and maggots are examples of scavengers. Decomposers and scavengers are "garbage collectors" who help clean up a community. Through decay and eating, decomposers and scavengers remove dead organisms from the environment. In so doing, they contribute to the recycling of matter and energy through an ecosystem.

Making Sure

4. How can an animal be both predator and prey?
5. Describe three kinds of relationships that exist in a community.
6. How are decomposers and scavengers important?

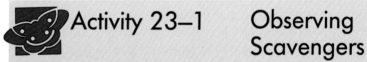

Activity 23–1   Observing Scavengers

Problem: What kinds of animals in the soil community are scavengers?

Materials   plastic cup, 14-cm long plastic drainpipe, 12-cm plywood square, 4 small rocks, raw meat

Procedure   (1) Find an area in your school yard near a tree, large rock, or shrub to place a scavenger trap. (2) Bury a 14-cm piece of plastic drainpipe vertically in the soil so that the top is just below the level of the soil. (3) Place the plastic cup in the drainpipe. Add the raw meat. (4) Cover the plastic cup with the plywood square. By placing the plywood square on small rocks, allow enough room for insects to crawl into the cup. (5) Observe the cup twice each day, early in the day and as late as possible.

Questions   (1) Record details of the cup's environment. (2) Record the number and types of animals in the trap each day. (3) What kinds of animals in a soil community are scavengers?

FIGURE 23–7.

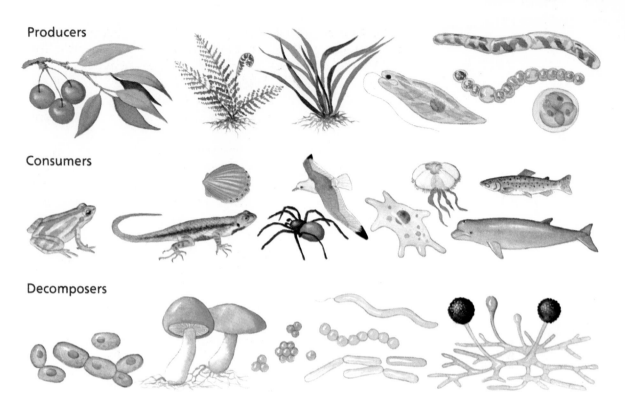

Producers

Consumers

Decomposers

23:4 Food

Food is important in every community because it provides the energy needed for life. Organisms may be classified into three groups based on how they obtain food. Organisms containing chlorophyll are **producers** because they produce food by photosynthesis. Plants and some simple organisms are producers. Plants use some of the food for themselves. However, the food they make will also help to feed all the other organisms in the community. Organisms that eat other organisms are **consumers**. Animals and some simple organisms are consumers. Organisms that cause the decay of dead organisms are decomposers. Fungi and most monerans are decomposers.

The consumers in a community depend on producers and other consumers for food. For example, mice eat acorns and owls eat mice. The oak trees on which the acorns grow are producers. The mice that eat the acorns are consumers. The owls that eat the mice are consumers also. When the oak trees, mice, and owls die, decomposers will cause their decay.

Define consumer.

FIGURE 23–9. A common food chain in forests is acorn–mouse–owl.

What are secondary consumers?

The acorns, mice, and owls in a community form a food chain. A **food chain** is a pathway of food and energy through an ecosystem. Acorns—mice—owls is an example of a simple food chain. Each species of organism is a link in the food chain. Each species is dependent on the other species in the food chain.

The first link in every food chain is the producer. There may be many links of consumers in a food chain. Consumers that eat producers are called primary consumers. Mice are primary consumers because they eat producers. Other primary consumers are squirrels, deer, cows, and sheep. Humans are primary consumers when they eat vegetables, fruits, and nuts. Consumers that eat primary consumers are called secondary consumers. Owls are secondary consumers because they eat primary consumers such as mice. Other secondary consumers are foxes, dogs, hawks, and snakes. Humans are secondary consumers when they eat meat.

The size of a population is limited by the sizes of the populations on which it feeds. For example, an increase in a mouse population will increase the numbers in an owl population. The larger owl population will then decrease the mouse population. This relationship produces a balance in nature.

Most consumers in communities use more than one species as food. For example, mice also eat corn and other plants. Rabbits and deer eat many of the same plants. Owls eat mice, but they eat rabbits, too. Hawks eat owls. Mountain lions eat rabbits and deer. These species are parts of food chains that together form a food web. A **food web** is a complex feeding system that contains several food chains.

Activity 23–2

Studying an Ecosystem

Problem: How do you study an ecosystem?

Materials

graph paper
notebook
pencil
hand lens
field guides
binoculars
other useful materials

Procedure

1. Choose a natural community near your school or home to be your ecosystem for study. For example, you may choose to study a pond, a forest area in a park, a rotten log, or an area in your school yard.
2. Decide the boundaries of the ecosystem you are studying. Make the ecosystem whatever size you think you can study well.
3. Make a map or drawing of the ecosystem on graph paper.
4. Observe the organisms that live in the ecosystem. Use a hand lens to study small creatures. Use binoculars to study organisms you cannot get near. Look for evidence such as tracks or feathers, or organisms you cannot see.
5. Record your observations. Make drawings. Use field guides to identify the organisms.
6. Visit the ecosystem as many times as you can and at different times of day for four weeks. Make

FIGURE 23–10.

observations and record them. Pay close attention to the relationships among organisms. Also note how the organisms interact with the nonliving environment.

Data and Observations

Date	Organisms observed	Comments

Questions and Conclusions

1. What is the ecosystem you chose?
2. Describe the nonliving environment of the ecosystem.
3. What organisms live in the ecosystem?
4. Which organisms are producers?
5. Which organisms are consumers?
6. Which organisms are decomposers?
7. Diagram a food web for the ecosystem.
8. What might happen if a population of producers was removed from the community?
9. What might happen if the predators were removed from the community?
10. What if the decomposers were removed from the community?
11. What relationships can you identify among the organisms, such as predator–prey, mutualism, commensalism, or parasitism?
12. How important is the nonliving environment in the ecosystem? Explain.
13. What might happen if the nonliving environment changed suddenly?
14. What biome would you consider the ecosystem to be a part of? Why?
15. How do you study an ecosystem?

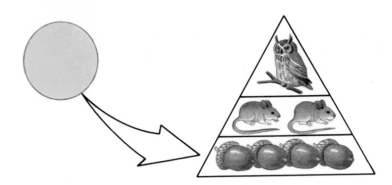

FIGURE 23–11. Energy pyramids show that the food energy in one level of a food chain is greater than in any level above it. In the transfer of energy from one level to the next, about 90 percent of the energy is lost as heat.

23:5 Energy

Food chains and food webs exist in communities because all organisms need energy. Food contains stored energy that organisms can use to carry on their life activities. All of the energy used by organisms comes originally from the sun. The sun's energy is stored in the food that producers make by photosynthesis. When a consumer eats a producer, some of the energy is passed to the consumer. The energy is passed through the food chain as one consumer eats another.

The flow of energy through a food chain can be shown as an **energy pyramid**. The energy pyramid is divided into levels that represent producers and consumers. Producers always form the base of an energy pyramid. Consumers make up the upper levels. Sometimes decomposers are shown at the top of an energy pyramid. The energy from food in each level of a pyramid is always less than the energy in the level below it. This is because as energy is passed from one organism to another, most of it is used or lost. The energy is used for life activities or is lost as body heat.

In the acorns—mice—owls food chain, acorns from oak trees form the base of the energy pyramid. The oak trees produce acorns that provide food (energy) for the mice. The mice form the second level of the pyramid. Only about ten percent of the energy in the acorns is passed to the mice. The rest is used for the acorns' life activities. The owls form the third level of the pyramid. Again, only a small part of the energy in a mouse is passed to an owl. The rest is used or lost in the mouse's metabolism. Thus, many acorns are needed to support small populations of mice and owls. A large animal requires more food than a smaller one. In a community, there are few large animals and a greater number of small animals. All these animals require an even greater number of plants as the base of their energy pyramid.

Describe an energy pyramid.

Making Sure

7. a. What is the original source of energy for every food chain?
   b. What kind of organism is the first link in every food chain?
8. Are bacteria consumers or decomposers?
9. Which of these food chains will support more people?
   a. corn—people
   b. corn—cow—people

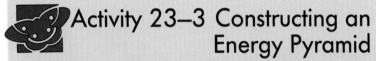

Activity 23–3 Constructing an Energy Pyramid

Problem: What does an energy pyramid represent?

Materials   paper, pencil, reference books

Procedure   (1) Arrange the following organisms in a food chain: hawks, grass, frogs, grasshoppers, snakes. (2) Estimate the number of producers that are needed to provide energy for the first level consumers. (3) Estimate the number of first level consumers that are needed to provide energy for the second level consumers. (4) Estimate the number of second level consumers that are needed to provide energy for the third level consumers. (5) Estimate the number of consumers that are needed to provide energy for the fourth level consumers. (6) Construct an energy pyramid using the organisms in the food chain.

Questions   (1) What happens in terms of energy each time an organism feeds on another organism? (2) What is the source of the energy in the bottom level? (3) How is energy lost as it passes through a food chain? (4) Why is the energy pyramid broad at the bottom? (5) Why does it narrow to a point at the top? (6) What does an energy pyramid represent?

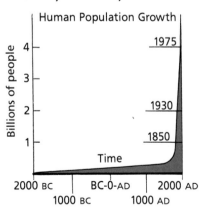

FIGURE 23–12. World population growth has increased dramatically in recent years.

23:6 Human Population Growth

As the number of people on Earth increases, so does their use of fossil fuels and other resources. During most of human history, the human population was small. It grew slowly and at times declined. Several thousand years were needed for the human population to reach one billion people. This figure was reached about 1850. Within 80 years, the human population doubled to two billion. It then doubled again in 45 years. Today there are more than 4 billion people on Earth.

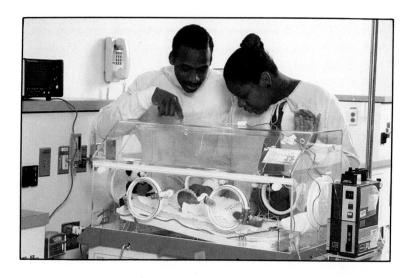

FIGURE 23–13. Years ago many children died as babies or young children. Modern medicine helps to lower the death rate by keeping young children alive.

Population size is controlled by the **birthrate** and **death rate**. Centuries ago most children did not live very long. They died at birth, as babies, or as young children. Death rate at birth was high. A newborn child in London in the sixteenth century was only expected to live nine years. Disease epidemics killed many children as well as adults. Few children lived to reproduce. The death rate was high and the birthrate was low. Population growth was limited.

Limiting factors of the past, such as disease and deaths at birth, have been changed by modern technology. Today, antibiotics, vaccinations, and improved sanitation help control the spread of disease. With modern health care, fewer people die young, and most children live to reproduce. As a result of these changes, the death rate has decreased and the survival of newborns has increased. The lower death rate and higher birthrate have caused the human population to increase rapidly.

Human population growth cannot continue at this rate forever. The carrying capacity of Earth is not known, but at present rates of growth, estimates are that the population will reach 11 billion by the year 2050. However, other predictions are that the population will stabilize at 8 billion due to limiting factors such as food shortages or diseases. Artificial control of human populations by family planning may be used to check the growth rate.

Define zero population growth.

In the United States, an average of 2.1 children per family would, over time, lead to zero population growth. With zero population growth, the population size would be stable. It would not increase nor decrease much overall. If the average birthrate per family is greater than that needed to replace the older generation, population growth will continue.

Making Sure

10. How does each affect population growth?
    a. death rate in children
    b. birthrate
11. How might population growth be reduced without increasing death rate?

Activity 23–4 Observing Overpopulation

Problem: What are the effects of overpopulation?

Materials two small milk cartons, scissors, labels, potting soil, 28 bean seeds, watering can, water

Procedure (1) Cut the tops off two small milk cartons. Label one carton A and the other B. (2) Fill each carton to the same level with potting soil. (3) Plant three bean seeds in carton A. Plant 25 bean seeds in carton B. (4) Predict what will happen to the seeds in each carton. (5) Place both cartons in a sunny place. Water regularly with the same amount of water for each carton. (6) Observe both cartons for three weeks. Record any differences between the plants in the two cartons.

Questions (1) Describe the plants in carton A. (2) Describe the plants in carton B. (3) What are the effects of overpopulation?

23:7 Food for People

When a population increases beyond its food supply, food shortages result and famine may occur. Such was the case in 1985 in Ethiopia, a country in Africa. Until 1985, there had been enough rainfall to produce the crops needed to feed Ethiopia's people. However, in 1985 a long drought decreased food production on farms. Many people died from starvation or became ill due to a lack of food. Food was imported in an attempt to save as many people as possible.

Lack of food is a problem in many poor or developing countries. It is estimated that at least 500 million people in the world are underfed. The actual figure may be three times as high, or about 1.5 billion people. In some parts of the world, the human population has increased at a much faster rate than food production. In these areas, most people are primary consumers. Their diet is

FIGURE 23–14. In 1985 a drought in Ethiopia decreased food production and caused starvation.

FIGURE 23–15. Irrigation in deserts is one way to increase the amount of cropland in production.

largely based on rice, wheat, or corn. These three plants provide people in less developed countries with about two-thirds of their required daily supply of Calories.

The average person in North America is a secondary consumer. A secondary consumer has meat in his or her diet. Meat is a more expensive food than rice, corn, and wheat because it takes more land to produce meat. Meat animals such as cattle, hogs, and chickens must be cared for and fed grain and other food. Much of the grain fed to the animals is used in their daily life activities and is not converted to meat. Therefore, in places where food is scarce, people usually have little meat in their diets. Most of the grain that is raised must be used to feed the human population.

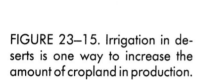

What is the diet of a secondary consumer?

To feed the growing population of the world, food production must increase. One way for this to happen is to increase the amount of land in crop production. However, care must be taken not to destroy stable ecosystems in which the soil or climate is not suited to farming. A tropical rain forest is an example of such an ecosystem. Irrigating fertile desert land is one method of bringing more land into crop production. Soil conservation aids crop production by maintaining the fertility of cropland already in use. Another way to increase food production is to increase crop yields by developing new varieties of plants. For example, new varieties of wheat and rice have been developed. These new plants produce more grain. Crop yields can also be increased by application of pesticides, but their use must be limited. Pesticides can cause damage to soil and wildlife and pollute water supplies. Pesticides interfere with food chains.

Name the methods used to increase food production.

Crop yields can also be increased by using fertilizers to make land more fertile or by using biocontrols for insects. **Biocontrols** involve the use of helpful organisms to control harmful organisms. Biocontrols do not harm the environment or wildlife. Ladybugs are an example of a biocontrol. They eat harmful insects.

How are biocontrols used?

In many parts of the world, the protein content of people's diets needs to be increased. Animal protein contains the amino acids that are essential for human health. Fish farming is one method scientists have developed to increase the supply of animal protein. In Japan, fish are raised in pens and fed organic waste. The farming of fish supplies animal protein and also disposes of the garbage.

FIGURE 23–16. The praying mantis may be used as a biocontrol for insect pests.

23:8 Open Space

Lack of open space in many cities is another problem caused by rapid growth of the human population. As the population increases, more space is needed for homes, schools, parks, stores, and industry. Overcrowding in cities creates social problems such as an increase in the crime rate. Automobile congestion in overpopulated cities causes air pollution and delays in the time it takes to get from one place to another. This can cause stress. Lack of contact with open space, fresh air, and sunlight may have a negative effect on mental health. The full effects of overcrowding on people are uncertain.

People can take actions to change their environment to a more healthy and pleasant place to live. Development of neighborhood parks and playgrounds within a city is one example. Cleaning up litter, trash, and weeds from vacant lots is another way to improve an environment. The development of mass transportation systems in urban areas can decrease motor traffic, pollution, and the need for parking space.

Planning can ensure that land is used in the best possible way. Land use planning promotes a healthy, productive environment. Cluster development of homes, apartments, condominiums, and marketplaces may be planned to make the best use of a limited area. Factories and warehouses can be located together in industrial parks away from residential areas.

Within many cities there are zoning regulations to control the use of land. For example, zoning may restrict the number of dwelling units that can be built in an area. It can regulate the size and height of buildings and the distance they are set back from the street. Zoning may also restrict the locations of new buildings to make sure they are in harmony with existing buildings. For example, factories cannot be built in areas that are zoned for homes. The regulations controlling development ensure that the original plans for the city are followed.

FIGURE 23–17. Some cities have special bicycle paths that help decrease motor traffic, pollution, and the need for parking space.

Making Sure

12. What are some problems of crowding in cities?
13. What are the advantages of land use planning?

Activity 23–5   Land Use Planning

Problem: How would you plan a new town?

Materials   large piece of paper, pencils, metric ruler

Procedure   Suppose a large construction company is planning to build a new town. The company wants to be sure that the town has everything a town needs. They also want to make the town clean, safe, energy efficient, and a pleasant place to live. The construction company decides to ask designers to submit plans for the new town. You are one of the designers. **(1)** Consider the following questions before you begin planning:

What industries will provide jobs? Where will people live? How will people get from place to place? What energy sources will be used? How will the town be kept clean, safe, and healthy? What will the people do for enjoyment and recreation?

(2) On a large sheet of paper, design and draw the plan you would submit for the new town.

Questions   **(1)** What will make people want to live in your town? **(2)** Compare your finished plan with those of your classmates. **(3)** Which plan do you think the construction company should build? **(4)** How would you improve your plan based on the ideas you learned from your classmates? **(5)** How would you plan a new town?

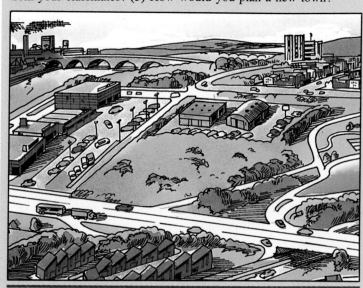

FIGURE 23–18.

Technology

Studying Ecology from Space

As a result of technology, humans have altered the biosphere. The amount of harm done is not easy to estimate. Since the first weather satellite was launched in 1960, the information provided from space has helped monitor the environment. Advances in satellite remote sensing technology and computer processing within the last decade have provided much detailed information concerning our planet.

Remote sensing is the identification and study of objects and processes from a great distance, and it can be done by satellites in space. One of the latest remote sensing methods is the Advanced Very High Resolution Radiometer (AVHRR). AVHRR sensors are carried by a satellite that orbits Earth. The sensors record the different colors of light reflected from Earth's surface and a computer produces a color-coded map. From these maps, scientists can determine the general health of a particular area. For example, a forest that is stressed from a drought or pollution will not reflect the same kinds of light that a healthy region would. This difference could be seen on the map. Scientists can now study the impact technology has had on various ecosystems.

The coastal zone color scanner (CZCS) is another remote sensing method that monitors the health of the oceans. The color-coded maps produced by CZCS show the abundance of phytoplankton that grows in the ocean. Phytoplankton are microscopic plants that drift with the ocean currents. They are at the base of the ocean food chain. A decline in phytoplankton levels could indicate a serious problem in the ocean. With data from CZCS, such problems could be studied, analyzed, and solved.

Satellite remote sensing can also be used in the preservation of endangered species. In 1984, a biologist from the United States Fish and Wildlife Service strapped a 171-gram transmitter on the back of a bald eagle. During the eagle's flights, two satellites received signals from the transmitter. These signals told the biologist where the eagle traveled. After its release from Maryland, the eagle flew across eight states to Florida in just nine months. The eagle is now in Charleston, South Carolina, where it had originally hatched. It was already known to scientists that eagles usually return to their hatching places, but they discovered that eagles might spend a long time flying along the mid-Atlantic coast. A similar study was done with a humpback whale. Scientists are more able to protect endangered species when they have information on migration routes.

FIGURE 23–19. A golden eagle wears a transmitter that sends signals monitored by two satellites.

Rachel Carson and the Story of DDT

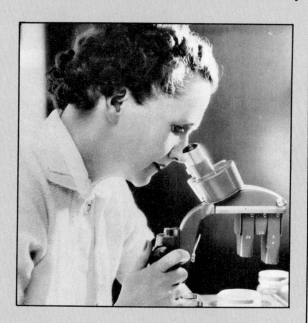

DDT (dichlorodiphenyl trichloroethane) was first made in 1874, but it was not used as an insecticide until 1939. During World War II, DDT protected soldiers from insects that carry typhus and mosquitoes that carry malaria. Between 1941 and 1947, DDT was intensively used to combat insect pests such as the potato beetle and the boll weevil, thus increasing crop yields. By 1948, however, warning signs were beginning to indicate that DDT might be harming the environment. Instead of using standard doses of DDT, it was necessary to double or triple the dose to be as effective. Resistant races of insects were developing.

Despite such warnings, DDT became the main insecticide used around the world. After trees were sprayed, the DDT remained on the leaves. After the leaves withered and fell to the ground, earthworms would feed on the leaf litter. The DDT from the leaves accumulated in the worms, which became food for songbirds in the spring. Thousands of birds were killed or became sterile. Sounds of spring were silenced in many parts of the United States.

Concerned about the dangers of DDT and its effects on the environment, Rachel Carson brought these dangers to the public's attention. In her 1962 book, *Silent Spring*, Rachel Carson warned that DDT not only poisoned insects, but fish, birds, mammals, and humans as well. She documented how DDT accumulated in the food chain. In one study of a marsh, the water was shown to contain less than 0.001 parts per million (ppm) DDT. The plankton contained between 0.01 and 0.1 ppm. The clams that fed on the plankton contained 1.0 ppm. The fish that fed on the clams and the plankton contained 2–3 ppm. The top level consumers, such as ospreys, had 10–100 ppm DDT. DDT at these levels can cause death or sterility. By the mid 1960s, ospreys and other marsh birds became endangered. Many of the birds that survived could only lay soft-shelled eggs that frequently broke in the nest. The numbers of these birds declined rapidly.

Carson also reported the effects of DDT on humans. DDT was shown to be stored in body fat and said to cause cancer and damage to the liver, adrenal glands, and nerves. Partly as a result of Rachel Carson's concern, DDT was finally banned by the Environmental Protection Agency (EPA) in 1972.

The large scale use of insecticides continues, despite our increasing knowledge of the hazardous effects. Recently, an insecticide known as difocol has been found to contain as much as 15 percent DDT. As of 1986, difocol was an ingredient in at least fifty other pesticides. Now, DDT is building up in wildlife tissues once again.

CHAPTER 23
Review

Summary

1. Organisms in a community interact with each other and the nonliving parts of their environment. 23:1
2. Individuals within a habitat compete with each other for food and living space. 23:2
3. Based on their food sources, organisms may be divided into three groups—producer, consumer, and decomposer. 23:3
4. Animals and plants in an area are parts of a food web. Each food web has several food chains. 23:4
5. The energy in each level of a food pyramid is less than the energy in the level below it. 23:5
6. The world's human population is growing at a rapid rate. 23:6
7. An increase in human population results in an increased demand for natural resources. 23:6
8. Increasing food production to feed more people is a major problem. 23:7
9. Zoning regulations are one way to control the use of land. 23:8
10. Land use planning can improve the human environment by making it healthier and more pleasant. 23:8

Vocabulary

Write a sentence using the following words or terms correctly.

biocontrol	death rate	niche
birthrate	decomposer	parasitism
carrying capacity	energy pyramid	predator
commensalism	food chain	prey
competition	food web	producer
consumer	habitat	scavenger

Questions

Do not write in this book.

A. True or False

Determine whether each of the following sentences is true or false. Rewrite the false statements to make them correct.

1. An organism may be the habitat for another organism.
2. A green plant is a food producer.
3. The world's human population will probably double by about year 2050.
4. Birthrate and death rate control the size of human populations.

5. Death rate among children does not affect the size of the human population.
6. Increased population causes increased use of resources.
7. Infectious diseases can prevent the growth of a population.
8. Food production can be increased through the use of irrigation of desert regions.
9. A chemical pesticide is an example of a biological control.
10. Animal protein is a relatively cheap nutrient.

B. Multiple Choice
Choose the word or phrase that correctly completes the following sentences.

1. A tapeworm living in an animal's intestine is an example of *(mutualism, commensalism, a scavenger, a parasite)*.
2. When the food supply of a species increases, the number of individuals usually *(increases, decreases, remains the same)*.
3. Most of the energy in an energy pyramid is at the *(lowest, highest, center)* level.
4. A snake is a *(predator, producer, decomposer)*.
5. Lack of open space in many cities is due to a rapid *(decrease, increase)* of the human population.
6. Plants are *(composers, producers, consumers)*.
7. Open space is most available in *(rural, suburban, city)* areas.
8. An increase in food supply tends to *(increase, decrease, have no effect on)* carrying capacity.
9. A termite, a moss, and a fungus all compete for a(n) *(niche, community, ecosystem)* on a fallen log.
10. A niche usually has *(one, two, few, many)* species.

C. Completion
Complete each of the following sentences with the correct word or phrase.

1. _____ are the first link in any food chain.
2. An organism that contains chlorophyll is a food _____.
3. The populations of _____ in a community would eventually be reduced by a decrease in mice.
4. The path through which food is passed from one species to another is called a(n) _____.
5. Squirrels and cows are _____ consumers.
6. Producers always form the _____ of an energy pyramid.
7. Land use _____ is a way to make sure that land is used wisely.

8. _____ of people in cities or buildings may have a bad effect on their mental health.

9. Conserving soil and increasing crop yields are ways to increase _____.

10. The death rate in _____ has more of an effect on population growth than the death rate in older people.

D. How and Why

1. Explain why a change in the population of one species might change the population size of another species.

2. How do stable populations differ from unstable populations?

3. All consumers and decomposers depend on the existence of plant producers. Explain why.

4. How can the urban environment be improved?

5. How can the world's food supply be increased?

6. What are the advantages of using biocontrols?

7. Identify an environmental issue or problem. Write a paragraph in which you state your informed opinion on the issue or problem.

Ideas to Explore

1. **Challenge:** Some people must live and work in close quarters with other people for long periods of time. Find out what techniques of human relations are used to train sailors for long voyages aboard nuclear submarines.

2. **Challenge:** Check with a local government building department to find out the zoning laws for your area. Obtain information on how people obtain permits to construct and remodel buildings.

3. **Project:** Make a map of an urban area that shows the different kinds of land use.

4. **Project:** Get permission from your parents or guardian to remove all the grass and plants from one square meter of land where you live. Observe the square meter once a week. Keep a record of changes that occur.

Readings

Branley, Franklyn M. *Feast or Famine? The Energy Future.* New York: T. Y. Crowell Books, 1980.

Pringle, Laurence. *Lives at Stake: The Science and Politics of Environmental Health.* New York: Macmillan Publishing Company, Inc., 1980.

Pringle, Laurence. *What Shall We Do With the Land? Choices for America.* New York: T. Y. Crowell Books, 1981.

Farming has been a way of life for centuries. Methods of farming, however, have changed drastically over the years. Technology has led to the use of bailers, tractors, harvesters, pesticides, and insecticides. The young man in the photo uses a horse-drawn cart for his farming needs. How will his method of farming affect the environment? Compare this to the fuels needed to run most farm equipment today. What are the advantages and disadvantages of technological changes? How do they affect Earth?

CHAPTER 24
Resources and the Environment

24:1 Resources

People use resources every day. A **resource** is something taken from the environment that is useful to living organisms. Resources include air, water, minerals, and fuels such as petroleum and natural gas. You must have air to breathe and water to drink. Minerals and other resources are used to make pens, pencils, paper, clothing, and the building in which you live. Fuels are used to provide energy. Electric lights and appliances operate on electricity generated by burning fuels.

Resources can be divided into two groups: renewable and nonrenewable. **Renewable resources** are those that can be replaced by nature. Trees, land, water, and animals and crops raised for food are renewable resources. Trees cut down for lumber to make buildings and furniture can be replanted. Animals reproduce and crops are replanted to ensure that future generations will have these resources. Ocean water is an inexhaustible resource.

Nonrenewable resources are those that take hundreds or millions of years to form. Topsoil is a nonrenewable resource that takes hundreds of years to form. Other nonrenewable resources are petroleum, natural gas, and coal. These fuels take millions of years to form within Earth. Nonrenewable resources are limited. Through conservation, the supply of all resources may be extended. **Conservation** is the wise and careful use of Earth's resources. Both renewable and nonrenewable resources are vital to life. Therefore, it is everyone's responsibility to conserve resources.

GOALS:
1. You will learn about Earth's resources.
2. You will learn about pollution and ways to prevent or reduce it.
3. You will learn about methods of resource conservation.

What is a renewable resource?

FIGURE 24–1. Rush-hour traffic in large cities pollutes the air with harmful chemicals.

What is pollution?

Describe three sources of air pollution.

FIGURE 24–2. Some industries contribute to air pollution.

24:2 Air Pollution

Air and water are renewable resources essential to life. Because these two resources are used by billions of organisms, air and water pollution are problems that affect all life forms. **Pollution** is a change in the environment that can be harmful to living organisms. Pollution can be natural or human-made. Natural pollutants include volcanic ash and dust that pollute the air; and seeps of natural oil that may kill fish and other aquatic life. Pollution from industries, motor vehicles, and agriculture are among the human-made sources of pollutants.

The major air pollutants produced by the burning of fuels in homes and industries are particulates (par TIHK yuh layts) and sulfur dioxide. **Particulates** are particles of all sizes that are emitted into the air. Ash and dust are particulates that contribute to smog, which causes respiratory problems. In December, 1952, smog contributed to the deaths of thousands of people in London. Sulfur dioxide is a colorless gas with a distinct odor. Sulfur dioxide can also cause respiratory problems, and it is poisonous. Sulfur dioxide combines with water vapor in the air to form acid rain and acid snow. The acid rain and snow harm plants and animals, corrode metals, and damage stone structures.

Motor vehicles are another source of air pollution. Carbon monoxide, hydrocarbons, and nitrogen oxides are pollutants in auto exhaust. Carbon monoxide is a toxic, colorless, odorless gas that can cause suffocation. Hydrocarbons and nitrogen oxides can cause photochemical smog. Photochemical smog results from chemical changes that occur in these gases in the presence of sunlight. Ozone gas, one of the products of the changes, irritates the linings of the nose and throat and causes the eyes to tear and sting. Photochemical smog is common in large cities such as Los Angeles because of the great number of motor vehicles.

Air pollution from sulfur dioxide, particulates, industry, and motor vehicles can be controlled. Sulfur pollutants and particulates can be reduced by burning low-sulfur coals and using filters called scrubbers in smokestacks. Gasoline engine designs have been modified to reduce air pollution from exhaust. Some gasoline, however, contains lead that becomes another exhaust pollutant. Lead in the air can be harmful to organisms, and lead poisoning can cause permanent damage to the brain and nervous system. New cars are designed to use lead-free fuels.

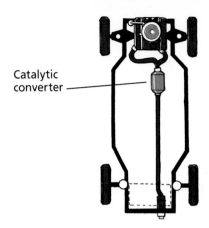

Catalytic converter

FIGURE 24–3. Since 1975, catalytic converters have been attached to car engines to reduce emissions.

Making Sure

1. Distinguish between renewable and nonrenewable resources.
2. How does air pollution affect organisms?

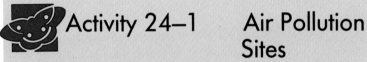

Activity 24–1   Air Pollution Sites

Problem: Where would you expect to find air polluted with particulates?

Materials   waxed paper, scissors, metric ruler, thumbtacks, cardboard, petroleum jelly, hand lens, pencil, string

Procedure   (1) Cut six sheets of waxed paper 8 cm square. **CAUTION:** *Be careful when using scissors.* (2) Cut six pieces of cardboard 8 cm square. (3) Use a pencil and a metric ruler to make each sheet into sixteen 2-cm squares. (4) Thumbtack each sheet of waxed paper to a cardboard square. (5) Thinly coat the waxed paper with petroleum jelly. (6) Place these six collectors in six open areas. Fasten them to an object so that they do not blow away. Label the collectors with their locations. (7) Record the locations. Predict which locations you expect to have the most particulate air pollution. (8) Wait four days, then gather the collectors. Be careful not to smudge the petroleum-coated side. (9) Examine the squares on each collector with a hand lens. (10) Determine which collector has the most and which has the least number of particulates.

Questions   (1) Where is the air most polluted with particulates? (2) Where is the air least polluted? (3) How do the particulates on different collectors compare? (4) How can you explain the differences? (5) How did your predictions compare with the results? (6) Where would you expect to find air polluted with particulates?

FIGURE 24–4.

FIGURE 24–5. Harmful chemicals, oil, and sewage dumped into waterways kill organisms and make the water unsuitable for human use.

What are the uses of water resources?

24:3 Water Pollution

Clean water is required by all plants and animals. People use water for drinking, bathing, laundering, watering lawns and gardens, and for recreation. Water is also needed for sewage disposal, electric power production, and transportation. Industry and agriculture use large amounts of water. It can take as much as 246 000 liters of water to produce one ton of steel. Livestock consume water, and crops need adequate rainfall or irrigation. Growth in population, industry, agriculture, and the use of water for recreation have increased the need for clean water.

Water can be obtained from lakes, streams, reservoirs (REZ urv worz), wells, and the oceans. Pollution of these sources by industry and agriculture is a growing concern. Harmful chemicals and oil dumped into water can be a threat to humans and other organisms. Pesticides and fertilizers can poison not only cattle and other livestock that drink the water, but also the aquatic inhabitants of the lake, river, or stream.

Some industries pollute water supplies by disposing of their wastes into nearby waterways. In the 1950s, in Minamata, Japan, a factory had been discharging water that contained mercury, a toxic element, into Minamata Bay. People who ate a lot of fish from the bay suffered from mercury poisoning. As a result, babies were born with birth defects, people became disabled, and 93 people died.

Some industries pollute waterways with hot water used in cooling processes. **Thermal pollution** raises the temperature of the water in a waterway. The higher temperature promotes algae growth. The algae exhaust the supply of oxygen in the waterway and fish may die as a result. One solution to thermal pollution is the use of cooling towers. Industries can pump hot water through pipes into these towers where the water is cooled before it is discharged into a waterway.

Sewage (soo uj) is another source of water pollution. **Sewage** is waste matter carried off by sewers. Cities and factories sometimes pollute water by dumping sewage into rivers, lakes, or the ocean. As sewage decays, oxygen is often removed from the water. This loss in oxygen can be fatal to fish and other aquatic life. Sewage pollution problems can be solved with treatment plants where sewage is converted to less harmful substances before it is disposed.

Water covers over 66 percent of Earth's surface, but the amount of clean water available depends partly on conservation. Household water use can be decreased by fixing leaky faucets and taking shorter showers. Water for agricultural and industrial uses, in many cases, can be recycled several times. For example, the amount of water used in steel production can be reduced by 75 percent if the water is recycled.

FIGURE 24–6. Some industries use cooling towers to avoid thermal pollution of waterways.

How can people conserve water?

Making Sure

3. Name three sources of water pollution.
4. How can sewage treatment reduce water pollution?

Activity 24–2   Acid Rain

Problem: What is acid rain?

Materials   six aluminum pie pans, masking tape, six jars with lids, labels, pH paper, distilled water

Procedure   (1) Place six clean pie pans in areas to catch rainwater. Tape the pans securely in place so they will not blow away. (2) After the first rain, collect the pie pans one at a time. Pour the contents of each pan into a jar. Label each jar with the location where the water was collected. (3) Test the water in each jar with pH paper. Record the pH of each sample. (4) Test the pH of a sample of distilled water. Record this value.

Questions   (1) How does the acidity of rainwater compare with the acidity of distilled water? (2) How can you explain the difference? (3) What does the term acid rain mean? (4) What causes the rainwater to be acidic? (5) Where do you expect rainwater to be the most acidic? (6) How are acid rain and air pollution related? (7) How does acid rain affect lakes and streams? (8) What is acid rain?

FIGURE 24–7.

a

b

FIGURE 24–8. Shelter belts protect farm fields from wind erosion (a). Mulch helps garden soil retain moisture (b).

Define erosion.

What was the "Dust Bowl"?

Explain four methods of soil conservation.

24:4 Soil Conservation

The formation of 2.5 centimeters of topsoil takes between 500 and 1000 years. Topsoil is often removed by the process of erosion (ih ROH zhun). **Erosion** is the removal of soil by water, wind, ice, or gravity. When topsoil is eroded, the subsoil is exposed. Plants do not grow well in subsoil.

During the 1930s, drought occurred in the Great Plains of the United States. These weather conditions and poor farming practices caused the "Dust Bowl." Tons of topsoil were eroded from farmland. Although the Dust Bowl has been over for many years, severe erosion is still occurring. In 1977, nearly three billion metric tons of soil were eroded from United States farmland. However, soil conservation efforts are being made to reduce erosion of topsoil, increase the amount of water absorbed by the soil, and maintain the fertility of the soil.

Planting rows of dense evergreens, called shelter belts, helps protect fields from wind erosion. Gardeners may use mulch, a cover of organic material such as grass clippings, to help retain soil moisture. Because soil left unplanted during winter is likely to be eroded by wind and water, many farmers plant a cover crop after the main crop has been harvested. A cover crop protects the soil and reduces runoff, in addition to adding minerals and organic matter to the soil. In spring, when the main crop is planted again, the cover crop is plowed under.

Some farmers use a soil conservation method called no-till farming. With this method, cover crops or the remains of previous crops are not plowed under. New crops are planted directly in the unplowed field. Because the soil is not exposed by plowing, there is less erosion by wind and water.

Contour plowing and contour planting are other methods of soil conservation. Fields are plowed and crops are planted across

a

b

the slope of the land rather than up and down. Also, crop rotation helps maintain the fertility of soil that is farmed year after year. In crop rotation, a different crop is planted each year in a two- or three-year cycle. If a crop that requires a lot of nitrogen, such as corn, is planted in the first year of a two-year cycle, a crop that restores nitrogen to the soil, such as peas or beans, is planted the second year. Another method is strip cropping, or alternating rows of crops such as corn and grass. Farmers may also add fertilizers to fields to improve crops yields and help maintain soil fertility from year to year.

FIGURE 24–9. Contour plowing (a) and strip cropping (b) are important methods of soil conservation.

Making Sure

5. Why is topsoil important to plants?
6. Discuss four methods of soil conservation.
7. Why are crop rotation farming and fertilizers used by some farmers?

FIGURE 24–10. Farmers may add fertilizers to fields to maintain soil fertility.

Activity 24–3   Soil Characteristics

Problem: Does peat moss help soil hold water?

Materials

dry soil
2 empty food cans
labels
old nylon stockings
rubber bands
2 glass jars
2 pieces of screen wire
peat moss
balance
metric ruler
can opener
deep pan
spoon
scissors

Procedure

1. Measure 50 g of dry soil. Set aside.
2. Measure 35 g more of dry soil. Measure 15 g of peat moss. Mix the two well.
3. Carefully remove the bottoms of two clean food cans with a can opener.
4. Cut six 14-cm squares from old nylon stockings.
5. Use rubber bands to fasten three squares over one end of each can.

6. Label one can dry soil.
7. Label the other can dry soil and peat moss.
8. Place the correct contents in each can.
9. Determine the mass of each can and its contents. Record the measurements.
10. Predict which can will have the most water after being submerged in water overnight.
11. Submerge the cans in a pan of water overnight.
12. Place two pieces of wire screen over each jar.
13. Turn the cans upside down on the screen. Allow the contents of the cans to drain for 30 minutes.
14. Determine the mass of each can after it was soaked and drained. Record the measurements.

Data and Observations

Can	Dry soil	Dry soil and peat moss
Dry mass		
Wet mass after draining		
Amount of water held		

FIGURE 24–11.

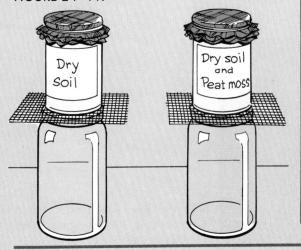

Questions and Conclusions

1. How much water did the dry soil hold?
2. How much water did the dry soil and peat moss hold?
3. How much more did the dry soil and peat moss hold than the dry soil alone?
4. Why was it important that each can contain the same amount (50 grams) of mass when you began the activity?
5. What part of soil does the peat moss represent?
6. If you were a gardener or farmer, why might you add peat moss to your soil?
7. Does peat moss help soil hold water?

24:5 Forest Conservation

Forests are important renewable natural resources. They provide natural beauty, prevent erosion, and furnish food and cover for wildlife. Also, forests provide lumber to make furniture and buildings. Wood pulp is used in making paper and turpentine. Bark is a source of mulch, fertilizers, and glues. As with Earth's other resources, careful management is needed to conserve forests.

The major causes of forest destruction are diseases and insects. Parasites cause diseases that kill trees. For example, chestnut blister and Dutch elm disease are caused by fungi. Insects such as spruce budworms, gypsy moths, and pine weevils also destroy trees. Methods of controlling diseases in forests include removing infected trees and treating diseased trees with antibiotics. Insect pests may be controlled by introducing natural insect predators into a forest or using pesticides.

Careful forest management is needed to conserve forests. Certain methods of cutting down trees do not destroy forests but aid in forest conservation. Improvement cutting is the practice of removing unhealthy trees and those with little commercial value. Improvement cutting increases the lumber yield and quality of a forest. Selective cutting removes only mature trees. Younger trees are left to grow for use in the future. Harvesting of trees also may be done by block cutting in which all trees in a small section, or block of a forest, are cut down. The trees around the block produce seeds that fall onto the open land. In time, new trees grow. Reforestation is another method of conservation. **Reforestation** is the practice of renewing a forest by seeding or planting small trees.

FIGURE 24–12. The elms on the left are afflicted with Dutch elm disease.

What is reforestation?

FIGURE 24–13. Reforestation is an important method of forest conservation.

FIGURE 24–14. When people go camping, they should build fires in fire rings.

How are natural fires important to forests?

FIGURE 24–15. Fuels such as coal (a), wood (b), and natural gas (c) contain potential energy that is released when they are burned.

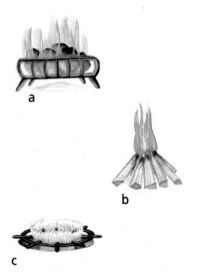

Natural fires, such as those caused by lightning, may be important to maintaining balance in a forest. Controlled fires may be used to thin the growth of young trees. These prescribed fires keep the forest "clean." They can prevent a large fire from occurring that might destroy the whole forest. To avoid accidental fires, matches, fuels, gas stoves, and lanterns should always be handled carefully in and around forests.

Conservation of forest resources involves the reduction of waste in harvesting and using timber. Waste wood particles produced in cutting and sanding wood can be compressed and glued together to form particle board. Waste wood can be heated in the absence of oxygen to produce turpentine, charcoal, and wood alcohol. Cellulose can be extracted from waste wood and used to make plastics. Moving outdoor wooden furniture indoors during the winter and painting wood exposed to the weather also help conserve forests by decreasing the need to replace wood products.

24:6 Energy Resources

The main sources of energy today are fossil fuels. **Fossil fuels** are nonrenewable resources that include coal, natural gas, and petroleum. These fuels formed over millions of years as the result of burial and decay of organisms deep within Earth. Supplies of these fuels are rapidly decreasing and the need for conservation is growing.

Only about one third of all energy produced is used wisely. There are many ways to conserve energy. Reducing automobile speeds and driving smaller cars help save fuel. Using mass trans-

FIGURE 24–16. Many buildings being constructed have solar panels, such as this library.

portation, such as buses and car pools, also saves fuel. Setting thermostats at lower temperatures in winter and higher in summer reduces the use of energy for home heating and cooling. Increasing insulation in homes and buildings reduces heat losses that waste energy. Using electric lights and appliances wisely also saves energy.

In addition to conservation, however, it is necessary to develop alternative energy resources that will decrease peoples' dependence on fossil fuels. One alternative is solar energy. The sun provides a continuous source of energy that can be used for heating and cooling and for generating electricity. Energy from the sun can be stored in water, rocks, or electric batteries for use when there is no sunlight.

What are the advantages of solar heating?

Another alternative to using fossil fuels is nuclear energy. Nuclear power plants use fuels such as uranium or plutonium, which are radioactive elements. The energy released from the fuel by a fission reaction is used to generate electricity. Another nuclear reaction called fusion also releases large amounts of energy. With nuclear power plants, however, there exists the danger of the release of harmful radiation into the environment. Also, the long-term effects of the storage of radioactive wastes are not fully understood.

FIGURE 24–17. Nuclear power plants generate electricity.

Geothermal energy is obtained from hot spots in Earth such as areas of volcanic activity and natural geysers. Steam produced by geothermal energy is used to generate electricity. Use of geothermal energy, however, is limited to certain geographic areas. Another problem is that salts in the heated water corrode pipes and machinery and can pollute the nearby land area.

Hydroelectric power plants are another source of energy. The energy of water falling over a dam is converted to electrical energy by generators.

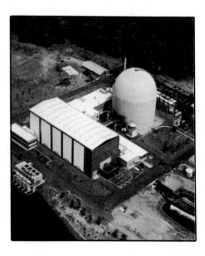

Making Sure

8. What are the major causes of forest destruction?
9. List three methods of forest conservation.
10. Define fossil fuels.
11. Discuss two uses of solar energy.
12. Discuss the advantages and disadvantages of nuclear energy.
13. How is water used to generate electricity?

24:7 Wildlife Conservation

Wildlife refers to any wild animal or plant. In recent years, many wildlife populations have been decreasing, largely due to changes in the environment. People have cleared forests, plowed grasslands, drained swamps, dammed streams, and polluted the air. These practices destroy the habitats of wildlife. Unwise hunting practices have also reduced wildlife populations.

Only small numbers of some species are living. These species are said to be **endangered** and could become extinct if the living members are not protected. **Extinction** occurs when there are no longer any living members of a species. Dinosaurs are extinct organisms.

In 1941, only 15 wild whooping cranes were living. Loss of habitat was the main reason for the decreasing population. Efforts were begun to preserve the whooping cranes' habitat. Although these measures were successful, the whooping crane is still an endangered species.

To avoid extinction, wildlife must be conserved. Preserving the habitat of wildlife aids conservation. Wildlife refuges are areas in which wildlife and their habitats are protected. In some refuges,

Distinguish between endangered and extinct wildlife.

FIGURE 24–18. The whooping crane (a) and American alligator (b) are endangered species.

a

b

FIGURE 24–19. Fence rows are habitats for many wildlife species.

no hunting is allowed. In others, hunting is carefully restricted. Wildlife refuges are usually owned and managed by governments. Special efforts are made to provide water, protective cover, and breeding areas. Also, winter feeding within a refuge helps assure that wild animals survive and reproduce. Planting new forests provides shelter and food for wildlife.

Another wildlife conservation practice is to set aside permanent wilderness areas. People can camp and hike in these areas, but no roads, motor vehicles, or power lines are allowed. The aim is to preserve the wilderness for present and future generations to enjoy. Wildlife habitats also can be preserved by planting trees and bushes in windbreaks. The vegetation is not only decorative, but it also provides food and cover for birds and other wildlife. Allowing brush to grow along farm fences increases the area in which wild rabbits, quail, and pheasant can survive and multiply.

What are some methods of wildlife conservation?

Government regulations are important to wildlife conservation. Managing wildlife habitats and populations helps maintain balance. Regulated hunting and fishing are methods of wildlife management. These laws restrict the number of animals that may be killed and limit hunting and fishing to times when the populations are at their peaks.

For example, the deer population in some states is controlled through hunting because the natural predators of deer are no longer present. Some government departments raise fish and game birds for stocking streams and fields. Stocking keeps the population large enough to allow fishing and hunting.

Making Sure

14. How can endangered species be saved from extinction?
15. Describe two ways in which a wildlife refuge aids in wildlife conservation.

FIGURE 24–20. Recycling paper, such as newspapers, reduces the number of trees that must be cut each year to make new paper.

24:8 Environmental Management

The use of methods that conserve resources and protect the ecosystem is called **environmental management**. In addition to conservation measures, recycling is an important method in good management of the environment. **Recycling** means using over again. Perhaps you have saved old newspapers and aluminum cans for recycling. Recycled newspapers are used to make paper bags, writing paper, and cardboard. Aluminum cans are refined to produce new aluminum products.

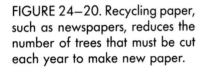

Pollution prevention, too, requires proper environmental management. Nuclear power plants, oil refineries, and other factories must use proper safety devices and methods to reduce pollution. Special disposal techniques must be provided for hazardous chemical wastes.

In addition to industrial and human pollutants, plant and animal wastes contribute to the environment. These organic wastes, however, are biodegradable. **Biodegradable** (bi oh duh GRAYD uh bul) wastes decompose into compounds that do not harm the environment. The wastes are broken down by microbes in soil, water, and air, and become a natural part of the ecosystem. However, people have added many materials to the environment that are not biodegradable such as some detergents, metals, plastics, glass, and most litter.

An important part of environmental management is weighing the risks and benefits of a certain situation. Do the economic benefits outweigh the environmental risks? Building the Alaskan oil pipeline involved many risks. Damage to the permafrost and wildlife, and potential oil spills were among the many factors involved. The benefits included a vast supply of petroleum for the United States. But, risks and benefits do not always have a dollar value. Preserving the beauty of the wilderness or the nation's heritage are factors that cannot be determined financially.

Define recycling.

What is biodegradable?

List the risks and benefits of the Alaskan pipeline.

Activity 24–4   Managing the Environment

Problem: Which substances are not biodegradable?

Materials

2 clay flowerpots
2 petri dish lids to fit clay pots
sand or gravel
potting soil
2 small aluminum pie pans
newspaper
dead leaf
apple peeling
plastic milk container
aluminum foil
Styrofoam®
scissors
metric ruler
water

Procedure

1. Place a layer of sand or gravel in the bottom of each clay flowerpot. Fill the pots with moistened potting soil to within 1 cm of the top.
2. Into one pot, place a 2-cm square of newspaper, a dead leaf, and a 2-cm square of apple peeling.
3. Into the second pot, place a 2-cm square of plastic, a 2-cm square of aluminum foil, and a 2-cm square of Styrofoam.®

FIGURE 24–21.

4. Cover each pot with the top of a petri dish. Make sure it fits tightly over the materials in the pot.
5. Place each pot in an aluminum pie pan. Add water to the aluminum pan. The water will rise through each pot and keep the contents moistened.
6. Observe the two pots every other day for four weeks. Record your observations.

Data and Observations

Pot 1

Date	Substance	Observations
	newspaper	
	leaf	
	apple peeling	

Pot 2

Date	Substance	Observations
	plastic	
	aluminum foil	
	Styrofoam®	

Questions and Conclusions

1. Which substances were biodegradable?
2. Which substance decomposed most rapidly?
3. What kinds of organisms were you able to observe?
4. How do substances that are not biodegradable affect our environment?
5. How can you use what you learned in this activity to help conserve our environment?
6. Which substances are not biodegradable?

FIGURE 24–22. Visual pollution refers to unsightly aspects of the environment.

What effects does noise pollution have on people?

FIGURE 24–23. Workers may be required to wear ear protection if they work in noisy places.

24:9 Healthy Environments

Conservation, pollution control, safe disposal of wastes, and recycling are several methods of environmental management that will lead to a healthy environment. What other factors are necessary for a clean, healthy environment?

Visual pollution refers to sights such as unpleasant signs, wires, telephone poles, litter and discarded trash. Efforts to reduce visual pollution include limiting the number, size, and location of outdoor billboards and other signs. New electric wires and communication lines can be buried underground. Trees can be planted to beautify the surroundings.

Loud or unpleasant sounds are called **noise pollution**. People differ in what they consider to be noise. For you, the ring of a telephone when a friend is calling may be a pleasant sound. For someone working in an office, the continual ring of many phones can be unpleasant noise. Pressure changes caused by loud noises can strain the inner parts of a person's ears. If the loud noise is continual, a permanent loss of hearing may occur. Noise can also affect other parts of the body. Changes in breathing and heart rates, an increase in blood pressure, and changes in digestion may be responses to noise. Too much noise can make people grouchy and tired. Noise can cause headaches and lack of appetite. People who work in noisy areas should wear ear covers that protect against the effects of loud noise.

What can be done to reduce noise pollution? Jet engines are being modified to reduce the amount of noise they make. Insulation and sound-absorbent material in buildings reduce noise levels inside. Manufacturers are producing appliances that run more quietly. Lowering the volume of stereos and televisions also helps reduce noise pollution. Planting trees near busy highways not only beautifies the area, but helps reduce noise levels because the trees absorb sound.

24:10 Looking to the Future

Our future depends on how we plan and manage what we do. Wise and careful planning and analysis of new developments can create a bright future for humans. Although technology has improved our lives, it also has created many environmental problems. A supersonic jet airplane may be faster, but it creates noise pollution and burns much fuel. Pesticides and fertilizers may increase crop yields, but in large quantities, they are hazardous to the environment.

Wise development and use of land areas as well as conservation of all Earth's resources is needed. Development of alternative energy resources will ensure a good supply of energy for future generations. The future of all people and Earth depends on the wise application of ecological principles.

Making Sure

16. Define environmental management.
17. Name three examples of noise pollution.

FIGURE 24–24. The future of all people and Earth depends on the application of ecological principles.

Technology

Ozone's Effect on Forests

Ecologists have recently discovered that some forests are not healthy. Forest growth is declining and many trees are dying. The causes of this destruction include insects, disease, drought, and air pollution.

Over two-thirds of Germany's Black Forest is dying due to a combination of disease and industrial pollution. Scientists have evidence to believe that nitrogen oxides from car and truck emissions are carried from the cities and highways up into the atmosphere. Ozone is a gas formed when oxygen combines with oxides, such as nitrogen oxide, in the presence of sunlight. In high concentrations, ozone can be fatal to trees. Ozone breaks down the protective membranes of the needles and leaves causing a loss of nutrients, such as magnesium. Magnesium is vital to photosynthesis.

Researchers from Cornell University have also studied the effects of ozone on forest trees and crop plants. In laboratory studies, plants were placed in controlled-environment fumigation chambers. The ozone levels in these chambers ranged from those found in clean air, to levels found in heavily polluted air. To determine the effects of ozone, they estimated the rate of photosynthesis by measuring the amount of carbon dioxide used by plants. The researchers used an infrared carbon dioxide analyzer to measure the carbon dioxide. Results showed reduced rates of photosynthesis in forest trees and crop plants exposed to high levels of ozone. Similar results were obtained with experiments in the field. Based on these results, ozone is considered to be a major factor responsible for the decline in forest growth and health. Unhealthy trees are more vulnerable to insects, diseases, extreme temperatures, and drought.

FIGURE 24–25. As more and more trees of the Black Forest dry out and turn brown, whole forests must be cut down.

Environmentalists

Dr. Larry McKinney holds a bachelor of science degree and a master of science degree in education. He earned his doctor of philosophy degree in science education. Of the many career opportunities available to him, Dr. McKinney chose teaching. After teaching for ten years, he was appointed as the science supervisor of a state department of education.

During his nine years as science supervisor, Dr. McKinney promoted outdoor education projects by setting up outdoor classrooms for hands-on study of the environment. Later, under his leadership as a middle school principal, the school district's science teachers developed a model outdoor education site that supports many kinds of plant and animal life.

The area has a path known as the study trail. It has numbered sites and lists of suggested activities appropriate for each area. At first, Dr. McKinney intended the outdoor education site to be used by middle school and high school students only. Its fame spread, however, and now elementary students attend day camps at the site.

According to Dr. McKinney, students seem to retain much of what they learn at an outdoor education site. "Students enjoy science activities in an informal situation," he says.

Although Dr. McKinney knows that he could have earned a greater salary in another career, he feels that money is no substitute for the joy of watching young people learn. He says, "Teaching is the most important profession in society."

Walter Fletcher has a different approach to teaching young people about their environment. As a sergeant in the United States Army, he taught airborne troops how to survive if they were forced down behind enemy lines. Now a civilian volunteer, he teaches wilderness survival to members of a youth organization.

Each year, emergency teams search for lost backpackers, campers, or survivors of small aircraft crashes. Mr. Fletcher believes that knowing basic survival techniques can mean the difference between life and death.

Members of Mr. Fletcher's youth group learn that boot laces can be used to snare small animals, and that a belt buckle sharpened on a flat stone becomes a skinning knife. At night the group members listen to the sounds of nocturnal animals in order to locate breakfast, and during the day they watch for the burrows of small animals. They learn to use compasses, read topographic maps, and practice first aid techniques on each other. Mr. Fletcher uses his military training, combined with his imagination and creativity, to give young people the ability to save their own lives in case of outdoor emergencies.

Summary

1. Resources can be divided into two groups: those that are renewable and those that are nonrenewable.   24:1
2. Sources of air pollution include industries and motor vehicles.   24:2
3. Thermal pollution is caused by pumping hot water into lakes, rivers, and streams.   24:3
4. Soil conservation methods reduce erosion and add necessary nutrients to the soil.   24:4
5. Forest conservation ensures an adequate supply of lumber, wood pulp, and bark for all organisms.   24:5
6. Fossil fuels are nonrenewable resources that include coal, natural gas, and petroleum.   24:6
7. Wildlife conservation protects wild animals and plants from becoming endangered or extinct.   24:7
8. Environmental management is the use of methods that conserve and protect the ecosystem.   24:8
9. Controlling noise and visual pollution are necessary to maintain a healthy environment.   24:9
10. The future of all organisms and Earth depends on the wise application of ecological principles.   24:10

Vocabulary

Write a sentence using each of the following words or terms correctly.

biodegradable	fossil fuel	reforestation
conservation	noise pollution	renewable resource
endangered	nonrenewable resource	resource
environmental	particulate	sewage
management	pollution	thermal pollution
erosion	recycling	visual pollution
extinction		

Questions

Do not write in this book.

A. True or False

Determine whether each of the following sentences is true or false. Rewrite the false statements to make them correct.

1. In no-till farming, a new crop is planted directly in an unplowed field.
2. A resource is something taken from the environment that is harmful to organisms.

3. Particulates and sulfur dioxide are the major air pollutants.
4. Filters in smokestacks help to reduce air pollution.
5. Photochemical smog occurs most often in small cities with little traffic.
6. Changes in habitat often decrease an organism's chances of survival.
7. Hunting is allowed in all wildlife refuges.
8. Sonic booms, jet planes, and large trucks all contribute to noise pollution.
9. Technology can be both beneficial and harmful to the environment.
10. Supplies of fossil fuels are rapidly increasing.

B. Multiple Choice
Choose the word or phrase that correctly completes the following sentences.
1. Contour plowing reduces *(sewage, erosion, the amount of topsoil)*.
2. Reforestation aids *(soil, wildlife, soil and wildlife)* conservation.
3. A species that no longer exists is *(protected, abundant, extinct, nongame)*.
4. Wildlife that is in danger of extinction is said to be a(n) *(game animal, endangered species, wildlife refuge)*.
5. *(Insulation materials, Improvement cuttings, Reservoirs, Telephone poles)* are used to decrease noise pollution.
6. *(Particulates, Carbon monoxide, Lead, Sewage)* is (are) not a form of air pollution.
7. Thermal pollution is caused by *(organic wastes, minerals, heated water, sewage)*.
8. Planting new trees to replace those cut down is called *(reforestation, improvement cutting, selective cutting)*.
9. Geothermal energy comes from *(coal, natural gas, hot spots in Earth)*.
10. *(Ozone, Carbon monoxide, Smog)* is a toxic, odorless gas that can cause suffocation.

C. Completion
Complete each of the following sentences with the correct word or phrase.
1. _____ and _____ can increase crop yields but can also pollute the environment.
2. Particles of any size emitted into the air are _____.
3. Untreated _____ can cause a decrease in oxygen in a lake, river, or stream that could kill fish or other life.
4. The removal of soil by water, wind, ice, or gravity is _____.
5. In Minamata, Japan, polluted water that contained _____ caused birth defects.
6. Poles, wires, unpleasant signs, trash, and litter are forms of _____ pollution.

7. Ash and dust are _____ that contribute to smog and respiratory problems.
8. Glass, aluminum, and paper can be conserved by _____ .
9. Coal and topsoil are _____ resources.
10. _____ power is produced by water falling over a dam.

D. How and Why

1. Why is conservation of soil and water important to people?
2. How is water conservation related to soil and forest conservation?
3. What is noise pollution and why is it harmful?
4. Write a paragraph in which you explain how you can help conserve resources.
5. Explain how three resources can be conserved by recycling.
6. How can science and technology aid in the conservation of natural resources?

Ideas to Explore

1. **Project:** Tour a solar home if one is available in your area. Report on how solar energy is used to heat and cool the home.
2. **Challenge:** Obtain information on the advantages and disadvantages of nuclear energy. Present a report to your class.
3. **Project:** Visit a water supply station to learn how your community obtains its water and how the water is purified.
4. **Project:** Obtain information from a library on endangered species. Make a poster listing several such species with drawings or pictures.
5. **Project:** Design a decal based on the "Save Wildlife" theme. Obtain information from a local art or hobby store on making a decal transfer for clothing based on your design.

Readings

Ardley, Neil. *Our Future Needs*. New York: Franklin Watts, Inc., 1982.

Asimov, Isaac. *How Did We Find Out About Solar Energy?* New York: D. Walker, 1981.

Burt, Olive W. *Rescued: America's Endangered Wildlife on the Comeback Trail*. New York: Julian Messner, 1980.

Koopowitz, Harold and Hilary Kaye. *Plant Extinction: A Global Crisis*. Washington, D. C.: Stone Wall Press, 1983.

Moore, Tara. *The Endangered Species: Elephants*. Champaign, IL: Garrard, 1982.

Moore, Tara. *The Endangered Species: Polar Bears*. Champaign, IL: Garrard, 1982.

Life Through Time
Background Data

This feature focuses on changes in the plant and animal population of Earth since the beginning of geologic time. If you were to let your mind wander, you could picture an array of plants and animals. Many different types of organisms inhabited Earth in the geologic past. Fossils are evidence of past life. Scientists study fossils to learn about Earth's history. Fossils indicate the type of environment in which an organism lived, and the relative numbers of the organism. Fossils also help scientists determine when a particular organism evolved, flourished, and became extinct. Scientists also study fossils to determine the succession of organisms through geologic time. As you work with this program, notice how the abundance and complexity of life has increased from the beginning of geologic time to the present. Also note that as the types and numbers of populations increase, the likelihood of change also increases.

Input/Output

Enter the program into your computer exactly as it is printed. After you enter the entire program, type RUN. If there is a problem, type LIST and check that you have entered the program exactly as it is printed. Remember, symbols and punctuation are important and must be typed as printed here. REM statements are provided in the program to help you. They do not need to be entered in order for the program to run. When all corrections have been made, save the program.

Once the program is running, the computer will ask how much of Earth's history you want displayed on the screen. You may choose (1) Earth's entire history from formation to present, or (2) Earth's history from the beginning of the Cambrian, when the first fossils are found, to the present. After you make your choice, the computer will ask the number of seconds that you wish to represent your selected period of Earth's history. When you enter your choice, the computer will clear the screen and print your choices and the major biologic event associated with that time period. As changes occur more rapidly, events will stay on the screen for a shorter period of time.

Programming Notes

The computer reads each line of the program and executes the command listed there. Line 90 is used to clear the screen. Some computers use the command CLS, others use HOME. Use the command your computer recognizes.

The variables used are listed below.

M	long or short history
X	length of time in seconds
E$	event listed
A$	name of age
A	age in years
T	time period between ages
C, Q, B	temporary variables

Lines 20 through 40 utilize several PRINT statements to generate the menu on the screen. The computer asks for your choice in line 50, and the number of seconds in line 60. An IF/THEN statement in line 50 causes the program to move to line 70 if the long history is chosen. Line 70 calculates the length of time and reads the first event and age from the data. If a short history is chosen in line 50, the program moves to line 80 where the time is calculated, the data are read, and the first five events are discarded. Line 100 utilizes a device that checks for the end of the data. PRINT statements again are used in lines 100 through 140 to print the event, age, and time period on the screen. The number of seconds that each event will last and the total number of seconds that have passed are calculated in lines 150 and 160. Line 170 incorporates a loop, and lines 180 through 340 contain the data.

Program

```
10 Q = 1: GOTO 90
20   PRINT : PRINT "HISTORY OF TH
     E WORLD": PRINT
30   PRINT "      1    THE ENTIRE HI
     STORY"
40   PRINT "      2    ONLY FROM CAM
     BRIAN"
50   PRINT : PRINT "WHICH HISTORY
     TO USE";: INPUT M: IF M < 0
     OR M > 2 THEN 50
60   PRINT : PRINT "HOW MANY SECO
     NDS SHOULD THIS LAST";: INPUT
     X
70   IF M = 1 THEN X = X / 7.05: READ
     E$,A$,A:B = A: GOTO 90
80   IF M = 2 THEN X = X * 1.065:
     FOR C = 1 TO 4: READ E$,A$,
     A: NEXT C:B = A
90   HOME : IF Q = 1 THEN Q = 0: GOTO
     20: REM  MAY BE DIFFERENT O
     N YOUR COMPUTER
100  IF E$ = "END" THEN  PRINT :
     PRINT : PRINT "R E A C H E
     D  T O D A Y": FOR C = 1 TO
     1000: NEXT C: RUN
110  PRINT : PRINT : PRINT E$: PRINT
120  PRINT "YEARS AGO = ";A;",00
     0,000": PRINT
130  PRINT "TIME PERIOD = ";A$: PRINT
140  READ E$,A$,A:T = B - A:B =
     A: PRINT : PRINT
150  PRINT "         ";( INT (((((T
     * X) / 635) * 10) + .05) /
     10);"  SECS": PRINT
160  PRINT "TOTAL ";:N = N + ( INT
     (((((T * X) / 635) * 10) + .0
     5) / 10): PRINT N;"  SECS"
170    FOR S = 1 TO (T * X): NEXT
       S: GOTO 90
180    DATA   INFERED AGE OF THE EA
       RTH,BEGINING OF EARTH,4500
190    DATA   FIRST ALGAE TYPE PLAN
       TS,ARCHEOZOIC,3200
200    DATA   FIRST JELLYFISH OCEAN
       ANIMALS,PROTEROZOIC,1200
210    DATA   FOSSILS SHOW ANIMAL
       & PLANT LIFE OCEAN,CAMBRIAN,
       600
220    DATA   THE FIRST MARINE VERT
       ABRATES,ORDOVICIAN,475
230    DATA   FIRST FISHES & PLAN
       TS ON LAND, SILURIAN,430
240    DATA   ABUNDANT FISHES IN OC
       EANS,DEVONIAN,400
250    DATA   ANIMALS LIVING IN BO
       TH LAND & WATER,MISSISSIPPIA
       N,350
260    DATA   LARGE SWAMPS COVER NO
       RTHEAST,PENNSYLVANIAN,310
270    DATA   FIRST REPTILES & LAND
       ANIMALS,PERMIAN,260
280    DATA   LARGE LAND REPTILES,T
       RIASSIC,230
290    DATA   MANY KINDS OF DINOSAU
       RS,JURASSIC,180
300    DATA   SUDDEN DISAPPEARANCE
       OF DINOSAURS,CRETACEOUS,130
310    DATA   MODERN MAMMALS INCLU
       DING PRIMATES,TERTIARY,65
320    DATA   BEGINING OF MAN,QUAT
       ERNARY,1
340    DATA   END,END,0
```

Challenge: On Your Own

An easy modification to this program would be to add additional organisms to the data. You will need to research their placement in geologic history carefully. To make this modification, add the organisms between the word DATA and the first comma of the statement. You may want to change the program so that it traces one type of plant or animal through geologic time. You would need to research the organism's evolutionary history and change each data statement to incorporate this information.

If you enjoy programming, you may wish to expand the menu to allow different time intervals to be selected. You would need to add additional lines similar to lines 30, 40, 70, and 80. Be sure to follow the format shown in the program when making any modifications or additions.

APPENDIX A
International System of Measurement

The International System (SI) of measurement is accepted as the standard for measurement throughout most of the world. Three base units in SI are the meter, kilogram, and second. Frequently used SI units are listed below.

Table A–1

Frequently Used SI Units
LENGTH
1 millimeter (mm) = 1000 micrometers (µm)
1 centimeter (cm) = 10 millimeters (mm)
1 meter (m) = 100 centimeters (cm)
1 kilometer (km) = 1000 meters (m)
1 light-year = 9 460 000 000 000 kilometers (km)
AREA
1 square meter (m^2) = 10 000 square centimeters (cm^2)
1 square kilometer (km^2) = 1 000 000 square meters (m^2)
VOLUME
1 milliliter (mL) = 1 cubic centimeter (cc) (cm^3)
1 liter (L) = 1000 milliliters (mL)
MASS
1 gram (g) = 1000 milligrams (mg)
1 kilogram (kg) = 1000 grams (g)
1 metric ton = 1000 kilograms (kg)
TIME
1 s = 1 second

Temperature measurements in SI are often made in degrees Celsius. Celsius temperature is a supplementary unit derived from the base unit kelvin. The Celsius scale (°C) has 100 equal graduations between the freezing temperature (0°C) and the boiling temperature of water (100°C). The following relationship exists between the Celsius and kelvin temperature scales:

$$K = °C + 273$$

Several other supplementary SI units are listed below.

Table A–2

Supplementary SI Units			
Measurement	**Unit**	**Symbol**	**Expressed in base units**
Energy	Joule	J	kg · m^2/s^2
Force	Newton	N	kg · m/s^2
Power	Watt	W	kg · m^2/s^3 (J/s)
Pressure	Pascal	Pa	kg/m · s^2 (N · m)

APPENDIX B
Safety in the Science Classroom

The science classroom is a safe place in which to perform activities if you are careful. You must assume responsibility for the safety of yourself and your classmates. These safety rules will help you protect yourself and others from injury.

1. Do not perform activities that are unauthorized. Always obtain your teacher's permission before beginning an activity.
2. Study your assignment. If you have questions, ask your teacher.
3. Use the safety equipment provided for you. Know the location of the fire extinguisher, safety shower, fire blanket, first aid kit, fire alarm, and the nurse.
4. Safety glasses and safety apron should be worn when any activity calls for heating, pouring, or using chemicals.
5. Smother fires with a towel. If clothing should catch fire, smother it with a blanket or coat or quench it under a safety shower. **NEVER RUN.**
6. Handle chemicals and bend glassware only under the direction of your teacher. If you spill acid or another corrosive chemical, wash it off immediately with water. **Never** taste any chemical substance or draw poisonous materials into a glass tube with your mouth. **Never** inhale chemicals. Keep combustible materials away from open flames.
7. Place broken glass and solid substances in designated containers. Keep insoluble waste material out of the sink. Dispose of chemicals properly. Do not dispose of them in the sink.
8. When your activity is completed, be sure to turn off the water and gas and disconnect electrical connections. Clean your work area. Return all materials to their proper places.

REPORT ALL ACCIDENTS AND SPILLS TO YOUR TEACHER IMMEDIATELY

Table B–1

Classroom Safety	
Injury	**Safe response**
burns	Flush with water. Call your teacher immediately.
cuts and bruises	Follow the instructions in the first aid kit. Report to the school nurse.
fainting or collapse	Provide the person with fresh air. Have the person recline so that his or her head is lower than his or her body. Call your teacher. A nurse or a doctor may be needed to provide artificial respiration.
fire	Wrap person in fire blanket. Extinguish all flames.
foreign matter in eye	Flush with plenty of water. Use eyewash bottle or fountain.
poisoning	Note the suspected poisoning agent and call your teacher.
severe bleeding	Apply pressure directly to the wound and get medical attention.
spills on skin acid spills base spills	Flush with water or use safety shower. Apply baking soda and call your teacher. Apply boric acid and call your teacher.

Fungus Kingdom

Phylum	Some characteristics	Examples
Zygomycota (sporangium fungi)	multicellular spores produced in sporangia	Bread mold / Water mold
Basidiomycota (club fungi)	multicellular spores produced in club-shaped structures	Bracket fungi / Mushrooms
Ascomycota (sac fungi)	multicellular or unicellular spores produced in saclike structures	Morel / Yeast

Moneran Kingdom

Phylum	Some characteristics	Examples
Cyanophyta (blue-green algae)	unicellular algae can make own food contain chlorophyll most are blue-green	Nostoc / Gloecapsa / Rivularia
Schizomycophyta (bacteria)	unicellular bacteria most cannot make own food round, spiral- or rod-shaped	Bacilli / Cocci / Spirilla

Protist Kingdom

Phylum	Some characteristics	Examples
Euglenophyta (euglenoids)	unicellular most make own food most have one flagellum	*Euglena* *Phacus*
Chrysophyta (golden algae)	most are unicellular make own food yellow-brown color	Diatoms *Synedra*
Pyrrophyta (dinoflagellates)	unicellular make own food have two flagella	*Ceratium* *Peridinium*
Sarcodina (sarcodines)	unicellular cannot make own food have pseudopods	*Amoeba* *Foraminifera*
Ciliophora (ciliates)	unicellular cannot make own food have cilia	*Vorticella* *Paramecium* *Didinium*
Mastigophora (flagellates)	unicellular cannot make own food have more than one flagellum	*Trichomonas* *Trypanosoma*
Sporozoa (sporozoans)	unicellular parasitic no means of movement	*Gregarina* *Plasmodium*
Myxomycota (slime molds)	multicellular cannot make own food change form during life cycle	*Dictyostelium* *Physarum*

Plant Kingdom

Phylum	Some characteristics	Examples
Chlorophyta (green algae)	nonvascular, unicellular, green live on land or in water	*Volvox* Sea lettuce
Phaeophyta (brown algae)	nonvascular, multicellular, brown most live in salt water	Sea palm Gulfweed Rockweed
Rhodophyta (red algae)	nonvascular, multicellular, red most live in deep salt water	Irish "moss" *Polysiphonia* *Corallina*
Bryophyta Class Hepaticae (liverworts)	nonvascular, multicellular, green grow flat in moist land areas rhizoids	*Marchantia* Horned liverwort

Phylum	Some characteristics	Examples
Bryophyta Class Musci (mosses)	nonvascular, multicellular, green grow upright stalks in moist land areas rhizoids	Hairy cap moss *Sphagnum* Rock moss
Tracheophyta Class Filicineae (ferns)	vascular, multicellular, green live in moist land areas feathery leaves called fronds	Floating fern Adder's tongue Maidenhair fern
Tracheophyta Class Gymno-spermae (gymno-sperms)	vascular, multicellular, green live on land produce seeds in cones or conelike structures	Ginkgo Douglas fir Bald cypress
Tracheophyta Class Angio-spermae (angio-sperms)	vascular, multicellular, green live on land produce flowers and seeds in fruits	Rhododendron Aspen Barrel cactus

Animal Kingdom

Phylum	Some characteristics	Examples
Porifera (sponges)	thick sack of cells with pores, canals, chambers live in water, attached to one place	Velvet sponge · Elephant ear · Venus's flower basket
Coelenterata (coelenterates)	have central cavity, mouth most have tentacles live in water, floating or attached to one place	Jellyfish · Brain coral · Sea anemone
Platyhelminthes (flatworms)	flattened body freeliving in water or parasitic	Planarian · Tapeworm · Liver fluke
Nematoda (roundworms)	round body freeliving in water or on land or parasitic	Ascaris · Filaria · Hookworm

Phylum	Some characteristics	Examples
Annelida (segmented worms)	body divided into segments that have bristles freeliving in water or on land	Earthworm Leech Bristle worm
Mollusca (mollusks)	soft bodies most have hard shells or shell-like coverings live in water or on land	Snail Octopus Scallop
Arthropoda (arthropods)	body divided into sections jointed legs have exoskeletons live in water or on land	Spider Honeybee Shrimp
Echinodermata (echinoderms)	spiny or leathery skin radial symmetry water vascular system live in salt water	Sea cucumber Sea urchin
Chordata (chordates)	internal skeleton specialized body systems paired appendages live in water and on land	Vertebrates

Glossary

The glossary contains all of the major science terms of the text and their definitions. Below is a pronunciation key to help you use these terms. The word or term will be given in boldface type. If necessary, the pronunciation will follow the term in parentheses.

a . . . **b**ack (bak)	oo . . . **foot** (foot)	
ay . . . **d**ay (day)	ew . . . **foo**d (fewd)	
ah . . . **f**ather (fahth ur)	yoo . . . **p**ure (pyoor)	
ow . . . **flow**er (flow ur)	yew . . . **f**ew (fyew)	
ar . . . **c**ar (car)	uh . . . **c**omma (cahm uh)	
e . . . **l**ess (les)	u (+con) . . . flow**er** (flow ur)	
ee . . . **l**eaf (leef)	sh . . . **sh**elf (shelf)	
ih . . . **tr**ip (trihp)	ch . . . **nat**ure (nay chur)	
i (i + con + e) . . . **id**ea	g . . . **g**ift (gihft)	
(i dee uh), **l**ife (life)	j . . . **g**em (jem)	
oh . . . **g**o (goh)	ing . . . **sing** (sing)	
aw . . . **s**oft (sawft)	zh . . . **vis**ion (vihzh un)	
or . . . **or**bit (or but)	k . . . **c**ake (kayk)	
oy . . . **c**oin (coyn)	s . . . **s**eed, **c**ent (seed, sent)	
	z . . . **z**one, **r**aise (zohn, rayz)	

A

acquired behavior: behavior that is learned

active immunity: immunity gained when the body produces antibodies

active transport: process that requires energy to move materials from areas of low concentration to areas of high concentration

adaptation: change in an organism that makes it suitable or fit to survive and reproduce in a particular environment

addictive: quality of a drug that causes a physical dependence

adolescence (ad uh LES uns): stage in human development that follows childhood

aerobic (ehr ROB ihk): with oxygen

agar (AH gur): organic compound obtained from seaweed that is used to form a medium for growing microorganisms

albino (al BI noh): organism that has no pigment as a result of a genetic mutation

alcohol: depressant drug that can be habit-forming

alga (AL guh): single-celled or multi-celled organism that contains chlorophyll but no vessels and no roots, stems, or leaves

amino (uh MEE noh) **acid:** organic compound that contains nitrogen

amoeba (uh MEE buh): single-celled organism with changeable form that moves by pseudopods.

amphetamine: habit-forming stimulant

amphibian (am FIHB ee un): cold-blooded, smooth-skinned vertebrate that usually passes through stages of metamorphosis from a larva with gills to an adult with lungs

anaerobic: without oxygen

anaphase: stage of cell division during which paired or doubled chromosomes separate and move to opposite poles of the cell

angiosperm (AN jee uh spurm): seed plant that produces flowers

antibiotic (an ti bi AHT ihk): substance produced by a living organism, that slows down or stops the growth of microbes

antibody: organic compound in blood that attacks a germ or the poison it produces

antiseptic: chemical that kills or prevents the growth of microbes on living tissue

arachnid (uh RAK nihd): arthropod with two body segments, no antennae, and four pairs of legs

artery: blood vessel that carries blood away from the heart

arthropod (AHR thruh pahd): invertebrate with jointed legs and an exoskeleton

asexual (ay SEKSH wul) **reproduction:** process that results in the production of offspring from a cell of only one parent

atom: smallest particle of an element that has properties of the element

atrium: (AY tree um): one of two upper chambers of the human heart that receives blood from the veins

auxin (AHK sihn): plant hormone that controls growth

axon: long fiber attached to a thickened area of a neuron

B

bacterium (bak TIHR ee um) (*pl.* **bacteria**): one-celled moneran with a cell wall, no nuclear membrane, and usually no chlorophyll; shape is coccus (spherical), bacillus (rod-shaped), or spirillum (spiral)

barbiturate (bar BIHCH uh'rut): depressant drug

behavior: the way an organism acts

bilateral (bi LAT uh ruhl) **symmetry:** arrangement of an organism so that lengthwise division would produce two sides that are alike

bile: digestive juice produced in the liver, that breaks down fats into tiny particles

biocontrol: use of helpful organisms to control harmful organisms

biodegradable (bi oh duh GRAYD uh bul): capable of being broken down into harmless compounds by microbes

biome (BI ohm): geographical region with a characteristic climate and particular organisms

biosphere (BI uh sfihr): narrow zone surrounding Earth in which life can exist

biotechnology: application of biological and engineering data to problems; as in the industrial processing of materials by microorganisms to provide useful products

bird: warm-blooded vertebrate with feathers, a four-chambered heart, and a high rate of metabolism

birthrate: number of offspring born in a population in a given length of time

blood type: one of the classes into which blood can be grouped based on its composition

blue-green alga: (also known as Cyanobacterium) moneran with chlorophyll and blue or red pigments; an important food producer for aquatic life

brain: major control center of the body

breed: variety or type of animal or plant developed through selection

budding: kind of asexual reproduction in which a piece of tissue grows from an organism, breaks off, then develops into a new organism

C

Caesarean section: method of childbirth in which the baby is delivered through an incision in the mother's abdominal wall and uterus

caffeine: habit-forming, mild stimulant found in some coffees, teas, and chocolate, cocoa, and many soft drinks

Calorie (KAL uh ree): amount of heat needed to raise the temperature of 1 kg of water 1°C

cambium (KAM bee um): growth tissue that produces new xylem and phloem cells in vascular plants

capillary: blood vessel that connects an artery to a vein

carbohydrate: sugar or starch made of carbon, hydrogen and oxygen that is a good source of energy

carbon monoxide: poisonous gas found in tobacco smoke and car exhaust

carrier: individual who has a gene for a recessive trait that can be passed on to offspring; transmitter of disease microbes

carrying capacity: number of individuals of a population that a habitat can support

cartilage (KAHRT uhl ihj): tough, flexible connective tissue of vertebrates in which cells are widely separated by fine fibers

cell: basic unit of structure and function in an organism; cytoplasm bounded by a membrane or wall

cell membrane: thin layer that surrounds and holds the parts of a cell together

cell wall: rigid layer that surrounds a plant cell membrane

cellulose (SEL yuh lohs): carbohydrate in the cell walls of plants

Celsius (SEL see us): temperature scale on which the freezing point of water is 0° and the boiling point is 100°

centi-: prefix meaning one hundredth 1/100

centipede (SENT uh peed): arthropod with flat, segmented body and one pair of legs per segment

central nervous system: vertebrate brain and spinal cord

cerebellum (ser uh BEL um): smaller part of brain behind the cerebrum; part of the brain that controls sense of balance and coordinates muscular activity

cerebrum (suh REE brum): largest part of the vertebrate brain, located in the upper part of the head; part of the brain that controls memory, learning, and voluntary movements

chemical change: change in which one or more new substances are formed

chemotherapy: treatment of disease by strong and potent chemicals

chitin (KI tun): hard, lightweight substance that composes exoskeletons of arthropods

chlorophyll: green pigment in plants that traps energy from light during photosynthesis

chloroplast (KLOR uh plast): cell organ that contains chlorophyll and in which photosynthesis takes place

Chordata (kohr DAHT uh): phylum that includes vertebrates, tunicates, and lancelets

chromosome (KROH muh sohm): long strand of genetic material or DNA that appears in a cell nucleus during the first stage of cell division

cilia (SIHL ee uh): short, hairlike parts on the outside of a cell

cirrhosis (suh ROH sus): disease of the liver caused by long-term use of alcohol

classification: system of grouping things into categories

climax community: last stage in community succession

club fungus: saprophyte or parasite with a body of hyphae and spores produced in club-shaped structures

club moss: vascular plant with creeping or erect stems having scalelike, overlapping leaves and reproducing by spores

cocaine: strong stimulant that is very habit-forming

cochlea (CAHK lee uh): nerve-containing spiral tube of the inner ear

coelenterate (sih LENT uh rayt): simple invertebrate animal with radial symmetry and a saclike body cavity

cold-blooded: having a body temperature that changes with the temperature of the environment

commensalism: relationship in which one organism lives on another without harm to the host

communicable (kuh MYEW nih kuh bul) **disease:** disease that can be passed from one person to another

community: all the organisms that live together in a certain area

competition: contest among organisms to obtain all their requirements for life

compound: two or more elements bonded together

conception (kun SEP shun): time at which fertilization occurs in mammals

conclusion: answer to a question, or solution to a problem based on observations

conditioning: type of learning that occurs in response to a stimulus that does not normally cause the response

conifer (KAHN uh fur): gymnosperm that produces seeds in cones

conjugation (kahn juh GAY shun): method of sexual reproduction in which a tube of cytoplasm grows between two cells, and through which nuclear material is exchanged

conservation: careful use of resources to maintain quality and avoid waste

consumer: organism that eats other organisms because it cannot make its own food

control: constant in an experiment used to compare changes that occur in the variables of the experiment

coronary circulation: flow of blood through the tissues of the heart

cotyledon (kaht ul EED un): seed leaf that contains food that a plant embryo uses during its early growth

cross: process of pollination and fertilization of one plant by another producing hybrid seeds

crossbreed: organism produced by the mating of two different varieties or breeds

cross-pollination: transfer of pollen from the stamens of one flower to the pistil of another

crustacean (kruh STAY shun): arthropod with two pairs of antennae, a fused head and thorax, and an abdomen

culture: medium with a growing organism

cuticle: (KYEWT ih kul): waxy covering of the epidermis of some leaves

cytoplasm (SITE uh plaz um): material inside a cell membrane that is not nuclear material

D

data: facts obtained through observations

death rate: number of organisms in a population that die in a certain length of time

deciduous (dih SIHJ uh wus): falling off or shedding, at a particular stage of growth or at a specific season; shedding of leaves

decomposer: microbe that brings about the decay of dead organisms

dehydration: process of removing water from a substance

dendrite: structure attached to a neuron that receives stimuli

depressant: drug that slows down body processes

diatom: marine species of algae whose cell has a two-part outer shell

dicot (DI kaht): angiosperm with two seed leaves, vascular bundles arranged in a circle in the stem, leaves with branched veins, and flower parts arranged in fours or fives

diffusion (dihf YEW zhun): movement of molecules in solution from a more concentrated area to a less concentrated area

digestion: process of making food absorbable by the body through the action of secreted enzymes

digestive tract: system of body organs that are connected from the mouth to the anus and through which food passes for digestion

disinfectant: chemical used to destroy microbes on nonliving objects

DNA: deoxyribonucleic acid; the genetic material in cells

dominant trait: trait that is expressed over another trait when both are present

dormancy (DOR mun see): period of time when an organism's metabolism is greatly reduced

drug: substance that can change life processes within the body

drug interaction: effects of one drug on another within an organism

E

eardrum: thin, tightly stretched membrane that transmits sound in a vertebrate's ear

echinoderm (ih KI nuh durm): invertebrate with radial symmetry, a skeleton made of spines inside its body, and a water vascular system for obtaining food

ecology (ih KAHL uh jee): study of relationships between organisms and their environments

ecosystem: living organisms interacting with each other and their nonliving environment

ecotone (EE kuh tohn): area where one biome blends gradually into another

effector: (ih FEK tur): body part that responds when stimulated by nerve impulses

egg: female reproductive cell

element: substance that cannot be broken down into simpler substances

embryo (EM bree oh): first stage of growth after fertilization; young growing plant inside a seed

emphysema: disease of the lungs that prevents normal breathing

endangered: threatened with extinction

endocrine (EN duh krihn) **system:** group of glands in different parts of the body that produce hormones transported by blood

endoplasmic reticulum (en duh PLAZ mihk • rih TIK yuh lum) (ER): network of tubes in the cytoplasm that may be connected to the cell membrane, or to the nuclear membrane; helps move materials through the cell

endospore: small asexual spore with a wall around it that protects a cell

energy: ability to do work

energy pyramid: diagram that shows the flow of energy through a food chain with producers at the base and consumers in the upper levels

environment: part of the biosphere that surrounds and influences an organism

environmental management: use of methods that conserve resources and protect the ecosystem

enzyme (EN zime): protein that regulates the rate of a chemical change in cells

epidemic: condition in which large numbers of people have a certain disease at the same time

epidermis (ep uh DUR mus): thin protective layer of cells that covers a tissue

equation: notation that shows how elements combine to form compounds

erosion: removal of soil by water, wind, ice, or gravity

esophagus (ih SAHF uh gus): tube about 30 cm long that connects the mouth to the stomach

estrus (ES trus): time when a female animal can mate with a male to produce offspring

ethyl alcohol: alcohol used to make beer, wine, whiskey, and other alcoholic beverages

euglena (yew GLEE nuh): animallike, one-celled protist that contains chlorophyll

euglenoid: one-celled protist that belongs to a group of varied flagellates having chlorophyll

evergreen: tree whose leaves remain green throughout the year

evolution: change over time in the hereditary features of a species

excretion: process by which waste products of the body are removed

exoskeleton: hard, outer covering that protects the internal body parts of an arthropod

experiment: operation carried out under controlled conditions to test a hypothesis

external fertilization: fusion of egg and sperm outside the female animal's body

extinction: condition in which there are no longer any living members of a species

F

fat: nutrient made of many carbon atoms and some hydrogen, phosphorus, and oxygen atoms that is rich in energy

feedback: signal to a device that controls an activity; in organisms, signal to decrease, increase, or maintain a life activity

fermentation: process by which energy is released when sugar is changed to ethyl alcohol and carbon dioxide

fern: vascular plant that has roots, leaves, rhizomes and reproduces by spores

fertilization: joining of a sperm and an egg

fetus (FEET us): stage in the development of an animal that has the shape and form of its species but is not yet fully developed; stage between embryo and birth

fish: cold-blooded, aquatic vertebrate with a two-chambered heart and gills for obtaining oxygen from water

fission: nuclear reaction that releases energy during splitting of an atomic nucleus

flagellate (FLAJ uh layt): one-celled protozoan that has one or more flagella

flagellum (fluh JEL um): whiplike thread

flatworm: parasitic or invertebrate animal with a flattened, ribbonlike body and no legs

food chain: series of organisms that feed on other organisms

food web: complex feeding system that contains several food chains

formula: abbreviation for a compound showing its atomic components and the proportions in which they combine

fossil (FAHS ul): any evidence of prehistoric life preserved in rocks

fossil fuel: nonrenewable resource such as coal, petroleum, or natural gas

fraternal twins: twins who develop when two eggs are released and fertilized at the same time

frond (FRAHND): fern leaf

fungus: saprophytic or parasitic organism that does not move around, has a body made of hyphae with no chlorophyll, and reproduces by spores

fusion: nuclear reaction in which an atomic nucleus is formed from the combination of two other nuclei

G

gene (JEEN): unit of inheritance that is passed from parents to offspring

genetic disease: disease that is inherited from one or both parents through genes

genetics (juh NET ihks): study of heredity

genus (JEE nus): largest division in a family; first part of an organism's scientific name

geothermal energy: energy obtained from hot spots within Earth

geotropism: response to gravity in the growth of plant roots and shoots

germination (jur muh NAY shun): period of early growth of a plant from a seed

gestation (juh STAY shun): time between fertilization and the birth of offspring

gibberellic (jihb uh REL ik) **acid:** plant hormone that controls growth

glaucoma: disease of the eyes that can cause blindness

glycogen (GLI kuh jun): carbohydrate formed from glucose that is stored in the liver and muscle cells

Golgi (GAWL jee) **body:** cylindrical stack of unconnected disklike structures in cells that looks like endoplasmic reticulum; is involved in carbohydrate metabolism

gram: SI unit of mass

guard cell: one of a pair of cells surrounding a stoma that relaxes and contracts to change the size of the stoma

gymnosperm (JIHM nuh spurm): seed plant that does not have flowers and produces unprotected seeds

H

habitat: place in an ecosystem where a population lives and grows

hallucination: drug-induced situation in which a person sees and hears images and sounds that do not exist

hallucinogen (huh LEWS un uh jun): drug such as LSD, PCP, or mescaline that causes hallucinations

Haversian (huh VUR zhun) **canal:** tube in a bone through which a blood vessel runs

heart muscle: involuntary muscle that makes up the heart and that contracts and relaxes to pump blood; also called cardiac muscle

hemoglobin: protein pigment in red blood cells that contains iron and carries oxygen to tissues

hemophilia (hee muh FEE lee uh): disease in which blood does not clot

herbaceous (hur BAY shus) **stem:** stalk of a plant that is green, soft, and flexible

heredity (huh RED ut tee): the passing of traits from parents to offspring

heroin: dangerous narcotic made from morphine

homeostasis (hoh mee oh STAY sus): tendency of an organism to maintain a balanced state

homologous: refers to a condition of structures that are similar in origin and structure

hormone: chemical that regulates a body function

horsetail: branched and bushy vascular plant with a hollow skin surrounded by vascular tissue

humus (HYEW mus): decayed organic matter in soil

hybrid (HY brud) **trait:** trait that is made up of a dominant and a recessive trait

hyphae (HI fee): threadlike structures in the body of a fungus

hypothesis (hi PAHTH uh sus): proposed solution to a problem; a prediction or "best guess" based on known facts

I

identical twins: twins who develop from the same zygote and are always the same sex

immunity: ability to produce antibodies that fight a specific disease

inborn behavior: behavior inherited from parents

incomplete dominance: the inheritance of a pair of traits that show up independently; one is not dominant over the other

inferring: drawing conclusions based on observations

insect: arthropod with head, thorax, abdomen, and three pairs of legs

instinct: inborn behavior that involves complicated responses to a stimulus

interferon: substance produced by cells when first attacked by a virus; it interferes with the reproduction of viruses

interneuron: nerve cell in the spinal cord and brain that connects sensory neurons and motor neurons

invertebrate: animal with no backbone

involuntary muscle: muscle that cannot be consciously controlled

iris (I rus): colored part of a vertebrate's eye.

K

kilo-: prefix meaning 1000

kingdom: one of five main groups into which organisms are classified

Koch's postulates (KAHKS • PAHS chuh lutz): set of steps used to prove whether or not a disease is caused by a microbe

L

lancelet (LAN slut): nonvertebrate classified in phylum Chordata

large intestine: organ that removes excess water from undigested food

larva (LAHR vuh), *pl.* **larvae** (LAHR vee): stage of development between egg and pupa in complete metamorphosis of an insect

lens: part of the eye that forms an image on the retina

lichen (LI kun): organism consisting of both an alga and a fungus

life cycle: progression of changes that occurs as an organism grows, matures, ages, and dies

ligament: strand of tough tissue that holds bones together

limiting factor: condition in the environment that stops a population from increasing in size

liter: SI unit of volume

liver: organ that produces bile used in digestion

liverwort: nonvascular plant that grows as flat, ribbonlike or leafy structures that lie on the ground, and that reproduce by spores

loam: soil mixture of sand, clay, and humus considered ideal for gardening and farming

lymph: colorless liquid that supplies body tissues with nutrients from the blood

M

mammal: warm-blooded vertebrate with a four-chambered heart, hair, and mammary glands

mandible (MAN duh bul): tough, sharp body part on each side of an arthropod's mouth that is used for biting and chewing

marijuana: drug that can be a stimulant or a depressant and can become habit-forming

marine: relating to the sea

marrow: soft tissue in the center of many bones

marsupial (mahr SOO pee uhl): mammal whose young is not fully developed when born, and crawls into a pouch in the mother's body where it completes its development

mass: measure of the amount of matter in an object or organism

maturity (muh TOOHR ih tee): stage in human development marked by full physical and mental development

medium: special organic material on or in which bacteria are grown

medulla (mih DEW luh): enlarged upper end of the spinal cord; part of the brain that controls involuntary functions

meiosis (mi OH sus): cell division resulting in the formation of sex cells with half the body cell number of chromosomes

melanin: brown pigment that gives color to eyes, skin, and hair

menopause: human female's loss of ability to reproduce

menstrual (MEN strul) **cycle:** series of changes in the human female reproductive system that include development and release of egg, and preparation of uterus for possible pregnancy

menstruation (men STRAY shun): discharge of blood and tissues from a female's uterus

metabolism (muh TAB uhl iz um): total of the chemical changes that keep an organism alive

metamorphosis (met uh MOHR fuh sus): set of changes that occurs in an organism as it develops into an adult

metaphase: stage of cell division during which paired or double chromosomes move to the center of the cell

meter: SI unit of length

methyl alcohol: alcohol used for heating that can cause blindness or even death if consumed

microscope: tool that magnifies objects that are too small to be seen by the naked eye

milli-: prefix meaning 1/1000

millipede (MIHL uh peed): arthropod with round, segmented body and two pairs of legs on each segment

mineral: element or compound needed as a nutrient by the body for the formation of hormones, enzymes, and other substances

mitochondria (mite uh KAHN dree uh): rod-shaped bodies in the cytoplasm; involved in respiratory changes that release energy for use in the cell

mitosis (mi TOH sus): process by which a body cell divides to form two cells

mixture: two or more substances blended, but not bonded together

molecule (MAHL uh kyewl): two or more atoms bonded together into one particle; the smallest particle of a compound that still has the properties of the compound

mollusk (MAHL usk): invertebrate with a soft body, a shell or shell-like covering, and a muscular foot

molting: shedding of exoskeleton (arthropods) or outer layer of skin (reptiles)

moneran (muh NIR un): single-celled or many-celled organism with no nuclear membrane and with or without chlorophyll

monocot (MAHN uh kaht): angiosperm with one seed leaf, scattered vascular bundles in stem, long narrow leaves with parallel veins, and flower parts arranged in threes

moss: nonvascular plant with a stem, small overlapping leaves, and rhizoids; it reproduces by spores

motor neuron: nerve cell that carries impulses away from the central nervous system to effectors

multiple genes: genes that control most human traits including eye, hair, and skin color

muscle: tissue that moves part of the body

mutation (myew TAY shun): inheritable change in the genetic code that causes a new trait

mutualism (MEW chul ihz um): relationship between two different organisms that live together in which both organisms benefit

N

narcotic: addictive depressant that relieves pain and often causes sleep

natural selection: process by which the factors in an organism's surroundings determine whether or not the organism will survive and reproduce

neuron (NOO rahn): nerve cell that carries impulses

niche: status or role of an organism within its community

nicotine: drug found in tobacco and tobacco smoke

noise pollution: loud or unpleasant sounds in the environment

nonrenewable resource: resource that takes hundreds or millions of years to form

nonvascular plant: organism that lacks vessels in stems, leaves, or roots

nuclear energy: energy obtained from fusion or fission reactions

nucleolus: part of cell nucleus where ribosomes are made

nucleus (NEW klee us): spherical body that contains nucleic acids and controls the activities of the cell

nutrient (NEW tree unt): material needed by the body for food

nutrition (new TRIHSH un): study of food and its use by the body

O

observation: an act of noting and recording something made by the senses

organ: group of tissues that work together to perform one or more life activities

organic (or GAN ihk) **compound:** compound that contains carbon

organism: whole or complete living thing

osmosis (ahs MOH sus): diffusion of water through a membrane; the overall direction of movement is controlled by concentrations of solutions on either side of the membrane

ossification (ahs uh fih KAY shun): formation of bone tissue

ovaries: reproductive organs located in the abdominal cavity of a female

ovary: bottom, rounded part of a pistil

over-the-counter drug: drug that can be bought without a prescription

ovulation (ahv yuh LAY shun): release of the egg from the ovary in females

ovule: female plant reproductive part that contains an egg

ozone: type of oxygen that blocks much of the sun's ultraviolet radiation

P

palisade (pal uh SAYD) **layer:** layer of cylindrical-shaped cells just under the epidermis in a leaf

pancreas (PAN kree us): organ that produces pancreatic juice used in digestion

paramecium (par uh MEE see um): protozoan with two nuclei and a covering of cilia

parasite: organism that gains food and protection from another living organism while contributing nothing to the survival of the host

parasitism: relationship in which one organism lives on and may harm another organism called a host

particulate: particle that is emitted into the air

passive immunity: immunity acquired when antibodies to a disease are directly introduced into the body

pasteurization: process of heating milk to a temperature below boiling to kill harmful bacteria without changing the flavor

pedigree: record of an organism's ancestors

perennial (puh REN ee ul): plant that lives from one growing season to another

periosteum (per ee AHS tee um): membrane of tissue that covers all bones except at joints

peripheral (puh RIHF uh rul) **nervous system:** all nerves outside the brain and spinal cord

permafrost: ground that remains frozen for most of the year

pesticide: chemical that kills pests, including insects, fungi, and weeds

petal: showy leaflike part of a flower

pH: measure of the acidity or basicity of a substance or solution

pheromone (FAIR uh mone): chemical with an odor that conveys information to other members of a species

phloem (FLOH em): tissue made of tubes that transport food in vascular plants

photoperiodism: flowering response of a plant to the number of daylight hours per day

photosynthesis (foht ah SIN thuh sus): chemical change in which light is used to produce food

phototropism: response to light in the growth of plant shoots and roots

phylum (FI lum): largest division in a kingdom

physical dependence: condition in which a user of drugs must continue to take the drugs, or else withdrawal will occur

pigment: substance that colors the tissues of organisms

pistil: female reproductive organ of angiosperm

pituitary gland: small endocrine organ attached to the brain that secretes hormones, which control secretions by other endocrine glands

placenta (pluh SENT uh): organ that develops in the wall of the uterus in female mammals during pregnancy; it supplies blood to the developing fetus to which it is attached by the umbilical cord

planarian (pluh NAR ee un) (*pl.* **planaria**): freeliving flatworm

plasma: liquid part of blood in which nutrients and some oxygen are dissolved

plasmolysis (plaz MAHL uh sus): shrinking of cytoplasm caused by the loss of water from cells

platelet: a colorless disk-shaped body in blood that assists in blood clotting

pollen grain: male reproductive structure of a plant that contains sperm

pollination: transfer of pollen grains from stamens to stigmas in plants

pollution: changes caused by man-made chemicals in the environment that can be harmful to organisms

polyploidy: condition in which an organism has more than the usual two sets of chromosomes

population: all the organisms of one species in a community

predator: animal that captures other animals for food

prey: animal that is eaten by a predator

primary consumer: organism that eats producers

problem: question to be answered or a hypothesis to be tested in a science experiment

procedure: series of steps followed in an experiment that usually involve the use of materials and equipment

producer: organism that makes its own food

prophase: first stage of cell division during which chromosomes become visible

protective coloration: adaptation in which the color of an organism resembles its surroundings

protein (PROH teen): compound made of amino acids

protist: one-celled organism that has both animallike and plantlike characteristics and has a nucleus bounded by a membrane

protozoan (proh tuh ZOH un): animallike one-celled protist that has no chlorophyll

pseudopod (SEWD uh pahd): temporary protrusion of cytoplasm from a cell as a means of locomotion and surrounding food

psychological dependence: condition in which a user of drugs has developed a craving for or mental dependence on a drug

puberty: time when a human being is first able to reproduce.

pulmonary circulation: flow of blood from the heart to the lungs and back to the heart

Punnett (PUN ut) **square:** table used to show the possible ways genes are combined when passed from parents to offspring

pupa (PYEW puh): stage of development between larva and adult in complete metamorphosis of an insect

pupil: opening in the vertebrate eye that controls the amount of light that enters

pure trait: trait that is made up of all dominant or all recessive traits

purebred: organism bred from members of a certain breed without a mixture of another breed

Q

quarantine (KWOR un teen): state of isolation of an infected organism to prevent the spread of disease microbes

R

radial (RAY dee uhl) **symmetry:** arrangement of similar parts around a central axis that can be divided in any direction to give two equal halves

radioactive element: element whose atoms give off nuclear radiation as it decays to form a more stable element

reasoning: ability to remember past experience and use it to solve a problem

receptor (rih SEP tur): part of the nervous system that detects stimuli

recessive (rih SES ihv) **trait:** trait that does not appear when a dominant trait is present

recycling: the process of using something over and over again, such as paper or glass

red blood cell: saucer-shaped cell in plasma that carries oxygen

reflex act: inborn behavior that is an automatic response to a stimulus; it occurs in animals with a central nervous system

reforestation: process of renewing a forest by seeding or planting small trees

refuge: area in which wildlife and their habitats are protected

regeneration (rih jen uh RAY shun): regrowth of lost or damaged parts of an organism

renewable resource: resource that can be replaced by nature

reproduction (ree pruh DUK shun): process by which organisms generate others of the same kind

reptile: cold-blooded, usually egg-laying vertebrate having an external covering of dry scales and breathing by means of lungs

reservoir: artificial lake where water is collected and stored

resource: something taken from the environment that is useful to living organisms

respiration (res puh RAY shun): physical and chemical processes by which an organism supplies its cells and tissues with oxygen for cell metabolism and withdraws carbon dioxide formed in the breakdown of food

response: action of an organism as a result of a stimulus

retina (RET nuh): part of the vertebrate eye that receives light

Rh factor: protein in the red blood cells of most persons that causes production of antibodies if injected into persons without it

rhizoid (RI zoyd): thin, threadlike structure that grows out from the bodies of mosses and liverworts and attaches them to the substrate

rhizome (RI zohm): stem that grows underground

ribosome (RI buh sohm): tiny grainlike particle in the cytoplasm or along the edges of endoplasmic reticulum in cells; the site where proteins are made

RNA: nucleic acid that carries the genetic information from the DNA life code to ribosomes, forms ribosomes, and aids in protein synthesis in the cell

root hair: threadlike structure growing from a root

roughage (RUF ij): coarse, bulky food that is not digested

roundworm: freeliving or parasitic round, tubelike animal whose body is unsegmented and tapers to a point at each end

S

sac fungus: fungus that produces spores in an ascus

saprophyte (SAP ruh fite): organism that obtains food from dead organisms or from the waste products of living organisms

scavenger: animal that feeds on and removes dead animals

secondary consumer: organism that eats primary consumers

segmented worm: animal with tubelike body divided into sections or segments

selective breeding: process of choosing and mating only those individuals that have desired traits

self-pollination: transfer of pollen from stamens of a flower to the pistil of the same flower

semen: mixture of sperm and fluids

sensory neuron: nerve cell that carries impulses from receptors to the central nervous system

sepal: one of several leaflike structures that surrounds a flower and provides protection to the young flower

sewage: liquid and solid waste that is carried off with ground water in sewers or drains

sex chromosomes: a special pair of chromosomes that determines the sex of an organism

sex-linked trait: a trait controlled by genes on a sex chromosome

sexual reproduction: process that results in the production of offspring when nuclear material from two different sex cells combine

shelter belt: row of dense evergreen trees that protects fields from wind erosion

side effect: unintended result caused by a drug

skeleton: network of bones that supports the body and protects internal organs

slime mold: protist with a three-stage life cycle

small intestine: coiled tube about 7 m long that secretes digestive juices onto food that passes from the stomach

smog: foglike pollution that can cause respiratory problems in humans

smooth muscle: involuntary muscle in the walls of many internal body organs

solar energy: energy from the sun

solution: mixture in which one substance is dissolved in another

species (SPEE seez): smallest division in a kingdom; organisms that may produce more of their own kind; second part of an organism's scientific name

sperm: male reproductive cells

spinal cord: thick cord of nerves encased in the bony spinal canal that relays messages between the brain and the rest of the body

spiracle (SPIHR ih kul): pore in an insect's abdomen through which oxygen enters

sponge: simplest kind of many-celled invertebrate animal with a porous skeleton of spicules and no symmetry

spongy layer: layer of irregularly-shaped cells below palisade layer in leaves that contain chlorophyll

spontaneous generation (spahn TAY nee us • jen uh RAY shun): idea that organisms originate directly from nonliving matter.

sporangium (spuh RAN jee um): spore case

sporangium fungus: saprophyte or parasite with a body of hyphae and spores produced in sporangia

spore: special reproductive cell of many plants, fungi, monerans, and protists

sporozoan (spor uh ZOH un): protozoan that reproduces by forming spores

stamen (STAY men): male reproductive organ of an angiosperm

starch: kind of carbohydrate

stimulant: drug that speeds up the rate of body activities

stimulus (STIHM yuh lus) (*pl.* **stimuli**): something in the environment that causes a response by an organism

stomach: body digestive organ with muscular walls that contract forcefully and mix the food inside

stoma (STOH muh) (*pl.* **stomata**): opening in the epidermis of a leaf through which gases are exchanged and water is lost

striated (STRI ayt ud) **muscle:** voluntary muscle attached to the skeleton; also called skeletal muscle

subsoil: layer of soil beneath topsoil that contains mostly rock particles and little humus

succession: process of gradual change in a community in which different species become dominant

symbol: letter that represents an element

symmetry (SIH muh tree): the property of being similar or having like parts

synapse (SINN aps): space between the axon of one neuron and the dendrites of another

system: group of organs that work together to carry on life activities

systemic circulation: flow of blood from the heart to the body tissues and back to the heart

T

tar: black gummy substance that remains in the lungs after smoking

taxonomy (tak SAHN uh mee): science of classifying living things

technology (tek NAHL uh jee): use of scientific knowledge in a practical way

telophase: final stage of cell division during which the nuclear membrane reforms around each of the daughter nuclei and the cell divides into two

tendon: tough band of tissue that connects a muscle to a bone

tentacle (TENT uh kul): ropelike piece of tissue that contains stinging cells; body part of a coelenterate

territoriality: pattern of behavior in which an animal defends a particular area

testes (TES teez): two oval-shaped male sex glands in which sperm are produced

theory (THIHR ee): idea that explains things or events based on hypotheses and many observations

thermal pollution: pollution caused by the dumping of heated water into waterways

tissue: group of similar cells that together perform a special job

tolerance: condition in which the body develops a resistance to the action of a drug

topsoil: upper level of soil that contains rock fragments, living organisms, and humus

trait: property or characteristic of an organism

tranquilizer: depressant used to reduce stress and relax muscles

transpiration (trans puh RAY shun): process of losing water vapor through the stomata of a leaf

trial and error: learning process in which an animal develops a behavior based on avoiding mistakes

tropism (TROH pihz um): directional response of a plant growth to a stimulus

tunicate (TEW nuh kayt): nonvertebrate classified in phylum chordata

U

ultrasound (UL truh sound) **machine:** machine that produces a sound wave picture of a fetus

umbilical cord: ropelike tube in a mammal that supplies a fetus with blood from the placenta

urethra: passageway that carries urine from the bladder to the outside of an animal's body

uterus: hollow, sac-shaped organ in which the embryo develops in a female mammal

V

vaccine (VAK seen): solution of dead or weakened germs that can stimulate the formation of antibodies to a disease to protect the body against that disease

vacuole (VAK yuh wohl): liquid-filled sac that stores water and dissolved materials in cells

vagina (vuh JI nuh): canal that leads to the uterus in female mammals

variable (VER ee uh bul): factor that can cause changes in an experiment

variation: trait that makes an individual different from others in its species

vascular (VAS kyuh lur) **plant:** organism with vessels that transport water and nutrients throughout roots, stems, and leaves

vegetative propagation (VEJ uh tayt ihv • prahp uh GAY shun): kind of asexual reproduction in which a new plant is grown from part of another plant

vein: blood vessel that carries blood to the heart

ventricle (VEN trih kul): one of two lower chambers of the human heart from which blood is forced into the arteries

vertebrate (VURT uh brayt): animal with a backbone

villi: small fingerlike structures in the uterus that later develop into the placenta

virus: complex of organic compounds composed of a nucleic acid core surrounded by a coat of protein; has living and nonliving characteristics; can replicate only inside a host cell

visual pollution: unsightly aspects of the environment due to human activities

vitamin: essential nutrient needed in small amounts for the control of cell activities

volume: amount of space something occupies

voluntary muscle: muscle that can be consciously controlled

W

warm-blooded: having a body temperature that is maintained no matter what the temperature of the surroundings

white blood cell: cell in the blood that destroys harmful microbes and removes dead cells

wildlife: any wild plant or animal

withdrawal: sickness that results when a physically dependent person stops taking an addictive drug

woody stem: stalk of a plant that has a secondary growth of xylem tissue

X

xylem (ZI lum): tissue made of vessels that transport water and dissolved minerals throughout vascular plants

Z

zygospore: zygote having a resistant shell or wall

zygote (ZI goht): single cell formed from the joining of a sperm and an egg cell

INDEX

PHOTO
CREDITS

COVER: Front: Breck P. Kent, **Back:** John Gerlack/Tom Stack & Assoc.; **2–3,** BIO-TEC Images/ © George D. Lepp 1962; **3,** C.C. Lockwood; **4,** Cobalt Productions; **8,** Ken Van Dyne Studio; **9,** Cobalt Productions; **10**(l) Stephen J. Krasemann/DRK Photo, (r) USDA; **12,** Larry Hamill; **14**(t) George Anderson, (b) The Bettmann Archive, Inc.; **15,** Ted Rice; **19,** "Fluorescence Digital Imaging Microscopy in Cell Biology," Donna J. Arndt-Jovin, Michel Robert-Nicoud, Stephen J. Kaufman, and Thomas M. Jovin, *SCIENCE*, Vol. 230, Fig. 2a,b,c,d, & e, 18 October 1985; **24,** Dwight R. Kuhn; **26**(l) Audio-Visual Productions, (c) Larry Day, (r) Tracy Borland; **27,28,** Hickson-Bender Photography; **29,** Frank Cezus; **30,** Colour Library International USA, Ltd.; **31**(all) Dwight R. Kuhn; **32**(l) Manfred Kage/Peter Arnold, Inc., (r) File Photo; **34**(t) Ward's Natural Science, (b) Robert D. Warmbrodt, Dept. of Botany, Ohio State Univ., Columbus, OH; **36,**(all) Kessel/Shih © 1976, Springer-Verlag; **38,** Walter Chandoha, (inset) Runk/Schoenberger from Grant Heilman; **41,** Bruce Dale/ © National Geographic Society; **46,** Tom Myers; **50,** Ted Rice; **51,** National Cotton Council of America; **55,** Dan Hulburt-Stock/Carolina; **57**(t) Jim Bradshaw, (b) Keith Porter; **58**(both) Ted Rice; **60**(both) Phillips Petroleum Co.; **64,** Hickson-Bender Photography; **66**(tl) The Metropolitan Museum of Art, Bequest of Lillian S. Timken, 1959, (tr) Ken Heinen/National Museum of African Art, Elisofon Archives, Smithsonian Institution, (bl) Photo by: Malcolm Varon, N.Y.C. © Copyright, (br) David L. Perry; **68**(tl) Joey Jacques, (tr) Manfred Kage/Peter Arnold, Inc., (bl) John MacGregor/Peter Arnold, Inc., (br) Joey Jacques; **72**(l) Warren Garst/Tom Stack & Assoc., (r) Don Nieman; **73,** Michele Wigginton; **78**(l) Paul Strother, (r) Field Museum of Natural History, Chicago; **79,** NASA; **86–87,** S. Rannels/Grant Heilman; **87,** © Manfred Kage/Peter Arnold, Inc.; **88,** Dan McCoy/Rainbow; **90**(t) Hickson-Bender Photography, (c) Omikron for Photo Researchers, Inc., (b) Centers for Disease Control; **92,** Steve Lissau; **93**(both) Alvin E. Staffan; **94**(l) John Hanson, Ohio State Univ.; (c) Reprinted courtesy of Jones & Bartlett Publishers, Inc., Boston, MA, 02116. From *LIVING IMAGES: Biological Microstructures Revealed by Scanning Electron Microscopy,* by Gene Shih and Richard Kessel, (r) A. Ottolenghi, Ohio State Univ.; **96**(both) Cobalt Productions; **98**(l) Walter Chandoha, (r) James Farley; **99**(l) Photo Courtesy of Wisconsin Division of Tourism, (r) James N. Westwater; **100**(both) John Hanson, Ohio State Univ.; **104,** Manfred Kage/Peter Arnold, Inc.; **107,** Harris Biological Supplies; **108**(l) Roger K. Burnard, (r) Manfred Kage/Peter Arnold, Inc.; **110,** Carolina Biological Supply Co.; **111,** BioMedia Assoc.; **113,** Harry Ellis/Tom Stack & Assoc.; **115**(t) Cobalt Productions, (b) William Patterson/Tom Stack & Assoc.; **117**(t) James E. Stahl, (b) Morgan Photos; **118**(t) Richard Brommer, (b) Pfizer, Inc.; **120**(l) Robert P. Carr/Bruce Coleman, Inc., (r) Ruth Dixon; **122**(both) Mike Beals; **128–129,** Michael Collier; **129,** Stephen J. Krasemann/DRK; **130,** George W. Folkerts; **134,** Colour Library International USA, Ltd.; **138**(l) Roger K. Burnard, (r) Debbie Dean; **139,** Kessel/Shih, © 1976 Springer-Verlag; **141,** Robert Fridenstine; **144**(both) Adrian Davies/Bruce Coleman, Inc.; **145,** Grant Heilman Photography; **146,** Hickson-Bender Photography; **147,** USDA; **148,** Mike Beals; **152,** *SEM IN BIOLOGY,* © 1976, Kessel/Shih, Springer-Verlag; **154**(tl) Richard Brommer, (tr) Ruth Dixon, (bl) William D. Popejoy, (br) File Photo; **156,** Dan McCoy/Rainbow; **157**(l) Carolina Biological Supply Co., (r) Alvin E. Staffan; **158,** Lynn M. Stone; **159**(l) Roger K. Burnard, (r) Alvin E. Staffan; **160**(l) Runk/Schoenberger from Grant Heilman, (r) Barry L. Runk/Grant Heilman; **161**(l) William Ferguson, (c) Steve Lissau, (r) Alvin E. Staffan; **162,** Roger K. Burnard; **163,** Dr. George Hall, Ohio State Univ.; **172,** Michael DiSpezio; **174**(both) Runk/Schoenberger from Grant Heilman; **175**(l) Grant Heilman Photography, (r) Horticultural Photography, Corvallis, Oregon; **178,** Science Photo Library/Photo Researchers, Inc.; **181,** Gerard Photography; **183**(l) Kessel/Shih, © 1976, (r) Morgan Photos; **185,** Ken Van Dyne Studio; **187,** Phillip A. Harrington/Fran Heyl Assocs.; **188,** Courtesy of E.E. Roos/USDA, National Seed Storage Laboratory; **194–195,** Carleton Ray/Photo Researchers, Inc.; **195,** Dr. D. Macdonald, Oxford Univ.; **196,** Animals Animals/Zig Leszczynski; **198**(both) Allan Roberts; **202,** Animals Animals/© Stouffer Productions, Ltd.; **205,** John Bova/Audubon Society Collection/Photo Researchers, Inc.; **207**(l) Doug Wechsler, (r) Steve Lissau; **208**(both) Richard Brommer; **209,** Roger K. Burnard; **211**(both) Harry Knollman; **213**(both) Reprinted with permission of the present publisher, Jones & Bartlett Publishers, Inc., from Shih and Kessel: *LIVING IMAGES,* Science Books International, 1982, page 92(t), page 122(r); **215,** Animals Animals/Fred Whitehead; **220,** E.R. Degginger/Bruce Coleman, Inc.; **222,** Sharon Kurgis; **223,** Joey Jacques; **224**(t) Breck P. Kent, (b) T.E. Adams/Peter Arnold, Inc.; **225**(t) Animals Animals/Breck P. Kent, (b) Roger K. Burnard; **226,** Latent Image; **227,** Animals Animals/© Oxford Scientific Films, G.I. Bernard; **229,** Ward's Natural Science Establishment; **234,** Dale A. Glantz; **237**(l) David Dennis, (r) Geri Murphy; **239**(l) Ward's Natural Science, (r) William J. Weber; **240**(l) Latent Image, (c) Harris Biological Supplies Ltd., (r) Sharon Kurgis; **242**(l) Roger K. Burnard, (r) Centers for Disease Control; **243,** Lynn Stone; **245**(t) Geri Murphy, (b) Barbara Bentley and Glenn Prestwich; **248,** Mike Beals; **252,** Helen Rhode; **254**(l) Geri Murphy, (r) Photography by Carolina Biological Supply Co.; **255,** Runk/Schoenberger from Grant Heilman; **259,** Geri Murphy; **260**(l) Joey Jacques, (r) Mac Albin; **262**(l) William J. Weber, (r) Animals Animals/Zig Leszczynski; **263**(l) Animals Animals/Zig Leszczynski, (r) Alvin E. Staffan; **264,** Richard G. Langer/Taurus Photos; **266,** © Tom McHugh/Photo Researchers, Inc.; **268,** Alan Carey; **271,** Reprinted with permission of the present publisher, Jones and Bartlett Publishers, Inc., from Shih and Kessel: *LIVING IMAGES,* Science Books International, 1982, page 151; **272**(all) Kessel/Shih, © 1976 Springer-Verlag; **273,** Runk/Schoenberger from Grant Heilman; **274,** Paul Schrock; **275,276,** © Tom McHugh/Photo Researchers, Inc.; **282–283,** David Brownell 1985; **283,** Cobalt Productions; **284,** Doug Martin; **290**(both) Carolina Biological Supply Co.; **291,** D. Davidson/Tom Stack & Assoc.; **293**(l) Marshall Sklar/Photo Researchers, Inc., (c) File Photo, (r) © Michael

Abbey, Science Source, Photo Researchers, Inc.; **295,** Cobalt Productions; **297**(both) Cobalt Productions; **301**(l) Ken Van Dyne Studio, (r) Doug Martin; **305,** Reprinted from *PSYCHOLOGY TODAY* Magazine, Copyright © 1985 American Phychological Association; **306,** Eli Lilly & Co.; **310,** Mobil Oil Corporation; **313**(t) Eric Hoffines, (b) Dr. B.L. Wismar, Dept. of Anatomy, Ohio State Univ.; **320**(t) Manfred Kage/Peter Arnold, Inc., (b) Kessel/Shih, © Springer-Verlag; **321**(t) Carolina Biological Supply Co., (b) John Hanson, Ohio State Univ.; **322,** *SEM IN BIOLOGY,* © 1976, Kessel/Shih, Springer-Verlag; **323,** Science Photo Library/Photo Researchers, Inc.; **324,** Cobalt Productions; **334,** Kraft, Inc.; **336,** National Dairy Council; **337,** Gerard Photography; **339**(t) Young/Hoffines, (b) Dr. Peter Baker, Ohio State Univ.; **340,** Eric Hoffines; **341,** Gerard Photography; **342,** Steve Lissau; **344,** Gerard Photography; **348,** John Hanson, Ohio State Univ.; **351,** Cobalt Productions; **352,** Mike Beals; **356,** Eli Lilly & Co.; **358,** The Bettmann Archive, Inc.; **360,** John Hanson, Ohio State Univ.; **361,** © D. Fawcett, E. Shelton/Photo Researchers, Inc.; **363,** Lab of A.M. Siegelman; **365,** March of Dimes Birth Defects Foundation; **366,** Tim Courlas; **369,** D.C. Lowe/Medichrome; **370**(t) Doug Martin, (b) D. Davidson/Tom Stack & Assoc.; **372,** Dan McCoy/Rainbow; **373**(t) Ralph C. Eagle MD/Photo Researchers, Inc., (b) Doug Martin; **374, 375**(l) Doug Martin, (r) Berg & Associates; **380,382,** Larry Hamill; **383,384,** Wright State Univ.; **385,** Ted Rice; **386,** Young/Hoffines; **387**(t) Al-Anon Family Group Headquarters, Gerard Photography, (bl&r) Martin M. Rotker/Taurus Photos; **388,** Tom Stack/Tom Stack & Assocs.; **389,** William E. Ferguson; **390**(t) Hickson-Bender, (b) Jeff Rotman/Peter Arnold, Inc.; **391,** Michael S. Renner/Bruce Coleman, Inc.; **393**(t) Robert Frerck/Odyssey Productions, (bl) Hans Pfletschinger/Peter Arnold, Inc., (bc) Joy Spurr/Bruce Coleman, Inc., (br) Carolina Biological Supply Co.; **394,** © C.C. Lockwood; **395**(l) W.H. Hodge/Peter Arnold, Inc., (r) Charles Marden Fitch/Taurus Photos; **396,** Doug Martin; **397**(l) Mimi Cotter, International Stock Photography, (r) Doug Martin; **398**(both) Mike Beals; **404–405,** Chip Clark/Smithsonian Institution; **405,** Dr. Larry D. Agenbroad, Northern Arizona Univ.; **406,** Doug Martin; **409,** © John Gignnicchi/Photo Researchers, Inc.; **412,** Lennart Nilsson, *A CHILD IS BORN,* Dell Publishing Co., N.Y.; **415,** Pictures Unlimited; **416,** Gerard Photography; **418**(l) Elaine Comer, (r) Paul Brown; **419**(l) George Anderson, (r) Cobalt Productions; **420,** Cobalt Productions; **422**(both) Mike Beals: **426,** Animals Animals/Zig Leszczynski; **433,** Courtesy of Watt Publishing; **438,** Photograph by Carolina Biological Supply Co.; **440**(l) Earl Kubis/Tom Stack & Assoc., (r) William A. Paff/Tom Stack & Assoc.; **441,** Ohio State Univ.; **444,** Grant Heilman; **446,** Phillip A. Harrington/Peter Arnold, Inc.; **447,** R.L. Brinster and R.E. Hammer, School of Veterinary Medicine, Univ. of Pennsylvania; **448,** Science Source/Photo Researchers; **452,** © S.C. Johnson & Son, Inc. and Smithsonian Institution; **454**(l) Roger K. Burnard, (c) MJW, (r) Don C. Arms/Tom Stack & Assoc.; **455**(t) William E. Ferguson, (b) Keith Grunnar/Tom Stack & Assoc.; **457**(tl,tr) The American Museum of Natural History, (b) David L. Brill © National Geographic Society, Museo Arqueologico Nacional, Madrid; **458**(tl,tr) The American Museum of Natural History, (b) David L. Brill © National Geographic Society, Institut du Quarternaire, Universite de Bordeaux I, Talence, France; **459,** David L. Brill © National Georgraphic Society, Musee des Antiquites Nationales, Saint-Germain-en-Laye, France; **465**(l)(l) Maurice & Sally Landrel/FPG, (r) Leonard Lee Rue III/Tom Stack & Assoc.; **466**(l) Alvin E. Staffan, (r) Craig Fusaro/Tom Stack & Assoc.; **467,** The Stock Shop; **470**(t) Roger K. Burnard, (b) © Zoological Scoiety of San Diego; **472**(t) Tim Courlas, (b) Leonard Lee Rue III/Photo Researchers, Inc.; **474,** The Cleveland Museum of Natural History; **480–481**(both) George Herben; **482,** © 1986 Gary Braasch; **484**(l) Colour Library International USA, Ltd., (r) James N. Westwater; **485**(l) Dr. George Gerster/Photo Researchers, Inc., (r) James N. Westwater; **487,** Thomas Russell; **488,** Animals Animals; **492**(l) Joe McDonald/Bruce Coleman, Inc., (r) Paul Von Baich/First Light, Toronto; **494**(t) © Zoological Society of San Diego, (b) M.W.F. Tweedie/Photo Researchers, Inc.; **495**(t) Huber/The Stock Shop, (b) T. Alvez/FPG; **496**(t) Stephen J. Krasemann/DRK, (b) Lynn Stone; **497**(t) David M. Dennis, (b) Jeff Foott/Bruce Coleman, Inc.; **498**(t) James E. Stahl, (b) © Zoological Society of San Diego; **499**(t) Grant Heilman, (b) Tom McHugh/Photo Researchers, Inc.; **500**(t) Johnny Johnson, (b) Pat & Tom Leeson/Photo Researchers, Inc.; **501**(t) Pat Morrow, First Light, Toronto, (b) Photo Researchers, Inc.; **502**(t) Carolina Biological Supply Co., (b) William J. Weber; **504,** Frank Balthis; **508,** William Roston; **510**(t) Grant Heilman, (b) Dwight R. Kuhn; **511,** John Gerlach; **512,** Runk/Schoenberger from Grant Heilman; **513**(t) Ruth Dixon, (b) Animals Animals/Frank Allan; **516**(all) Alvin E. Staffan; **520,** Doug Martin; **521,** William E. Ferguson; **522,** Gene Alexander/Soil Conservation Service; **523**(t) Roger K. Burnard, (b) Cobalt Productions; **525,** Gary Hensler/U.S. Fish & Wildlife Service; **526,** The Bettmann Archive, Inc.; **530,** Dennis Stock/Magnum; **532**(t) Ruth E. Bogart, (b) Roger K. Burnard; **534,** Earth Scenes/© C.C. Lockwood; **535,** Roger K. Burnard; **536**(l) Don Parsisson, (r) Thomas Hovland/Grant Heilman; **537**(tl) USDA, (tr) David M. Dennis, (b) Wallace Kirkland/Tom Stack & Assoc.; **539**(t) Runk/Schoenberger from Grant Heilman, (b) William E. Ferguson; **540,** Clyde H. Smith/FPG; **541**(t) Debbie Dean, (b) File Photo; **542**(l) William J. Weber, (r) Stuart L. Craig, Jr./Bruce Coleman, Inc.; **543,** Ruth Dixon; **544,** Cobalt Productions; **546**(t) Ruth E. Bogart, (b) David R. Frazier; **547**(t) Greg Miller, (b) Uta Hoffmann; **548**(both) Mike Beals.

2 3 4 5 6 7 8 9 10 11 12 13 14 15—95 94 93 92 91 90 89 88 87 86